# 2000 Solved Problems in Digital Electronics

# About the Author

**S P Bali** has been associated with the field of electronics for over 45 years. As a professional trainer, he has directed job-oriented courses on Audio/Video Appliances and Consumer Electronics in Haryana and Delhi. He has over twenty years of teaching experience, inducting new entrants into the field of electronics and teaching basic and diploma level courses in Military College of Electronics and Mechanical Engineering (MCEME), Secunderabad. He has contributed articles to magazines and authored three other books, namely, *Colour Television: Theory and Practice* (TMH), *Consumer Electronics* and *Solid State Devices and Circuits*.

His fields of interest are A/V Appliances, Consumer Electronics, Electronic Devices and Circuits and Electrical and Electronic Instruments and Instrumentation.

# 2000 Solved Problems in Digital Electronics

**S P Bali**

*Former Faculty Member*
*Military College of Electronics and Mechanical Engineering*
*Secundrabad, India*

**McGraw Hill Education (India) Private Limited**

NEW DELHI

**McGraw Hill Education Offices**

**New Delhi** New York St Louis San Francisco Auckland Bogotá Caracas
Kuala Lumpur Lisbon London Madrid Mexico City Milan Montreal
San Juan Santiago Singapore Sydney Tokyo Toronto

**McGraw Hill Education (India) Private Limited**

Copyright © 2005, by McGraw Hill Education (India) Private Limited.

Ninth reprint 2013
**RLZBCRZODRARR**

This edition can be exported from India only by the publishers,
McGraw Hill Education (India) Private Limited.

ISBN (13 digit): 978-0-07-058831-8
ISBN (10 digit): 0-07-058831-7

Published by McGraw Hill Education (India) Private Limited,
P-24, Green Park Extension, New Delhi 110 016, typeset in Times at
The Composers, 260, C.A. Apt., Paschim Vihar, New Delhi 110063
and printed at Akash Press, New Delhi 110020

Cover: SDR Printer

*This book is dedicated to my grandchildren*

**Parth, Niharika** and **Mallika**

# Brief Contents

# Detailed Contents

# Preface

> *Always design a thing by considering it in its next larger context—a chair in a room, a room in a house, a house in an environment, an environment in a city plan.*

Over the years, the design and construction of electronic circuits have changed dramatically. New devices have been discovered and old devices improved. Electronic circuits have shrunk considerably in size, and construction techniques have shifted from discrete components to the use of plug-in integrated circuits that already contain the complete circuit. The needs of the technician and the experimenter have also changed over the years. This book is an attempt to meet that need, by presenting a wide variety of related material together in just one volume. You will find theoretical concepts and design information on digital circuits, helpful data sheets and know-how about an assortment of integrated circuits. Throughout the text the author has endeavoured to bridge the gap between Blackboard and Breadboard.

In order to build and design digital circuits you have to have a firm grasp of the fundamentals. The material in this book is appropriate for introductory courses on digital logic design in electrical or computer engineering or computer science curricula. The background required is familiarity with basic electronics concepts. Though the level of this book is introductory, it contains much more material than can be taught in a typical introductory course.

No technical book ever made light bedtime reading. Nor is it possible, in just over four-hundred and fifty pages of legible type, to transform the novice into a full fledged circuit designer. What can be done, however, is to present the most important information to the largest number of users, in such a way that it can be absorbed as readily as possible.

Each chapter begins with a review of relevant topics in digital circuit theory which will be useful throughout the text. There are a large number of worked out examples in the text to illustrate how the theory may be applied to obtain quantitative results and to emphasize the order of magnitude of the effects under consideration.

In addition, a summary of the keypoints, review questions, supplementary problems, fill in the blanks, true and false statements and multiple-choice questions (chapter-wise) are provided to motivate the students, and strengthen the group of basic concepts, help in self evaluation, and give the students an experience in the design of the circuits discussed in the text and of other configurations to perform similar functions. Answer/Hints for solution are provided chapter-wise.

In almost all numerical problems, realistic parameters, values and specifications have been chosen. Considerable care has been exercised in the development of these problems, which are an integral and important part of the text.

There is always a time-lag between the introduction of a new device with its technical data, which enables the circuit designer to go ahead; and the production of a circuit for some particular application, which can be put in the hands of the general user. Broadly speaking the circuits have been restricted to devices which are available now.

A digital signal is modeled as taking on, at any time, only one of two discrete values, which we call 0 or 1 (or LOW and HIGH, FALSE and TRUE, Negated and Asserted or whatever). The students might ask a *very geniune question*.

What are we going to do with ( ⎓⎓⎓D⎯ ) AND, ( ⎓⎓⎓⊃⎯ ) OR, ( ⎯▷o⎯ ) INVERT!

> *What are you able to build with your blocks?*
>
> *Castles and palaces, temples and docks.*
>
> **Robert Louis Stevenson**

The book comprises eighteen chapters. Chapter 1 on **Digital Concepts** is of an introductory nature and introduces the student to the domain of digital electronics.

Chapter 2 on **Number Systems** gives a comprehensive coverage of the four number systems (decimal, binary, octal, or hexadecimal) and conversion of any number in one system to its equivalent value in any of the remaining three numbering systems.

Chapter 3 deals with **Codes and Parity**. There are many specialized codes used in digital systems. Some codes are strictly numeric, like the BCD, while others are alphanumeric like the ASCII, they are used to represent numbers, letters, symbols, and instructions. Also, the detection of errors in codes using a parity bit is covered. Information on codes that use other methods of error detection and an error correcting code are also discussed.

**Logic Gates**, (Chapter 4), are the basic building blocks for forming digital electronic circuitry. Gates allow or retard the flow of digital information. The seven logic gates AND, OR, NAND, NOR, INVERT, XOR and XNOR are explained in detail with the help of timing diagrams.

**Boolean Algebra**, (Chapter 5), uses many of the same laws as those of ordinary algebra. The OR function ($X = A + B$) is the Boolean addition and the AND function ($X = AB$) is the Boolean multiplication. By using the laws of Boolean algebra you can rearrange Boolean equations to form simpler equivalent circuits using fewer gates.

All Boolean expressions, regardless of their form, can be converted into either of two standard forms: the sum-of-products (SOP) form or the product-of-sums (POS) form. Standardization makes the evaluation, simplification, and implementation of Boolean expressions much more systematic and easier. There are two methods of systematically reducing Boolean expressions, the graphical method or Karnaugh map and the Quine McClusky or tabulation method. Both of these methods are discussed under the heading **Reduction Techniques** in Chapter 6.

Chapter 7 on **Pulse and Switching Devices** deals with the characteristics of pulse waveforms (both ideal and non-ideal) and the use of electromechanical relays, diodes, transistors, JFETs, MOSFETs, and CMOS for switching applications.

Linear waveshapers (integrators and differentiators) and non-linear waveshapers (limiters, clippers and clampers) are discussed in Chapter 8 on **Waveshaping**. This chapter also includes sweep circuits.

The various approaches to digital logic design are called **Logic Families** (Chapter 9). Logic specifications and a detailed description of the various logic families is given in this chapter. A comparison of the logic families and their relative advantages and disadvantages are also discussed.

Chapter 10 on **Arithmetic Circuits** discusses the four arithmetic operations—addition, subtraction, multiplication and division—and digital hardware to facilitate these operations. Sign-magnitude representation of numbers, one's and two's complement representation, two's complement addition and subtraction and floating-point numbers are discussed in detail.

Combinational logic circuits may contain an arbitrary number of logic gates and inverters but no feedback loops. In combinational circuit analysis we start with a logic diagram and proceed to a formal description of the function performed by that circuit, such as a truth table or a logic expression. In synthesis we do the reverse, starting with a formal description and proceeding to a logic diagram. The purpose of Chapter 11 on **Combinational Logic Circuits** is to give the student a solid theoretical foundation for the analysis and synthesis of combinational logic circuits, a foundation that will be doubly important later when we move on to sequential circuits.

The outputs of sequential logic circuits depend not only on current inputs, but also on the past sequence of inputs. Latches and flip-flops are the basic building blocks of most sequential circuits. Typical digital systems use latches and flip-flops that are prepackaged, functionally specified devices in a standard integrated circuit. We study these discrete designs for two reasons—to understand the behaviour of the prepackaged elements better, and to gain the capability of building a latch or flip-flop from scratch, as is required occasionally in digital-design practice and often in digital-design exams. These topics are covered in Chapter 12 on **Flip-Flops**.

In a generic computer registers are used extensively for temporary storage of data in areas other than memory. Data is shifted to left or right in a shift register. Counters time the duration of various events and count events. These applications are called sequential because they follow a predetermined sequence of digital states and are triggered by a timing pulse or clock. **Registers and Counters** form the subject of Chapter 13.

A large digital system cannot be understood through a detailed electrical analysis of all its circuits. The system as a whole can be understood only by a model that simplifies the system. One such model is the sequential (finite state) machine. Both Mealy and Moore machine are explained in Chapter 14 on **Sequential Machines**.

Any sequential circuit has memory of a sort, since each `flip-flop` or latch stores one bit of information. However, we usually reserve the word **Memory** (Chapter 15) to refer to bits that are stored in a structured way, usually as a two-dimensional array in which one row of bits is accessed at a time. This chapter describes several different memory organisations and commercially available memory chips.

Since their introduction years ago **Programmable Logic Devices** (Chapter 16) have been very flexible workhorses of digital design. As IC technology advanced, there was naturally greater interest in creating larger PLD architectures to take advantage of increased chip density. Programmable Logic Arrays (PLAs), Programmable Array Logic (PAL), Generic Array Logic (GAL), Complex Programmable Logic Devices (CPLDs) and Field Programmable Gate Array (FPGA) are also discussed.

The real world is analog in nature. A common boundary between two physical or functional units is called an interface. Converters for **Interfacing** (Digital-to-Analog and Analog-to-Digital) form the subject of study in Chapter 17. Digital-to-Analog conversion (DAC) involves translation of digital information into equivalent analog information. Analog-to-Digital converters (ADCs) are used for the conversion of analog signals into digital signals. All digital systems have ADCs as part of their structure. The problems encountered in interfacing logic families are also discussed in this chapter.

In recent years the microprocessor has become an integral part of many electronic systems. Apart from its obvious use in personal computers, the microprocessor is commonly found in industrial equipment and is frequently incorporated into domestic equipment, such as video recorders and washing machines. **Microprocessor Basics** are discussed in Chapter 18.

**Appendices A to E** provide a wealth of information. A **Glossary** of key terms is given at the end of the book. Also included is a list of reference books (**Bibliography**) for those students interested in higher studies.

The project has taken considerable time to see the light of day—precious time has been spent in giving the book the shape you find it in today; the major setback being the constraint of space.

I personally feel the book will prove to be a constant companion of engineering students irrespective of the discipline they opt for.

I gratefully acknowledge the help from different reviewers in answering a comprehensive questionnaire and making valuable suggestions for the improvement of the text.

I would like to put on record the valuable suggestions and cooperation of Ms Vibha Mahajan, and the entire editorial and production teams of Tata McGraw-Hill in bringing out this book.

Finally, I would like to thank my wife, Suksham, for her patience, understanding, support and encouragement.

I hope the students will enjoy studying this book as much as I have enjoyed writing it.

**S P BALI**

# Digital Concepts

## INTRODUCTION

The main difference between analog and digital operation is the way the loadline is used. With *analog* circuits, adjacent points on the loadline may be used, so that the output voltage is *continuous*. Because of this, the output voltage can have an infinite number of values. One way to get analog operation is with a *sinusoidal* input. The continuously changing input voltage produces a continuously changing output voltage.

*Digital* circuits are different. Almost all digital circuits are designed for *two-state* operation. This means using only two non-adjacent points on the loadline, typically *saturation* and *cut-off*. As a result, the output voltage has only two states (values), either *LOW* or *HIGH*. One way to get digital operation is with a *square-wave* input. If large enough, this type of input drives the transistors into saturation and cut-off, producing a two-state operation, as illustrated in Fig. 1.1.

## DIGITAL/ANALOG SIGNALS

A *signal* can be defined as useful information transmitted within, to, or from electronic circuits. The circuit in Fig. 1.2(a) puts out an *analog signal* or voltage. As the wiper on the potentiometer is moved upward, the voltage from points *A* to *B* gradually increases. When the wiper is moved downward, the voltage gradually decreases. The waveform diagram in Fig. 1.2(b) is a graph of the analog output. On the left side, the voltage from *A* to *B* is gradually increasing to 5 V; on the right side, the voltage is gradually decreasing to 0 V. By stopping the wiper at any midpoint, we can get an output voltage anywhere between 0 and 5 V. *An analog device then, is*

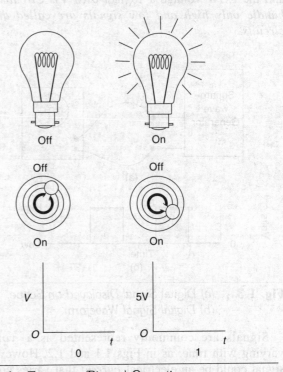

**Fig. 1.1** *Two-state (Binary) Operation.*

*one that has a signal which varies continuously in step with the input.*

A *digital device* operates with a digital signal. The generator in Fig. 1.3(a) produces a square waveform that is displayed on the oscilloscope. The *digital signal* is either at +5 V or at 0 V as shown in Fig. 1.3(b). The voltage at point *A* moves from 0 to 5 V. The voltage then stays at +5 V for a time. At point *B* the voltage drops immediately from +5 V to 0 V. The voltage then stays at 0 V for a time. *Only two voltages are present*

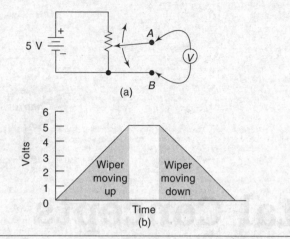

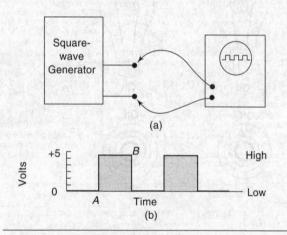

**Fig. 1.2** *(a) Analog Output from a Potentiometer. (b) Analog Signal Waveform.*

*in a digital electronic circuit.* In the waveform diagram in Fig. 1.3(b) these voltages are labelled HIGH and LOW. The HIGH voltage is called a *logical 1* (5 V) and the LOW voltage a *logical 0* (0 V). *Circuits that handle only high and low signals are called digital circuits.*

**Fig. 1.3** *(a) Digital Signal Displayed on Scope. (b) Digital Signal Waveform.*

Signals are commonly represented as a *voltage* varying with time, as in Figs 1.1 and 1.2. However, a signal could be an electrical *current* that varies continuously (analog) or has an *on-off characteristic* (digital).

Within most digital circuits, it is customary to represent signals in the *voltage versus time* format. When digital circuits are *interfaced* with non-digital devices, such as lamps and motors, then the signal can be thought of as *current versus time*. Interfacing refers to the design of interconnections that shift the *levels* of voltage and current to make them *compatible*.

## DIGITAL DEVICES

An *analog device* is one in which data is represented by *physical variables*. A *digital device* is one in which data is represented by *numerical quantities*.

Figure 1.4 shows an analog clock and a digital clock. Both are in common use today. The analog device can be thought of as showing the information desired as an *analog*; the position of the hands of the clock is *analogous* to the time of day. The digital clock, on the other hand, shows the time of day as a *set of numbers*.

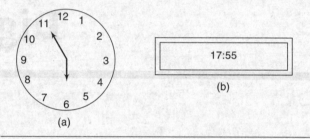

**Fig. 1.4** *(a) An Analog Clock. (b) A Digital Clock.*

The standard volt-ohm milliammeter (VOM) shown in Fig. 1.5(a) is another example of an *analog measuring device*. As the voltage, resistance, or current being measured by the VOM increases, *the needle gradually and continuously moves up the scale*. The digital multimeter shown in Fig. 1.5(b) is an example of a *digital measuring device*. As the voltage, resistance, or current being measured by the DMM increases, *the display jumps upward in small steps*. The DMM is an example of digital circuitry taking over tasks previously performed only by analog devices.

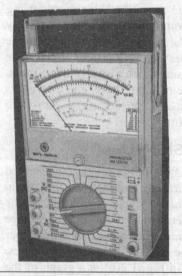

**Fig. 1.5** *(a) Analog Multimeter (BPL). (b) Digital Multimeter (Philips).*

## ADVANTAGES OF DIGITAL CIRCUITS

Digital circuits which use only two signal states have the following *advantages:*

(1) Changes in component values have very little effect on digital signals.

(2) Noise and other interfering signals have very little effect on digital signals.

(3) The voltage anywhere in a digital circuit will always be in one state or the other, so that there is very little chance of confusion or error.

(4) Digital signals are ideally suited for logic use, and for counting in the binary scale.

(5) Information storage is easy.

(6) Operation can be programmed.

(7) More digital circuitry can be fabricated on IC chips.

**1.1 Draw the waveform of (a) an analog signal, (b) a digital signal, and (c) a digital binary signal. Explain briefly.**

*Solution:*

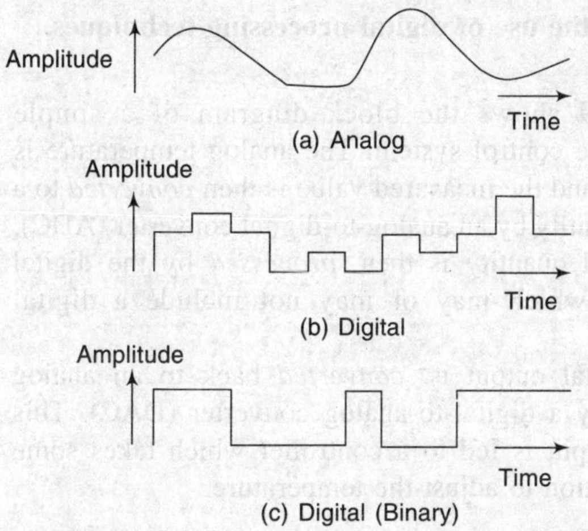

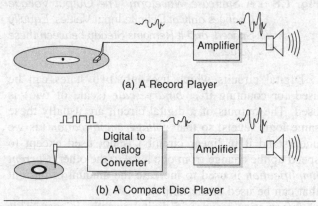

**Fig. 1.6**

(a) An analog signal is *smooth* and not abrupt.

(b) A digital signal is abrupt and not smooth.

(c) A digital binary signal is a digital signal *so constrained* as to take on the values +5 V (1 or *high*) and 0 V (0 or *low*).

**1.2 Compare two very common electronic systems— one an analog system and the other, its counterpart, a digital system.**

*Solution:*

*Record player* (Fig. 1.7(a)): A sensor is used to detect the motion of a stylus as it tracks the displacement of a groove in a vinyl disc (record). The signal produced by this sensor is *analog* in form and corresponds to the sound pressure of the original recording. To reproduce

this sound, the sensor's output is amplified to produce a signal of sufficient power to drive a loudspeaker.

*Compact disc player* (Fig. 1.7(b)): Sound is stored on a compact disc in a *digital* format. This is achieved by repeatedly measuring the magnitude of the original analog sound signal and representing these measurements by numbers. This information is converted into a *binary form* and written onto the CD as a series of pits. The space between two pits is called *land*. The data stored on the disc is retrieved by a sensing arrangement that uses a laser to detect the presence or absence of these pits as the disc spins at high speed. The result is a train of binary information that is a *coded form* of the original measurements. In order to reproduce the recorded sound, this data is first *decoded* and then *converted* back to analog form using a digital-to-analog converter. This signal is then amplified to drive a loudspeaker in a CD player.

(a) A Record Player

(b) A Compact Disc Player

**Fig. 1.7**

**1.3 Explain in detail the advantages of digital circuits.**

*Solution:*

Let us look at the *reasons* for these advantages. Because any voltage which is close to the reference (earth) voltage counts as logic zero and any voltage which is close to the supply voltage counts as logic 1, *small changes* in signal voltages, which might be caused by resistors going higher or lower in value, or changes in the current gain of transistors, have no effect *unless the changes are very great*. Only a voltage change which causes the output of a digital circuit to be *indeterminate*—that is half way between 0 and 1—will cause problems. Similarly *unwanted noise signals* which are added to the 0 or 1 signals have no effect unless their amplitude is *comparatively large*, around half the supply voltage.

An *earthed input* in a digital circuit is a signal input— it sets the input voltage to *logic level 0*. An input which is connected to the *supply voltage* is also a signal input— it sets the input to *logic level 1*.

The use of only two states is an advantage because *it reduces the possibility of errors*—a volt or so change in a level will not mean that it can be mistaken for a different level. A digital type of signal, such as the staircase waveform in Fig. 1.8, which uses several levels, is very likely to cause errors because voltage levels cannot be kept within close limits.

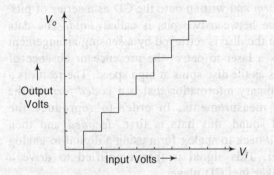

**Fig. 1.8**   *A Staircase Waveform. The Output Voltage Changes only at* Definite Input Values, *Equally Spaced, and it Remains Steady between these Values.*

Digital circuits which use only two states can be used for counting if a *binary scale* (scale of two) is used. The outputs of a digital circuit are usually these same logic levels, so that *voltage amplification* (as we understand it in linear circuits) is not used except to speed up the change from one level to the other. *Current amplification* is used to increase the amount of current that can be used at the output.

*Information storage* in digital systems is easy. This is accomplished by special devices and circuits that can latch onto digital information and hold it for as long as necessary. *Mass storage* techniques can store billions of bits of information in a relatively small space. Analog storage capabilities are, by contrast, extremely limited.

It is fairly easy to design digital systems whose operation is controlled by a set of stored instructions called a *program*. Analog circuits can also be *programmed*, but the variety and complexity of the available operations is extremely limited.

Analog circuits have also benefited from the unprecedented development of IC (integrated circuit) technology, but its relative complexity and its use of devices that cannot be economically integrated (high-value capacitors, precision resistors, inductors, transformers) have prevented analog systems from achieving the same degree of integration—*much more digital circuitry can be fabricated on digital ICs.*

## LIMITATIONS OF DIGITAL CIRCUITS

There is only one major drawback when using digital techniques. *The real-world is analog in nature.* To take advantage of digital techniques when dealing with *analog inputs and outputs,* three steps must be followed:

(1) *Convert* the real-world analog inputs to digital form (analog-to-digital conversion, *ADC*).

(2) *Process* (operate on) the digital information.

(3) *Convert* the digital outputs back to real-world analog form (digital-to-analog converstion, *DAC*).

**1.4 Explain a simple temperature control system that requires analog/digital conversions in order to allow the use of digital processing techniques.**

*Solution:*

Figure 1.9 shows the block diagram of a simple temperature control system. The analog temperature is measured and the measured value is then *converted* to a digital quantity by an analog-to-digital converter (ADC). The digital quantity is then *processed* by the digital circuitry, which may or may not include a digital computer.

Its digital output is *converted* back to an analog quantity by a digital-to-analog converter (DAC). This analog output is fed to a controller which takes some kind of action to adjust the temperature.

## DIGITAL (BINARY) OPERATION OF A SYSTEM

A digital system functions in a binary manner. It employs devices which are permitted to exist in only two possible states. A transistor is allowed to operate at cut-off or in

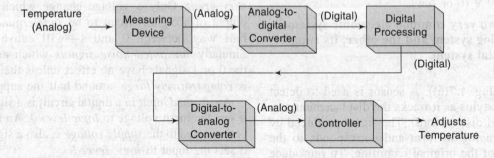

**Fig. 1.9**   *Temperature Control System.*

saturation, *but not in its active region*. A node may be at a high voltage, say, 12 ± 2 V or at a low voltage of, say 0 ± 0.2 V, *but no other values are allowed*. Various designations are used for these *quantized states*, and the most common of these are listed in Table 1.1. In logic, a statement is characterized as *true* or *false*, and this is the first binary classification listed in the table. A switch may be *closed* or *open*, which is the notation under 9, etc. Binary arithmetic and mathematical manipulation of switching and logic functions are best carried out with classification 3, which involves two symbols, 0 (*zero*) and 1 (*one*).

**Table 1.1** *Binary-state Terminology*

|  | 1 | 2 | 3 | 4 | 5 | 6 | 7 | 8 | 9 | 10 | 11 |
|---|---|---|---|---|---|---|---|---|---|---|---|
| One of the states . . . | True | HIGH | 1 | Up | Pulse | Excited | Off | Hot | Closed | North | Yes |
| The other state. . . | False | LOW | 0 | Down | No pulse | Non-excited | On | Cold | Open | South | No |

In a digital system all the electronic components operate in switching mode, because most of the devices act very much like switches, being either ON or OFF. For a variety of technical reasons, devices that function in the *switching mode* are simpler and cheaper to construct than those that function in the *continuous mode* and they function much more efficiently and reliably.

**1.5 An open switch represents 0 and a closed switch represents 1. What number do the switches in Fig. 1.10 represent?**

*Solution:*

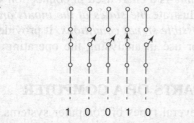

1    0    0    1    0

**Fig. 1.10**

**1.6 The absence or presence of holes in paper represent 0 and 1, respectively. What binary numbers does the punched tape in Fig. 1.11 store?**

*Solution:*

Hole   No Hole

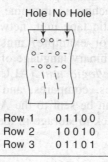

Row 1    0 1 1 0 0
Row 2    1 0 0 1 0
Row 3    0 1 1 0 1

**Fig. 1.11**

## WHY BINARY

A computer is often referred to as a *data processor*. Data means names, numbers, facts, anything needed to work out a problem. *Data* goes into a computer, where it is processed or manipulated to get new information. *A computer's circuits can respond only to binary numbers.*

Besides the data, someone has to work out a *program,* a list of instructions telling the computer what to do. *The program must be coded in binary form before it goes into the computer.*

So the two things we must *input* to a computer are the program and data. These are *stored* inside the computer before the processing begins. Once the run starts, each instruction is executed and the data is processed.

The electronic, magnetic, and mechanical devices of a computer are known as *hardware*. Programs are called *software*. Without software, a computer is a pile of 'dumb' metal.

Computers use *integrated circuits* (ICs) with thousands of transistors, either bipolar or MOS. These computer ICs work remarkably well despite variations. How is it possible? The answer is *two-state* design.

**1.7 Explain the difference between computer hardware and software with the help of a suitable analogy.**

*Solution:*

A *phonograph* is like hardware and *records* are like software. The phonograph is useless without records. Furthermore, the music you get depends on the record you play. A similar idea applies to computers. A *computer* is the hardware and *programs* are the software. The computer is useless without programs. The program stored in the computer determines what the computer will do: change the program and the computer processes the data in a different way.

## MEMORY

When an input signal is applied to most devices or circuits, the output somehow changes in response to the input, and when the input signal is removed, the output returns to its original state. These circuits do not exhibit the property of memory. *Since their outputs revert back to normal, they are classed as non-memory circuits.*

In digital circuitry certain types of devices and circuits do have memory. When an input is applied to such a circuit, the output will change its state, but will remain in the same state even after the input is removed. *The property of retaining its response to a momentary input is called memory.* Figure 1.12 illustrates non-memory and memory operations.

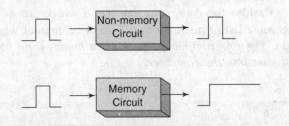

**Fig. 1.12**    *Comparison of Memory and Non-memory Elements.*

Memory devices and circuits play an important role in digital systems because they provide means for *storing* binary numbers, either temporarily or permanently, with the ability to *change* the stored information at any time.

A *register* is a string of devices that store data. Early computers used magnetic cores to store data.

### 1.8 Explain the working of a 4-bit (*binary digit*) core register.

*Solution:*
Figure 1.13(a) shows a *4-bit core register*. With the right-hand rule you can see that conventional current into a wire produces a *clockwise* flux; reversing the current produces a *counter-clockwise* flux. The same result is obtained if electron-flow is assumed and the left-hand rule is used.

The cores have rectangular hysteresis loops; this means that the flux *remains* in the core even after the magnetizing current is *removed* (see Fig. 1.13(b)). This is why a core register can *store* binary data indefinitely. By changing the magnetizing currents in Fig. 1.13(a) we can *change* the stored data.

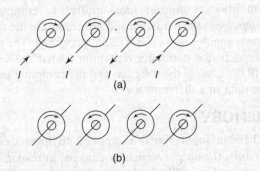

**Fig. 1.13**    *Four-bit Core Register.*

### 1.9 What binary number is stored in Fig. 1.13(b)?

*Solution:*
Using the following code:

| Flux | Binary |
|---|---|
| Counterclockwise | 0 |
| Clockwise | 1 |

Then, the core register of Fig. 1.13(b) stores binary 1001.

## LOGIC CIRCUITS

We use many logical truths in everyday life. Most of the simple logical problems are distinguished by words such as *and, or, not, if, else and then*. Once a verbal reasoning process has been completed and results put into statements, the basic laws of logic can be used to evaluate the process. Simple *logic operations* can be performed by manipulating *verbal statements*. More complex relationships can be usefully represented by the use of symbols. These operations are known as *logic symbols*.

The circuits which perform the logic operations *sense the input conditions and provide an output only if certain input conditions exist.* They can be classified generally as *gate* circuits and they may employ transistors, semiconductor diodes, or magnetic cores. Logic gates most commonly employed are OR, AND, NOT and FLIP-FLOP. They are used to implement Boolean algebraic equations. Logic gates are used extensively in digital computers.

A *truth table* is a chart used in connection with logic circuits to illustrate *the states of the inputs and outputs under all possible signal conditions.* It provides a *ready reference* for use in analysing the operating theory of logic circuits.

## MAJOR PARTS OF A COMPUTER

There are several types of computer systems, but each can be broken down into the same *functional units*. Each unit performs specific functions and all units function together to carry out the instructions given in the program. Figure 1.14 shows the five major functional parts of a digital computer and their *interaction*.

The *input device* lets us pass information from *person to machine* or machine to machine. The input device (keyboard, magnetic tape unit, network connection or telephone line, for example) must *encode* human language into the binary language of the computer.

The *arithmetic/logic unit* (ALU) adds, subtracts, multiplies, divides, compares, and does other logic functions. Data can be sent to the ALU for action and the results sent back to storage in the memory.

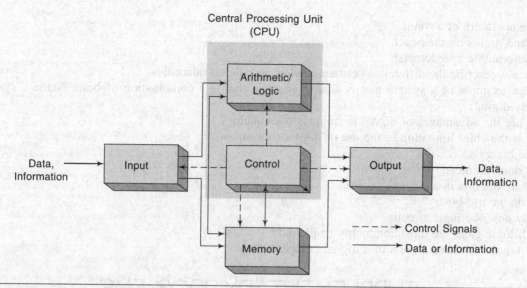

**Fig. 1.14** *Functional Parts of a* Digital Computer.

The *memory unit* is the storage area for both data and programs. This storage can be *supplemented* by storage outside the processing unit.

*The control unit* is the *nervous system of the computer*. It directs all other sections to operate in the proper order and tells the input *when and where* to place information in memory. This unit takes instructions from the memory unit one at a time and interprets them. It then sends appropriate signals to all the other units to cause the specific instruction to be executed.

The *output unit* is the link between the *machine and a person* (or to a device or network). The output unit must *decode* the language of the computer into human language.

## SUMMARY

> An analog device is one that has a signal which varies continuously in step with the input.
> A digital device is one that has a signal with two-state operation.
> An analog device is one in which data is represented by physical variables.
> A digital device is one in which data is represented by numerical quantities.
> Digital signals are ideal for logic use, and for counting in the binary scale. Noise and other interfering signals have very little effect on digital signals. Information storage in digital systems is easy.
> Digital systems can be programmed. Much more digital circuitry can be fabricated on digital ICs.
> The real world is analog in nature.
> When dealing with analog inputs and output: convert (ADC), process, convert (DAC)
> Digital systems work in a binary manner.
> In a digital system all the components operate in switching mode.
> A computer's circuit can respond only to binary numbers.
> The property of retaining its response to a momentary input is called memory.
> A register is a string of devices that store data.
> Logic gates most commonly employed are OR, AND, NOT, and FLIP-FLOP.
> A truth table is a chart used in connection with logic circuits.
> A digital computer has five functional units: input, ALU, memory, control and output.

## REVIEW QUESTIONS

**Test your understanding**

1. Which of the following involve analog quantities and which involve digital quantities?
   (a) Ten-position switch
   (b) Current flowing out of an electrical outlet

(c) Temperature of a room

(d) Sand grains on the beach

(e) Automobile speedometer

2. Concisely describe the difference between analog and digital quantities.

3. Give an example of a system that is analog and one that is a combination of both. Name a system that is entirely digital.

4. What are the advantages of digital techniques over analog?

5. What is the chief limitation to the use of digital techniques?

6. Define binary.

7. What does bit mean?

8. What are the bits in a binary system?

9. Why do we use binary?

10. Briefly describe logic circuits.

11. Which logic gates are most commonly employed?

12. What are the functional units of a digital computer?

# SUPPLEMENTARY PROBLEMS

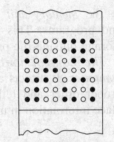

13. How will you generate a digital signal?

14. What type of signal will a push button generate?

15. How will you generate a string of digital pulses?

16. Figure 1.15 shows a strip of magnetic tape. The black circles are magnetized points and the white circles are unmagnetized points. What binary number does each horizontal row represent?

17. In Fig. 1.16, clockwise flux stands for binary 1 and counterclockwise flux stands for binary 0. What is the binary number stored in the 8-bit core register?

**Fig. 1.15** *Numbers on Magnetic Tape.*

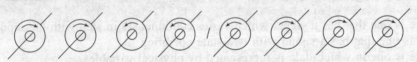

**Fig. 1.16**   *An 8-bit Core Register.*

18. Figure 1.17 shows a 5-bit switch register. By opening and closing the switches you can set up different binary numbers. HIGH output voltage stands for binary 1 and LOW output voltage for binary 0. What is the number stored in switch register?

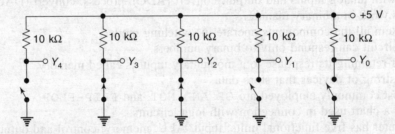

**Fig. 1.17**   *A 5-bit Switch Register.*

# OBJECTIVE TYPE QUESTIONS

## *Fill in the Blanks*

19. Analog signals are continuous and not _____.

20. A digital signal does not change voltage _____ it does so _____.

21. Only two voltages are present in a _____ electronic circuit.
22. An analog device is one in which data is represented by _____.
23. A digital device is one in which data is represented by _____.
24. The real world is _____ in nature.
25. In a digital system all the electronic components operate in a _____ mode.
26. The property of retaining its response to a momentary input is called _____.
27. Memory devices provide a means of _____ binary numbers.
28. The program must be coded in _____ before it goes into the computer.
29. Programs are called _____.
30. The input device lets us pass information from _____ to machine.
31. A truth table provides a _____ for use in analysing the operating theory of logic circuits.
32. Each functional unit performs a _____ function and all functional units function _____ to carry out program instructions.
33. The _____ unit is the nervous system of the computer.

## True/False Questions

State whether the following statements are True or False.
34. The exact value of an input voltage is critical for a digital circuit.
35. A digital circuit is also referred to as a logic circuit.
36. One way to get analog operation is with a square-wave input.
37. Non-memory devices provide means for storing binary numbers.
38. The output unit of a computer is the link between machine and a person.
39. There is no interaction between the functional units of a computer.

## Multiple Choice Questions

40. A quantity having continuous values is
    (a) a digital quantity
    (b) an analog quantity
    (c) a binary quantity
    (d) a natural quantity
41. Which of the following systems are digital:
    (a) electronic calculator
    (b) pressure gauge
    (b) clinical thermometer
    (d) ordinary electric switch
42. The term bit means
    (a) a small amount of data
    (b) a 1 or 0
    (c) a binary digit
    (d) both answers (b) and (c)
43. The property of retaining its response to a momentary input is called
    (a) conversion
    (b) memory
    (c) storing
    (d) coding
44. In a digital system all the electronic components operate in
    (a) continuous mode
    (b) pulse mode
    (c) active mode
    (d) switching mode
45. A digital signal can be generated with the help of a
    (a) mechanical switch
    (b) push button switch
    (c) mechanical relay
    (d) multiplexer

# ANSWERS

1. (a) Digital (b) Analog (c) Analog (d) Digital (e) Analog, if needle type; digital, if numerical readout type.
2. Analog quantities can take on *any* values over a continuous range; digital quantities can take on only *discrete* values.
3. A public address system is analog. A CD player is analog and digital. A computer is all digital.
4. Greater accuracy and precision; less affected by noise; easier to design; easier to store information; ideally suited for logic use; operations can be programmed; higher degree of integration.
5. Real world physical quantities are analog.
6. Binary means having two states or values.
7. A bit is a binary digit.

8. The bits are 1 and 0.

9. A computer's circuits can respond only to binary numbers; the program must be coded in binary form before it goes into the computer; computer ICs work remarkably well, despite variations, because of two-state design.

10. Logic circuits sense the input conditions and provide an output only if certain input conditions exist.

11. OR, AND, NOT and FLIP-FLOP.

12. Input, ALU, memory, control and output.

13.

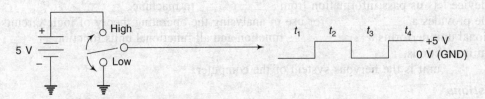

**Fig. 1.18**   *Generating a Digital Signal.*

14.

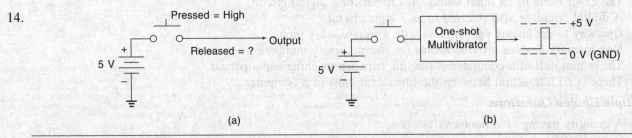

(a)                                                                                  (b)

**Fig. 1.19**   *(a) Push button will not Generate a Digital Signal. (b) Push Button used to Trigger a One-shot Multivibrator for a Single-pulse Digital Signal.*

15.

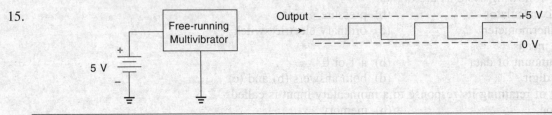

**Fig. 1.20**   *A Free-running Multivibrator Generates a String of Digital Pulses.*

16. Row 1   0 0 0 0 1 1 1 1          Row 5   1 1 1 0 0 1 1 0
    Row 2   1 0 0 0 0 1 1 0          Row 6   0 1 0 0 1 0 0 1
    Row 3   1 0 1 1 0 1 1 1          Row 7   1 1 0 0 1 1 0 1
    Row 4   0 0 1 1 0 0 0 1

17. 1 1 0 0 0 1 1 1       18. 1 0 0 1 1       19. abrupt            20. continuously, abruptly
21. digital              22. physical variables   23. numerical quantities
24. analog               25. switching      26. memory            27. storing
28. binary               29. software       30. man               31. ready reference
32. specific, together   33. control        34. False             35. True
36. False                37. False          38. True              39. False
40. (b)                  41. (a) and (d)    42. (c)               43. (b)
44. (d)                  45. (a)

# Number Systems

## INTRODUCTION

The base or *radix* of a chosen number system comes about through some particular *convenience*. Doubtless human beings prefer the decimal system based upon a radix of 10, because they began by counting on their fingers. A radix of 10 gives 10 different states. Since digital systems are based upon circuitry having only two different states, *binary arithmetic* is employed because this has a radix of 2.

Large numbers in the binary system become *unwieldy* in length, and whilst this presents no problems to the electronics of a system, it does present problems at the *human interface*. Because of this there are various other number systems in use which conveniently interface with the binary system. These systems express numbers in a more convenient and shorter form, e.g. *octal, binary coded decimal, and hexadecimal.*

### 2.1 How will you express the form of a number in any number system?

*Solution:*

Using the letter $r$ to represent the radix of any number system, the form of any number can be expressed as:

$$Y = d_n r^n + d_{n-1} r^{n-1} + \ldots + d_1 r^1 + d_0 r^0 \qquad (2.1)$$

where $Y$ is the value of the entire number, $d_n$ is the value of the $n$th digit from the radix point and $r$ is the radix or base.

### 2.2 Explain the terms:
**(a) most significant digit (b) least significant digit (c) radix point.**

*Solution:*

(a) The most significant digit (*MSD*), the one with the *highest* power of the radix, is always at the left.

(b) The least significant digit (*LSD*), the one with the *lowest* power of the radix, is always at the right.

(c) Any decimal number can be expressed as:

$$\ldots 10^4 \ 10^3 \ 10^2 \ 10^1 \ 10^0 \ . \ 10^{-1} \ 10^{-2} \ 10^{-3} \ 10^{-4} \ldots$$
$$\downarrow$$
$$decimal\ point$$

Any binary number can be expressed as:

$$\ldots 2^4 \ 2^3 \ 2^2 \ 2^1 \ 2^0 \ . \ 2^{-1} \ 2^{-2} \ 2^{-3} \ 2^{-4} \ldots$$
$$\downarrow$$
$$binary\ point$$

Using the letter $r$ to represent the radix of any number system, the form of any number can be expressed as:

$$\ldots r^4 \ r^3 \ r^2 \ r^1 \ r^0 \ . \ r^{-1} \ r^{-2} \ r^{-3} \ r^{-4} \ldots$$
$$\downarrow$$
$$radix\ point$$

### 2.3 Explain the idea of positional weighting.

*Solution:*

Any number of any magnitude can be expressed by using the system of *positional weighting*. The position of the digit with reference to the *radix point* determines the weight. The principle of positional weighting can be extended to any number system.

### 2.4 What weight does the digit 7 have in each of the following numbers?
**(a) 1370 (b) 6725 (c) 7501 (d) 75,898**

*Solution:*
(a) 10    (b) 100    (c) 1,000    (d) 10,000

### 2.5 Evaluate the four digit decimal number 3264.

*Solution:*

In a four digit decimal number, the *least significant* position (right most) has a weighting factor of $10^0$; the *most significant* position (left most) has a weighting factor of $10^3$:

$$10^3 \quad 10^2 \quad 10^1 \quad 10^0$$

where $10^3 = 1000$, $10^2 = 100$, $10^1 = 10$ and $10^0 = 1$

To evaluate the decimal number 3264, the digit in each position is multiplied by the *appropriate weighting factor*:

$$
\begin{aligned}
3 \quad 2 \quad 6 \quad 4 \\
4 \times 10^0 &= \quad 4 \\
6 \times 10^1 &= \quad 60 \\
2 \times 10^2 &= \quad 200 \\
3 \times 10^3 &= +3000 \\
\hline
&\quad 3264
\end{aligned}
$$

## THE BINARY NUMBER SYSTEM

Binary numbers are used extensively in all digital systems because of the very *nature of electronics*. A $\underline{1}$ can be represented by a saturated transistor, a light turned on, a relay energized, or a magnet magnetized in a particular direction. A $\underline{0}$ can be represented by a cut-off transistor, a light turned off, a de-energized relay, or a magnet magnetized in the opposite direction. In each case there are *only two values* that the device can assume. The binary number system has a *radix* of 2.

### 2.6 Illustrate binary elements.

*Solution:*
*Binary elements* are illustrated in Fig. 2.1.

### 2.7 Evaluate the five bit binary numbers 10101.

*Solution:*
We can find its weighting value simply by adding the weighting value of each position that has a 1 below it. Adding from right to left, we obtain:

$$10101 = 1 \times 2^0 + 1 \times 2^2 + 1 \times 2^4$$
$$= 1 + 4 + 16 = 21$$

### 2.8 Evaluate the number $(312.4)_5$.

*Solution:*

$$(312.4)_5 = 3 \times 5^2 + 1 \times 5^1 + 2 \times 5^0 + 4 \times 5^{-1}$$
$$= 75 + 5 + 2 + 0.8$$
$$= (82.8)_{10}$$

*Note:* If there is any doubt about the number system being employed, it should be clarified by writing the radix of the number as a subscript to the number. Thus,

$125_{10}$    decimal number system
$100_2$    binary number system

### 2.9 How will you use your fingers for coding binary numbers?

*Solution:*
A basic unit which we personally can use as a counter is the finger. If it is raised, we say it has value; if it is

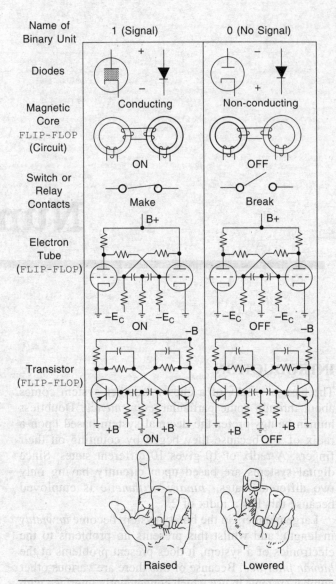

| Name of Binary Unit | 1 (Signal) | 0 (No Signal) |
|---|---|---|
| Diodes | Conducting | Non-conducting |
| Magnetic Core FLIP-FLOP (Circuit) | ON | OFF |
| Switch or Relay Contacts | Make | Break |
| Electron Tube (FLIP-FLOP) | ON | OFF |
| Transistor (FLIP-FLOP) | ON | OFF |

Raised    Lowered

**Fig. 2.1**    *Binary Elements.*

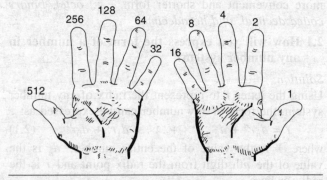

**Fig. 2.2**    *A ready-made Binary Digital Computer.*

lowered, it has no value. It is, therefore, a *binary element*. Ten fingers provide us with a ready-made binary digital computer. By assigning values to the fingers of each hand, we can count any number between 0 and 1023.

## 2.10 Discuss the significance of *zeros* in binary numbers.

*Solution:*

Zeros, whether they are to the right or left, never add to the value of the binary number. Zero times any number is zero. Thus, for practical purposes, only the 1's have to be multiplied by their weighting values and added to each other as shown in Fig. 2.3.

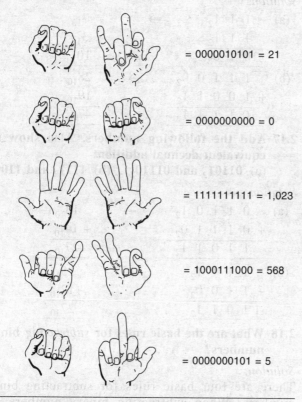

= 0000010101 = 21

= 0000000000 = 0

= 1111111111 = 1,023

= 1000111000 = 568

= 0000000101 = 5

**Fig. 2.3**  *Finding the Value of Binary Numbers.*

Some zeros are required however. The zeros to the *right* of the highest valued 1 serve as *place-keepers* or *spaces* to retain the 1's in their correct position. The zeros to the *left* however provide no information about the number, and hence can be eliminated. Thus, 00101 can be written as 101.

## 2.11 How will you write a *binary sequence*?

*Solution:*

An easy way to write a binary sequence is illustrated in Fig. 2.4.

1. The right-most column begins with a 0 and *alternates each bit*.
2. The next column begins with two 0's and *alternates every two bits*
3. The next column begins with four 0's and *alternates ever four bits*.
4. The next column begins with eight 0's and *alternates every eight bits*.
5. The next column begins with sixteen 0's and *alternates every sixteen bits*.

| Binary | | | Sequence | | Decimal |
|---|---|---|---|---|---|
| 0 | | 0 | | 0 | 0 |
| 0 | | 0 | | 1 | 1 |
| 0 | | 0 | | 1 | 0 | 2 |
| 0 | | 0 | | 1 | 3 |
| 0 | | 1 | | 0 | 0 | 4 |
| 0 | | 1 | | 0 | 1 | 5 |
| 0 | | 1 | | 1 | 0 | 6 |
| 0 | | 1 | | 1 | 1 | 7 |
| 1 | | 0 | | 0 | 0 | 8 |
| 1 | | 0 | | 0 | 1 | 9 |
| 1 | | 0 | | 1 | 0 | 10 |
| 1 | | 0 | | 1 | 1 | 11 |
| 1 | | 1 | | 0 | 0 | 12 |
| 1 | | 1 | | 0 | 1 | 13 |
| 1 | | 1 | | 1 | 0 | 14 |
| 1 | | 1 | | 1 | 1 | 15 |

**Fig. 2.4**  *Writing Binary Sequence.*

## FRACTIONAL BINARY NUMBERS

Although seldom used in digital systems, binary weightings for values less than 1 (fractional binary numbers) are possible. These factors are developed by successively dividing the weighting factors by 2 for each decrease in power of 2 as shown in Fig. 2.5.

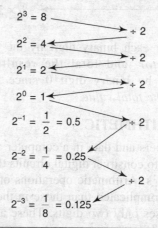

$$2^3 = 8$$
$$2^2 = 4 \quad \div 2$$
$$2^1 = 2 \quad \div 2$$
$$2^0 = 1 \quad \div 2$$
$$2^{-1} = \frac{1}{2} = 0.5 \quad \div 2$$
$$2^{-2} = \frac{1}{4} = 0.25 \quad \div 2$$
$$2^{-3} = \frac{1}{8} = 0.125$$

**Fig. 2.5**  *Successive Division by 2 to Develop Fractional Binary Weighting Factors.*

## BINARY-TO-DECIMAL CONVERSION

Converting a binary number to decimal merely requires *substitution* of numbers into Eq. (2.1) remembering that the $d$'s will all be 0's or 1's, the $r$'s will all be 2 (the radix), and the $n$'s will be the various powers of 2, depending on the position of the digit with reference to the radix point.

## 2.12 Convert $10111_2$ to decimal.

*Solution:*

$$Y = d_4 r^4 + d_3 r^3 + d_2 r^2 + d_1 r^1 + d_0 r^0$$
$$= 1 \times 2^4 + 0 \times 2^3 + 1 \times 2^2 + 1 \times 2^1 + 1 \times 2^0$$
$$= 16 + 0 + 4 + 2 + 1$$
$$10111_2 = 23_{10}$$

## 2.13 Convert the following binary numbers to decimal:
    (a) 110101        (b) 101001

*Solution:*

| Powers of two | $2^5$ | $2^4$ | $2^3$ | $2^2$ | $2^1$ | $2^0$ |
|---|---|---|---|---|---|---|
| Decimal weights | 32 | 16 | 8 | 4 | 2 | 1 |

  (a) $110101 = 32 + 16 + 4 + 1 = 53$
  (b) $101001 = 32 + 8 + 1 = 41$

*Note:* Long binary expressions are broken up into groups of bits to aid in readability. These groups are called *bytes*. A byte is defined as a sequence of adjacent *bits* located as a unit. Bytes are commonly made up of four, eight, or more bits (binary digits), but greater numbers of bytes that are grouped together usually then form a *word*.

## 2.14 Convert the fractional binary number 1011.1010$_2$ to decimal.

*Solution:*

$$1\ 0\ 1\ 1\ .\ 1\ 0\ 1\ 0$$

$$1 \times 2^{-3} = 0.125$$
$$1 \times 2^{-1} = 0.500$$
$$1 \times 2^{0} = 1$$
$$1 \times 2^{1} = 2$$
$$1 \times 2^{3} = 8$$
$$\overline{\qquad 11.625}$$

*Note:* Multiply each binary digit by the *appropriate weighting factor* and total the results. Skip the multiplication by binary digit 0 since it *does not contribute to the total value*.

## BINARY ARITHMETIC

Since all numbers and data in a computer are in *binary form* it is easy to construct digital circuits that recognise only 0's and 1's. Arithmetic operations on these numbers are less complicated than those in the digital system since it uses only two digits. These are illustrated through examples.

## 2.15 What are the basic rules for *adding* binary numbers?

*Solution:*

There are four basic rules for adding binary numbers. Three of the rules result in a single bit. The addition of two 1's yields a binary two ($10_2$). When binary numbers are added, the latter condition creates a sum of 0 in a given column and a *carry* of 1 over to the next higher column.

$$\left\{ \begin{array}{l} 0 + 0 = 0 \\ 0 + 1 = 1 \\ 1 + 0 = 1 \\ 1 + 1 = 10_2 \end{array} \right\}$$

When three bits are being added (a bit in each of the two numbers and a carry bit) the rules for this are illustrated.

$$\left\{ \begin{array}{ll} 1 + 0 + 0 = 01_2 & \text{1 with a carry of 0} \\ 1 + 0 + 1 = 10_2 & \text{0 with a carry of 1} \\ 1 + 1 + 0 = 10_2 & \text{0 with a carry of 1} \\ 1 + 1 + 1 = 11_2 & \text{1 with a carry of 1} \end{array} \right\}$$

## 2.16 Add the following numbers. Also show the equivalent decimal addition.
    (a) 111$_2$ and 11$_2$    (b) 11100$_2$ and 10011$_2$

*Solution:*

(a)
$$\begin{array}{r} 1\ 1\ 1_2 \\ +\ 1\ 1_2 \\ \hline 10\ 1\ 0_2 \end{array} \quad \rightarrow \quad \begin{array}{r} 7_{10} \\ +\ 3_{10} \\ \hline 10_{10} \end{array}$$

(b)
$$\begin{array}{r} 1\ 1\ 1\ 0\ 0_2 \\ +\ 1\ 0\ 0\ 1\ 1_2 \\ \hline 10\ 1\ 1\ 1\ 1_2 \end{array} \quad \rightarrow \quad \begin{array}{r} 28_{10} \\ 19_{10} \\ \hline 47_{10} \end{array}$$

## 2.17 Add the following numbers. Also show the equivalent decimal addition:
    (a) 01101$_2$ and 01110$_2$    (b) 1111$_2$ and 1100.

*Solution:*

(a)
$$\begin{array}{r} 0\ 1\ 1\ 0\ 1_2 \\ +\ 0\ 1\ 1\ 1\ 0_2 \\ \hline 1\ 1\ 0\ 1\ 1_2 \end{array} \quad \rightarrow \quad \begin{array}{r} 13_{10} \\ +\ 14_{10} \\ \hline 27_{10} \end{array}$$

(b)
$$\begin{array}{r} 1\ 1\ 1\ 1_2 \\ +\ 1\ 1\ 0\ 0_2 \\ \hline 1\ 1\ 0\ 1\ 1_2 \end{array} \quad \rightarrow \quad \begin{array}{r} 15_{10} \\ +12_{10} \\ \hline 27_{10} \end{array}$$

## 2.18 What are the basic rules for *subtracting* binary numbers?

*Solution:*

There are four basic rules for subtracting binary numbers. When subtracting binary numbers, we sometimes have to *borrow* from the next higher column. A borrow is required in binary only when we try to subtract a 1 from a 0. In this case when a 1 is borrowed from the next higher column, a 10 is created in the *column being subtracted*, and the last of the basic rules must be applied.

$$\left\{ \begin{array}{l} 0 - 0 = 0 \\ 1 - 0 = 1 \\ 1 - 1 = 0 \\ 10_2 - 1 = 1 \end{array} \right\}$$

## 2.19 Subtract the following numbers. Also show the equivalent decimal subtraction:
    (a) 10$_2$ from 11$_2$    (b) 011$_2$ from 101$_2$

*Solution:*

(a)
$$\begin{array}{r} 11_2 \\ -10_2 \\ \hline 1_2 \end{array} \quad \rightarrow \quad \begin{array}{r} 3_{10} \\ 2_{10} \\ \hline 1_{10} \end{array}$$

(b)
$$\begin{array}{r} 101_2 \\ -011_2 \\ \hline 10_2 \end{array} \quad \rightarrow \quad \begin{array}{r} 5_{10} \\ -3_{10} \\ \hline 2_{10} \end{array}$$

**2.20 Subtract the following numbers. Also show the equivalent decimal subtraction:**
   **(a) $01011_2$ from $11011_2$   (b) $011_2$ from $101_2$**

*Solution:*

(a)
$$\begin{array}{r} 1\,1\,0\,1\,1_2 \\ -\,0\,1\,0\,1\,1_2 \\ \hline 1\,0\,0\,0\,0_2 \end{array} \rightarrow \begin{array}{r} 27_{10} \\ 11_{10} \\ \hline 16_{10} \end{array}$$

(b)
$$\begin{array}{r} 1\,0\,1_2 \rightarrow 5_{10} \\ 0\,1\,1_2 \rightarrow 3_{10} \\ \hline 1\,0_2 \rightarrow 2_{10} \end{array}$$

**2.21 What are the basic rules for *multiplying* binary numbers?**

*Solution:*

There are four basic rules for multiplying binary numbers. Multiplication involves forming the *partial products*, shifting each partial product left one place and then adding all the partial products.

$$\left.\begin{array}{l} 0 \times 0 = 0 \\ 0 \times 1 = 0 \\ 1 \times 0 = 0 \\ 1 \times 1 = 1 \end{array}\right\}$$

**2.22 Carry out the following multiplications. Also show the equivalent decimal multiplication.**
   **(a) $111_2 \times 101_2$      (b) $1011_2 \times 1001_2$**

*Solution:*

(a)
$$\begin{array}{r} 1\,1\,1_2 \\ \times\ 1\,0\,1_2 \\ \hline 1\,1\,1_2 \\ 0\,0\,0_2 \\ 1\,1\,1_2 \\ \hline 1\,0\,0\,0\,1\,1_2 \end{array} \rightarrow \begin{array}{r} 7_{10} \\ \times\,5_{10} \\ \hline 35_{10} \end{array}$$

(b)
$$\begin{array}{r} 1\,0\,1\,1_2 \\ \times\ 1\,0\,0\,1_2 \\ \hline 1\,0\,1\,1_2 \\ 0\,0\,0\,0_2 \\ 0\,0\,0\,0_2 \\ 1\,0\,1\,1_2 \\ \hline 1\,1\,0\,0\,0\,1\,1_2 \end{array} \rightarrow \begin{array}{r} 11_{10} \\ \times\,9_{10} \\ \hline 99_{10} \end{array}$$

**2.23 Carry out the following multiplications. Also show the equivalent decimal multiplication.**
   **(a) $10101_2 \times 101_2$   (b) $11111_2 \times 10011_2$**

*Solution:*

(a)
$$\begin{array}{r} 1\,0\,1\,0\,1_2 \\ \times\ 1\,0\,1_2 \\ \hline 1\,0\,1\,0\,1_2 \\ 0\,0\,0\,0\,0_2 \\ 1\,0\,1\,0\,1_2 \\ \hline 1\,1\,0\,1\,0\,0\,1_2 \end{array} \rightarrow \begin{array}{r} 21_{10} \\ \times\,5_{10} \\ \hline 105_{10} \end{array}$$

(b)
$$\begin{array}{r} 1\,1\,1\,1\,1_2 \\ 1\,0\,0\,1\,1_2 \\ \hline 1\,1\,1\,1\,1_2 \\ 1\,1\,1\,1\,1_2 \\ 0\,0\,0\,0\,0_2 \\ 0\,0\,0\,0\,0_2 \\ 1\,1\,1\,1\,1_2 \\ \hline 1\,0\,0\,1\,0\,0\,1\,1\,0\,1_2 \end{array} \rightarrow \begin{array}{r} 31_{10} \\ 19_{10} \\ \hline 279_{10} \\ 31_{10} \\ 589_{10} \end{array}$$

**2.24 What are the basic rules for *division* in binary?**

*Solution:*

Division in binary follows the same procedure as division in decimal.

**2.25 Carry out the following divisions. Also show the equivalent decimal division.**
   **(a) $110_2 \div 11_2$      (b) $1111_2 \div 110_2$**

*Solution:*

(a)
$$11_2\overline{)110_2} \rightarrow 3_{10}\overline{)6_{10}}$$
with quotient $10_2 \rightarrow 2_{10}$
$$\begin{array}{r} 10_2 \\ 11_2)\overline{110_2} \\ \underline{11_2} \\ 000_2 \end{array} \qquad \begin{array}{r} 2_{10} \\ 3_{10})\overline{6_{10}} \\ \underline{6_{10}} \\ 0_{10} \end{array}$$

(b)
$$\begin{array}{r} 10.1 \\ 110_2)\overline{1111.0_2} \\ \underline{110_2} \\ 110_2 \\ \underline{110_2} \\ 000_2 \end{array} \qquad \begin{array}{r} 2.5_{10} \\ 6_{10})\overline{15_{10}} \\ \underline{12_{10}} \\ 30_{10} \\ \underline{30_{10}} \\ 00_{10} \end{array}$$

**2.26 Carry out the following divisions. Also show their equivalent decimal division.**
   **(a) $11111111_2 \div 110011_2$   (b) $110000_2 \div 100_2$**

*Solution:*

(a)
$$\begin{array}{r} 101_2 \\ 110011_2)\overline{11111111_2} \\ \underline{110011_2} \\ 110011_2 \\ \underline{110011_2} \\ 000000_2 \end{array} \qquad \begin{array}{r} 5_{10} \\ 51_{10})\overline{255_{10}} \\ \underline{255_{10}} \\ 000_{10} \end{array}$$

(b)
$$\begin{array}{r} 1100_2 \\ 100_2)\overline{110000_2} \\ \underline{100_2} \\ 100_2 \\ \underline{100_2} \\ 000_2 \end{array} \rightarrow \begin{array}{r} 12_{10} \\ 4_{10})\overline{48_{10}} \\ \underline{4} \\ 08_{10} \\ \underline{8_{10}} \\ 0_{10} \end{array}$$

## COMPLEMENTS IN NUMBER SYSTEMS

The complement number system was invented to make addition and subtraction faster and easier to implement by omitting the need for sign and magnitude comparison. Instead it requires *complementation* which is performed quite efficiently on binary numbers.

The *true complement* of a binary number is formed by subtracting each digit of the number from radix-minus-one of the number system and then adding 1 to the least significant digit. The true complement of a number in the decimal system is referred to as the *10's complement* and in the binary system it is referred to as the *2's complement*.

The *radix-minus-one complement* in each system is formed by subtracting each digit of the number from the radix-minus-one. It is *9* for the decimal system and *1* for the binary system.

The *1's complement* and *2's complement* of a binary number are important because they permit the representation of *negative numbers*. The method of 2's complement arithmetic is commonly used in computers to handle negative numbers.

**2.27 How will you carry out 9's complement subtraction?**

*Solution:*
Subtraction of a *smaller* decimal number from a *larger* decimal number is accomplished by adding 9's complement of the subtrahend (in this case the smaller number) to the minuend and then adding the carry to the result. This is called *end-around-carry*.

When subtracting a *larger* decimal number from a *smaller* decimal number, there is no carry, and the result is in 9's complement form and negative. This procedure has a distinct advantage in certain types of arithmetic logic.

**2.28 Find the 9's complement of**
    **(a) 28**        **(b) 562**        **(c) 3497**

*Solution:*

| (a) | 99 | (b) | 999 | (c) | 9999 |
|---|---|---|---|---|---|
| | −28 | | −562 | | −3497 |
| | 71 | | 437 | | 6502 |

**2.29 Perform the following subtractions using the 9's complement method.**
    **(a) 13 − 7**        **(b) 15 − 28**

*Solution:*

|  | Regular subtraction | | 9's complement subtraction | |
|---|---|---|---|---|
| (a) | 13 | | 13 | |
| | −07 | | +92 | 9's complement of 07 |
| | 06 | | ① 05 | |
| | | | → +1 | Add carry to result |
| | | | 06 | |

(b)

| 15 | | 15 | |
|---|---|---|---|
| −28 | | +71 | 9's complement of 28 |
| −13 | | 86 | 9's complement of result |
| | | −13 | *No carry indicates that the answer is negative and in complement form.* |

**2.30 How will you carry out *10's complement subtraction*?**

*Solution:*
The 10's complement of a decimal number can be used to perform subtraction by adding the minuend to the 10's complement of the subtrahend and *dropping the carry*.

**2.31 Convert the following decimal numbers to their 10's complement form:**
    **(a) 52**        **(b) 428**

*Solution:*

| (a) | 99 | (b) | 999 | |
|---|---|---|---|---|
| | −52 | | −428 | |
| | 47 | | 571 | 9's complement form |
| | ⊕ 1 | | ⊕ 1 | Add 1 |
| | → 48 | | → 572 | 10's complement |

**2.32 Perform the following subtractions by using the 10's complement method.**
    **(a) 54 − 21**        **(b) 196 − 155**

*Solution:*

|  | Regular subtraction | 10's complement subtraction | |
|---|---|---|---|
| (a) | 54 | 54 | |
| | −21 | +79 | 10's complement of 21 |
| | 33 | ✗33 | Drop carry |
| (b) | 196 | 196 | |
| | −155 | +845 | 10's complement of 155 |
| | 41 | ✗041 | Drop carry |

**2.33 How will you carry out *1's complement subtraction*?**

*Solution:*
1's complement method allows us to subtract using only addition.

To subtract a *smaller* number from a *larger* one, the following steps are involved:
1. Determine the 1's complement of the smaller number.
2. Add the 1's complement to the larger number.
3. *Remove the carry and add it to the result* (end-around carry).

To subtract a *larger* number from a *smaller* number the following steps are involved:

1. Determine the 1's complement of the larger number.
2. Add the 1's complement to the smaller number.
3. The answer has an opposite sign and is the 1's complement of the result. *There is no carry.*

**2.34 Find the 1's complement of the following binary numbers:**

**(a) $101_2$     (b) $1101_2$     (c) $11100_2$**

*Solution:*

|     | Binary number | 1's complement |
|-----|---------------|----------------|
| (a) | $101_2$       | $010_2$        |
| (b) | $1101_2$      | $0010_2$       |
| (c) | $11100_2$     | $00011_2$      |

**2.35 Subtract $10011_2$ from $11001_2$ using the 1's complement method. Also show direct subtraction for comparison.**

*Solution:*

| Direct subtraction | 1's complement subtraction |  |
|---|---|---|
| $11001_2$ | $11001_2$ | |
| $-10011_2$ | $+01100_2$ | 1's complement |
| $\overline{00110_2}$ | $\overline{①00101_2}$ | |
| | $\quad\longrightarrow +1$ | Add end-around carry |
| | $\overline{00110_2}$ | |

**2.36 Subtract $1101_2$ from $1001_2$ using the 1's complement method.**
**Also show direct subtraction for comparison.**

*Solution:*

| Direct subtraction | 1's complement subtraction |  |
|---|---|---|
| $1001_2$ | $1001_2$ | |
| $-1101_2$ | $+0010_2$ | 1's complement |
| $\overline{-0100_2}$ | $\overline{1011_2}$ | Answer in 1's complement form and opposite in sign |
| | $\downarrow$ | |
| | $-0100$ | Final answer. |

**2.37 How will you obtain the 1's complement of a binary number with a digital circuit?**

*Solution:*
The simplest way to obtain the 1's complement of a binary number with a digital circuit is to use parallel inverters (NOT circuits) as shown in Fig. 2.6 for an 8-bit binary number. *An inverter negates the input.*

**2.38 How will you obtain the 2's complement of a *negative binary number* with a digital circuit?**

*Solution:*
The 2's complement of a negative binary number can be realised using inverters and an adder as shown in

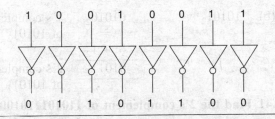

**Fig. 2.6** *Example of Inverters to Obtain 1's Complement of a Binary Number.*

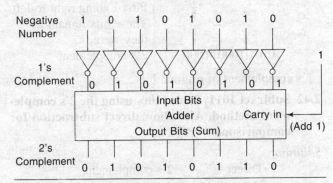

**Fig. 2.7** *Obtaining the 2's Complement of a Negative Binary Number.*

Fig. 2.7. *Invert each bit* to take 1's complement and then *add 1* to the 1's complement with an adder circuit.

**2.39 How will you carry out *2's complement subtraction*?**

*Solution:*
To subtract *a smaller number from a larger number*, the following steps are involved:

1. Determine the 2's complement of the smaller number.
2. Add the 2's complement to the larger number.
3. Discard the carry (*there is always a carry in this case*).

To subtract *a larger number from a smaller number* the following steps are involved:

1. Determine the 2's complement of the larger number.
2. Add the 2's complement to the smaller number.
3. *There is no carry. The result is in 2's complement form and is negative.*
4. To get the answer in true form, take the 2's complement and change the sign.

**2.40 Find the 2's complement of**
**(a) $110_2$ and     (b) $10101_2$**

*Solution:*

|     | Binary number | 2's complement |  |
|-----|---------------|----------------|---|
| (a) | $110_2$       | $001_2$        | 1's complement of $110_2$ |
|     |               | $+ 1_2$        | Add 1 |
|     |               | $\overline{010_2}$ | 2's complement of $110_2$ |

(b)    $10101_2$                  $01010_2$    1's complement
                                              of $10101_2$

                                  $\underline{+\ 1_2}$

                                  $01011_2$    2's complement
                                              of $10101_2$

### 2.41 Find the 2's complement of $1101011101000_2$.

*Solution:*

$\underbrace{1101011}\ \underbrace{101000}$

{ First 1 going right-to-left.
These bits remain as
they were.

$\underbrace{0010100}011000$    2's complement

1's complement of original bits.

### 2.42 Subtract $1011_2$ from $1100_2$ using the 2's complement method. Also show direct subtraction for comparison.

*Solution:*

| Direct subtraction | 2's complement method | |
|---|---|---|
| $1100_2$ | $1100_2$ | |
| $-1011_2$ | $+0101_2$ | 2's complement |
| $\overline{0001_2}$ | $\cancel{1}0001_2$ | Discard carry |
| | $\rightarrow 0001_2$ | |

### 2.43 Subtract $11100_2$ from $10011_2$ using the 2's complement method. Also show direct subtraction for comparison.

*Solution:*

| Direct subtraction | 2's complement method | |
|---|---|---|
| $10011_2$ | $10011_2$ | |
| $-11100_2$ | $+00100_2$ | 2's complement |
| $\overline{-01001_2}$ | $\overline{10111_2}$ | No carry 2's complement of answer. |
| | $\rightarrow -01001_2$ | |

## DECIMAL-TO-BINARY CONVERSION

Decimal-to-binary conversion is a more lengthy process. One method is the *repeated subtraction of powers of two* until there is no remainder or the remainder that is left is sufficiently small for the desired conversion. This method works best for *whole numbers*. The second method, *two-part method,* is used to convert a number containing a *fraction*. First the whole number is converted by successively dividing the number by two. Then the decimal part is converted by repeatedly multiplying by two until the decimal part of the number becomes exactly zero or until the desired accuracy is obtained.

### 2.44 How will you perform a decimal-to-binary conversion using the *subtraction method*?

*Solution:*

1. Write down the powers of two *upto and including* the one closest to the number being converted.
2. *Sequentially subtract* each of these powers of two from the decimal number.
3. If the powers can be subtracted, *write a binary 1* in the bit position corresponding to that power of two.
4. If the power is larger than the decimal number, *write a 0* in that position and try the next lower power of two.

### 2.45 Convert $50_{10}$ to binary using the *subtraction method*.

*Solution:*

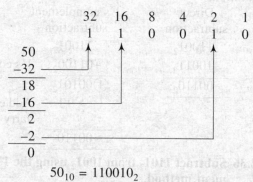

$$50_{10} = 110010_2$$

### 2.46 How will you perform a decimal-to-binary conversion using the two-part method?

*Solution:*

First convert the *whole part* of the decimal number by repeatedly dividing by two.

1. If there is no remainder (it divides evenly or is *even*) write down a 0.
2. If there is a remainder (answer is odd) write down a 1.
3. The first division represents the *least significant digit*.
4. The last division represents the *most significant digit*.

This method does not require writing down the powers of two. The fractional part is converted by repeatedly multiplying by two.

1. If the multiplication produces a whole number equal to one plus some fractional part, write a 1.
2. Multiplications by two are repeated until the fractional part exactly equals zero or until the desired accuracy is obtained.

**2.47 Convert $53_{10}$ to binary by *two-part method*.**

*Solution:*

| Division | Remainder | |
|---|---|---|
| $53 \div 2 = 26$ | 1 | → LSD |
| $26 \div 2 = 13$ | 0 | |
| $13 \div 2 = 6$ | 1 | |
| $6 \div 2 = 3$ | 0 | |
| $3 \div 2 = 1$ | 1 | |
| $1 \div 2 = 0$ | 1 | → MSD |

$53_{10} = 110101$

**2.48 Convert $0.3125_{10}$ to binary.**

*Solution:*

| Multiplication | Whole Number Part | |
|---|---|---|
| 0.3125 | | |
| $\times 2$ | | |
| 0.6250 | 0 | → MSD |
| $\times 2$ | | |
| 1.2500 | 1 | |
| $\times 2$ | | |
| 0.5000 | 0 | |
| $\times 2$ | | |
| 1.0000 | 1 | → LSD |

$0.3125_{10} = 0.0101_2$

## SIGNED BINARY NUMBERS

Binary numbers that carry identification as to their polarity are called signed binary numbers. Plus and minus signs for positive and negative numbers can be represented in a digital format. Further, if a binary number is negative, there are several convenient ways of representing that number. Each representation has its own features. The three major *signed binary notations* are: sign magnitude notation, 1's complement notation, and 2's complement notation.

**2.49 Describe the *sign magnitude notation* for representing signed binary numbers.**

*Solution:*

The most straight forward method is to add a 0 or 1 to the most significant digit of the overall number. This notation is called *sign magnitude* because the *sign* bit is given first, and then the positive *magnitude* of the number follows. A *sign bit of $\theta$* indicates the number is positive, while a *sign bit of 1* indicates the number is negative. All other bits of the number indicate the magnitude of the number just as for unsigned binary numbers.

Sign magnitude notation is *very easy to read*, but it is *not easy to use* when adding or subtracting binary numbers.

**2.50 Express the decimal number 13 as a signed magnitude number.**

*Solution:*

$$13_{10} = 1101_2$$
$$\text{Sign}$$
$$+13_{10} = \boxed{0}1101_2$$
$$-13_{10} = \boxed{1}1101_2$$

**2.51 Describe the *1's complement notation* for representing signed binary numbers.**

*Solution:*

Another way to represent a signed binary number is to attach a *sign bit*, just as with sign magnitude notation, and *invert all of the bits if the number is negative*. 1's complement numbers are easy to form, but there are two representations of zero. Also, when 1's complement numbers are added or subtracted, a process known as *end-around-carry* is necessary to obtain the correct answer.

**2.52 Express the decimal number 13 as signed magnitude number in *1's complement notation*.**

*Solution:*

$$13_{10} = 1101_2$$
$$+13_{10} = 0\boxed{1101_2} \quad \text{same as in problem 2.50}$$
$$-13_{10} = 1\boxed{0010_2} \quad \text{invert all the bits if the}$$
$$\text{number is negative.}$$
$$\text{Sign bit}$$

This number representation is called 1's complement notation.

**2.53 Describe the *2's complement notation* of expressing signed magnitude numbers.**

*Solution:*

The most common representation for signed binary numbers is 2's complement notation. The 2's complement is generated by *inverting the bits* as in 1's complement, *then adding 1 to the least significant digit*. 2's complement is a little more difficult to generate, but it simplifies addition and subtraction. Further, there is only one representation for zero in 2's complement.

**2.54 Express the decimal number 13 in *2's complement notation*.**

*Solution:*

$$13_{10} = 1101_2 \quad \text{same as in problem 2.52}$$
$$+13_{10} = 0\boxed{1101_2}$$
$$-13_{10} = 1\boxed{0011_2}$$

This number representation is called *2's complement notation*.

## OCTAL NUMBERS

The octal number system is *composed of eight digits*, which are

$$0, 1, 2, 3, 4, 5, 6, 7$$

To count above 7, we begin another column and start over.

$$10, 11, 12, 13, 14, 15, 16, 17$$
$$20, 21, 22, 23, 24, 25, 26, 27$$
$$30, 31, 32, 33, 34, 35, 36, 37$$

Counting in octal is the same as counting in decimal, except that any number with an 8 or 9 is omitted. We use the *subscript 8* to indicate on octal number.

## OCTAL-TO-DECIMAL CONVERSION

Since the octal number system has a *base of 8*, each successive digit position is an *increasing power of 8*, beginning in the right-most column with $8^0$. The evaluation of an octal number in terms of its decimal equivalent is accomplished by multiplying each digit by its weight and summing the products.

**2.55 Convert $2374_8$ to its decimal equivalent.**

*Solution:*

| Weight | $8^3$ | $8^2$ | $8^1$ | $8^0$ |
|---|---|---|---|---|
| Decimal value | 512 | 64 | 8 | 1 |
| Octal number | 2 | 3 | 7 | 4 |

$$2374_8 = 2 \times 8^3 + 3 \times 8^2 + 7 \times 8^1 + 4 \times 8^0$$
$$= 2 \times 512 + 3 \times 64 + 7 \times 8 + 4 \times 1$$
$$= 1024 + 192 + 56 + 4$$
$$= 1276_{10}$$

## DECIMAL-TO-OCTAL CONVERSION

Whole octal numbers are represented by digits to the left of the octal point. The *column weights* are
$$8^n \ldots 8^6.8^5.8^4.8^3.8^2.8^1.8^0$$

A method of converting a decimal number into an octal number is the *repeated-division-by-8 method*, which is similar to the method used for conversion of decimal to binary. Each successive division by 8 yields a remainder that becomes a digit in the equivalent octal number. The first remainder generated is the *least significant digit* (LSD).

**2.56 Convert 359 decimal to octal.**

*Solution:*

```
                          44              Remainder
                      8) 359
                         32
                         ─────
                         39
                         32
                         ─────
                          7        →    7   (LSD)
                          5
                      8) 44
                         40
                         ─────
                          4        →    4
                          0
                      8) 5
                          0
                         ─────
                          5        →    5   (MSD)
                                       547₈
```
$$547_8$$

## FRACTIONAL OCTAL NUMBERS

Fractional octal numbers are represented by digits to the right of octal point. The column weights are:
$$8^0.8^{-1}.8^{-2}.8^{-3}.8^{-4}.8^{-5}.8^{-6} \ldots 8^{-n}$$

octal point

All digits to the left of octal point have weights that are *positive powers of eight*. All digits to the right of octal point have weights that are *negative powers of eight*.

To convert fractional octal numbers to decimal numbers determine the weights of each digit and *sum the weight times the digit*.

**2.57 Determine the decimal value of the octal fraction $0.325_8$.**

*Solution:*
First determine the weights of each digit and then sum the weight times the digit.

| Octal weight: | $8^{-1}$ | $8^{-2}$ | $8^{-3}$ |
|---|---|---|---|
| Decimal value: | 0.125 | 0.015625 | 0.001953 |
| Octal number: | 0.3 | 2 | 5 |

$$0.325_8 = 3(0.125) + 2(0.015625) + 5(0.001953)$$
$$= 0.375 + 0.03125 + 0.009765$$
$$= 0.416015_{10}$$

## OCTAL-TO-BINARY CONVERSION

The conversion from octal to binary is performed by converting each octal digit to its *3-bit binary equivalent*.

**Table 2.1**   *Octal Numerals*

| Octal Digit | 0 | 1 | 2 | 3 | 4 | 5 | 6 | 7 |
|---|---|---|---|---|---|---|---|---|
| Binary Equivalent | 000 | 001 | 010 | 011 | 100 | 101 | 110 | 111 |

Using these conversions, any octal number is converted to binary by *individually* converting each digit.

**2.58 Convert $472_8$ to binary.**

*Solution:*

| 4 | 7 | $2_8$ |
|---|---|---|
| 100 | 111 | 010 |

Hence octal $472 = 100111010_2$

**2.59 Convert $5431_8$ to binary.**

*Solution:*

| 5 | 4 | 3 | 1 |
|---|---|---|---|
| 101 | 100 | 011 | 001 |

Thus, $5431_8 = 101100011001_2$

## BINARY-TO-OCTAL CONVERSION

Converting from binary to octal is the *reverse* of octal-to-binary conversion. The bits of binary numbers are arranged into *groups of three bits* starting at the least significant bit. Then each group is converted to its equivalent, as shown in Table 2.1.

### 2.60 Convert $100111010_2$ to octal.

*Solution:*

$$\underbrace{100}_{4} \quad \underbrace{111}_{7} \quad \underbrace{010}_{2}{}_8$$

$$= 472_8$$

### 2.61 Convert $11010110_2$ to octal.

*Solution:*

$$\underbrace{011}_{3} \quad \underbrace{010}_{2} \quad \underbrace{110}_{6}{}_8$$

$$= 326_8$$

### 2.62 Why do we need the octal system?

*Solution:*

When dealing with a large quantity of binary numbers of many bits, it is *convenient and more efficient* for us to write the numbers in octal rather than binary. *Digital circuits and systems work strictly in binary; we are using octal only as a convenience for the operators of the system.*

### 2.63 Discuss the usefulness of the octal system.

*Solution:*

The octal system is attractive as *a shorthand means of expressing large binary numbers*. In computer work, binary numbers with up to 64 bits are not uncommon. These binary numbers do not always represent a *numerical* quantity but are always some type of *code* that conveys *non-numerical* information. In computers, binary numbers might represent:
1. actual non-numerical data;
2. numbers corresponding to a location (address) in memory;
3. an instruction code;
4. a code representing alphabetic and other non-numerical characters; or
5. a group of bits representing the status of devices internal or external to the computer.

## HEXADECIMAL NUMBERS

Hexadecimal (*hex*) uses sixteen different digits. Because hex digits must be represented by a single character; *letters are chosen to represent values greater than 9.* The sixteen allowable hex digits are:

0, 1, 2, 3, 4, 5, 6, 7, 8, 9, A, B, C, D, E and F.

To signify a hex number, a subscript 16 or the letter H is used (that is $A7_{16}$ or A7H, for example). Two hex digits are used to represent a *byte*. Four bits (one hex digit) are sometimes called a *nibble*.

### 2.64 What is the *practical application* of hexadecimal number system?

*Solution:*

Binary numbers are long. *The hexadecimal system was born out of the need to express numbers concisely, and is by far the most commonly used number system in computer literature.*

The hexadecimal number system, like the octal system, is *a method of grouping bits to simplify entering and reading the instructions or data present in digital computer systems.* Hexadecimal uses *4-bit groupings*, therefore, instructions or data used in 8-16-, or 32-bit computer systems can be represented as a two-, four-, or eight-, digit hexadecimal code instead of using a long string of binary digits.

### 2.65 How do we count in hex?

*Solution:*

Once we get to F, simply start over with another column and continue as follows:

> 10, 11, 12, 13, 14, 15, 16, 17, 18, 19,
> 1A, 1B, 1C, 1D, 1E, 1F
> 20, 21, 22, 23, 24, 25, 26, 27, 28, 29,
> 2A, 2B, 2C, 2D, 2E, 2F
> 30, 31, 32, 33, 34, 35, 36, 37, 38, 39,
> 3A, 3B, 3C, 3D, 3F, 3F
> 40, 41, and so forth.

### 2.66 Tabulate and *compare* binary, hexadecimal, and decimal numbers.

*Solution:*

**Table 2.2**  *Binary, Hex, and Decimal Numbers—a Comparison*

| Binary | Hexadecimal | Decimal |
|--------|-------------|---------|
| 0000 | 0 | 0 |
| 0001 | 1 | 1 |
| 0010 | 2 | 2 |
| 0011 | 3 | 3 |
| 0100 | 4 | 4 |
| 0101 | 5 | 5 |
| 0110 | 6 | 6 |
| 0111 | 7 | 7 |
| 1000 | 8 | 8 |
| 1001 | 9 | 9 |
| 1010 | A | 10 |
| 1011 | B | 11 |
| 1100 | C | 12 |
| 1101 | D | 13 |
| 1110 | E | 14 |
| 1111 | F | 15 |
| 1  0000 | 10 | 16 |

### 2.67 What is the maximum count of a two-digit, three-digit, and four-digit hex number?

*Solution:*

With two hexadecimal digits, $FF_{16}$, we can count up to $255_{10}(16^2 - 1)$. To count beyond this, three hexadecimal digits are required. The maximum three-digit hexadecimal number is $FFF_{16}$, or $4095_{10}$ ($16^3 - 1$). The maximum four-digit hexadecimal number is $FFFF_{16}$, or $65,535_{10}$ ($16^4 - 1$).

## HEXADECIMAL-TO-DECIMAL CONVERSION

One method to evaluate a hexadecimal number in terms of its decimal equivalent is to first convert it to *binary* and then convert from *binary to decimal.*

Another method of converting a hexadecimal number to its decimal equivalent is by multiplying each hexadecimal digit by its *weight* and then taking the sum of these products. *The weights of a hexadecimal number are increasing powers of 16.*

### 2.68 Convert $2A6_{16}$ to decimal.

*Solution:*

$$
\begin{array}{ccc}
2 & A & 6 \\
0010 & 1010 & 0110
\end{array}
$$
$$
\begin{aligned}
001010100110 &= 2^1 + 2^2 + 2^5 + 2^7 + 2^9 \\
&= 2 + 4 + 32 + 128 + 512 \\
&= 678_{10}
\end{aligned}
$$

## DECIMAL-TO-HEXADECIMAL CONVERSION

*Repeated division* of a decimal number by 16 will produce the equivalent hexadecimal number formed by the remainders of each division. This is analogous to repeated division-by-2 for decimal-to-binary conversion and repeated division-by-8 for decimal-to-octal conversion.

### 2.69 Convert $B2F8_{16}$ to decimal.

*Solution:*

$$
\begin{aligned}
B2F8_{16} &= B \times 16^3 + 2 \times 16^2 + F \times 16^1 + 8 \times 16^0 \\
&= 11 \times 4096 + 2 \times 256 + 15 \times 16 + 8 \times 1 \\
&= 45,816_{10}
\end{aligned}
$$

### 2.70 Convert $498_{10}$ to hexadecimal.

$$
\begin{array}{llll}
498 \div 16 = 31 & \text{remainder} & 2 & \text{(LSD)} \\
31 \div 16 = 1 & \text{remainder} & 15(= F) & \\
1 \div 16 = 0 & \text{remainder} & 1 & \text{(MSD)} \\
498_{10} = 1F2_{16} & & &
\end{array}
$$

## HEXADECIMAL-TO-BINARY CONVERSION

To convert from hex to binary *replace each hex symbol with the appropriate four bits.*

### 2.71 Convert $A9_{16}$ to binary.

*Solution:*

$$
\begin{array}{cc}
A & 9 \\
1010 & 1001
\end{array}
$$
$$
10101001_{16}
$$

## BINARY-TO-HEXADECIMAL CONVERSION

To convert a binary number to hex, simply *break the binary number into four-bit groups, starting at the binary point, and replace each group with the equivalent hex symbol.*

### 2.72 Convert $01101101_2$ to hex.

*Solution:*

$$
\begin{array}{cc}
0110 & 1101 \\
6 & D \\
& 6D_{16}
\end{array}
$$

## HEXADECIMAL ARITHMETIC

Hexadecimal *addition* can be done directly with hex numbers remembering that:

1. *hex* digits 0 through 9 are equivalent to *decimal* digits 0 through 9, and
2. the *hex digits* A through F are equivalent to *decimal digits* 10 through 15.

Since a hexadecimal number can be used to represent a binary number, it can also be used to represent the 2's complement of a binary number. *The 2' complement allows us to subtract by adding binary numbers.* We can also use this method for hexadecimal subtraction.

### 2.73 What are the rules for hexadecimal addition?

*Solution:*

When adding two hexadecimal numbers, the following rules apply:

1. In any given column of an addition problem, think of the two hexadecimal digits in terms of their decimal value.
2. If the sum of these two digits is $15_{10}$ or less, bring down the corresponding hexadecimal digit.
3. If the sum of these two digits is greater than $15_{10}$, bring down the amount of the sum that exceeds $16_{10}$ and *carry* a one to the next column.

### 2.74 Add the following hexadecimal numbers:

(a) $58_{16} + 22_{16}$    (b) $2B_{16} + 84_{16}$
(c) $DF_{16} + AC_{16}$

*Solution:*

(a)
$$
\begin{array}{r}
58_{16} \\
+22_{16} \\
\hline
7A_{16}
\end{array}
$$
right column: $8_{16} + 2_{16}$
$= 8_{10} + 2_{10} = 10_{10} = A_{16}$
left column: $5_{16} + 2_{16}$
$= 5_{10} + 2_{10} = 7_{10} = 7_{16}$

(b)
$$
\begin{array}{r}
2B_{16} \\
+84_{16} \\
\hline
AF_{16}
\end{array}
$$
right column: $B_{16} + 4_{16}$
$= 11_{10} + 4_{10} = 15_{10} = F_{16}$
left column: $2_{16} + 8_{16}$
$= 2_{10} + 8_{10} = 10_{10} = A_{16}$

(c)      $DF_{16}$      right column: $F_{16} + C_{16}$
$$= 15_{10} + 12_{10} = 27_{10}$$

     $+AC_{16}$      $27_{10} - 16_{10} = 11_{10} = B_{16}$
*with a 1 carry*

     $18B_{16}$      left column: $D_{16} + A_{16} + 1_{16}$
$$= 13_{10} + 10_{10} + 1_{10} = 24_{10}$$
$$24_{10} - 16_{10} = 8_{10} = 8_{16}$$
*with a 1 carry*

### 2.75 Subtract the following hex numbers:
(a) $84_{16} - 2A_{16}$      (b) $C3_{16} - 0B_{16}$

*Solution:*

(a)   $2A_{16} = 00101010_2$
2' complement of $2A_{16} = 11010110 = D6_{16}$

     $84_{16}$
     $+D6_{16}$
     $\cancel{1}5A_{16}$          Drop carry as in 2's complement addition.

     $5A_{16}$

(b)   $0B_{16} = 00001011_2$
2's complement of $0B_{16} = 11110101 = F5_{16}$

     $C3_{16}$
     $+ F5_{16}$
     $\cancel{1}B8_{16}$          Drop carry

## CONVERSION ALGORITHMS

An *algorithm* is a method of arriving at an answer that always works. The first algorithm presented in this chapter is:

$$Y = d_n r^n + d_{n-1} r^{n-1} + \ldots + d_0 r^0 + d_{-1} r^{-1}$$
$$+ \ldots + d_{-m} r^{-m}$$

The second algorithm requires successive division for integers. Both algorithms are universal. *A flow chart is a graphical means of expressing an algorithm.*

### 2.76 Illustrate and explain the *conversion algorithm.*

*Solution:*

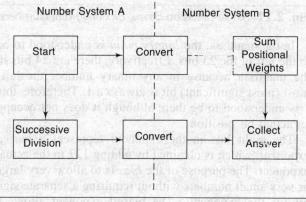

**Fig. 2.8** *Conversion Algorithm.*

Numbers from number system A are first converted to those of the system B. Then calculation takes place within the system B. For example, to convert from the *binary system to the decimal system* each digit (a 1 or 0) is converted to decimal and then multiplied by the radix (expressed in the decimal system) raised to some decimal power. The operations could be described as: (a) *convert* (b) *arithmetic* and (c) *collect the answer.*

*Decimal-to-octal* conversion is usually done using *successive division*, because it is easier to do the arithmetic in the decimal system. If, however, the arithmetic is done in octal, the *positional weighting* method can be used.

*Octal-to-decimal* conversion is usually done using the *positional weighting* method. However, if the arithmetic is done in octal, the same answer can be found using *successive division*.

### 2.77 Draw the *flowchart* for repeated-division method of decimal-to-binary conversion of integers.

*Solution:*

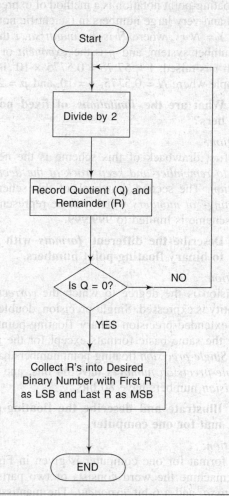

**Fig. 2.9** *Flowchart for Repeated-division Method of Decimal-to-binary Conversion of Integers. The Same Process can be used to Convert a Decimal Integer to any Other System.*

## FLOATING-POINT NUMBERS

In *decimal* very small and very large numbers are expressed in *scientific notation* (powers of 10). $2.7 \times 10^9$ and $1.56 \times 10^{-12}$ are typical examples. *Binary numbers* can also be expressed in the same notation by stating a number (*mantissa*) and an *exponent of 2*. There are many *formats* of the floating-point number, each computer having its own. On some machines, the programmer can *select* from various formats, depending on the *accuracy* desired. Some use *excess-notation* for the exponent; some use *2's complement*; some use *signed magnitude* for both the mantissa and the exponent.

### 2.78 Differentiate between a *fixed-point* number and *floating-point* number.

*Solution:*

Any number with a *fixed location of the radix point* is called a fixed-point number, e.g. $01101.111_2$, $66.575_{10}$, and $9AF. AB_{16}$. The *range* of numbers that can be represented in fixed-point notation is *limited*.

Floating-point notation is a method of expressing very small and very large numbers in (scientific notation) the form $Y = N \, r^p$, where $N$ is the *mantissa*, $r$ the *base* of the number system, and $p$ is the *exponent* or power to which $r$ is raised. $Y = 57.75 = 0.5775 \times 10^2$ is a typical example where $N = 0.5775$, $r = 10$, and $p = 2$.

### 2.79 What are the *limitations* of fixed point numbers?

*Solution:*

The first drawback of this scheme is the need of the user *to remember and keep track of the decimal point location*. The second drawback of this scheme is that the *range of numbers* which can be represented, using this scheme is limited to 999.999.

### 2.80 Describe the different *formats* with reference to binary floating-point numbers.

*Solution:*

Precision is the degree to which the *correctness* of a quantity is expressed. Single-precision, double-precision and extended-precision binary floating-point numbers have the same basic formats except for the number of bits. *Single-precision* floating-point numbers have 32 bits, *double-precision numbers* have 64 bits, and *extended-precision* numbers have 80 bits.

### 2.81 Illustrate and describe the floating-point format for one computer.

*Solution:*

The format for one computer is given in Fig. 2.10. In this machine the word consists of two parts: a 10-bit *mantissa*, and a 6-bit *exponent*. The mantissa is in *2's complement form*; the left-most bit is the *sign bit*. The *binary point* is to the right of this sign bit. The 6 bits of the exponent could represent 0 through 63. However, to express *negative exponents* the number 32 ($100000_2$) has been added to the desired exponent. This is a

common system used in floating-point formats. It represents *excess-32 notation*.

| Mantissa | | | | | | | | | | Exponent | | | | | |
|---|---|---|---|---|---|---|---|---|---|---|---|---|---|---|---|
| 0 | 1 | 0 | 0 | 1 | 0 | 0 | 0 | 0 | 0 | 1 | 0 | 0 | 0 | 1 | 1 |

**Fig. 2.10** *Floating-point Format.*

### 2.82 What is the *floating-point number* in Fig. 2.10?

*Solution:*

Excess-32 notation is given in Table 2.3.

| | |
|---|---|
| The mantissa portion is | $+0.100100000$ |
| The exponent portion is | $100011$ |
| Subtracting $100000(32_{10})$ | $000011$ |
| The entire number is | $+0.1001_2 \times 2^3$ |
| $N$ | $= 100.1_2$ |
| | $= 4.5_{10}$ |

**Table 2.3**   *Excess-32 Notation*

| Desired Exponent | Binary Representation |
|---|---|
| −32 | 000000 |
| −1 | 011111 |
| 0 | 100000 |
| +6 | 100110 |
| +31 | 111111 |

### 2.83 Illustrate and describe the format for *single-precision* binary floating-point numbers with the help of an example.

*Solution:*

In the standard format for a single-precision binary number, Fig. 2.11, the *sign bit* ($S$) is the left-most bit, the *exponent* ($E$) includes the next eight bits and the *mantissa or the fractional part* ($F$) includes the remaining 23 bits.

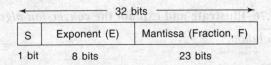

| S | Exponent (E) | Mantissa (Fraction, F) |
|---|---|---|
| 1 bit | 8 bits | 23 bits |

32 bits

**Fig. 2.11** Single-precision *Binary Floating Point Numbers.*

In the mantissa, the *binary point* is understood to be to the left of the 23 bits. Effectively, there are 24 bits in the mantissa because in any binary number the left-most (most significant) bit is always a 1. Therefore, this 1 is understood to be there although it does not occupy an actual bit position.

The eight bits in the exponent represent a *biased exponent*, which is obtained by adding 127 to the actual exponent. The purpose of the *bias* is to allow very large or very small numbers without requiring a separate sign bit for the exponents. The biased exponent allows a range of actual exponent values from −126 to +128. Let's use 1011010010001 as an example.

It can be expressed as 1 plus a fractional binary number by moving the binary point 12 places to the lelt and then multiplying by the appropriate power of 2.

$$1011010010001 = 1.011010010001 \times 2^{12}$$

Assuming that this is a positive number, the *sign bit* (S) is 0. The exponent, 12 is expressed as a *biased exponent* by adding it to 127 (12 + 127 = 139). The biased exponent (E) is expressed as the binary number 10001011. The *mantissa* is the fractional part (F) of the binary number 0.011010010001. Because there is always 1 to the left of the binary point in the power-of-two expression, *it is not included in the mantissa.* The complete floating-point number is

| S | E | F |
|---|---|---|
| 0 | 10001011 | 011010010001000000000000 |

**Fig. 2.12** *The Format for 1011010010001.*

**2.84 When is a floating-point number said to be *normalized*?**

*Solution:*

In a 16-bit format (see Fig. 2.10), the *mantissa* is 10 bits long and the *exponent* 6-bits. The system is, therefore, capable of 9-bit *accuracy* (allowing 1 bit for the sign). *The exponent bits add, nothing to accuracy, only to magnitude.* Fixed-point 2's complement numbers expressed in 16 bits are accurate to 15 bits. Thus, although floating-point numbers can be much larger or smaller than equivalent length fixed-point numbers they are *less accurate.*

To keep the full 10 bits of accuracy in the floating-point number *the most significant bit must be placed next to the sign bit.* Under these conditions the floating-point number is said to be *normalized*. Most computers normalize the result of floating-point operations.

# SUMMARY

> Digital systems require the use of decimal, binary, octal, and hexadecimal number systems.
> The binary system is used by the hardware; the octal and hexadecimal systems are used as a shorthand language for representing binary numbers.
> A binary number is a weighted number. The weight of each whole number digit is a positive power of two. The weight of each fractional digit is a negative power of two. The whole number weights increase from right to left—from least significant digit to most significant digit.
> A binary number can be converted to a decimal number by summing the decimal values of the weights of all the 1's in the binary number.
> A decimal whole number can be converted to binary by using the sum-of-weights or by repeated division-by-2 method.
> A decimal fraction can be converted to binary by using the sum-of-weights or by repeated multiplication-by-2 method.
> The basic rules for binary addition are:
> $\qquad 0 + 0 = 0 \qquad 0 + 1 = 1 \qquad 1 + 0 = 1 \qquad 1 + 1 = 10$
> The basic rules for binary subtraction are:
> $\qquad 0 - 0 = 0 \qquad 1 - 1 = 0 \qquad 1 - 0 = 0 \qquad 10 - 1 = 1$
> The 1's complement of a binary number is derived by changing 1's to 0's and 0's to 1's.
> The 2's complement of a binary number can be derived by adding 1 to the 1's complement.
> Binary subtraction can be accomplished with addition by using the 1's or 2's complement method.
> A positive binary number is represented by a 0 sign bit.
> A negative binary number is represented by a 1 sign bit.
> For arithmetic operations, negative binary numbers are represented in 1's complement or 2's complement form.
> The hexadecimal number system consists of 16 digits and characters, 0 through 9 followed by A through F.
> One hexadecimal digit represents a 4-bit binary number.
> A decimal number can be converted to hexadecimal by the repeated division-by-16 method.
> The octal number consists of eight digits, 0 through 7.
> A decimal number can be converted to octal by the repeated division-by-8 method.
> Octal-to-binary conversion is accomplished by simply replacing each octal digit by its 3-bit binary equivalent. The process is reversed for binary-to-octal conversion.
> Each of the systems uses the two basic conversion algorithms, and each can perform all the arithmetic operations.
> Floating point numbers provide the widest range of binary numbers.

# REVIEW QUESTIONS

1.  What is the largest decimal number that can be represented in binary with eight bits?
2.  What weight does the digit 7 have in 58.72?
3.  How many bits are required to count up to decimal 1 million?
4.  Draw the table of hexadecimal and binary equivalences for 0 through $16_{10}$.
5.  Convert decimal 23 to binary.
6.  Convert $1011101001_2$ to decimal.
7.  Tabulate binary and decimal positional weighting.
8.  Write the next three numbers in the octal counting sequence: 624, 625, 626.
9.  What range of decimal values can be represented by a four-digit octal number?
10. Convert $614_8$ to decimal.
11. Convert $146_{10}$ to octal, then from octal to binary.
12. What range of decimal values can be represented by a four-digit hex number?
13. What are the advantages of using the hexadecimal system over binary, octal, or decimal system?
14. Convert $24CE_{16}$ to decimal.
15. Convert $3117_{10}$ to hex, then from hex to binary.
16. Write the next four numbers in this hex counting sequence: E9A, E9B, E9C, E9D.
17. Solve the following equation for $x$:

$$x_{16} = 1111 \quad 1111 \quad 1111 \quad 1111_2$$

18. Convert hexadecimal 7E to its decimal equivalent.
19. Convert decimal 141 to hexadecimal.
20. Add $1011_2$ and $110_2$.
21. Subtract 1 from $100_2$.

# SUPPLEMENTARY PROBLEMS

22. Express each of the following numbers as a sum of the products of each digit and its appropriate weight:
    (a) $51_{10}$     (b) $173_{10}$     (c) $1492_{10}$     (d) $10.658_{10}$
23. How are the weighting factors determined for each decimal position in a base 10 number?
24. Convert $1101.0110_2$ to decimal.
25. What is the weight of the MSB of a 16-bit number?
26. What is the decimal value of $110110_2$?
27. Derive the 9's complement representation of
    (a) $61_{10}$     (b) $235_{10}$
28. Evaluate $9_{10} - 6_{10}$ using the binary 1's complement system.
29. Draw the diagram to show all the 4-bit binary combinations in the 2's complement system to represent positive and negative numbers from 0 to 8.
30. Obtain the 1's and 2's complements of the following numbers:
    (a) $101101_2$     (b) $101100_2$
31. Convert $41_{10}$ to binary.
32. Convert $170_{10}$ to binary.
33. Convert $614_8$ to decimal.
34. Convert $146_{10}$ to octal, then from octal to binary.
35. Convert $975_{10}$ to binary by first converting to octal.
36. Convert binary $1010111011_2$ to decimal by first converting to octal.
37. Convert $11110011_2$ to hexadecimal system.
38. Convert $F80B_{16}$ to binary.
39. Add $18_{16} + 34_{16}$.
40. Subtract $5C_{16}$ from $94_{16}$.
41. How will you evaluate a binary number that is already in floating-point format?
42. Convert the decimal number $3.248 \times 10^4$ to a single-precision floating-point binary number.

# OBJECTIVE TYPE QUESTIONS

## Fill in the Blanks

43. Large numbers in the binary system become _____ in length.
44. There are various number systems in use which conveniently _____ with the binary system.
45. It is not necessary to design _____ circuits to perform binary arithmetic.
46. If an application calls for extensive mathematics, it is the domain of a _____.
47. Any number of any magnitude can be expressed by using the system of _____ weighting.
48. The position of a digit with reference to the _____ point determines its weight.
49. Digital computers function in the _____ number system.
50. Any number assigning process is called _____.
51. The highest weighting value is on the _____ left.
52. Positional weighting values increase from _____ to _____.
53. The zeros to the right of the highest valued 1 serve as _____ to retain the 1's in their correct positions.
54. The least significant digit is the _____ right digit.
55. The most significant digit is multiplied by the highest _____ value.
56. With *n* bits we can count up to _____.
57. Binary digits are referred to as _____.
58. The radix in any number system equals the number of _____ in the system.
59. Three number systems are used in computer work: binary, _____, and hexadecimal.
60. The binary number system is sometimes called the _____ system.
61. The 1 in the binary number 1000 has a place value of _____ in decimal.
62. The binary number 1010 equals _____ in decimal.
63. The number $2^7$ equals _____ in decimal.
64. When subtracting numbers, we sometimes have to _____ from the next higher column.
65. The 1's complement method of subtraction is particularly useful in _____ circuits.
66. The decimal number 39 equals _____ in binary.
67. The binary number 101010 equals _____ in decimal.
68. Signed binary numbers carry _____ as to their polarity.
69. There are _____ representations of zero in 1's complement notation.
70. The octal number system is composed of _____ digits.
71. The most common representation for signed binary numbers is _____ notation.
72. There is only one representation for _____ in 2's complement notation.
73. The octal system is a _____ means of expressing large binary numbers.
74. Hexadecimal uses _____ groupings.
75. In hexadecimal system _____ are chosen to represent values greater than 9.
76. Four bits (one hex digit) are sometimes called a _____.
77. Any number system is only a set of _____ symbols.
78. The weights of a hexadecimal number are increasing powers of _____.
79. The 2' complement allows us to subtract by _____ binary numbers.
80. Write the next four numbers in this hex counting sequence:
    E9A, E9B, E9C, E9D, _____, _____, _____, _____.
81. In decimal, very small and very large numbers are expressed by _____ notation.
82. An algorithm is a method of arriving at an answer that _____ works.
83. Conversion from decimal-to-octal is usually done by _____ division.
84. Conversion from octal-to-decimal is usually done using the _____ weightage.
85. There are many _____ for floating-point numbers.
86. Floating point numbers have the advantage of expressing _____, _____ and _____ _____ numbers.
87. Floating-point numbers are less accurate than _____ numbers.

### True/False Questions

State whether the following statements are True or False.

88. Binary number are to the base 2.
89. A radix of 10 gives 10 different states.
90. If an application calls for extensive mathematics, it is the domain of an encoder.
91. The most significant digit is the right-most digit.
92. We have names for the weighting of digits in their various places of significance.
93. Larger numbers cannot be expressed by positional weightage.
94. The position of a digit with reference to radix point determines its weight.
95. A raised finger can represent a 1 and a 0 can be represented by a lowered finger.
96. Octal numbers are to base 16.
97. $1 + 1 + 1 = 11_2 \rightarrow 1$ with a carry of 1.
98. When subtracting numbers, we sometimes have to borrow from the next higher column.
99. The complement number system was invented to make addition and subtraction faster and easier.
100. The 2' complement of a binary number is obtained by subtracting 1 from the 1's complement.
101. The method of repeated subtraction of powers of two works best for fractional binary numbers.
102. In sign magnitude notation, a sign bit of 1 indicates that the number is positive.
103. Sign magnitude notation is easy to use but not easy to read when adding and subtracting binary numbers.
104. There is only one representation of zero in 2's complement notation.
105. The primary advantage of hex number system is the ease with which conversions can be made.
106. In a hex system letters are chosen to represent values greater than 9.
107. An algorithm is a method of arriving at an answer that sometimes works.

### Multiple Choice Questions

108. The number system with radix 2 is known as
    (a) binary number system        (b) octal number system
    (c) decimal number system       (d) hexadecimal number system
109. A group of 8 bits is known as
    (a) a nibble                    (b) a byte
    (c) a bit                       (d) an octal number
110. Knowledge of binary number system is required by the designers of computers and other digital systems because
    (a) it is easy to learn binary number system
    (b) it is easy to learn Boolean algebra
    (c) it is easy to use binary codes
    (d) the devices used in these systems operate in a binary manner
111. One's complement of binary number 10001011 is
    (a) 01110101                    (b) 01110111
    (c) 01110100                    (d) 11110100
112. One's complement of 1's complement of the binary number 11000101 is
    (a) 00111010                    (b) 10111010
    (c) 00111011                    (d) 11000101
113. Two's complement of the binary number 10010100 is
    (a) 01101011                    (b) 01101100
    (c) 11101100                    (d) 10001011
114. Two's complement of 2's complement of the binary number 01101100 is
    (a) 10010100                    (b) 01101100
    (c) 10010011                    (d) 11101100
115. The radix of hexadecimal system is
    (a) 2           (b) 4           (c) 8           (d) 16
116. Hexadecimal number system is used in digital computers and digital systems to
    (a) perform arithmetic operations    (b) input binary data into the system
    (c) perform logical operations       (d) perform arithmetic and logic operations
117. The hexadecimal equivalent of the binary number 11101101111010 is
    (a) EDEB        (b) 35572       (c) FB7A        (d) 3B7A

118. The binary equivalent of the hexadecimal number AOB5 is
  (a) 0101110100001010  (b) 0101111101001010
  (c) 1010000010110101  (d) 1011000011000101
119. The binary equivalent of octal number 362 is
  (a) 011110010  (b) 101101010
  (c) 001101100010  (d) 100001101
120. The octal equivalent of the binary number 11010111 is
  (a) 656  (b) 327  (c) 653  (d) D7
121. In a digital computer binary subtraction is performed
  (a) in the same way as we perform subtraction in decimal number system
  (b) using two's complement method
  (c) using 9's complement method
  (d) using 10's complement method
122. The binary equivalent of decimal number 0.0625 is
  (a) 1001110001  (b) 0.1001110001
  (c) 0.0110001110  (d) 0.0001
123. The maximum positive and negative numbers which can be represented in 2's complement form using $n$ bits are respectively
  (a) $+(2^{n-1} - 1), -(2^{n-1} - 1)$  (b) $+(2^{n-1} - 1), -2^{n-1}$
  (c) $+2^{n-1}, -2^{n-1}$  (d) $+2^{n-1}, -(2^{n-1} + 1)$
124. When two $n$-bit binary numbers are added, the sum will contain at the most
  (a) $n$ bits  (b) $n + 1$ bits
  (c) $n + 2$ bits  (d) $n + n$ bits
125. The minimum number of bits required to represent negative numbers in the range of $-1$ to $-9$ using 2's complement representation is
  (a) 2  (b) 3  (c) 4  (d) 5
126. The minimum number of bits required to represent positive numbers in the range 1–31 using 2's complement representation is
  (a) 5  (b) 6  (c) 8  (d) 10
127. Two's complement representation of $-8$ is
  (a) 0111  (b) 1000  (c) 01000  (d) 10100
128. The number of bits required to encode 80 pieces of information is
  (a) 4  (b) 5  (c) 6  (d) 7

# ANSWERS

1. $2^8 - 1 = 255$,  2. 0.1  3. 20 bits,  4. see problem 2.66,
5. 10111,  6. $745_{10}$
7. **Table**  *Binary and Decimal Positional Weighting*

| *(a) Binary* | *(b) Decimal* |
|---|---|
| $1_2 = 1 \times 2^0 = 1_{10}$ | $1_{10} = 1 \times 10^0 = 1_{10}$ |
| $10_2 = 1 \times 2^1 = 2_{10}$ | $10_{10} = 1 \times 10^1 = 10_{10}$ |
| $100_2 = 1 \times 2^2 = 4_{10}$ | $100_{10} = 1 \times 10^2 = 100_{10}$ |
| $1000_2 = 1 \times 2^3 = 8_{10}$ | $1000_{10} = 1 \times 10^3 = 1000_{10}$ |
| $10000_2 = 1 \times 2^4 = 16_{10}$ | $10000_{10} = 1 \times 10^4 = 10000_{10}$ |

8. 627, 630, 631  9. 0 to 4095  10. 396  11. 222, 010010010
12. 0 to 65, 535
13. It is most compact among the four systems and requires the fewest digit symbols,
14. 9422  15. C2D, 110000101101  16. E9E, E9F, EA0, EA1
17. $x = \text{FFFF}_{16}$  18. 126  19. 8D  20. $10001_2$
21. $11_2$

22. (a) $5 \times 10^1 + 1 \times 10^0$
    (b) $1 \times 10^2 + 7 \times 10^1 + 3 \times 10^0$
    (c) $1 \times 10^3 + 4 \times 10^2 + 9 \times 10^1 + 2 \times 10^0$
    (d) $1 \times 10^1 + 0 \times 10^0 + 6 \times 10^{-1} + 5 \times 10^{-2} + 8 \times 10^{-3}$

23. The form of every decimal number is

$$\ldots 10^4 \ 10^3 \ 10^2 \ 10^1 \ 10^0 \ . \ 10^{-1} \ 10^{-2} \ 10^{-3} \ 10^{-4} \ldots$$

$$\downarrow$$

decimal point

24. $13.375_{10}$               25. $32768_{10}$               26. $54_{10}$

27. (a) $38_{10}$                 (b) $764_{10}$               28. $0011_2$; $3_{10}$

29.              **Table**   *Two's Complement Numbers*

| Binary | Decimal |
|--------|---------|
| 0111 | +7 |
| 0110 | +6 |
| 0101 | +5 |
| 0100 | +4 |
| 0011 | +3 |
| 0010 | +2 |
| 0001 | +1 |
| 0000 | 0 |
| 1111 | –1 |
| 1110 | –2 |
| 1101 | –3 |
| 1100 | –4 |
| 1011 | –5 |
| 1010 | –6 |
| 1001 | –7 |
| 1000 | –8 |

30. 1's complement  (a) $010010_2$     (b) $010011_2$
    2's complement  (a) $010011_2$     (b) $010100_2$

31. $101001_2$         32. $10101010_2$         33. $396_{10}$         34. $222_8$; $10010010_2$

35. $1717_8$, $1010111011_2$     36. $1273_8$, $699_{10}$     37. $F3_{16}$         38. $1111100000001011_2$

39. $4C_{16}$         40. $38_{16}$

41. Number $= (-1)^S (1 + F)(2^{E-127})$

Consider the following floating-point binary numbers.

| S | E | F |
|---|---|---|
| 1 | 10010001 | 10001110001000000000000 |

The sign bit is 1. The biased exponent is 10010001 = 145. Applying the formula we get

Number $= (-1)(1.10001110001)(2^{18}) = -1100011100010000000$

$$= -407,688_{10}$$

42. $3.248 \times 10^4 = 32480 = 111111011100000_2 = 1.11111011100000 \times 2^{14}$

The MSB will not occupy a bit position because it is always a 1. Therefore, the mantissa is the fractional 23-bit binary number 11111011100000000000000 and the biased exponent is

$$14 + 127 = 141 = 10001101_2$$

The complete floating-point number is

| 0 | 10001101 | 11111011100000000000000 |
|---|----------|--------------------------|

43. unwieldy         44. interface         45. complicated         46. microprocessor
47. positional       48. radix             49. binary              50. coding
51. extreme          52. right to left     53. spacers             54. extreme
55. place            56. $2^n - 1$         57. bits                58. digits

| | | | |
|---|---|---|---|
| 59. octal | 60. base-2 | 61. 8 | 62. 10 |
| 63. 128 | 64. borrow | 65. arithmetic/logic | 66. 100111 |
| 67. 42 | 68. identification | 69. two | 70. eight |
| 71. sign magnitude | 72. zero | 73. shorthand | 74. four-bit |
| 75. letters | 76. nibble | 77. sequential | 78. sixteen |
| 79. adding | 80. E9E, E9F, EA0, EA1 | | 81. scientific |
| 82. always | 83. successive | 84. positional | 85. formats |
| 86. very small, and very large | 87. fixed point | 88. True | 89. True |
| 90. False | 91. False | 92. True | 93. False |
| 94. True | 95. True | 96. False | 97. True |
| 98. True | 99. True | 100. False | 101. False |
| 102. False | 103. False | 104. True | 105. True |
| 106. True | 107. False | 108. (a) | 109. (b) |
| 110. (d) | 111. (c) | 112. (d) | 113. (b) |
| 114. (b) | 115. (d) | 116. (b) | 117. (d) |
| 118. (c) | 119. (a) | 120. (b) | 121. (b) |
| 122. (d) | 123. (b) | 124. (b) | 125. (d) |
| 126. (b) | 127. (b) | 128. (d) | |

# Codes and Parity

## INTRODUCTION

When numbers, letters, or words are represented by a special group of symbols we say that they are being *encoded*, and the group of symbols is called a *code*. Probably one of the most familiar codes is the *Morse Code*, where series of dots and dashes represent letters of the alphabet.

Any decimal number can be represented by an equivalent binary number. The group of 0's and 1's in the binary number can be thought of as a code representing the decimal number. When a decimal number is represented by its *equivalent* binary number, we call it *straight binary coding*.

All digital systems use some form of binary numbers for their internal operation, but *the external world is decimal in nature*. This means that conversions between decimal and binary numbers are being performed often. *Conversions* between decimal and binary can become long and complicated for large numbers. For this reason a means of encoding decimal numbers that combine some features of *both* the decimal and binary systems is used in certain situations. In many applications special codes are used for such *auxiliary functions* as error detection.

## WEIGHTED BINARY CODES

In order to represent the 10 decimal digits, 0 through 9, it is necessary to use at least 4 binary digits (0 = 0000 and 9 = 1001). Since there are 16 combinations of four binary digits, of which only 10 combinations are used, it is possible to form a very large number of distinct codes. Of particular importance is the class of *weighted codes*, whose main characteristic is that *each binary digit is assigned a weight*, and for each group of four-bits, the sum of the weights of those binary digits whose value is 1 is equal to the decimal digit which they represent. In other words, if $w_1$, $w_2$, $w_3$ and $w_4$ are the weights of the binary digits and $x_1$, $x_2$, $x_3$ and $x_4$ are the corresponding digit values, then the decimal digit $N = w_4 x_4 + w_3 x_3 + w_2 x_2 + w_1 x_1$ is represented by the binary sequence $x_4 x_3 x_2 x_1$. *A sequence of binary digits which represents a decimal digit is called a code word.* Thus, the above sequence $x_4 x_3 x_2 x_1$ is the code word for *N*. A number of *weighted four-digit binary codes* are shown in Table 3.1.

**Table 3.1**  *Examples of Weighted Binary Codes*

| Decimal digit | 8 | 4 | 2 | 1 | $w_4$ 2 | $w_3$ 4 | $w_2$ 2 | $w_1$ 1 | 6 | 4 | 2 | −3 |
|---|---|---|---|---|---|---|---|---|---|---|---|---|
| 0 | 0 | 0 | 0 | 0 | 0 | 0 | 0 | 0 | 0 | 0 | 0 | 0 |
| 1 | 0 | 0 | 0 | 1 | 0 | 0 | 0 | 1 | 0 | 1 | 0 | 1 |
| 2 | 0 | 0 | 1 | 0 | 0 | 0 | 1 | 0 | 0 | 0 | 1 | 0 |
| 3 | 0 | 0 | 1 | 1 | 0 | 0 | 1 | 1 | 1 | 0 | 0 | 1 |
| 4 | 0 | 1 | 0 | 0 | 0 | 1 | 0 | 0 | 0 | 1 | 0 | 0 |
| 5 | 0 | 1 | 0 | 1 | 1 | 0 | 1 | 1 | 1 | 0 | 1 | 1 |
| 6 | 0 | 1 | 1 | 0 | 1 | 1 | 0 | 0 | 0 | 1 | 1 | 0 |
| 7 | 0 | 1 | 1 | 1 | 1 | 1 | 0 | 1 | 1 | 1 | 0 | 1 |
| 8 | 1 | 0 | 0 | 0 | 1 | 1 | 1 | 0 | 1 | 0 | 1 | 0 |
| 9 | 1 | 0 | 0 | 1 | 1 | 1 | 1 | 1 | 1 | 1 | 1 | 1 |

**3.1 Describe the binary-coded decimal (BCD) system. How will you form a BCD number?**

*Solution:*

Binary-coded decimal (BCD) means that each decimal digit is represented by a binary code of four-bits. This code is useful for outputting to displays that are always numeric (0 to 9), such as those found in digital clocks or digital voltmeters.

To form a BCD number, simply *convert* each decimal digit to its four-bit binary code. To convert BCD to decimal, just *reverse* the process. Start at the decimal point and *break the code into groups of four-bits.* Then write the decimal digit represented by each four-bit group.

**3.2 Represent the number 562₁₀ in 8421 code.**

*Solution:*

$$5 \quad 6 \quad 2_{10}$$
$$0101 \quad 0110 \quad 0010$$

**3.3 Convert each of the following decimal numbers to BCD.**
   **(a) 9.2    (b) 34.8    (c) 92    (d) 321**

*Solution:*

(a)      9      2
        1001   0010

(b)   3    4    8
     0011 0100 1000

(c)      9      2
        1001   0010

(d)    3    2    1
      0011 0010 0001

**3.4 Find the decimal numbers corresponding to the following BCD codes.**
   **(a) 10000110      (b) 0001100001100000.0111**

*Solution:*

(a)    1000    0110
         8       6

(b)  0001 1000 0110 0000    0111
       1    8    6    0       7

## BCD ADDITION

BCD is a *numerical code.* Many applications require that arithmetic operations be performed. *Addition* is the most important operation because the other three operations (subtraction, multiplication and division) can be accomplished using addition. To add two BCD numbers proceed as follows:

(1) Add the two numbers using the rules for binary addition.
(2) If a four-bit sum is equal to or less than 9, it is a *valid* BCD number.
(3) If a four-bit sum is greater than 9, or if a carry-out of the sum is generated it is an invalid result. *Add 6(0110) to the four-bit sum to skip the six invalid*

*states and return the code to 8421.* If a *carry* results when 6 is added, simply add the carry to the next four-bit group.

**3.5 Add the following BCD numbers:**
   **(a) 0110 and 0010**
   **(b) 1000 0110 and 0001 0011**

*Solution:*

(a)        0110              6
          +0010            +2
          ─────            ───
           1000              8

(b)     1000  0110          86
       +0001  0011         +13
       ──────────         ────
        1001  1001          99

*Note:* (1) The decimal addition is shown for comparison.
   (2) The sum in any four-bit column does not exceed 9, and the results are *valid BCD numbers.*

**3.6 Add the following BCD numbers:**
   **(a) 0110 0111 and 0101 0011**
   **(b) 0100 0100 1000 and 0100 1000 1001**

*Solution:*

(a)      0110  0111         67
        +0101  0011        +53
        ──────────        ────
         1011  1010        120
          ⏟11₁₀  ⏟10₁₀

Both groups are *invalid* (>9). Add 6 to both groups.

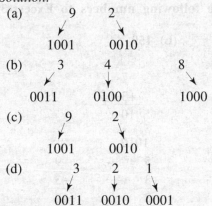

(b)     0100   0100   1000       448
       +0100   1000  +1001      +489
       ─────   ────  ─────      ────
        1101  10001   0111      +937
       +0110  +0110
       ─────  ─────
        1001  10011   0111
         ⏟9    ⏟3     ⏟7

This is a case of *invalid sum* (greater than 9 or a carry). Add 6 (0110) to skip the invalid states.

**3.7 Express the number 137₁₀ in BCD and binary. Explain any difference between the two results.**

*Solution:*

$$137_{10} = 10001001 \qquad \text{straight binary code}$$
$$137_{10} = 0001 \quad 0011 \quad 0111 \qquad \text{BCD code}$$
$$\phantom{137_{10} = }\ 1 \qquad\ \ 3 \qquad\ \ 7$$

(1) A straight binary code takes the *complete decimal number* and expresses it in binary.

(2) The BCD code converts each decimal digit to binary *individually*.

(3) BCD requires more bits than straight binary to represent decimal numbers with more than one digit.

## 3.8 Compare BCD and binary.

*Solution:*

BCD is not another number system like binary, octal, decimal and hexadecimal. It is, in fact, the decimal system with each digit encoded in its binary equivalent. A *BCD number* is not the same as a straight binary number. A *straight binary code* takes the complete decimal number and represents it in binary. The BCD code converts each decimal digit to binary individually. BCD requires more bits than straight binary to represent decimal numbers with more than one digit. This is because BCD does not use all possible four-bit groups, and is therefore *somewhat inefficient*.

The main advantage of the BCD code is the relative ease of converting to and from decimal. Only the four-bit code groups for the decimal digits *0 through 9* need to be remembered. This *ease of conversion* is especially important from a hardware standpoint because in a digital system it is the logic circuits that perform conversions to and from decimal.

## THE 8421 BCD CODE

The designation 8421 indicates the *binary weights* of the four-bits ($2^3$, $2^2$, $2^1$, $2^0$). The *ease of conversion* between 8421 code numbers and the familiar decimal numbers is the main advantage of this code. The 8421 code is the *predominant BCD code*, and when we refer to BCD, we always mean the 8421 code unless otherwise stated.

In the 8421 code only 10 of the 16 combinations are used. The six combinations that are not used-1010, 1011, 1100, 1101, 1110 and 1111-are *invalid* in the 8421 BCD code.

The BCD code is not self-complementing. *A necessary condition for a weighted code to be self-complementing is that the sum of the weights must equal 9.*

## NON-WEIGHTED CODES

Non-weighted codes are *codes that are not positionally weighted*. That is, each position within the binary number is not assigned a fixed value; For example: Excess-3 and Gray code.

*Excess-3 Code:* Excess-3, also called *XS3*, is a non-weighted code used to express decimal numbers. Used in some old computers, the code derives its name from the fact that *each binary code is the corresponding 8421 code plus 3 (011).*

## 3.9 What is the key feature of the Excess-3 code?

*Solution:*

The key feature of the Excess-3 code is that it is *self-complementing*. That is, the 1's complement of an Ex-

cess-3 number is the Excess-3 code for the 9's complement of the corresponding decimal number. For example, the Excess-3 code for decimal 4 is 0111. The 1's complement of 0111 is 1000, which is the Excess-3 code for decimal 5, and 5 is the 9's complement of 4.

The 1's complement is easily produced with logic circuits by simple *inverting* each bit. The self-complementing property makes the Excess-3 code useful in some arithmetic operations, because subtraction can be performed using the *9's complement method*.

## EXCESS-3 ADDITION

To add in Excess-3, add the binary numbers. If there is no carry out of the four-bit group *subtract 011*; if there is a carry out *add 011*.

## 3.10 Convert the following numbers to Excess-3 code.

(a) 87          (b) 159

*Solution:*

(a)

| 8 | 7 |
|---|---|
| +3 | +3 |
| 11 | 10 |
| ↓ | ↓ |
| 1011 | 1010 |

(b)

| 1 | 5 | 9 |
|---|---|---|
| +3 | +3 | +3 |
| 4 | 8 | 12 |
| ↓ | ↓ | ↓ |
| 0100 | 1000 | 1100 |

## 3.11 Add 3 and 2 in Excess-3.

*Solution:*

```
3 = 0011    binary      2 = 0010    binary
   +0011                   +0011
    0110    Excess-3        0101    Excess-3
    0110
   +0101
    1011
   -0011   There is no carry out. Subtract 0011.
5 = 1000
```

## 3.12 Add 6 and 8 in Excess-3.

*Solution:*

```
6  = 0110   binary      8 = 1000   binary
    +0011                  +0011
     1001   Excess-3        1011   Excess-3
     1001
    +1011
    10100   There is a carry out.
    +0011   Add 0011
14 = 10111
```

*Note:* The answer *includes six invalid combinations* also (14 + 6 + 3)

## GRAY CODE

The Gray code belongs to a class of codes called *minimum change code*. Successive coded characters never differ in more than one-bit. The Gray code is an *unweighted code*. Because of this the Gray code is not suitable for arithmetic operations but finds application in input/output devices, some types of analog-to-digital converters, and designation of rows and columns in a Karnaugh map.

### 3.13 How will you *generate* Gray code?

*Solution:*

The basic Gray code configuration is shown in Fig. 3.1 (a). A three-bit Gray code may be obtained by merely *reflecting* the two-bit code about an axis at the end of the code and assigning a third-bit as 0 above the axis and as 1 below the axis. This is illustrated in Fig. 3.1(b). By reflecting the three-bit code, a four-bit code may be obtained as in Fig. 3.1(c).

| | | | | | | | | |
|---|---|---|---|---|---|---|---|---|
| 0 | 0 | 0 | 0 | 0 | 0 | 0 | 0 | 0 |
| 0 | 1 | 0 | 0 | 1 | 0 | 0 | 0 | 1 |
| 1 | 1 | 0 | 1 | 1 | 0 | 0 | 1 | 1 |
| 1 | 0 | 0 | 1 | 0 | 0 | 0 | 1 | 0 |
| | | 1 | 1 | 0 | 0 | 1 | 1 | 0 |
| | | 1 | 1 | 1 | 0 | 1 | 1 | 1 |
| | | 1 | 0 | 1 | 0 | 1 | 0 | 1 |
| | | 1 | 0 | 0 | 0 | 1 | 0 | 0 |
| | | | | | 1 | 1 | 0 | 0 |
| | | | | | 1 | 1 | 0 | 1 |
| | | | | | 1 | 1 | 1 | 1 |
| | | | | | 1 | 1 | 1 | 0 |
| | | | | | 1 | 0 | 1 | 0 |
| | | | | | 1 | 0 | 1 | 1 |
| | | | | | 1 | 0 | 0 | 1 |
| | | | | | 1 | 0 | 0 | 0 |
| (a) | | (b) | | | (c) | | | |

**Fig. 3.1** *Generating Gray Code.*

### 3.14 What is a *cyclic code*?

*Solution:*

In many practical applications, e.g. analog-to-digital conversion, it is desirable to use codes in which all successive code words differ in only one digit. Codes that have such a property are referred to as *cyclic codes*. A particularly important cyclic code is the Gray code. The feature that makes this cyclic code useful is the simplicity of the procedure for converting from the binary number system into the Gray code.

### 3.15 Explain the term resolution.

*Solution:*

The Gray code, also referred to as the *reflected code*, can have as many bits as necessary, and *the more the bits, the more the possible combinations of output codes*

(number of combinations = $2^n$). A four-bit Gray code, for example, has $2^4 = 16$ different representations giving a *resolution* of 1 out of 16 possible angular positions at 22.5° each

$$2^4 = 16 \quad \text{and} \quad 360°/16 = 22.5°$$

### 3.16 Explain the relevance of Gray code in reducing errors in *position indicators*.

*Solution:*

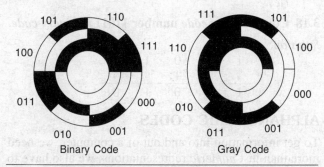

**Fig. 3.2** *Positional Indicating Codes.*

Consider a rotating disk that must provide an output of the position in three-bit binary (Fig. 3.2). When the brushes are on the black part, they output a 1, when on a white part, they output a 0. However, consider what happens when the brushes are on the 111 sector and almost ready to enter the 000 sector. If one brush were slightly ahead of the other, say the 4's brush, the position would be indicated by a 011 instead of a 111 or 000. Therefore, a 180-degree (°) error in disk position would result. Since it is physically impossible to have all the brushes precisely aligned, *some error will always be present at the edges of the sectors*.

The Gray code was introduced to reduce this error. *It assures that only one-bit will change each time the decimal number is incremented*. Whereas the binary system requires four-bits to change when going from 7 (0111) to 8 (1000), the Gray code requires only one-bit to change (0100 to 1100).

## BINARY-TO-GRAY CONVERSION

To convert from binary-to-Gray code the following rules apply:
(1) The MSD (left-most digit) in the Gray code is *the same as* the corresponding digit in the binary number.
(2) Going from left to right, add each pair of binary digits to get the next Gray code digit. *Disregard carries.*

### 3.17 Convert the *binary number* $10110_2$ to *Gray code.*

*Solution:*

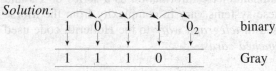

*Note:* Disregard carry. 1 + 1 = 0 and not 10

## GRAY-TO-BINARY CONVERSION

To convert from Gray to binary, a similar procedure is adopted, but there are some differences. The following rules apply:

(1) The MSD in the binary code is *the same as* the corresponding digit in the Gray code.
(2) Add each binary digit generated to the Gray code digit in the *next* adjacent position. *Disregard carries.*

**3.18 Convert *Gray code* number 11011 *to binary code*.**

*Solution:*

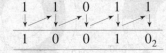

$$1 \quad 0 \quad 0 \quad 1 \quad 0_2$$

## ALPHANUMERIC CODES

To get information into and out of a computer, we need more than just *numeric* representations; we also have to take care of *letters and symbols* used in day-to-day processing. Information such as names, addresses, and item descriptions must be input and output in a readable format. But a digital system can deal only with 1's and 0's. Therefore, *we need a special code to represent all alphanumeric data* (letters, symbols, and numbers).

In the strictest sense, codes that represent numbers and alphabetic characters (letters) are called *alphanumeric codes.* Most of these codes, however, also represent symbols and various instructions necessary for conveying *intelligible information.*

**3.19 What are the requirements of an alphanumeric code?**

*Solution:*
At a minimum, an alphanumeric code must represent 10 decimal digits and 26 letters of the alphabet, for a total of 36 items. This requires 6 bits in each code combination, because five bits are insufficient ($2^5 = 32$). There are 64 total combinations of 6 bits, so we have 28 unused code combinations. Obviously, in many applications, symbols other than just numbers and letters are necessary to communicate completely. We need spaces to separate words, periods to mark the end of sentences or for decimal points, instructions to tell the receiving system what to do with the information, and more. So, with codes that are 6 bits long, we can handle decimal numbers, the alphabet, and 28 other symbols. This gives an idea of *the requirements of a basic alphanumeric code.*

Several coding systems have been invented that represent alphanumeric information as a series of 1's and 0's. These systems vary in complexity from the Morse code used in *telegraph work* to the Hollerith code used with *punched cards.*

## THE ASCII CODE

Most industry has settled on an input/output (I/O) code called the *American Standard Code for Information Interchange.* The ASCII (pronounced "as-kee") code uses 7 bits to represent all the alphanumeric data used in computer I/O. Seven bits will yield 128 different code combinations, as listed in Table 3.2. ASCII is basically a *7-bit code.* An 8th bit is usually added and is (a) always set to a 1, (b) always set to a 0, or (c) used as a parity bit.

**Table 3.2** *American Standard Code for Information Interchange*

|      | 000 | 001 | 010 | 011 | 100 | 101 | 110 | 111 |
|------|-----|-----|-----|-----|-----|-----|-----|-----|
| 0000 | NUL | DLE | SP  | 0   | @   | P   | `   | p   |
| 0001 | SOH | DC₁ | !   | 1   | A   | Q   | a   | q   |
| 0010 | STX | DC₂ | "   | 2   | B   | R   | b   | r   |
| 0011 | ETX | DC₃ | #   | 3   | C   | S   | c   | s   |
| 0100 | EOT | DC₄ | $   | 4   | D   | T   | d   | t   |
| 0101 | ENQ | NAK | %   | 5   | E   | U   | e   | u   |
| 0110 | ACK | SYN | &   | 6   | F   | V   | f   | v   |
| 0111 | BEL | ETB | '   | 7   | G   | W   | g   | w   |
| 1000 | BS  | CAN | (   | 8   | H   | X   | h   | x   |
| 1001 | HT  | EM  | )   | 9   | I   | Y   | i   | y   |
| 1010 | LF  | SUB | *   | :   | J   | Z   | j   | z   |
| 1011 | VI  | ESC | +   | ;   | K   | [   | k   | {   |
| 1100 | FF  | FS  | ,   | <   | L   | \   | l   | |   |
| 1101 | CR  | GS  | -   | =   | M   | ]   | m   | }   |
| 1110 | SO  | RS  | .   | >   | N   | ^   | n   | ~   |
| 1111 | SI  | US  | /   | ?   | O   | —   | o   | DEL |

*Definitions of Control Abbreviations:*

| | | | |
|---|---|---|---|
| ACK | Acknowledge | FS | Form separator |
| BEL | Bell | GS | Group separator |
| BS | Backspace | HT | Horizontal tab |
| CAN | Cancel | LF | Line feed |
| CR | Carriage return | NAK | Negative acknowledge |
| DC₁-DC₄ | Direct control | NUL | Null |
| DEL | Delete idle | RS | Record separator |
| DLE | Data link escape | SI | Shift in |
| EM | End of Medium | SO | Shift out |
| ENQ | Enquiry | SOH | Start of heading |
| EOT | End of transmission | STX | Start of text |
| ESC | Escape | SUB | Substitute |
| ETB | End of transmission block | SYN | Synchronous idle |
| ETX | End text | US | Unit separator |
| FF | Form feed | VT | Vertical tab |

## 3.20 How will you use the ASCII Code?

*Solution:*
Each time a key is depressed on the ASCII keyboard, that key is converted into its *ASCII code* and processed by the computer. Then, before outputting the computer connects to a display terminal or printer, all information is converted from ASCII into standard English.

To use this table, place the *4-bit group* in the least significant positions and the *3-bit group* in the most significant positions.

## 3.21 (a) What is ASCII code for G?
## (b) Using Table 3.2 determine the ASCII code for *p*.

*Solution:*
(a) ASCII code for G is

$$\underbrace{100}_{\text{3-bit group}} \qquad \underbrace{0111}_{\text{4-bit group}}$$

(b) ASCII code for lower case letter *p* is

$$1\ 1\ 1\ 0\ 0\ 0\ 0$$

## 3.22 Write your name in ASCII.

*Solution:*

| | S | . | P | . | BALI |
|---|---|---|---|---|---|

```
        S       .       P       .       B       A
1010011 0101110 1010000 0101110 1000010 1000001
        S       .       P       .       B       A

        1001100   1001001
           L         I
```

## EBCDIC CODE

Another alphanumeric code frequently encountered is called *Extended Binary Coded Decimal Interchange Code.* EBCDIC (pronounced "eb-si-dic") is an 8 bit code in which the decimal digits are represented by the 8421 BCD code preceded by 1111. Both lower case and upper case letters are represented in addition to various other symbols and commands.

## THE HOLLERITH CODE

The Hollerith code is the code used in *punched cards.* Each card has 80 columns oriented vertically, and 12 rows oriented horizontally. The *rows* are numbered 0 through 9, 11 and 12. The *columns* are numbered 1 through 80, each one containing one character. Each character is uniquely identified by the rows punched in that column. The letter A is 12-1 punch (A punch in the 12-row and a punch in the 1-column), for example.

## 3.23 What is the practical application of Hollerith code?

*Solution:*
The Hollerith code is BCD, rather than natural binary oriented. Thus, translation to and from EBCDIC is fairly simple. Since most large computers use punched cards, they use Hollerith for their card readers and punches and EBCDIC within the computer itself.

## 3.24 What is the need for error detection and correction codes?

*Solution:*
The codes for *error detection and correction* are used whenever we need to transmit data from one processor to another over noisy channels or whenever errors are likely to result from unstable environmental conditions. Such codes require *special encoding and decoding hardware,* which increases the cost and decreases the performance of a digital system, thus forcing the designer who uses these codes to trade cost and performance for *data security.*

Most modern digital equipment is designed to be relatively *error-free,* and the probability of errors is very low. However, we must realize that digital systems often transmit thousands, even millions of bits per second so that even a very low *rate of occurrence of errors* can produce an occasional error that might prove to be bothersome, if not disastrous. For this reason many digital systems employ some method of *detection* (and sometimes *correction*) of errors. *One of the simplest and most widely used schemes for error detection is the parity method.*

## 3.25 Explain how parity testing is done?

*Solution:*
*Parity testing* is done by adding a small amount of redundant information to each word of data to allow it to be checked. The extra information takes the form of a *parity bit* which is added at the end of each data bit. The *polarity* of the added bits is chosen so that the total number of 1's within the data word (including the added parity bit) is either always even (*even parity*) or always odd (*odd parity*). An even parity system is shown in Fig. 3.3.

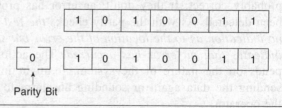

**Fig. 3.3** *An Even-parity System.*

If the parity is incorrect on reception, an error has been detected and the system must take appropriate action. Although this technique indicates that an error has occurred, it cannot determine which bit or bits are incorrect. If two errors are present, the errors will not be detected. This simple error detecting technique will either detect an even, or an odd, number of errors. Random numbers thus have a 50% chance of passing the parity test.

Parity testing is often used in communication channels where it is used to give confidence that the line is working correctly. Although the *reliability* of testing any one word is low, when applied to a large number of words it is sure to detect errors if the line is unreliable.

When the parity method is being used, the transmitter and the receiver must be *in agreement*[1], *in advance*[1], as to whether odd or even parity is being used. There is no specific advantage of one over the other, although even parity seems to be used more often. The transmitter must attach an appropriate parity bit to each unit of information that it transmits.

### 3.26 Give three examples of (a) *odd* parity and (b) *even* parity.

*Solution:*
(a) Odd parity

| Parity | ┌──── | Data | ────┐ | | | | | Total 1's |
|--------|-------|------|-------|---|---|---|---|-----------|
| 1 | 1 | 0 | 1 | 0 | 1 | 1 | 0 | 5 |
| 0 | 1 | 0 | 1 | 0 | 1 | 1 | 1 | 5 |
| 1 | 0 | 0 | 1 | 0 | 0 | 1 | 0 | 3 |

(b) Even parity

| Parity | ┌──── | Data | ────┐ | | | | | Total 1's |
|--------|-------|------|-------|---|---|---|---|-----------|
| 1 | 1 | 0 | 1 | 0 | 1 | 1 | 1 | 6 |
| 1 | 0 | 0 | 0 | 0 | 1 | 1 | 1 | 4 |
| 0 | 1 | 0 | 0 | 0 | 1 | 0 | 0 | 2 |

## CHECK SUM

An alternative method of checking the correctness of data is to use a checksum. *This provides a test of integrity of a block of data rather than of individual words.* When a group of words is to be transmitted, the words are summed at the transmitter and the sum is transmitted after the data. At the receiver, the words are again summed and compared with the sum produced by the transmitter. If both the results agree, the data is probably correct. If they don't, an error has probably been detected. As with the parity check, *the test gives no indication as to the location of the error but simply indicates that an error has occurred.* The action depends on the nature of the system. It might involve sending the data again or sounding an alarm to warn the operator.

## HAMMING CODE

The parity and check sum techniques both send a small amount of redundant information to allow the integrity of the data to be tested. If one is prepared to send additional redundant information, it is possible to construct codes that not only detect the *presence* of errors, but also indicate their *location* within a word, allowing them to be corrected. An example of this technique is the well-known *Hamming code.*

The performance of these codes in terms of their ability *to detect and correct multiple errors* depends upon the amount of redundant information that can be tolerated. The more the redundancy that is incorporated, the greater is the rate at which data must be sent and the more complicated the system. It is also not possible to construct a code that will allow an unlimited number of errors. This would imply that the system could produce the correct output with a random input, clearly an impossibility.

### 3.27 Explain the *format* for Hamming code.

*Solution:*
The Hamming code format for four data bits would be:

$$D_7 \quad D_6 \quad D_5 \quad P_4 \quad D_3 \quad P_2 \quad P_1 \rightarrow \text{7-bit code}$$

where the D-bits are the *data bits* and the P-bits are the *parity bits.* $P_1$ is set so that it establishes *even parity* over bits 1, 3, 5 and 7 ($P_1$, $D_3$, $D_5$ and $D_7$). $P_2$ is set for even parity over bits 2, 3, 6 and 7 ($P_2$, $D_3$, $D_6$ and $D_7$). $P_4$ is set for even parity over bits 4, 5, 6, and 7 ($P_4$, $D_5$, $D_6$ and $D_7$).

The above concept can be extended to any number of bits. A *15-bit code*, for example, would have the following format:

$$D_{15}, D_{14}, D_{13}, D_{12}, D_{11}, D_{10}, D_9, P_8, D_7, D_6, D_5,$$
$$P_4, D_3, P_2, P_1 \rightarrow \text{15-bit code}$$

*Note: Parity bits are inserted at each $2^n$ bit. This is true for Hamming codes of any length.*

### 3.28 Data bits 1011 must be transmitted. Construct *even-parity*, 7-bit, Hamming code for this data.

*Solution:*
$P_1$ must be a 1 in order for bits *1, 3, 5, and 7* to be even parity.
$P_2$ must be a 0 in order for bits *2, 3, 6 and 7* to be even parity.
$P_4$ must be a 0 in order for bits *4, 5, 6 and 7* to be even parity.

Therefore, the final code is

| $D_7$ | $D_6$ | $D_5$ | $P_4$ | $D_3$ | $P_2$ | $P_1$ |
|-------|-------|-------|-------|-------|-------|-------|
| 1 | 0 | 1 | 0 | 1 | 0 | 1 |

The Hamming code data are now ready for transmission and reception. At the receiving end, they are decoded to see if any errors have occurred. Bits 1, 3, 5 and 7; bits 2, 3, 6, and 7; and bits 4, 5, 6, and 7 are all checked for even-parity. *Should they check out, there is no error. However, should there be an error, the problem bit can be located by forming a 3-bit binary number out of the three parity checks.*

### 3.29 Encode data bits 0101 into a 7-bit *even-parity* Hamming code.

*Solution:*

| $D_7$ | $D_6$ | $D_5$ | $P_4$ | $D_3$ | $P_2$ | $P_1$ |
|-------|-------|-------|-------|-------|-------|-------|
| 0 | 1 | 0 | 1 | 1 | 0 | 1 |

**3.30 Assume that the data has been encoded in a 7-bit even-parity Hamming code and the number 1011011 is received. Find out the bit(s) in error. What will the *corrected code be*?**

*Solution:*

$$1 \quad 0 \quad 1 \quad 1 \quad 0 \quad 1 \quad 1$$
$$D_7 \quad D_6 \quad D_5 \quad P_4 \quad D_3 \quad P_2 \quad P_1$$

(1) Bits 1, 3, 5, and 7 associated with parity bit $P_1$ contain an error.
(2) Bits 2, 3, 6, and 7 associated with parity bit $P_2$ contain no error.
(3) Bits 4, 5, 6, and 7 associated with parity bit $P_3$ contain an error.

$$\begin{array}{ccc} P_4 & P_2 & P_1 \\ \text{Error word} = 1 & 0 & 1_2 = 5_{10} \end{array}$$

Therefore, bit 5 of the transmitted code is in error. The corrected code should read.

$$D_7 \quad D_6 \quad D_5 \quad P_4 \quad D_3 \quad P_2 \quad P_1$$
$$1 \quad 0 \quad \boxed{0} \quad 1 \quad 0 \quad 1 \quad 1$$

**3.31 A 7-bit Hamming code is received as 1111101. What is the *corrected code*? Assume even parity.**

*Solution:*

$$D_7 \quad D_6 \quad D_5 \quad P_4 \quad D_3 \quad P_2 \quad P_1$$
$$1 \quad 1 \quad 1 \quad 1 \quad 1 \quad 0 \quad 1$$

(1) Bits 4, 5, 6, and 7 → no error (0)
(2) Bits 2, 3, 6, and 7 → error (1)
(3) Bits 1, 3, 5, and 7 → error (0)

Error word = 0 10$_2$ = 2$_{10}$

Bit 2 is in error, and the corrected code is

$$1111111$$

# SUMMARY

> 8421 BCD code is the most *prominent* BCD code.
> A decimal number is *converted* to BCD by replacing each decimal digit with the appropriate 4-bit binary code.
> In weighted binary codes each binary digit is assigned a *weight*.
> In BCD addition if a 4-bit sum is equal to or less than 9, it is a *valid* BCD number.
> Non-weighted codes are *not positionally weighted*.
> Gray code is a *minimum change* code.
> Excess-3 code is obtained by *adding 3* to every decimal digit and then converting the result to 4-bit binary.
> In Excess-3 *addition*, if there is no carryout of the 4 bit group subtract 011; if there is a carryout add 011.
> *Alphanumeric* codes include binary codes for letters, numbers and symbols.
> ASCII and EBCDIC are the *most commonly used* alphanumeric codes.
> *Cyclic* codes are used to avoid errors when going from one binary number to the next.
> The ASCII is a 7-bit alphanumeric code that is widely used in computer systems for *input and output* of information.
> The Hollerith code is used in *punched cards*.
> Parity, check sums, and parity data codes are used for *error correction*.
> Hamming code is used for *error detection and correction*.

# REVIEW QUESTIONS

Test your understanding

1. Explain the difference between a *weighted* and a *non-weighted* code.
2. Give two examples of *weighted* codes.
3. Give two examples of *non-weighted* codes.
4. *Convert* 5429 to BCD.
5. Convert BCD 0100 0011 1001 1000 to decimal.
6. What is the main *advantage* of BCD?
7. What is the necessary condition for a weighted code to be *self-complementing*?
8. What is the *key feature* of the Excess-3 code?
9. What is the *key feature* of Gray code?

10. What is a *reflective code*?
11. Where is *reflectivity* desirable?
12. What is a *sequential* code?
13. Which code is used in *punched cards*?
14. What scheme is used for *error detection*?
15. What is the requirement of *parity method*?

# SUPPLEMENTARY PROBLEMS

Test your
understanding

16. Represent the number 2048 in:
    (a) binary          (b) BCD          (c) Excess-3 code  (d) Gray code
17. Encode the following decimal numbers in BCD code:
    (a) 46              (b) 327.89       (c) 20.305
18. Encode the numbers in Problem 17 to Excess-3 code.
19. Encode the numbers in Problem 17 to Gray code.
20. Express the following decimal numbers in 8421 BCD code:
    (a) 328            (b) 1497          (c) 9725
21. Express the following Excess-3 numbers as decimals:
    (a) 0110  1011  1100  0111    (b) 0011  0101  1010  0100
22. Convert the number 9450 to BCD code and show that it is not the same as the straight binary equivalent.
23. Convert 11100001110110 BCD to decimal.
24. Convert $9_{10}$ and $4_{10}$ to BCD. Add the conversions.
25. Add $8_{10}$ and $9_{10}$ in BCD.
26. Convert the following Gray numbers to equivalent binary numbers:
    (a) 111011        (b) 101110101
27. Write your full name in ASCII.
28. Attach an even-parity bit as MSB for ASCII code.
29. Repeat the above problem for odd parity.
30. Find the number of bits required to encode:
    (a) 56 elements of information   (b) 130 elements of information
31. Represent the decimal numbers
    (a) 27            (b) 396 and       (c) 4096 in binary form in
    (a) binary code  (b) BCD code      (c) Excess-3 code
    (d) Gray code    (e) Octal code    (f) Hexadecimal code
32. Represent the decimal number 2048 in
    (a) binary       (b) BCD code      (c) Excess-3 code  (d) Gray code
33. 7-bit Hamming code is received as 1101101. Locate the error position and find the correct code.
34. The message below has been coded in the Hamming code and transmitted through a noisy channel. Decode the message assuming that a single error has occurred in each word code:
    1001001   0111001   1110110   0011011
35. If odd parity is being used, what is the parity bit when the decimal number 43 is converted to binary?
36. The decimal number 6 is to be transmitted using the Hamming error correcting code. (a) What are the values of $P_1 P_2 P_3$ (b) What 7-digit binary number is transmitted? (c) If the binary number 1100111 is received, how can the location of the error be determined?
37. Typically, digital thermometers use BCD to drive their *digital displays*.
    (a) How many *BCD bits* are required to drive a 3-digit thermometer display?
    (b) What 12 *bits* are sent to the display for a temperature of 147°?
38. Most PC-compatible computer systems use a 20-bit address code to identify each of over 1 million binary locations.
    (a) How many *hexcharacters* are required to identify the address of each memory location?
    (b) What is the 5-digit *hexaddress* of the 200th memory location?
39. If the part number 651-M is stored in ASCII in a computer memory. List the *contents* of its memory location.

# OBJECTIVE TYPE QUESTIONS

## Fill in the Blanks

40. When a decimal number is represented by its _____ binary number we call it straight binary coding.
41. The external world is _____ in nature.
42. Conversions between decimal and binary can become _____ and _____ for large numbers.
43. In many applications special codes are used for _____ functions.
44. Error detection and correction codes are used whenever we want to transmit data from one processor to another over _____ channels.
45. Error detection and correction codes require special _____ and _____ hardware.
46. In weighted binary codes each binary digit is assigned a _____ .
47. A _____ of binary digits which represents a decimal digit is called a code word.
48. The _____ is the predominant BCD code.
49. The BCD code is not _____ .
50. In a self-complementing code, the sum of the _____ must equal 9.
51. If a 4-bit sum is equal to or less than 9, it is a _____ BCD number.
52. A BCD number is not the _____ as a straight binary number.
53. BCD is not another _____ system.
54. BCD converts each decimal digit to binary _____ .
55. The main advantage of BCD is _____ of conversion to and from decimal.
56. Because BCD does not use all possible 4-bit groups it is somewhat _____ .
57. Non-weighted codes are codes that are not _____ weighted.
58. Excess-3 code is _____ .
59. Gray code belongs to a class of codes called _____ change codes.
60. Gray code is not suited for _____ operations.
61. Gray code is employed in the designation of _____ and _____ in a Karnaugh map.
62. Gray code is also referred to as a _____ code.
63. The Gray code can be _____ to any number of bits.
64. The Morse code uses two _____ conditions.
65. The Hollerith code is _____ rather than natural binary oriented.
66. The ASCII code uses _____ to represent all the alphanumeric data used in computer I/O.
67. The _____ code is the code used in punched cards.
68. The EBCDIC is an _____ code.
69. The major cause of any transmission errors is _____ .
70. One of the simplest and most widely used schemes for error detection is the _____ method.
71. Parity bit is added at the _____ of each data word.
72. The _____ method of correctness of data provides a test of integrity of a block of data rather than individual words.
73. The checksum test gives no indication as to the _____ of the error.
74. When the parity method is being used, the transmitter and the receiver must be in _____ in advance.
75. _____ parity seems to be used more often.

## True/False Questions

State whether the following statements are True or False.
76. To form a BCD number, simply convert each decimal digit to its 8-bit binary code.
77. The designation 8421 indicates the binary weights of the 4 bits.
78. BCD is an alphanumeric code.
79. BCD is somewhat inefficient.
80. Non-weighted codes are not positionally weighted.
81. Gray code is a minimum change code.
82. ASCII is a numeric code.
83. ASCII is an 8-bit code.
84. Hollerith is a 7-bit code.

85. Parity testing is done by adding a small amount of redundant information.
86. The checksum method simply indicates an error has occurred.
87. Parity bits are inserted at each $2^n$-bit.

### Multiple Choice Questions

88. The parity of the binary number 1100110
    (a) is even
    (b) is not known
    (c) is odd
    (d) is same as the number of zeros
89. Decimal number 13 is represented in natural BCD as
    (a) 1101
    (b) 00010011
    (c) 00001101
    (d) 00011101
90. The code used in computer cards is
    (a) Gray code
    (b) natural BCD code
    (c) 12-bit Hollerith code
    (d) ASCII code
91. The decimal number 279 will be represented in Excess-3 code as
    (a) 001001111001
    (b) 010110101100
    (c) 100010111
    (d) 100011010
92. When representing in the following code the consecutive decimal numbers differ only in one-bit.
    (a) Excess-3
    (b) Gray
    (c) BCD
    (d) Hexadecimal
93. The number 27 is represented by 01011010 in
    (a) straight binary
    (b) natural BCD
    (c) Gray code
    (d) Excess-3 code
94. The number $6_{10}$ in Excess-3 is written as
    (a) 0110
    (b) 0011
    (c) 1101
    (d) 1001
95. The Hamming code has a minimum distance dm of
    (a) 3            (b) 4            (c) 5            (d) 6
96. The ASCII code is basically a
    (a) 7-bit code
    (b) 12-bit code
    (c) 4-bit code
    (d) 6-bit code
97. The Hollerith code is used in
    (a) floppy disk
    (b) hard disk
    (c) VDU
    (d) punched cards
98. A string of 8-bits is known as a
    (a) quad
    (b) octet
    (c) nibble
    (d) byte
99. The parity of the binary number 100110011 is
    (a) even         (b) odd         (c) 2           (d) 1
100. A necessary condition for a weighted code to be self-complementing is that the sum of its weights must be equal to
    (a) 9
    (b) 8
    (c) an even number
    (d) an odd number
101. If each successive code differs from its preceding code by a single bit only, then this code is called
    (a) BCD code
    (b) Gray code
    (c) weighted code
    (d) binary code

# ANSWERS

1. *Weighted codes* obey the positional weighting principles. *Non-weighted codes* are not positionally weighted.
2. The 8421 and the 2421 are *weighted codes*.
3. Excess-3 and Gray code are *non-weighted codes*.

4.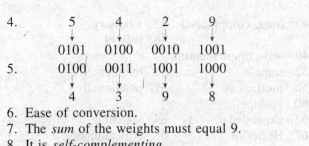

5.

| 0100 | 0011 | 1001 | 1000 |
|---|---|---|---|
| ↓ | ↓ | ↓ | ↓ |
| 4 | 3 | 9 | 8 |

6. Ease of conversion.
7. The *sum* of the weights must equal 9.
8. It is *self-complementing*.
9. It is a *minimum change* code.
10. A code is said to be *reflective* when the code for 9 is the complement of the code for 0, 8 for 1, 7 for 2, 6 for 3 and 5 for 4.
11. Reflectivity is desirable in a code when the *9's complement* must be found.
12. A code is said to be sequential when each succeeding code is *one binary number greater than* its preceding code.
13. Hollerith code.
14. One of the simplest and most widely used schemes for error detection is the *parity method*.
15. The transmitter and the receiver must be *in agreement* in advance.
16. (a) 100000000000       (b) 0010  0000  0100  1000
    (c) 0101  0011  0111  1011   (d) 11000000000
17. (a) 0100  0110        (b) 0011  0010  0111 · 1000  1001
    (c) 0010  0000 · 0011  0000  0101
18. (a) 0111  1001        (b) 0110  0101  1010 · 1011  1100
    (c) 0101  0011 · 0110 ₁ 0011  1000
19. (a) 0110  0101        (b) 0010  0011  0100 · 1100  1101
    (c) 0011  0000 · 0010  0000  0111
20. (a) 0011  0010  1000   (b) 0001  0100  1001  0111
    (c) 1001  0111  0010  0101
21. (a) 3894       (b) 0271
22. $9450_{10} = 1001\ 0100\ 0101\ 0000_{BCD}$; $9450_{10} = 10010011101010_2$ BCD form of the number requires more digits than the straight binary form
23. $3876_{10}$       24. $0001\ 0011_{BCD}$   25. $0001\ 0111_{BCD}$
26. (a) 101101       (b) 110100110   28. 11010010 (8-bit code) ASCII code for R
29. 00101110 (8-bit code) ASCII code for P
30. (a) 6       (b) 8
31. (a) 11011       (b) 00100111   (c) 01011010
    (d) 00110100     (e) 011011    (f) 00011011
32. (a) $100000000000_2$       (b) $0010000001001000_{BCD}$
    (c) $0101001101111011_{Excess-3}$   (d) $11000000000_{Gray\ code}$
33. Error in 5th position; 1101001
34. Correct message 1101001  0011001  1100110  0011001
35. 1
36. (a) 110       (b) 1100110
    (c) Check parity bits for received code parity bits are 111 ($P_3P_2P_1$). This means that the error in the seventh bit from the left.
37. (a) 12; 4-bits for each digit   (b) 0001  0100  0111
38. (a) five (each hex digit represents 4 bits)
    (b) 000C7H ($200_{10} = C8H$; but the first memory location is 00000H, so we have to subtract 1).
39.

| | | |
|---|---|---|
| 6 = | 0011 | 0110 |
| 5 = | 0011 | 0101 |
| 1 = | 0011 | 0001 |
| – = | 0010 | 1101 |
| M = | 0100 | 1101 |

If you look at these memory locations in hex, they will read

36  35  31  2D  4D

40. equivalent
41. decimal
42. long, complicated
43. auxiliary
44. noisy
45. encoding, decoding
46. weight
47. sequence
48. 8421
49. self-complementing
50. weights
51. valid
52. same
53. number
54. individually
55. ease
56. inefficient
57. positionally
58. self-complementing
59. minimum
60. arithmetic
61. rows, columns
62. reflected
63. expanded
64. signaling
65. BCD
66. 7 bits
67. Hollerith
68. Alphanumeric
69. electrical noise
70. parity
71. end
72. checksum
73. location
74. agreement
75. even
76. False
77. True
78. False
79. True
80. True
81. True
82. False
83. False
84. False
85. True
86. True
87. True
88. (a)
89. (b)
90. (c)
91. (b)
92. (b)
93. (d)
94. (d)
95. (c)
96. (a)
97. (d)
98. (d)
99. (b)
100. (a)
101. (b)

# Logic Gates

## INTRODUCTION

Logic gates are the *basic building blocks* for forming digital electronic circuitry. A logic gate has one output terminal and one or more input terminals. Its output will be HIGH (1) or LOW (0) depending on the *digital level(s)* at the input terminal(s). Through the use of *logic gates*, we can design digital systems that will evaluate digital input levels and produce a *specific output response* based on that particular logic circuit design. The seven logic gates are AND, OR, INVERTER, NAND, NOR, exclusive-OR, and exclusive-NOR.

A *logic system* may involve a great many gates, and each gate may have many components. Because of this, it would be confusing to show a logic system as an electronic circuit complete with all components. Instead, *each type of gate is represented by a particular graphic symbol.*

### 4.1 What is the difference between Boolean algebra and ordinary algebra?

*Solution:*

The algebra used to symbolically describe logic functions is *Boolean algebra*. As with ordinary algebra, the letters of the alphabet can be used to represent *variables*. The primary difference is that *Boolean algebra variables can have only the values 0 or 1.* Boolean algebra is ideally suited to dealing with the problems of binary arithmetic and electronic digital systems.

### 4.2 Differentiate between positive and negative logic.

*Solution:*

There are two values for logic-value assignment. Choosing the high-level $H$ to represent logic 1, as shown in Fig. 4.1(a), defines a positive-logic system. Choosing

the low-level $L$ to represent logic 1, as shown in Fig. 4.1(b), defines a negative-logic system. It is not signal polarity that determines the type of logic, but rather the assignment of logic values according to the relative amplitudes of the signals.

| Logic Value | Signal Value | | Logic Value | Signal Value |
|---|---|---|---|---|
| 1 | | H | 0 | H |
| 0 | L | | 1 | L |
| (a) Positive Logic | | | (b) Negative Logic | |

**Fig. 4.1** *Signal-amplitude Assignment and Type of Logic.*

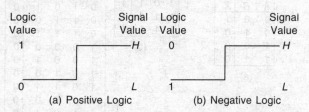

| Logic Equation | $A = B$ | | |
|---|---|---|---|
| Graphic Representation | Point $A$ | Wire | Point $B$ |
| Truth Table | $A$ $B$ <br> 0V 0V <br> +V +V | or | $A$ $B$ <br> 0 0 <br> 1 1 |
| Logic Symbol | $A$ | | $B$ |

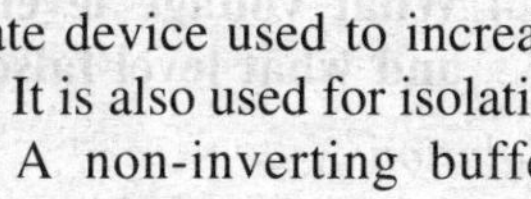

**Fig. 4.2** Function: Logical Equality. *Symbol denotes a Non-inverting Amplifier or* Buffer *(Performs no Logic Function)*

## BUFFER

A buffer is a special solid-state device used to increase the drive current at the output. It is also used for isolation between output and input. A non-inverting buffer, Fig. 4.2, has no logical function.

**4.3 What is the significance of a truth table? Draw the truth tables for two-input, three-input and four input circuits.**

*Solution:*
*A truth table simply shows all of the possible values for the inputs to a function, then shows the resultant outputs for each combination of inputs.* The purpose of truth tables is not to determine whether or not circuits are 'lying', rather they *verify 'truth' in the logical sense*—that a given set of input conditions will produce a 'true' output, while some other set of input conditions will produce a 'false' output. A *true state* is indicated by the digit 1, and a *false state* is indicated by the digit 0.

Figure 4.3 shows samples of truth tables for two-, three-and four-input logic circuits. Each table lists *all possible combinations* of input logic levels on the left, with *resultant logic levels* for output $X$ on the right. Of course, the actual value of $X$ will depend on the *type* of logic circuit.

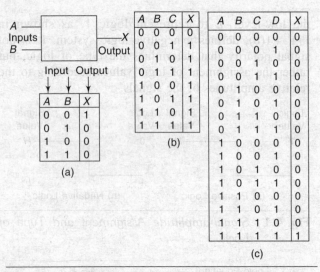

**Fig. 4.3**    *Examples of Truth Tables for (a) Two-input, (b) Three-input and (c) Four-input Circuits.*

*Note:* 1. The number of input combinations for an *n*-input truth table is $2^n$.
2. The list of all possible input combinations follows the binary counting sequence.

## THE AND FUNCTION

If a situation which may be described with Boolean variables gives a desired result *only when all* of several external conditions are satisfied, then that situation is said to obey the Boolean *AND function*. AND gates may have any number of inputs (Fig. 4.4).

**4.4 What voltage level is considered true (HIGH) and what level false (LOW)?**

*Solution:*
Many logic gates that are on the market today define a 5 V level as true and a 0 V level as false. In actual

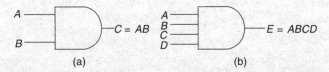

**Fig. 4.4**    *(a) Two-input* AND *Gate. (b) Four-input* AND *Gate.*

practice, any voltage *above* a certain level (for example 3 V) is considered true, and any voltage *below* a certain voltage level (for example 1V) is considered false.

**4.5 Represent the AND function by switch analogy.**

*Solution:*
The switch analogy of AND function is shown in Fig. 4.4. The lamp will light only if both $A$ *and* $B$ are closed. The lamp will not light if *either* $A$ *or* $B$ is closed.

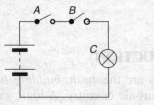

**Fig. 4.5**    *Switch Analogy of* AND *Function.*

**4.6 Draw the truth table of a four-input AND gate.**

*Solution:*
The truth table for a four-input AND gate is shown in Fig. 4.3(c).

## PULSED OPERATION

In a majority of applications, the inputs to a gate are not stationary levels but are *voltages that change frequently between two logic levels* and can be classified as pulse waveforms. *An* AND *gate obeys the truth table operation regardless of whether its inputs are constant levels or pulsed levels.*

A useful means of the output response of a gate to varying input-level changes is by means of a timing diagram. *A timing diagram illustrates graphically how the output levels change in response to input changes.*

**4.7 Illustrate and explain the pulsed operation of the AND gate.**

*Solution:*
In examining the pulsed operation of the AND gate, we will look at the inputs *with respect to each other* in order to determine the output level at any given time. For example, in Fig. 4.6, the inputs are both HIGH (1) during the interval $t_1$, making the output HIGH (1) during this interval. During interval $t_2$, input $A$ is LOW (0) and input $B$ is HIGH (1), so the output is LOW (0). During interval $t_3$, both inputs are HIGH (1) again, and therefore the output is HIGH (1). During interval $t_4$, input $A$ is HIGH (1) and input $B$ is LOW (0), resulting

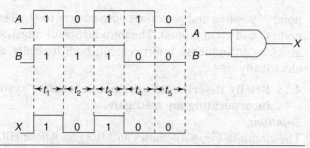

**Fig. 4.6**  *Example of Pulsed AND Gate Operation.*

in LOW (0) output. Finally, during interval $t_5$, input $A$ is LOW (0), input $B$ is LOW (0), and the output is therefore LOW (0).

## 4.8 Determine the output waveform for the AND gate in Fig. 4.7.

*Solution:*

The output $X$ will be HIGH only when both $A$ AND $B$ ($AB$) are HIGH at the same time. Using this fact the output waveform can be determined as shown in Fig. 4.6.

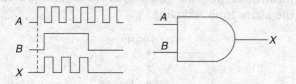

**Fig. 4.7**

## 4.9 What will happen to the $X$ output waveform if the $B$ input in 4.8 is kept at the 0 level?

*Solution:*

With $B$ kept low, the $X$ output will also stay LOW. This can be reasoned in two different ways. First, with $B = 0$ we have $X = A \cdot B = A \cdot 0 = 0$, since *anything multiplied (ANDed) by 0 will be 0.* Another way to look at it is that *an AND gate requires that all inputs be HIGH in order for the output to be HIGH* and this cannot happen if $B$ is kept low.

## 4.10 Determine the output $X$ for the three-input AND gate in Fig. 4.8.

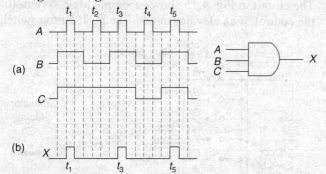

**Fig. 4.8**

*Solution:*

The output of a three-input AND gate will be HIGH only when all three inputs are HIGH as shown in Fig. 4.8.

## 4.11 Sketch the output waveform at $X$ for the two-input AND gates shown in Fig. 4.9.

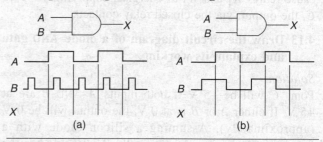

(a)                                    (b)

**Fig. 4.9**

*Solution:*

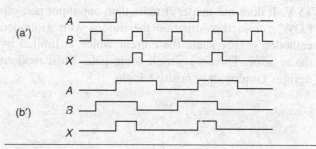

**Fig. 4.9a**

## AND CIRCUITS

The pinout diagram of a 7408, TTL (transistor-transistor logic) Quad two-input AND gate is given in Fig. 4.10. This digital IC contains *four 2-input AND gates*. After connecting a supply voltage of +5 V to pin 14 and a ground to pin 7, you can connect one or more AND gates to other TTL devices.

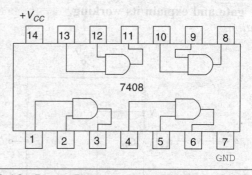

**Fig. 4.10**  *Pinout Diagram of the 7408 Quad Two-input AND Gates.*

## 4.12 Draw the circuit diagram of a relay AND circuit and explain its working.

*Solution:*

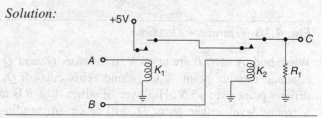

**Fig. 4.11**  *Relay AND Circuit.*

Input of +5 V applied to both points *A* AND *B* will cause relays $K_1$ and $K_2$ to energise, supplying +5 V to *C*, the output, via the closed relay contacts.

### 4.13 Draw the circuit diagram of a diode AND gate and explain its working.

*Solution:*

Point *C* will be +5 V if both inputs *A* AND *B* are at +5 V. If either *A* or *B* is at 0 V, the output will be 0 V (approximately). Assuming a silicon diode with a forward voltage drop of nominally 0.7 V, this has the effect of pulling the output *C* down to approximately 0.7 V. $R_1$ is called a common pull-up resistor tied to +5 V. It does not matter if more than one input is taken LOW, for in this situation the diodes with grounded cathodes simply share the current which is limited by the resistor. This is a simple logic gate. Most modern designs employ only positive logic.

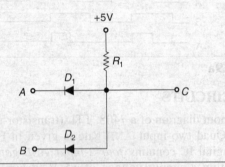

**Fig. 4.12**   *Diode AND Circuit.*

### 4.14 Draw the circuit diagram of a transistor AND gate and explain its working.

*Solution:*

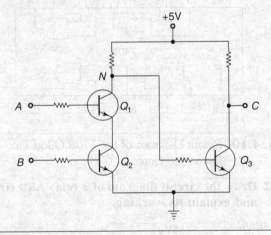

**Fig. 4.13**   *Transistor AND Gate.*

When both *A* AND *B* are at +5 V, transistors $Q_1$ and $Q_2$ conduct, moving point *N* to ground. This cuts-off $Q_3$, driving point *C* to +5 V. However, if either *A* or *B* is at a ground level, either $Q_1$ or $Q_2$ will be cut-off sending

point *N* positive and providing base current to $Q_3$. Thus, point *C* will go to ground. The introduction of transistors gives us an immense improvement, both logically and electrically.

### 4.15 Briefly describe an automobile's safety system incorporating an AND gate.

*Solution:*

The circuit in Fig. 4.14 shows an AND gate whose HIGH output activates a buzzer when three conditions are met on its inputs. When the ignition switch $S_1$ is ON, a HIGH is connected to the gate input *A*. When the seat belt is not properly buckled, switch $S_2$ is OFF and a HIGH is connected to the gate input *B*. At the instant the timer switch is turned ON, the timer is activated and produces a HIGH on gate input *C*. The resultant HIGH gate output activates the alarm. After a specified time, the timer's output goes LOW, disabling the AND gate and turning OFF the alarm. If the seat belt is buckled when the ignition is turned ON, a LOW is applied to input *B*, keeping the gate output LOW, thus preventing the alarm from sounding.

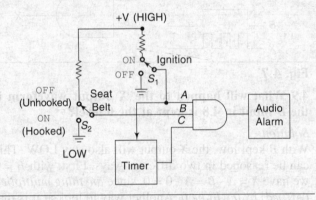

**Fig. 4.14**   *An Automobile's Safety System.*

### 4.16 Discuss a simple logic system, incorporating an AND gate, for control of an elevator motor.

*Solution:*

The circuit in Fig. 4.15 shows a simple logic system for the control of an elevator motor. The push-button switch

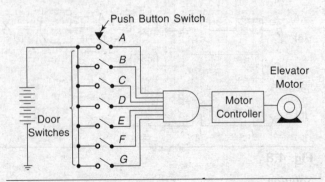

**Fig. 4.15**   *Control of an Elevator Motor.*

starts the elevator motor only when all of the door switches are closed. When one or more door switches is open, HIGH levels are not present at every input of the AND gate, and the motor cannot be started. When all the door switches are closed, HIGH levels are applied to each input of the gate, with the exception of input $A$. Closing the push-button switch now provides a HIGH level at $A$. Thus, the AND gate output goes from LOW to HIGH (0 to 1), and the motor controller is energised to start the motor. If one or more of the door switches is open, the AND gate output remains LOW when the push-button switch is pressed, and the motor cannot be started.

## ENABLE/INHIBIT FUNCTION OF AND GATE

A common application of the AND gate is to *enable* (allow) the passage of a signal (pulse waveform) from one point to another at certain times and to *inhibit* (prevent) the passage of the signal at other times.

### 4.17 How can a clock oscillator be enabled/disabled using an AND gate?

*Solution:*
The clock frequency of 1 MHz converts to 1 $\mu$s for each clock period. To transmit the clock pulses, we have to provide an enable signal. The illustration (Fig. 4.16) shows the circuit and waveforms to enable four clock pulses. For the HIGH clock pulses to get through the AND gate to point $X$, the second input to AND gate (enable signal input) must be HIGH, otherwise the output of the AND gate will be LOW. Therefore, when the enable signal is HIGH for 4 $\mu$s, four clock pulses pass through the AND gate. When the enable signal goes LOW, the AND gate disables (inhibits) any further clock pulses from reaching the receiving device.

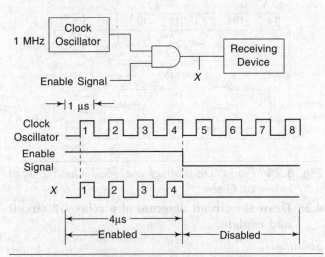

**Fig. 4.16** *Using an AND Gate to Enable/Disable a Clock Oscillator.*

## AND LAWS

There are three AND laws.
$$A \cdot 1 = A \qquad A \cdot 0 = 0 \qquad A \cdot A = A$$

All of these three AND laws can be verified by remembering what the AND symbol means.

### 4.18 Verify AND laws with the help of illustrations.

*Solution:*

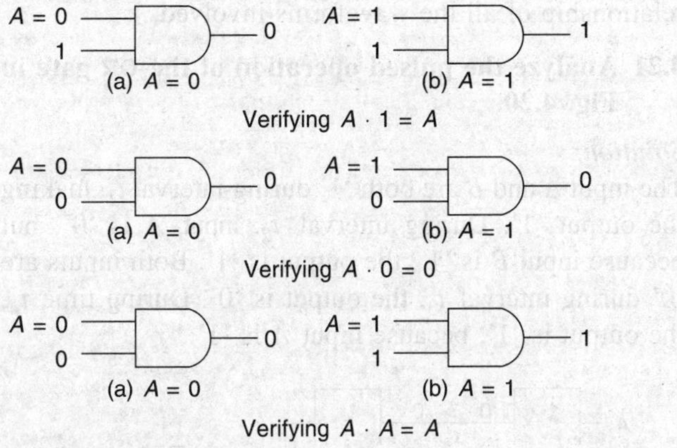

Verifying $A \cdot 1 = A$

Verifying $A \cdot 0 = 0$

Verifying $A \cdot A = A$

**Fig. 4.17** *Illustrating and Verifying AND Laws.*

## THE OR FUNCTION

If a situation which may be described with Boolean variables gives a desired result *only when any one or all* of several external conditions are satisfied, then that situation is said to obey the Boolean OR function. OR gates may have any number of inputs (Fig. 4.18).

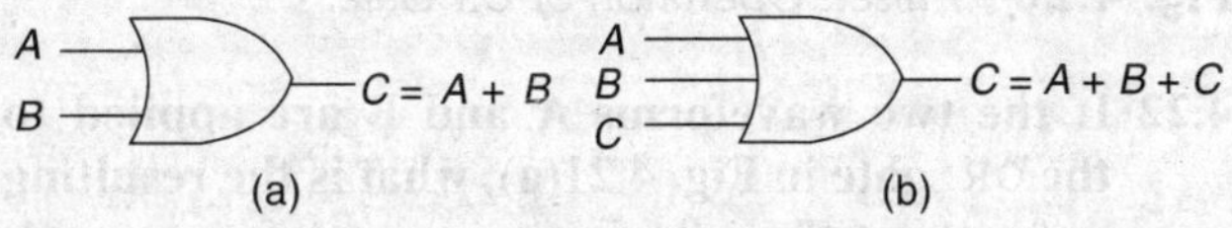

$C = A + B$

$C = A + B + C$

(a)                              (b)

**Fig. 4.18** *(a) Two-input OR Gate. (b) Three-input OR Gate.*

### 4.19 Represent the OR function by switch analogy.

*Solution:*
The switch analogy of OR function is shown in Fig. 4.19. The lamp will light if either $A$ OR $B$ is closed OR both $A$ and $B$ are closed.
*Note:* Compare Fig. 4.19 with Fig. 4.5.

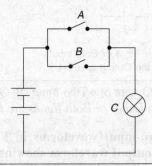

**Fig. 4.19** *Switch Analogy of OR Function.*

### 4.20 Draw the truth table for a three-input OR gate.

*Solution:*

The truth table for a three-input OR gate is given in Fig. 4.3(b).

*Note:* Compare Fig. 4.3(b) with Fig. 4.3(c).

## PULSED OPERATION

The important thing in pulsed operation is the mutual relationship of all the waveforms involved.

### 4.21 Analyze the pulsed operation of the OR gate in Fig. 4.20.

*Solution:*

The input $A$ and $B$ are both '1' during interval $t_1$, making the output '1'. During interval $t_2$, input $A$ is '0', but because input $B$ is '1', the output is '1'. Both inputs are '0' during interval $t_3$, the output is '0'. During time $t_4$, the output is '1', because input $A$ is '1'.

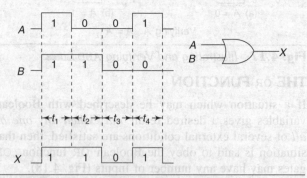

**Fig. 4.20** *Pulsed Operation of OR Gate.*

### 4.22 If the two waveforms A and B are applied to the OR gate in Fig. 4.21(a), what is the resulting output waveform?

*Solution:*

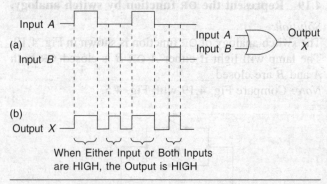

When Either Input or Both Inputs
are HIGH, the Output is HIGH

**Fig. 4.21** *The Output of a Two-input OR Gate is HIGH when Either or Both Inputs are HIGH.*

### 4.23 For the two-input waveforms in Fig. 4.22(a), sketch the output waveform showing its proper relationship to the inputs for the two-input OR gate.

*Solution:*

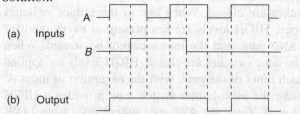

**Fig. 4.22** *The Output is HIGH when any of the Inputs are HIGH.*

### 4.24 For the three-input OR gate shown in Fig. 4.23, determine the output waveform in proper relationship to the inputs.

*Solution:*

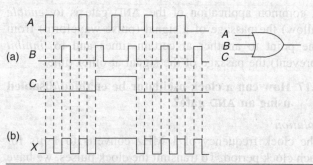

**Fig. 4.23** *The Output is HIGH when any of the Inputs are HIGH.*

## OR CIRCUITS

The pinout diagram of a 7432, TTL Quad 2-input OR gate is shown in Fig. 4.24. This digital IC contains 4 two-input OR gates inside a 14-pin dual-in-line package (DIP). After connecting a supply voltage of +5 V to pin 14 and a ground to pin 7, you can connect one or more of the OR gates to other TTL devices.

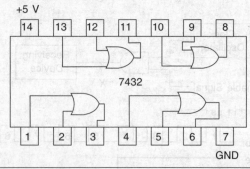

**Fig. 4.24** *Pinout Diagram of the 7432 Quad 2-input OR Gates.*

### 4.25 Draw the circuit diagram of a relay OR circuit and explain.

*Solution:*

If either $A$ OR $B$ is +5 V, one of the relay contacts, which are wired in parallel, will close applying +5 V to point $C$. (See Fig. 4.25.)

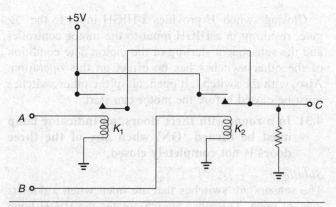

**Fig. 4.25** *Relay OR Circuit.*

## 4.26 Draw the circuit diagram of a diode OR gate and explain its working.

*Solution:*

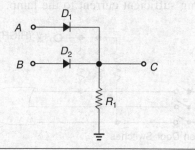

**Fig. 4.26** *Diode OR Circuit.*

Applying +5 V to input $A$ OR input $B$, OR both inputs $A$ and $B$, will forward bias $D_1$, OR $D_2$, OR both $D_1$ and $D_2$, causing point $C$ to go to +5 V.

## 4.27 Draw the circuit of a transistor OR gate and explain its working.

*Solution:*

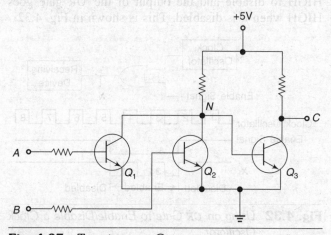

**Fig. 4.27** *Transistor OR Gate.*

Applying +5 V to point $A$ will cause $Q_1$ to conduct, causing point $N$ to go to ground. This, in turn, will cut off $Q_3$, causing point $C$ to go to +5 V. Applying +5 V to point $B$ will cause $Q_2$ to conduct, resulting in the output again going to +5 V. If both inputs are grounded

$Q_1$ and $Q_2$ will cut-off, causing point $N$ to go positive, supplying current to the base of $Q_3$. This results in input $C$ going to ground. Therefore, this circuit satisfies the definition for the OR gate.

## 4.28 Draw the logic system for controlling a boiler used in a hot-water space heating system. The boiler is switched 'ON' when the air temperature falls below a predetermined level OR when the water temperature falls below a preset level.

*Solution:*

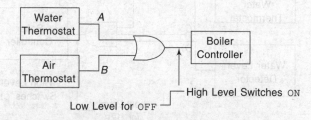

**Fig. 4.28** *Logic System for Controlling a Boiler used in a Water Heating System.*

When the *air temperature* falls below a predetermined level, the air thermostat provides a HIGH output, which calls for the boiler to be switched 'ON'. Similarly, when the *water temperature* falls below a preset level, a HIGH output is produced by the water thermostat to switch the boiler 'ON'. The desired operation is achieved by the use of an OR gate, as illustrated, and a controller that switches the boiler 'ON' when the OR gate output is HIGH.

## 4.29 The boiler control circuit in problem 4.28 is to be modified to provide safety functions. The boiler is to switch 'OFF' if the water temperature exceeds a prescribed maximum. A second water thermostat is included to detect the upper temperature limit. This produces a HIGH output level while the water temperature is below the maximum. Also, the boiler is to switch 'OFF' if the quantity of water is below a minimum safe level. A water level transducer is included, and this produces a HIGH output while the water level remains above the minimum. Make the necessary circuit modification.

*Solution:*
The statement which describes the operation of the circuit is as follows:

*The boiler starts when a HIGH input is provided at terminals A OR B.*

When the two additional parts are included, the circuit statement must be modified as follows:

*The boiler starts when a HIGH input is provided at terminals (A OR B) and at C AND D.*

It is clear that an AND gate and an OR gate are required.

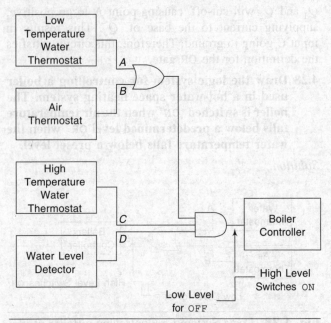

**Fig. 4.29** *Modification to the Boiler Control Circuit in Problem 4.29 to provide Safety Functions. The Boiler can be Switched 'ON' only if the Water Temperature remains below a prescribed Maximum and the Water Level remains above a Specified Minimum.*

**4.30** **The elevator control circuit in problem 4.16 is to be modified to permit a maintenance technician to start the motor regardless of the condition of other switches. Determine the necessary modification.**

*Solution:*
The motor starts when a HIGH input is provided at terminals (*A* AND *B* AND *C* AND *D* AND *E* AND *F* AND *G*) OR *H*. This statement shows that an AND gate and an OR gate are required. The modification is shown in Fig. 4.30.

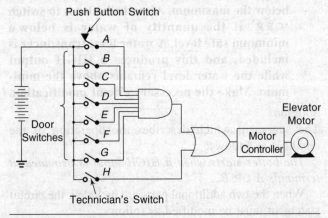

**Fig. 4.30** *Modification to the Motor Control Circuit in Problem 4.16 to Provide a Maintenance Technician Switch 'H' which Starts the Motor Regardless of the Condition of Other Switches.*

Closing switch *H* provides a HIGH input to the OR gate, resulting in a HIGH input to the motor controller and the subsequent starting of the motor. The condition of the other switches has no effect on this operation. Also, with the switch left open, all of the other switches must be closed before the motor can start.

**4.31** **In a room with three doors, an indicator lamp must be turned 'ON' when any of the three doors is not completely closed.**

*Solution:*
The sensors are switches that are open when a door is ajar, or open. This open switch creates the HIGH level for the OR gate input, as shown in Fig. 4.31. If any or all of the doors are open, the gate output is HIGH. The HIGH level is then used to illuminate the indicator lamp. The gate is, of course, assumed to be capable of supplying sufficient current to the lamp.

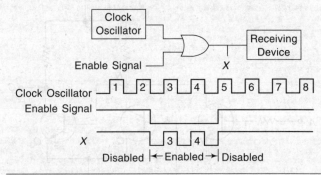

**Fig. 4.31** *An Example of an OR Gate Application.*

## ENABLE/INHIBIT FUNCTION OF OR GATE

An OR gate can also be used to *disable* a function. The only difference is that the enable input signal is made HIGH to disable and the output of the OR gate goes HIGH when it is disabled. This is shown in Fig. 4.32.

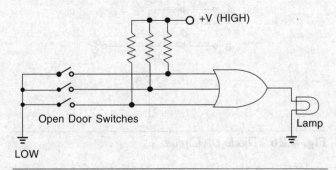

**Fig. 4.32** *Using an OR Gate to Enable/Disable a Clock Oscillator.*

## OR LAWS

There are three OR laws.
$$A + 1 = 1 \quad A + 0 = A \quad A + A = A$$
All of these OR laws can be verified remembering what the OR symbol means.

## 4.32 Verify OR laws with the help of illustrations.

*Solution:*

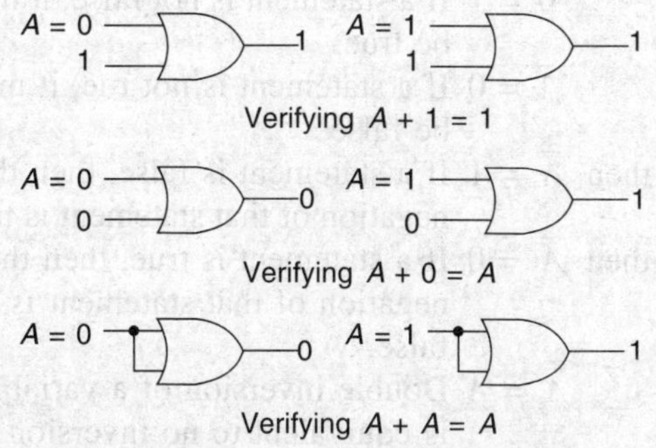

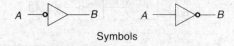

Verifying $A + 1 = 1$

Verifying $A + 0 = A$

Verifying $A + A = A$

**Fig. 4.33**  *Illustrating and Verifying OR Laws.*

## THE NOT FUNCTION

The NOT circuit performs a basic logic function called *negation* or *complementation*. It changes one logic level to the *opposite* logic level (negates the input). In terms of levels, it changes a HIGH level to a LOW level and LOW level to a HIGH level. In terms of bits it changes a '1' to a '0' and a '0' to a '1'. Each statement is called the negation or *inverse* of the other. A logic gate that negates the input is called an inverter. Inversion is indicated by an overline $\overline{A}$ (not $A$). The negation indicator is a bubble appearing on the *input* or output of a logic element. When appearing on the *input*, the bubble means that an external 0 produces an internal 1. When appearing on the *output*, the bubble means that an internal 1 produces an external 0. Typically, inputs are on the left of a logic symbol and outputs are on the right. The triangle, Fig. 4.34, represents an amplifier. When a single circuit is used for inversion alone the triangle is included with the symbol.

Symbols

**Fig. 4.34**  *The Inverter.*

## 4.33 Discuss the significance of a polarity indicator.

*Solution:*

The polarity indicator is a triangle ($\Delta$). When appearing on the input, it means that an external LOW level produces an internal HIGH level. When appearing on the output, it means that an internal HIGH level produces an external LOW level. The placement of the negation or polarity indicator does not imply a change in the way an inverter operates. Both indicators are equivalent and can be interchanged.

**Fig. 4.35**  *The Polarity Indicator.*

## PULSED OPERATION

Inversion of a variable $A$ gives $\overline{A}$. Conversely, inversion of $\overline{A}$ gives $A$. A *double* inversion of a variable is thus equivalent to no inversion. This is shown in Fig. 4.36.

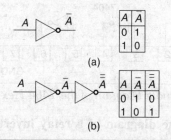

(a)

(b)

**Fig. 4.36**  *(a) Single Inversion. (b) Double Inversion.*

## 4.34 Illustrate the pulsed operation of an inverter.

*Solution:*

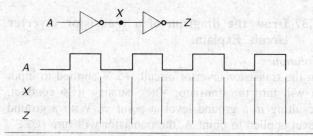

Input Pulse                Output Pulse

**Fig. 4.37**  *Inverter with Pulsed Input.*

## 4.35  Sketch the output waveform at X and Z if the timing waveform shown below is input at A.

*Solution:*

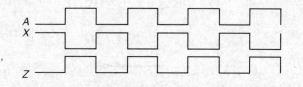

**Fig. 4.38**  *Double Inversion.*

**Fig. 4.39**  *Solution for 4.35.*

## INVERTER CIRCUITS

The 7404 is a TTL hex inverter. This integrated circuit (IC) contains six inverters. After applying +5 V to pin 14 and grounding pin 7, you can connect any or all of the inverters to other TTL devices. For instance, if you need only one inverter, you can connect an input signal to pin 1 and take the output signal from pin 2; the other five inverters can be left unconnected. (See Fig. 4.40)

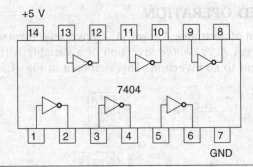

**Fig. 4.40** *Pinout Diagram of the 7404 Hex Inverter.*

### 4.36 Draw the diagram of a relay inverter circuit. Explain.

*Solution:*

With +5 V applied to the relay circuit, the relay will energise, opening the *normally closed* contacts, causing 0 V to appear on the output lead *B*. Thus, a HIGH on the input is inverted (negated) to a LOW on the output.

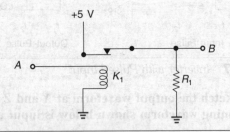

**Fig. 4.41** *Relay Inverter Circuit.*

### 4.37 Draw the diagram of a transistor inverter circuit. Explain.

*Solution:*

In the transistor invertor circuit, +5 V applied to input *A* will turn the transistor 'ON', causing it to conduct, resulting in a ground level at point *B*. With a ground level applied to point *A*, the transistor will turn 'OFF', resulting in +5 V at point *B*.

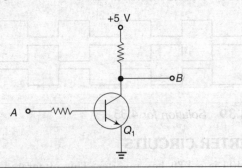

**Fig. 4.42** *Transistor Inverter Circuit.*

### NOT LAWS

There are several laws of Boolean algebra that become apparent when examining the inverter.

$\overline{0} = 1$, $\overline{1} = 0$, if $A = 0$ then $\overline{A} = 1$, if $A = 1$ then $\overline{A} = 0$, $\overline{\overline{A}} = A$

### 4.38 Give the verbal statements of NOT laws.

*Solution:*

$\overline{0} = 1$   If a statement is not false, it must be true.

$\overline{1} = 0$   If a statement is not rue, it must be false.

If $A = 0$ then $\overline{A} = 1$   If a statement is false, then the negation of that statement is true.

If $A = 1$ then $\overline{A} = 0$   If a statement is true, then the negation of that statement is false.

$\overline{\overline{A}} = A$   Double inversion of a variable is equivalent to no inversion.

### 4.39 Differentiate between even and odd number of negations.

*Solution:*

An *even* number of negations is equivalent to no negation.

An odd number of negations is equivalent to a single negation.

### THE NAND FUNCTION

The term NAND is a contraction of *NOT–AND* and implies an AND function with a complemented (inverted) output.

The circle at the output acts just like an *inverter*. So a NAND gate can be drawn symbolically as an AND gate with an inverter connected to its output as shown in Fig. 4.43.

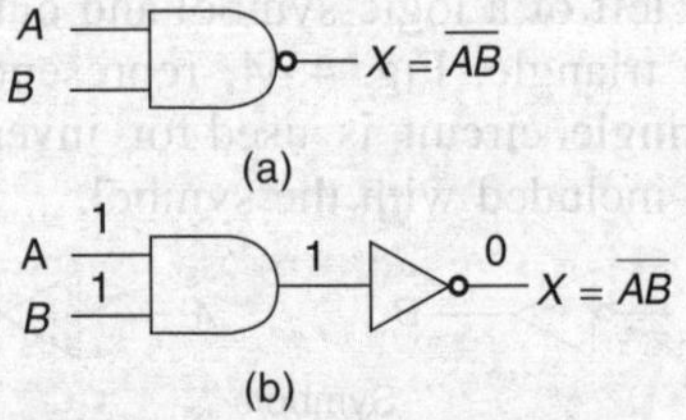

$$A \quad B \longrightarrow X = \overline{AB}$$
(a)

$$A \overset{1}{\longrightarrow} B \overset{1}{\longrightarrow} \boxed{\phantom{x}} \overset{1}{\longrightarrow} \overset{0}{\longrightarrow} X = \overline{AB}$$
(b)

**Fig. 4.43** *(a) Symbol for NAND Gate.*
*(b) AND–INVERT Equivalent of a NAND Gate with A = 1 and B = 1.*

### 4.40 Draw the truth table of NAND gate and write the Boolean equation for a two-input NAND gate.

*Solution:*

The Boolean equation for a NAND gate is written as $X = \overline{AB}$. The inversion bar is drawn over (*A* and *B*), meaning that the output of the NAND is the complement of (*A* AND *B*) i.e. [*NOT* (*A* AND *B*)]. Because we are inverting the output, the truth table outputs will be the complements of the AND gate. Think of how an AND gate would respond to the inputs and then invert your answer (see Fig. 4.44). We can see that *the output is LOW when both inputs are HIGH* (just the opposite of AND gate). Also, *the output is HIGH when any or all inputs are LOW*.

| A | B | X |
|---|---|---|
| 0 | 0 | 1 |
| 0 | 1 | 1 |
| 1 | 0 | 1 |
| 1 | 1 | 0 |

**Fig. 4.44**  *Two-input NAND Gate Truth Table.*

**4.41  Draw the logic symbols of, and write the Boolean expressions for a three-input and an eight-input NAND gate.**

*Solution:*

NAND gates can also have more than two inputs. Figure 4.45 shows the symbols and Boolean expressions for a three-input and an eight-input NAND gate.

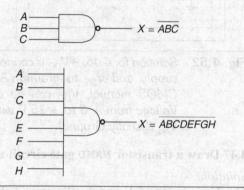

**Fig. 4.45**  *Symbols and Boolean Expressions for a Three-input and an Eight-input NAND Gate.*

**4.42  A NAND gate is also referred to as a negative OR gate. Why?**

*Solution:*

In Fig. 4.44, if $A$ is LOW or $B$ is low, or if both $A$ and $B$ are LOW then $X$ is HIGH. Here we have an OR operation that requires one or more LOW inputs to produce a HIGH output. This is referred to as *negative OR*. When a NAND gate is looking for one or more LOWs on its inputs, rather than for all HIGHs, it is acting as a negative OR, Fig. 4.46(b). The two symbols in Fig. 4.46 represent the same gate, but they also serve to define its role in a particular application.

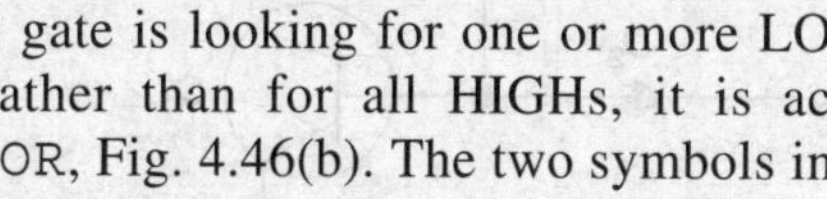

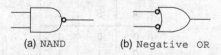

(a) NAND          (b) Negative OR

**Fig. 4.46**  *Standard Symbols Representing the Two Equivalent Functions of the NAND Gate.*

*Note:* 1.  In a NAND gate, the LOW level is the active output level. The bubble on the output indicates that *the output is active 0*.

2.  The unique output from a NAND gate is LOW only when *all* inputs are HIGH.

3.  The *universality* of the NAND gate means that logic systems incorporating many different functions may be designed with only a single type of gate.

**4.43  Discuss the implementation of NOT, AND, or OR gates by NAND gates.**

*Solution:*

The *NOT operation* is obtained from a one-input NAND gate, actually another symbol for an inverter circuit. The *AND operation* requires two NAND gates. The first NAND gate produces an inverted AND and the second NAND gate acts as an inverter to produce the normal output. The *OR operation* is achieved through a NAND gate with additional inverters in each input. All the three operations are shown in Fig. 4.47.

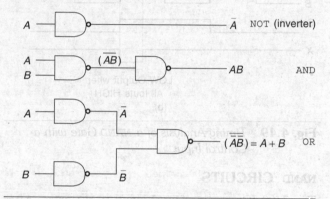

**Fig. 4.47**  *Universality of the NAND Gate.*

## PULSED OPERATION

In a NAND gate, the only time a LOW output occurs is when all inputs are HIGH.

**4.44  Sketch the output waveform at $X$ for the NAND gate in Fig. 4.48.**

*Solution:*

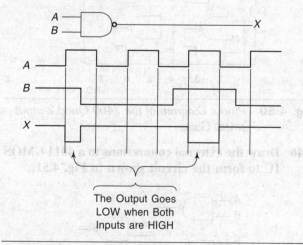

The Output Goes LOW when Both Inputs are HIGH

**Fig. 4.48**  *Timing Analysis of a NAND Gate.*

**4.45   Sketch the output waveform at *X* for the NAND gate shown in Fig. 4.49(a) with the given input waveforms at *A*, *B* and control in Fig. 4.49(b).**

*Solution:*
The control input waveform is used to enable/disable the NAND gate. When it is LOW, the output is stuck HIGH. When it is HIGH, the output will respond LOW when *A* and *B* go HIGH.

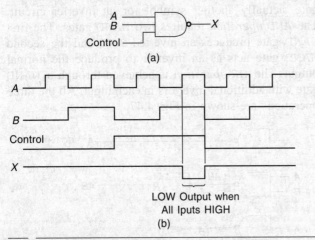

(a)

(b)

**Fig. 4.49**   *Timing Analysis of a NAND Gate with a Control Input.*

## NAND CIRCUITS

The 7400 IC contains four 2-input NAND gates. After connecting a supply voltage of +5 V to pin 14 and a ground to pin 7, you can connect one or more NAND gates to other TTL devices.

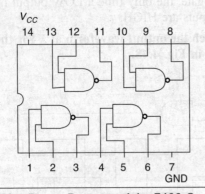

**Fig. 4.50**   *Pinout Diagram of the 7400 Quad 2-input NAND Gates.*

**4.46   Draw the external connections to a 4011 CMOS IC to form the circuit shown in Fig. 4.51.**

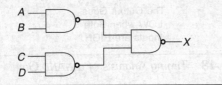

**Fig. 4.51**

*Solution:*

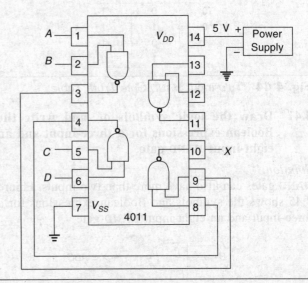

**Fig. 4.52**   *Solution for 4.46. +$V_{DD}$ is connected to +5 V supply and $V_{SS}$ to ground. According to CMOS manual, $V_{DD}$ can be any Positive Voltage from + 3 to + 15 V with respect to $V_{SS}$ (Usually Ground).*

**4.47 Draw a transistor NAND gate circuit and explain.**

*Solution:*
The 1's indicate +5 V and the 0's ground. The output *C* is LOW only when *A* and *B* are both 1.

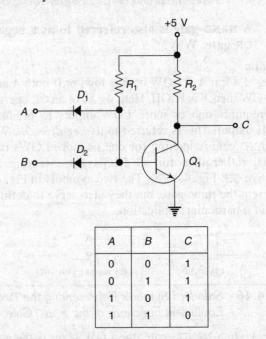

| A | B | C |
|---|---|---|
| 0 | 0 | 1 |
| 0 | 1 | 1 |
| 1 | 0 | 1 |
| 1 | 1 | 0 |

**Fig. 4.53**   *A Transistor NAND Gate Circuit Along with its Associated Truth Table.*

*Note:* A NAND gate is a purchasable piece of hardware, usually an integrated circuit. This piece of hardware can perform all three functions: AND, OR, and Invert.

**4.48 The simultaneous occurrence of two HIGH level voltages must be detected and indicated by a LOW level output that is used to illuminate a LED. Sketch the operation.**

*Solution:*

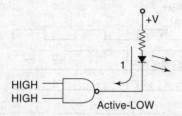

**Fig. 4.54**

The application requires a NAND function, since the output must be *active-LOW* in order to produce current through the LED when the two HIGHs occur on its outputs. The NAND symbol is, therefore, used to show the operation.

## THE NOR FUNCTION

The term NOR is a contraction of *NOT-OR* and implies an OR function with a complemented (inverted) output. The circle at the output acts just like an *inverter*. So a NOR gate can be drawn symbolically as an OR gate with an inverter connected to its output as shown in Fig. 4.55.

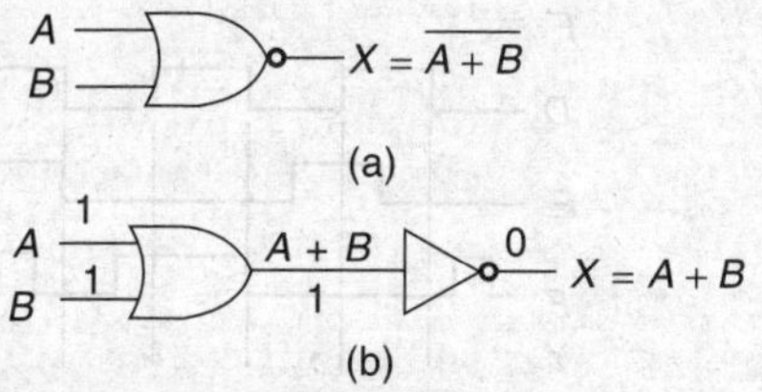

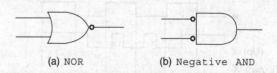

**Fig. 4.55** *(a) Symbol for NOR gate.*
*(b) OR-INVERT equivalent of a NOR gate with A = 1 and B = 1.*

**4.49 Draw the truth table of and write the Boolean equation for a two-input NOR gate.**

*Solution:*
The Boolean equation for a NOR gate is written as $X = \overline{A + B}$. The inversion bar is drawn over $(A + B)$, meaning that the output of the NOR is the complement of $(A$ or $B)$ i.e. $[NOT\ (A + B)]$. Because we are inverting the output, the truth table output will be the complement of the OR gate truth table output. Think of how an OR gate would respond to the inputs and then invert your answer (see Fig. 4.56). We can see that *the output is HIGH when both inputs are LOW* (just the opposite of OR gate). Also, *the output is LOW when any or all inputs are HIGH.*

**4.50 Draw the logic symbols of, and write the Boolean expressions for a three-input and an eight-input NOR gate.**

| A | B | X |
|---|---|---|
| 0 | 0 | 1 |
| 0 | 1 | 0 |
| 1 | 0 | 0 |
| 1 | 1 | 0 |

**Fig. 4.56** *Two-input NOR Gate Truth Table.*

*Solution:*
NOR gates can also have more than two inputs. Figure 4.57 shows the symbols and Boolean expressions for a three-input and eight-input NOR gate.

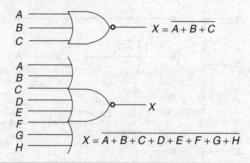

**Fig. 4.57** *Symbols and Boolean Expressions for a Three-input and Eight-input NOR Gate.*

**4.51 A NOR gate is also referred to as a 'Negative AND gate'. Why?**

*Solution:*
In Fig. 4.56, if both $A$ and $B$ are LOW then $X$ is HIGH. Here we have an AND operation that requires all LOW inputs to produce a HIGH output. This is referred to as *negative AND*. When a NOR gate is looking for all LOWs on its inputs, rather than one or more HIGHs, it is acting as a negative AND, Fig. 4.58(b). Also, the output is LOW when any of the inputs $A$ and $B$ are HIGH. The two symbols in Fig. 4.58 represent the same gate, but they also serve to define its role in a particular application.

(a) NOR       (b) Negative AND

**Fig. 4.58** *Standard Symbols Representing the Two Equivalent Functions of the NOR Gate.*

*Note:* 1. In a NOR gate, the low level is the active output level. The bubble on the output indicates that *the output is active 0.*
   2. The unique output from a NOR gate is HIGH only when *all* inputs are LOW.
   3. The *universality* of the NOR gate means that logic systems incorporating many different functions may be designed with only a single type of gate.

**4.52 Discuss the implementation of NOT, OR, or AND gates by NOR gates.**

*Solution:*

The *NOT operation* is obtained from a one-input NOR gate, yet another symbol for inverter circuit. The *OR operation* requires two NOR gates. The first NOR gate produces an inverted OR and the second acts as an inverter to obtain the normal output. The *AND operation* is achieved through a NOR gate with additional inverters at each input. All the three operations are shown in Fig. 4.59.

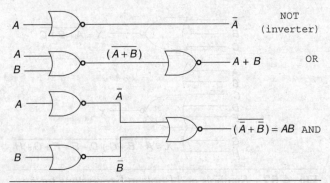

**Fig. 4.59** *Universality of the NOR Gate.*

## PULSED OPERATION

Again, as with other types of gates, we will simply follow the truth table operation to determine the waveforms in the proper time relationship to the inputs.

**4.53 Sketch the waveforms at *X* and *Y* with the switches in the 'down' (0) position. Repeat the problem with the switches in the 'up' (1) position.**

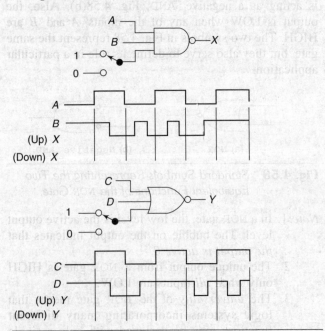

**Fig. 4.60**

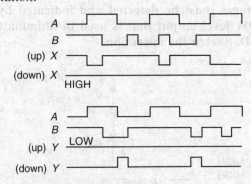

**Fig. 4.61** *Solution for 4.53.*

**4.54 Sketch the output at *X* and *Y* in Fig. 4.62, given the input waveforms.**

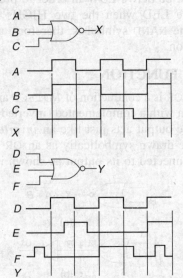

**Fig. 4.62**

*Solution:*

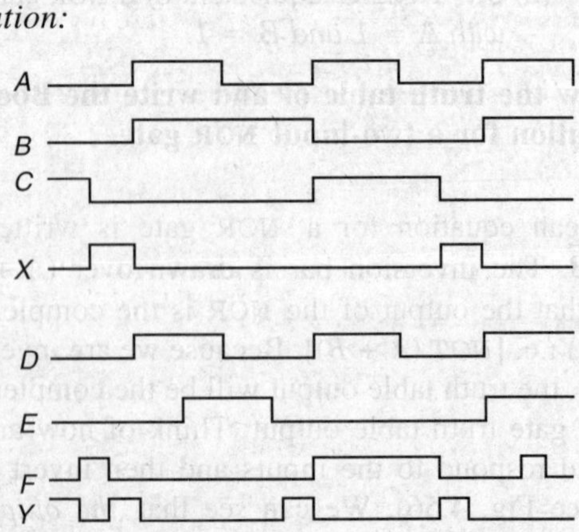

**Fig. 4.63** *Solution for 4.54.*

## NOR CIRCUITS

The most common ECL type is designated as the 10,000 series. The 10102 provides four 2-input NOR gates. An

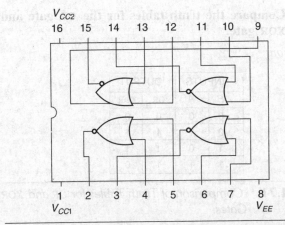

**Fig. 4.64** *Pinout Diagram of (Emitter-coupled Logic) (ECL) 10102 Quad 2-input NOR Gates.*

ECL gate may have two outputs, one for the NOR function and another for the OR function (pin 9 of the 10102 IC).

### 4.55 Draw the pinout diagram of CMOS 4002. Explain.

*Solution:*
CMOS circuits of the 4002 can accommodate only two 4 input NOR gates because of pin limitations. The IC has two unused terminals marked NC (no connection). The terminal marked $V_{DD}$ requires a power supply from 3 to 15 V, while $V_{SS}$ is connected to ground.

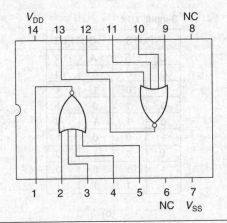

**Fig. 4.65** *Pinout Diagram of CMOS 4002.*

### 4.56 Draw the circuit diagram of a diode-transistor NOR gate. Explain.

*Solution:*
A diode-transistor NOR gate is shown in Fig. 4.66. When all of the inputs are LOW, transistor $Q_1$ is 'OFF' and the output is HIGH. A HIGH input at terminal $A$ OR $B$ OR $C$ biases the transistor 'ON' and produces a LOW output.

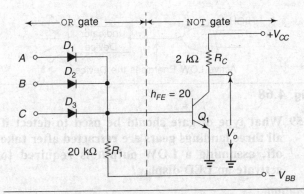

**Fig. 4.66** *Diode-transistor NOR Gate, consisting of an OR Gate and an Inverter Stage, or NOT Gate. A LOW Output is produced When HIGH Inputs are Present at Terminals A OR B OR C.*

### 4.57 A gate is required to monitor two lines and to generate a HIGH level output used to activate an electric motor whenever either or both lines are LOW. Sketch the operation.

*Solution:*

```
LOW ───┐
       )──── Active-     ┌──────────┐     Motor
LOW ───┘     HIGH        │Interface │──────⊙
                         │ circuit  │
                         └──────────┘
```

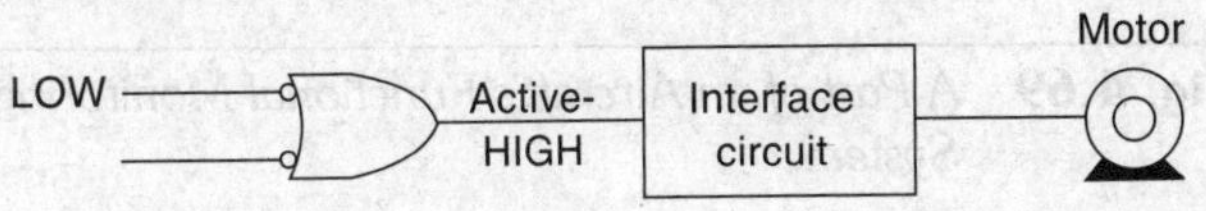

**Fig. 4.67**

This application requires an active-LOW input OR function because the output has to be active-HIGH in order to produce an indication of the occurrence of one or more LOW levels on its inputs. In this case, the gate functions as a `negative-OR` and is represented by the appropriate symbol shown in the diagram. A LOW on either input or both inputs causes an active-HIGH output to activate the motor through an appropriate interface circuit.

### 4.58 A certain application requires that two lines be monitored for the occurrence of a HIGH level voltage on either or both lines. Upon detection of a HIGH level, the circuit must provide a LOW voltage to energise a particular indicating device. Sketch the operation.

*Solution:*
The application requires a NOR function, since the output must be active-LOW in order to give an indication of at least one HIGH on its inputs. The NOR symbol is, therefore, used to represent the operation as shown in Fig. 4.68.

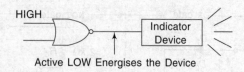

**Fig. 4.68**

**4.59 What type of gate should be used to detect if all three landings gears are retracted after take off, assuming a LOW output is required to activate an LED display?**

*Solution:*

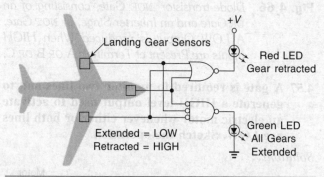

**Fig. 4.69** *A Part of an Aircraft's Functional Monitoring System.*

Power is applied to the circuit only when the 'gear-down' switch is activated. Use a NOR gate for each of the two requirements as shown in Fig. 4.69. One NOR gate operates as a negative-AND to detect a LOW from each of the three landing gear sensors. When all three of the gate inputs are LOW, the three landing gears are properly extended and the resulting HIGH output from the negative-AND gate turns on the green LED display. The other NOR gate operates as a NOR to detect if one or more of the landing gears remain retracted when the 'gear down' switch is activated. When one or more of the landing gears remain retracted, the resulting HIGH from the sensor is detected by the NOR gate, which produces a LOW output to turn on red LED warning display.

## THE EXCLUSIVE OR FUNCTION

The exclusive OR gate is sometimes referred to as the *any but not all gate*. The term 'exclusive OR gate' is often shortened to 'XOR gate'. The logic symbol for the XOR gate is shown in Fig. 4.70(a), the Boolean expression for the XOR function is shown in Fig. 4.70(b). The symbol ⊕ means that the terms are XORed together. Notice that if any but not all of the inputs are 1, then the output will be a binary or logical 1.

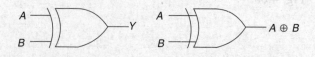

**Fig. 4.70** *(a) XOR Gate Symbol, (b) Boolean Expression.*

**4.60 Compare the truth tables for the OR gate and XOR gate.**

*Solution:*

| INPUTS | | OUTPUT | |
|---|---|---|---|
| *B* | *A* | OR | XOR |
| 0 | 0 | 0 | 0 |
| 0 | 1 | 1 | 1 |
| 1 | 0 | 1 | 1 |
| 1 | 1 | 1 | 0 |

**Fig. 4.71** *Comparison of Truth Tables for OR and XOR Gates.*

**4.61 What is the unique characteristic of the XOR gate?**

*Solution:*

The unique characteristic of the XOR gate is that it produces a HIGH output only when an *odd* number of HIGH inputs are present. If an *even* number of HIGH inputs to the XOR gate are present the output will be LOW. This is shown in Fig. 4.72. The XOR gates are used in a variety of arithmetic circuits.

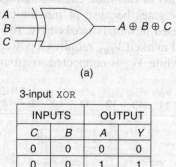

(a)

3-input XOR

| INPUTS | | | OUTPUT |
|---|---|---|---|
| *C* | *B* | *A* | *Y* |
| 0 | 0 | 0 | 0 |
| 0 | 0 | 1 | 1 |
| 0 | 1 | 0 | 1 |
| 0 | 1 | 1 | 0 |
| 1 | 0 | 0 | 1 |
| 1 | 0 | 1 | 0 |
| 1 | 1 | 0 | 0 |
| 1 | 1 | 1 | 1 |

(b)

**Fig. 4.72** *(a) Three-input XOR Gate Symbol and Boolean Expression (b) Truth Table.*

## XOR CIRCUITS

ECL-10107 IC provides three XOR gates. There are two outputs from each gate; the other output gives the XNOR function equivalence. ECL gates have three terminals for power supply. $V_{CC1}$ and $V_{CC2}$ are usually connected to ground and $V_{EE}$ to a –5.2 V supply. (See Fig. 4.73)

XOR and XNOR gates are available in both TTL and CMOS integrated-circuit packages. *The 7486 is a TTL quad XOR and the 4077 is a CMOS quad XNOR.*

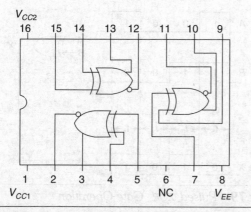

**Fig. 4.73** *Pinout of ECL-10107 Triple Exclusive OR-NOR Gate.*

## 4.62 Draw the combination of AND, OR, and NAND gates to provide the XOR function.

*Solution:*

The combination of AND, OR, and NAND gates shown in Fig. 4.74 will reduce to the *one or other but not both,* XOR function.

$$X = \bar{A}B + A\bar{B}.$$

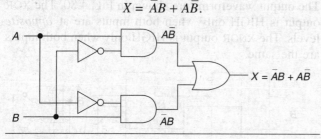

**Fig. 4.74**

## 4.63 Draw the switch analogy of the XOR function.

*Solution:*

Practically everyone who lives in a two-storeyed house uses an exclusive-OR gate every day. This consists of the switches at the top and bottom of the stairs that operate the *landing light.* When *both* switches are in the 'up' position, the lamp is not lit. If the switch at the *bottom* of the stairs is put on the 'down' position then the lamp will light. If the switch at the *top* of the stairs is also put in the 'down' position, the lamp will extinguish. Conversely, if *both* switches are in the 'down' position, the lamp will not be lit. *Putting one switch in the 'up' position and the other switch in the 'down' position will only light the lamp* (see Fig. 4.75)

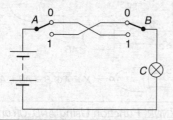

**Fig. 4.75** *Switch Analogy of the XOR Function.*

This can be described by the following statement: the lamp is lit only when the switches are in *different positions* or *X is true if A is true or B is true but not both.* This can be rephrased as: *X is true if A is true and B is false OR if B is true and A is false;* which can be written as the Boolean equation: $X = A\bar{B} + \bar{A}B$.

## 4.64 Exclusive-OR circuits used in Digital Comparator.

*Solution:*

Unlike the radio receiver, a digital system generally exhibits no *natural symptoms*—such as hum, distortion, or erratic volume—to warn the operator that something has gone wrong. Instead, the system simply provides the *wrong answer.* Furthermore, component failure is not the only way by which information can be made erroneous or be lost. There is some distortion each time a pulse passes from one circuit to another. Added to this is the distortion caused by the inductive effects from nearby circuits. Thus, it should be understood that *a pulse itself can sometimes become so distorted that it may produce an error.*

One method of detecting errors, which may be called a *redundancy method,* involves running the problem through the computer *twice* and noting whether the solutions are identical. However, a computer's major function is to save time, and this type of check doubles the amount of time that is required to solve a problem. In addition, this check is useless if a component has failed; for *the faulty component will probably distort both solutions in exactly the same manner.*

A better solution is to provide *two sets of identical circuitry,* as shown in Fig. 4.76. When this is done, *the same problem is run simultaneously through both circuits.* Unless both circuits commit exactly the same error, obtaining identical solutions indicates that the answer is correct. Recall that *an exclusive-OR circuit produces an output only when its two inputs are different.*

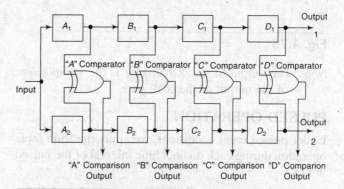

**Fig. 4.76** *Exclusive-OR Circuits used as Comparator in Error Detection.*

When using this method, the inputs should always be the same. A signal at the output of any of the exclusive-OR circuits indicates that the two parallel major section outputs are not identical and that one of them is in error. A signal at $B$, for example, means that either section $B_1$ or section $B_2$ is in error.

The *cost factor* must be considered. While parallel operation is an excellent technical concept and its use requires no extra time it does double the circuitry costs.

## THE EXCLUSIVE NOR FUNCTION

The 'exclusive NOR gate' is often shortened to 'XNOR gate'. The logic symbol for the XNOR gate and the Boolean expression for the XNOR gate are given in Fig. 4.77. It is the XOR symbol with the added invert bubble on the output side. The bar over $A \oplus B$ expression tells us we have inverted the output of the XOR gate. When the two input logic levels are opposite, the output of the XNOR gate is LOW.

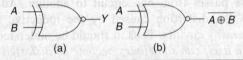

**Fig. 4.77**   *(a) XNOR Gate Symbol (b) Boolean Expression.*

**4.65 Compare the truth tables of XOR and XNOR gates.**

*Solution:*

| $X = AB + \overline{AB}$ | | | $X = \overline{A}B + A\overline{B}$ | | |
|---|---|---|---|---|---|
| A | B | X | A | B | X |
| 0 | 0 | 1 | 0 | 0 | 0 |
| 0 | 1 | 0 | 0 | 1 | 1 |
| 1 | 0 | 0 | 1 | 0 | 1 |
| 1 | 1 | 1 | 1 | 1 | 0 |
| Exclusive-NOR | | | Exclusive-OR | | |

**Fig. 4.78**

*Note:* The output of the XNOR gate is the *complement* of the output of the XOR gate.

## PULSED OPERATION

Under pulsed input conditions, we apply the truth table operation during each distinct time interval of the pulsed inputs.

**4.66 Find the output $X$ with the inputs $A$ and $B$ for the XOR gate in Fig. 4.79.**

*Solution:*
Input waveforms $A$ and $B$ are at opposite levels during time intervals $t_2$ and $t_4$. Therefore, the output $X$ is HIGH

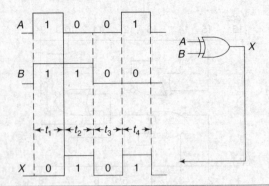

**Fig. 4.79**   *Pulsed XOR Gate Operation.*

during these two times. Since, both inputs are at the same level, either both HIGH or both LOW, during time intervals $t_1$ and $t_3$, the output is LOW during those times. This is illustrated in Fig. 4.79.

**4.67 Determine the output waveforms for the XOR gate and the XNOR gate, given the input waveforms, $A$ and $B$, in Fig. 4.80.**

*Solution:*
The output waveforms are shown in Fig. 4.80. The XOR output is HIGH only when both inputs are at *opposite* levels. The XNOR output is HIGH only when both inputs are the same.

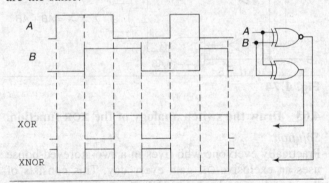

**Fig. 4.80**   *Pulsed XOR and XNOR Gate Operation.*

## XNOR CIRCUITS

The XNOR gate provides a HIGH output for both inputs HIGH or both inputs LOW (Fig. 4.81).

$$X = AB + \overline{A}\,\overline{B}$$

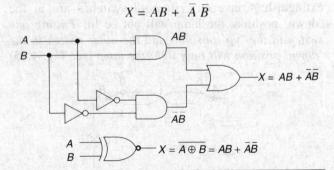

**Fig. 4.81**   *XNOR Function Using AND, OR and NAND Gates.*

**4.68 How will you use an XOR gate as a two-bit adder?**

*Solution:*

The output of the XOR gate is the *binary sum* of the two input bits. In the case where the inputs are both 1's, the output is the sum 0, but you lose the carry of 1. XOR gates are *combined* to make complete adding circuits.

| Input bits | | Output (sum) |
|---|---|---|
| A | B | Σ |
| 0 | 0 | 0 |
| 0 | 1 | 1 |
| 1 | 0 | 1 |
| 1 | 1 | 0 (without 1 carry) |

**Fig. 4.82**   *An XOR Gate as a Two-bit Adder.*

**4.69 A certain system contains two identical circuits operating in parallel. As long as both are operating properly, the outputs of both circuits are always the same. If one of the circuits fails, the outputs will be at opposite levels at sometime. Devise a way to detect that a failure has occurred in one of the circuits.**

*Solution:*

The outputs of the circuits are connected to the inputs of an XOR gate as shown in Fig. 4.83. A failure in either one of the circuits produces differing outputs, which cause the XOR inputs to be at opposite levels. This condition produces a HIGH on the output of the XOR gate, indicating a failure in one of the circuits.

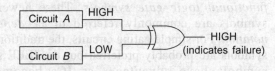

**Fig. 4.83**

**4.70 Give a summary of the basic logic gates in tabular form.**

*Solution:*

See Fig. 4.84.

**4.71 How will you perform gate inversions using inverters. Illustrate.**

*Solution:*

See Fig. 4.85.

| Logic Function | Logic Symbol | Boolean Expression | Truth Table | | |
|---|---|---|---|---|---|
| | | | Inputs | | Output |
| | | | B | A | Y |
| AND | A, B → Y | $A \cdot B = Y$ | 0 | 0 | 0 |
| | | | 0 | 1 | 0 |
| | | | 1 | 0 | 0 |
| | | | 1 | 1 | 1 |
| OR | A, B → Y | $A + B = Y$ | 0 | 0 | 0 |
| | | | 0 | 1 | 1 |
| | | | 1 | 0 | 1 |
| | | | 1 | 1 | 1 |
| Inverter | A → $\bar{A}$ | $A = \bar{A}$ | | 0 | 1 |
| | | | | 1 | 0 |
| NAND | A, B → Y | $\overline{A \cdot B} = Y$ | 0 | 0 | 1 |
| | | | 0 | 1 | 1 |
| | | | 1 | 0 | 1 |
| | | | 1 | 1 | 0 |
| NOR | A, B → Y | $\overline{A + B} = Y$ | 0 | 0 | 1 |
| | | | 0 | 1 | 0 |
| | | | 1 | 0 | 0 |
| | | | 1 | 1 | 0 |
| XOR | A, B → Y | $A \oplus B = Y$ | 0 | 0 | 0 |
| | | | 0 | 1 | 1 |
| | | | 1 | 0 | 1 |
| | | | 1 | 1 | 0 |
| XNOR | A, B → Y | $\overline{A \oplus B} = Y$ | 0 | 0 | 1 |
| | | | 0 | 1 | 0 |
| | | | 1 | 0 | 0 |
| | | | 1 | 1 | 1 |

**Fig. 4.84**   *Summary of Basic Logic Gates.*

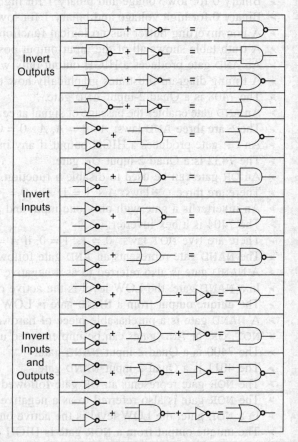

**Fig. 4.85**   *Gate Conversions using Inverters. The + Symbol here indicates Combining the Functions.*

**4.72 Briefly explain and compare traditional and IEEE logic gate symbols.**

*Solution:*

See Fig. 4.86.

The *traditional logic gate symbols* are recognised by all workers in the electronics industry. These symbols are very useful in that they have *distinctive shapes*. Manufacturers' data manuals include traditional logic symbols and are recently including the newer *IEEE functional logic gate symbols*. These newer *IEEE* symbols are commonly referred to as *dependency notation*. For simple gating circuits, the traditional logic symbols are probably preferred but the IEEE standard symbols have advantages as ICs become more complicated. Most military contracts call for use of IEEE standard symbols.

| Logic Function | Traditional Logic Symbol | IEEE Logic symbol* |
|---|---|---|
| AND | | |
| OR | | |
| NOT | | |
| NAND | | |
| NOR | | |
| XOR | | |
| XNOR | | |

**Fig. 4.86** *Comparing Traditional and IEEE Logic Gate Symbols.*

# SUMMARY

> - A logic gate is a digital circuit with one or more inputs but only one output. The output is HIGH only for certain combinations of input signals.
> - Binary 0 for low voltage and binary 1 for high voltage is called positive logic.
> - Binary 0 for high voltage and binary 1 for low voltage is called negative logic.
> - A non-inverting buffer has no logical function.
> - A truth table shows all of the input-output possibilities of a logic circuit.
> - An AND gate produces a HIGH output only when all inputs are HIGH.
> - A timing diagram illustrates graphically how the output levels change in response to input changes.
> - The 7408 is a Quad 2-input AND gate.
> - An AND gate enables the passage of signal at certain times and inhibits the passage of signal at other times.
> - There are three AND laws: $A \cdot 1 = A$, $A \cdot 0 = 0$, and $A \cdot A = A$.
> - An OR gate produces a HIGH output if any input is HIGH.
> - The 7432 is a Quad 2-input OR gate.
> - An OR gate can be used to disable a function.
> - There are three OR laws: $A + 1 = 1$, $A + 0 = A$, and $A + A = A$.
> - An inverter is a gate with only one input and a complemented output.
> - The 7404 is a hex inverter.
> - There are five NOT laws: $\overline{0} = 1$, $\overline{1} = 0$, if $A = 0$ the $\overline{A} = 1$, if $A = 1$ then $\overline{A} = 0$, and $\overline{\overline{A}} = A$
> - The NAND gate represents an AND gate followed by an inverter.
> - A NAND gate is also referred to as a negative OR gate.
> - In a NAND gate, the LOW level is the active output level.
> - The unique output from a NAND gate is LOW only when all its inputs are HIGH.
> - A NAND gate is a purchasable piece of hardware, usually an integrated circuit.
> - NOT, OR, or AND gates can be implemented using only NAND gates.
> - The 7400 is a Quad 2-input NAND gate.
> - The 4011 is a Quad 2-input NAND gate.
> - The NOR gate represents an OR gate followed by an inverter.
> - The NOR gate is also referred to as a negative AND gate.
> - In a NOR gate, the LOW level is the active output level.
> - The unique output from a NOR gate is HIGH only when all its inputs are LOW.
> - A NOR gate is a purchasable piece of hardware, usually an integrated circuit.

> NOT, OR, or AND gates can be implemented using only NOR gates.
> The 10102 is a Quad 2-input NOR gate.
> The CMOS. 4002 can accommodate only two 4-input NOR gates.
> The XOR gate has a HIGH output only when an odd number of inputs is HIGH.
> THe ECL-10107 is a triple exclusive OR-NOR gate.
> The 7486 is a TTL Quad XOR.
> The 4077 is a CMOS Quad XNOR.
> When the two logic levels are opposite, the output of the XNOR gate is LOW.

# REVIEW QUESTIONS

1. How many table entries are needed for a five-input circuit?
2. When is the output of an AND gate HIGH?
3. When is the output of an AND gate LOW?
4. What is the only input combination that will produce a HIGH at the output of a five-input AND gate?
5. What logic level should be applied to the second input of a two-input AND gate if the logic signal at the first input is to be prevented from reaching the output?
6. Describe the truth table for a three-input AND gate?
7. When is the output of an OR gate HIGH?
8. When is the output of an OR gate LOW?
9. What is the only set of input conditions that will produce a LOW output for any OR gate?
10. Write the Boolean expressions for a six-input OR gate?
11. Describe the truth table for a two-input OR gate.
12. If a 1 is on the input of an inverter what is the output?
13. Write a logic equation for each of the following:
    (a) $A = $ NOT $B$,   (b) $A$ OR $B = F$,   (c) $A$ AND $B$ AND NOT $C = F$
14. What is the only set of input conditions that will produce a HIGH output from a three-input NOR gate.
15. Change the NOR gate of Fig. 4.87 to a NAND gate and change the NAND gate to a NOR. What is the new expression for $X$?

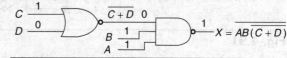

**Fig. 4.87**

16. When is the output of a NAND gate HIGH?
17. When is the output of a NAND gate LOW?
18. What is the functional difference between a NAND gate and a negative-OR gate? Do they both have the same truth table?
19. Write the output expression for NAND gate with inputs $A$, $B$, and $C$.
20. When is the output of a NOR gate HIGH?
21. When is the output of a NOR gate LOW?
22. Describe the functional difference between a NOR gate and a negative-AND gate? Do they both have the same truth table?
23. Write the output expression for a three input NOR with input variable $A$, $B$, and $C$.
24. When is the output of an XOR gate HIGH?
25. When is the output of XNOR gate HIGH?
26. How can you use an XOR gate to detect when two bits are different?
27. Describe the significance of a timing diagram.

# SUPPLEMENTARY PROBLEMS

28. Pins 1 and 2 are the input and output pins of an inverter. With the waveform shown in Fig. 4.88 as input to pin 1, sketch the output waveform at pin 2.

Pin 1 Input   A B C D E F G H I

**Fig. 4.88**

29. The input waveform shown below is applied to an inverter. Sketch the output waveform in proper relationship to the input.

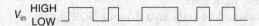

$$V_{in} \quad \begin{array}{l} \text{HIGH} \\ \text{LOW} \end{array}$$

**Fig. 4.89**

30. Sketch the output waveform at $X$ for the three-input AND gate shown below.

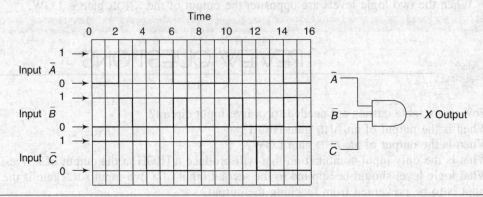

**Fig. 4.90**

31. Draw the truth table for the given diagram.

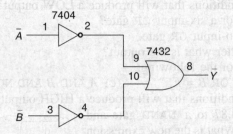

**Fig. 4.91**

32. Draw the truth table for the given diagram. (See Fig. 4.92)
33. Draw the truth table and its binary equivalent for a three-input AND gate.
34. Draw the timing diagram of a three-input NAND gate to show that the output is LOW only when all three inputs are HIGH.
35. Sketch the output waveform at $X$ for the NAND gate shown with given input waveforms. (See Fig. 4.93)
36. Sketch the output waveform at $X$ for the NOR gate shown with the given input waveforms. (See Fig. 4.94)

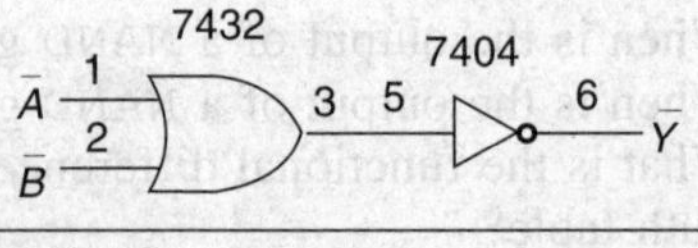

**Fig. 4.92**

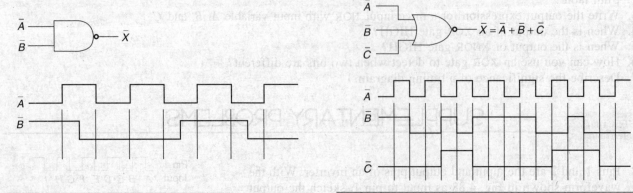

**Fig. 4.93**                                    **Fig. 4.94**

37. Using the given diagram, sketch the waveform that will allow only the even pulses (2, 4, 6, 8 etc.) to get through. (See Fig. 4.95)

38. Sketch the output waveform at $X$ for two-input NOR gate with the given input waveforms. (See Fig. 4.96)

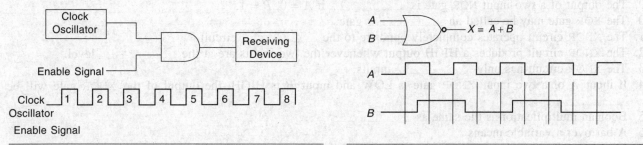

**Fig. 4.95**                                   **Fig. 4.96**

39. Sketch the output waveform at $X$ for the NAND gate shown with the given input waveforms at $A$, $B$, and control. (See Fig. 4.97)

40. Draw the truth table for a three-input NAND gate.

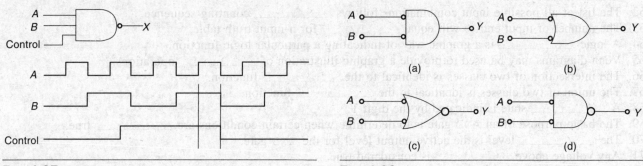

**Fig. 4.97**                                   **Fig. 4.98**

41. Find the relationship between the inputs and the outputs for each of the gates shown in Fig. 4.98. Name the operation performed in each case.

42. The input waveform at A is given for the two-input OR gate in Fig. 4.99. Sketch the input waveform at $B$ that will produce the output at $X$.

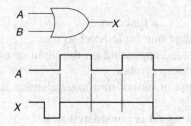

**Fig. 4.99**

# OBJECTIVE TYPE QUESTIONS

## Fill in the Blanks

43. NOT A is written as _____.
44. The output of an AND gate, if one of its input terminals is connected to logic 0, is _____.
45. The output of an AND gate when inhibited is logic 0 _____ of all other inputs.
46. The logic signal required to _____ an OR gate is logic 1.

47. The output of a two-input NAND gate is _____ if $A = 1$, $B = 0$.
48. The output side of a NAND gate logic symbol is _____ (flat with an added invert bubble, pointed with an added invert bubble, round with an added invert bubble.)
49. The output of a two-input NOR gate is _____ if $A = 0$, $B = 1$.
50. The XOR gate may be called an _____ gate.
51. The XNOR circuit operates completely opposite to the _____ circuit.
52. The XNOR circuit produces a HIGH output whenever the two inputs are at the _____ level.
53. The XNOR circuit has only _____ inputs.
54. If input $A$ of a two input XNOR gate is LOW and input $B$ is HIGH, the output of the XNOR gate will be _____.
55. Boolean multiplication is the same as _____.
56. A bar over a variable means _____.
57. Boolean addition is the same as _____.
58. A double bar over a variable means _____.
59. Complementation is the same as _____.
60. Boolean expressions can be _____ using algebraic methods.
61. If the higher of the two voltages represents a 0 and the lower voltage represents a 1, the system is called a _____ system.
62. The list of all possible input combinations follows _____ counting sequence.
63. The number of input entries will equal _____ for n-input truth table.
64. A logic _____ is a graphic way of indicating a particular logic function.
65. Venn diagrams may be used to provide a graphic illustration of _____ operations.
66. The intersection of two classes is identical to the _____ function.
67. The union of two classes is identical to the _____ function.
68. A _____ state is indicated by the digit 1.
69. The basic purpose of an AND gate is to determine when certain conditions are _____ true.
70. The _____ level is the active output level for the AND gate.
71. Any voltage above _____ is considered true.
72. Any voltage below _____ is considered false.
73. AND gates may have _____ of inputs.
74. An AND gate _____ the truth table operation regardless of whether its inputs are constant levels or pulsed levels.
75. An AND gate requires that _____ inputs be HIGH is order for the output to be HIGH.
76. AND and OR are called _____ connectives.
77. $A + 1 =$ _____ and $A \cdot 1 =$ _____.
78. An OR gate can be used to _____ a function.
79. The purpose of the inverter is to change one logic level to the _____ logic level.
80. The negation indicator is a _____ appearing on the input or output of a logic element.
81. Inputs are on the _____ of a logic symbol.
82. The placement of a bubble on the input or output of a logic element is determined by the _____ of the input signal.
83. The active state is the state when the signal is considered to be _____ on the input.
84. $\overline{1} =$ _____ , $\overline{\overline{1}} =$ _____.
85. An even number of negations is equal to _____.
86. An _____ number of negations is equal to a single negation.
87. The NAND function implies an AND function with a _____ output.
88. In a NAND gate, the output is _____ when any or all the inputs are LOW.
89. A NAND gate is equivalent to an active-LOW input _____ gate.
90. The _____ gate can perform an AND function and an OR function.
91. A NAND gate is a piece of _____.
92. The unique output from a NAND gate is a LOW only when all inputs are _____.
93. An _____ gate provides for the connection of additional diodes to increase the number of input terminals.
94. The NAND gate can be used as an _____ by connecting the input leads together.
95. A NOR gate is equivalent to a _____ AND gate.

96. A NOR gate is a universal _____ building block.
97. The NOR gate can be used as an _____ by connecting the input leads together.
98. The XOR gate produces a HIGH output only when an _____ number of HIGH inputs are present.
99. The XNOR gate is also called an _____ gate.

## True/False Questions

State whether the following statements are True or False.
100. A logic gate has an input terminal and one or more output terminals.
101. Each logic gate is represented by a particular logic symbol.
102. Boolean algebra variables can have only the values 0 or 1.
103. An open switch is equivalent to 1 and a closed switch equivalent to 0.
104. The + (plus) sign in Boolean algebra refers to the AND function.
105. A double bar has no effect on the logical value.
106. The list of all possible input combinations in a truth table follows the octal counting sequence.
107. The basic function of the AND gate is to determine when certain conditions are simultaneously true.
108. An inclusive OR function includes the possibility of $A$ being true, OR $B$ being true, OR both being true.
109. An AND gate can be used to enable/disable a clock oscillator.
110. An OR gate can be used to disable a function.
111. A logic gate that negates the input is called a buffer.
112. A bubble on the input means a double inversion.
113. An AND gate with inverters on its inputs and output is called a NAND gate.
114. Logic gates can have only two inputs.
115. XOR and XNOR gates have only two inputs.
116. It is possible to expand the XOR gate.
117. The XNOR gate may be called a non-equivalence gate.

## Multiple Choice Questions

118. The voltage levels for positive logic system
    (a) must necessarily be positive.     (b) must necessarily be positive or negative.
    (c) may be positive or negative.       (d) must necessarily be 0 or 5 V.
119. The digital operations such as AND, OR, NOT etc. can be performed by using
    (a) switches                           (b) amplifiers
    (c) rectifiers                         (d) oscillators
120. An inverter gate can be developed using
    (a) two diodes                         (b) a transistor
    (c) a resistance and a capacitance     (d) an inductance and a capacitance
121. If an input $A$ is given to an inverter, the output will be
    (a) $A$                                (b) $\bar{A}$
    (c) $1/A$                              (d) 1
122. The output of a two-input OR gate is HIGH
    (a) only if both the inputs are HIGH
    (b) only if both the inputs are LOW
    (c) only if one input is HIGH and the other is LOW
    (d) only if at least one of the inputs is LOW.
123. For an AND gate
    (a) All LOW inputs produce a HIGH output
    (b) All HIGH inputs produce a LOW output
    (c) All HIGH inputs produce a HIGH output
    (d) All LOW inputs produce a LOW output
124. The output of a gate is LOW when at least one of its inputs is HIGH. This is true for
    (a) AND                                (b) NAND
    (c) OR                                 (d) NOR
125. The output of a gate is LOW when at least one of its inputs is LOW. This is true of
    (a) AND                                (b) NAND
    (c) OR                                 (d) NOR

126. The output of a two-input AND gate is HIGH
    (a) only if both inputs are HIGH
    (b) only if both inputs are LOW
    (c) only if one input is HIGH and the other is LOW
    (d) if at least one of the inputs is LOW

127. NAND gate means
    (a) inversion followed by AND gate          (b) AND gate followed by an inverter
    (c) AND gate followed by an OR gate          (d) OR gate followed by an AND gate

128. The output of a gate is HIGH when at least one of its inputs is LOW. It is true for
    (a) XOR                                      (b) NAND
    (c) NOR                                      (d) OR

129. The output of a gate is HIGH when at least one of its inputs is HIGH. It is true for
    (a) NAND                                     (b) AND
    (c) OR                                       (d) XOR

130. The output of a gate is HIGH when all of its inputs are HIGH. It is true for
    (a) XOR                                      (b) AND
    (c) OR                                       (d) NAND

131. The output of a gate is LOW if and only if all of its inputs are HIGH. It is true for
    (a) AND                                      (b) XNOR
    (c) NOR                                      (d) NAND

132. The output of a gate is HIGH if and only if all of its inputs are LOW. It is true for
    (a) NOR                                      (b) XNOR
    (c) NAND                                     (d) XOR

133. The output of a two-input NAND gate is HIGH
    (a) only if both the inputs are HIGH
    (b) only if both the inputs are LOW
    (c) only if one input is HIGH and the other is LOW
    (d) if at least one of the inputs is LOW.

134. A NOR gate means
    (a) inversion followed by an OR gate         (b) OR gate followed by an inverter
    (c) NOT gate followed by an OR gate          (d) NAND gate followed by an OR gate.

135. An XOR gate gives a HIGH output
    (a) if there are odd number of 1's in the input
    (b) if there are even number of 1's in the input
    (c) if there are odd number of 0's in the input
    (d) if there are even number of 0's in the input.

136. An XNOR gate is logically equal to
    (a) inverter followed by XOR gate            (b) NOT gate followed by an XOR gate
    (c) XOR gate followed by an inverter         (d) complement of a NOR gate.

137. The logic expression $AB + \bar{A}\,\bar{B}$ can be implemented by giving inputs $A$ and $B$ to a two-input
    (a) NOR gate                                 (b) XNOR gate
    (c) XOR gate                                 (d) NAND gate

138. The logic expression $A\bar{B} + \bar{A}B$ can be implemented by giving inputs $A$ and $B$ to a two input
    (a) NAND gate                                (b) XOR gate
    (c) XNOR gate                                (d) NOR gate

139. The gate ideally suited for bit comparison is a
    (a) two-input XNOR gate                      (b) two-input XOR gate
    (c) two-input NOR gate                       (d) two-input NAND gate

140. Two-input XNOR gate gives HIGH output
    (a) when one input is HIGH and the other is LOW
    (b) only when both the inputs are LOW
    (c) when both the inputs are the same
    (d) only when both the inputs are HIGH.

141. The output of a gate is LOW if and only if all its inputs are LOW. It is true for
    (a) XOR                    (b) AND
    (c) OR                     (d) NOR
142. The output of a two-input gate is 1 if and only if its inputs are unequal. It is true for
    (a) OR                     (b) XOR
    (c) NOR                    (d) XNOR
143. The output of a two-input gate is 0 if and only if its inputs unequal. It is true for
    (a) XNOR                   (b) NOR
    (c) AND                    (d) NAND
144. The output of a two-input gate is 1 if and only if its inputs are equal. It is true for
    (a) XOR                    (b) XNOR
    (c) AND                    (d) NAND
145. The output of a two-input gate is 0 if and only if its inputs are equal. It is true for
    (a) AND                    (b) OR
    (c) NOR                    (d) XOR
146. Which of the following gates can be used as an inverter?
    (a) AND                    (b) OR
    (c) NAND                   (d) NOR
147. A gate is enabled when its enable input is at logic 1. The gate is
    (a) AND                    (b) OR
    (c) NAND                   (d) NOR
148. A gate is enabled when its enable input is at logic 0. The gate is
    (a) OR                     (b) AND
    (c) NOR                    (d) NAND
149. A gate is inhibited when its inhibit input is at logic 1. The gate is
    (a) AND                    (b) NAND
    (c) OR                     (d) NOR
150. A gate is disabled when its disable input is at logic 0. The gate is
    (a) NAND                   (b) NOR
    (c) OR                     (d) AND
151. The output of a logic gate is 1 when all its inputs are at logic 1. The gate is either
    (a) a NAND or a NOR        (b) an AND or an OR
    (c) an OR or an XOR        (d) an AND or a NOR
152. The output of a logic gate is 1 when all its inputs are at logic 0. The gate is either
    (a) an XOR or an XNOR      (b) an OR or a NAND
    (c) an AND or an XNOR      (d) a NAND or a NOR
153. Which of the following gates is known as an universal gate?
    (a) AND                    (b) NAND
    (c) OR                     (d) NOT
154. Any logical expression can be realized by using only
    (a) AND gates              (b) AND and NOT gates
    (c) OR and NOT gates       (d) AND, OR and NOT gates
155. The NAND gate is known as a universal gate because
    (a) it can be used as an inverter
    (b) AND operation can be realized using NAND gates
    (c) OR operation can be realized using NAND gates
    (d) AND, OR and NOT operations can be performed using NAND gates.
156. Which of the following gates is known as an universal gate?
    (a) OR                     (b) NOR
    (c) AND                    (d) NOT

# ANSWERS

1. 32
2. An AND gate output is HIGH when all inputs are HIGH.
3. An AND gate output is LOW when one or more inputs are LOW.
4. All five inputs = 1.
5. A LOW input will keep the output LOW.
6.

| A | B | C | X |
|---|---|---|---|
| 0 | 0 | 0 | 0 |
| 0 | 0 | 1 | 0 |
| 0 | 1 | 0 | 0 |
| 0 | 1 | 1 | 0 |
| 1 | 0 | 0 | 0 |
| 1 | 0 | 1 | 0 |
| 1 | 1 | 0 | 0 |
| 1 | 1 | 1 | 1 |

7. An OR gate output is HIGH when one or more inputs are HIGH.
8. An OR gate output is LOW when all inputs are LOW.
9. All inputs LOW.
10. $X = A + B + C + D + E + F$.
11.

| A | B | X |
|---|---|---|
| 0 | 0 | 0 |
| 0 | 1 | 1 |
| 1 | 0 | 1 |
| 1 | 1 | 1 |

12. When an inverter input is 1, the output is 0.
13. (a) $A = \bar{B}$        (b) $A + B = F$        (c) $AB\bar{C} = F$.
14. All inputs LOW.
15. $X = \overline{A + B + \overline{CD}}$
16. A NAND gate output is HIGH when one or more inputs are LOW.
17. A NAND gate output is LOW when all inputs are HIGH.
18. NAND: Active-LOW output for all HIGH inputs; Negative-OR: Active-HIGH output for one or more LOW inputs; Same truth table.
19. $X = \overline{ABC}$.
20. A NOR gate output is HIGH when all inputs are LOW.
21. A NOR gate output is LOW when one or more inputs are HIGH.
22. NOR: Active-LOW output for one or more HIGH inputs, Negative-And: Active-HIGH output for all LOW inputs. Same truth table.
23. $X = \overline{A + B + C}$.
24. An XOR gate output is HIGH when the inputs are at opposite levels.
25. An XNOR gate output is HIGH when all inputs are at the same level.
26. Apply the bits to the XOR gate inputs; when the output is HIGH, the bits are different.
27. A timing diagram is basically a graph that accurately displays the relationship of two or more waveforms with respect to each other on a time basis.

28. Pin 2 Output

A B C D E F G H I

29.

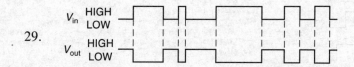

30. Output $X$

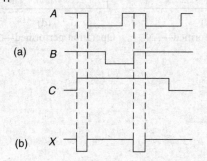

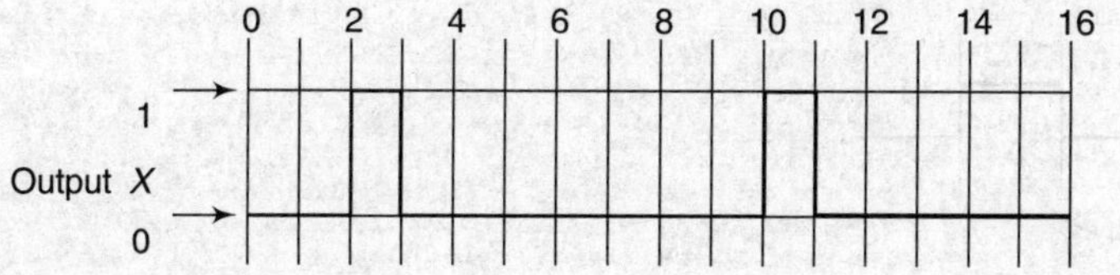

31.

| A | B | Y |
|---|---|---|
| L | L | H |
| L | H | H |
| H | L | H |
| H | H | L |

32.

| A | B | Y |
|---|---|---|
| L | L | H |
| L | H | L |
| H | L | L |
| H | H | L |

33.

| A | B | C | Y |
|---|---|---|---|
| L | L | L | L |
| L | L | H | L |
| L | H | L | L |
| L | H | H | L |
| H | L | L | L |
| H | L | H | L |
| H | H | L | L |
| H | H | H | H |

| A | B | C | Y |
|---|---|---|---|
| 0 | 0 | 0 | 0 |
| 0 | 0 | 1 | 0 |
| 0 | 1 | 0 | 0 |
| 0 | 1 | 1 | 0 |
| 1 | 0 | 0 | 0 |
| 1 | 0 | 1 | 0 |
| 1 | 1 | 0 | 0 |
| 1 | 1 | 1 | 1 |

34.

(a)

(b)

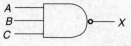

35.

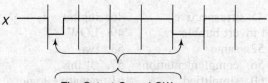

The Output Goes LOW
when both Inputs are HIGH

36.

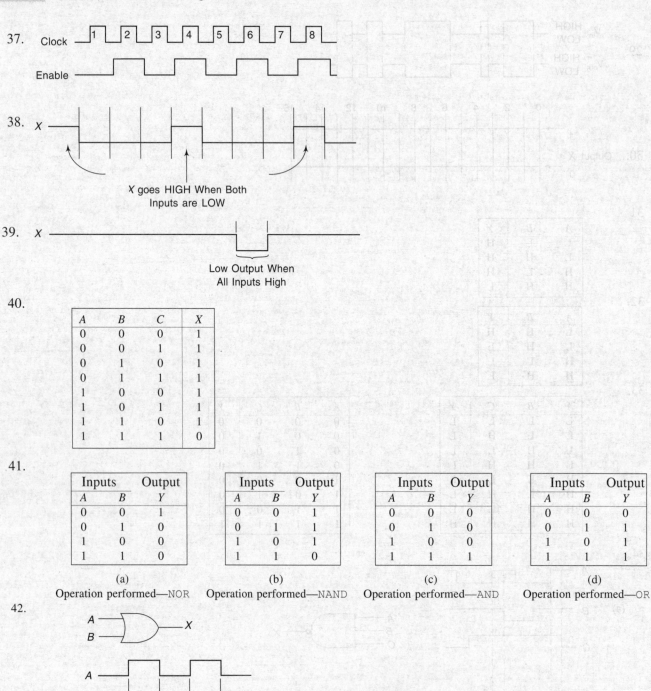

37. Clock / Enable

38. *X* goes HIGH When Both Inputs are LOW

39. *X* — Low Output When All Inputs High

40.

| A | B | C | X |
|---|---|---|---|
| 0 | 0 | 0 | 1 |
| 0 | 0 | 1 | 1 |
| 0 | 1 | 0 | 1 |
| 0 | 1 | 1 | 1 |
| 1 | 0 | 0 | 1 |
| 1 | 0 | 1 | 1 |
| 1 | 1 | 0 | 1 |
| 1 | 1 | 1 | 0 |

41.

| Inputs | | Output |
|---|---|---|
| A | B | Y |
| 0 | 0 | 1 |
| 0 | 1 | 0 |
| 1 | 0 | 0 |
| 1 | 1 | 0 |

(a)
Operation performed—NOR

| Inputs | | Output |
|---|---|---|
| A | B | Y |
| 0 | 0 | 1 |
| 0 | 1 | 1 |
| 1 | 0 | 1 |
| 1 | 1 | 0 |

(b)
Operation performed—NAND

| Inputs | | Output |
|---|---|---|
| A | B | Y |
| 0 | 0 | 0 |
| 0 | 1 | 0 |
| 1 | 0 | 0 |
| 1 | 1 | 1 |

(c)
Operation performed—AND

| Inputs | | Output |
|---|---|---|
| A | B | Y |
| 0 | 0 | 0 |
| 0 | 1 | 1 |
| 1 | 0 | 1 |
| 1 | 1 | 1 |

(d)
Operation performed—OR

42.

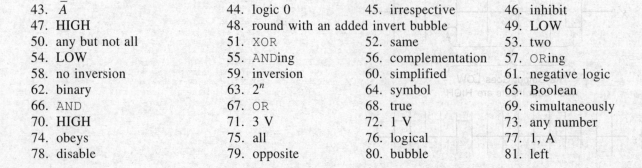

43. $\overline{A}$
44. logic 0
45. irrespective
46. inhibit
47. HIGH
48. round with an added invert bubble
49. LOW
50. any but not all
51. XOR
52. same
53. two
54. LOW
55. ANDing
56. complementation
57. ORing
58. no inversion
59. inversion
60. simplified
61. negative logic
62. binary
63. $2^n$
64. symbol
65. Boolean
66. AND
67. OR
68. true
69. simultaneously
70. HIGH
71. 3 V
72. 1 V
73. any number
74. obeys
75. all
76. logical
77. 1, A
78. disable
79. opposite
80. bubble
81. left

| | | | |
|---|---|---|---|
| 82. active state | 83. present | 84. 0, 1 | 85. no inversion |
| 86. odd | 87. complemented | 88. HIGH | 89. OR |
| 90. NAND | 91. hardware | 92. HIGH | 93. expandable |
| 94. inverter | 95. negative | 96. hardware | 97. inverter |
| 98. odd | 99. equivalence | 100. False | 101. True |
| 102. True | 103. False | 104. False | 105. True |
| 106. False | 107. True | 108. True | 109. True |
| 110. True | 111. False | 112. False | 113. False |
| 114. False | 115. True | 116. True | 117. False |
| 118. (c) | 119. (a) | 120. (b) | 121. (b) |
| 122. (d) | 123. (c) | 124. (c) | 125. (a) |
| 126. (a) | 127. (b) | 128. (b) | 129. (c) |
| 130. (b) | 131. (d) | 132. (a) | 133. (d) |
| 134. (b) | 135. (a) | 136. (c) | 137. (b) |
| 138. (b) | 139. (a) | 140. (c) | 141. (c) |
| 142. (b) | 143. (a) | 144. (b) | 145. (d) |
| 146. (c) and (d) | 147. (c) | 148. (a) | 149. (c) |
| 150. (d) | 151. (b) | 152. (d) | 153. (b) |
| 154. (d) | 155. (d) | 156. (b) | |

# Boolean Algebra

## INTRODUCTION

Named after its inventor, George Boole (1854), Boolean algebra defines constants, variables and functions to describe binary systems. It then describes a number of theorems that can be used to manipulate logic expressions. Boolean *operators* are the codes for the basic logic gates. You can use them as a short hand notation for digital circuits.

Boolean *constants* consist of 0 and 1. Boolean *variables* are quantities that can take different values at different times. They may represent *input, output or intermediate signals* and are given names consisting of alphabetic characters such as *A, B, C, X* or *Y*. Boolean variables may only take the values 0 or 1.

Each of the elementary *logic functions* is represented in Boolean algebra by a unique *symbol* as shown below:

| Function | Symbol | Example |
|----------|--------|---------|
| AND | dot (·) | $C = A \cdot B$ |
| OR | plus (+) | $C = A + B$ |
| NOT | overbar (⁻) | $C = \bar{A}$ |

**Fig. 5.1**   *Logic Functions.*

## BOOLEAN THEOREMS

Boolean expressions are not unique. We therefore require some method of *manipulating* expressions into their simplest forms. The rules of Boolean algebra consist of a set of *identities* and a set of *laws*. These are summarised in Table 5.1. It is easier to see the sense of the rules if they are converted into concrete examples when their meaning becomes clear. The identities on AND, OR and NOT functions have already been dealt with in details in Chapter 4. The various laws can also be understood by linking them to concrete examples.

**Table 5.1**   *Summary of Boolean Algebra Identities and Laws*

| AND function | Commutative law |
|---|---|
| (1)  $0 \cdot 0 = 0$ | (24)  $AB = BA$ |
| (2)  $0 \cdot 1 = 0$ | (25)  $A + B = B + A$ |
| (3)  $1 \cdot 0 = 0$ | **Distributive law** |
| (4)  $1 \cdot 1 = 1$ | (26)  $A(B + C) = AB + AC$ |
| (5)  $A \cdot 0 = 0$ | (27)  $A + BC = (A + B)(A + C)$ |
| (6)  $0 \cdot A = 0$ | **Associative law** |
| (7)  $A \cdot 1 = A$ | (28)  $A(BC) = (AB)C$ |
| (8)  $1 \cdot A = A$ | (29)  $A + (B + C) = (A + B) + C$ |
| (9)  $A \cdot A = A$ | **Absorption law** |
| (10)  $A \cdot \bar{A} = 0$ | (30)  $A + AB = A$ |
| **OR  function** | (31)  $A(A + B) = A$ |
| (11)  $0 + 0 = 0$ | **DeMorgan's law** |
| (12)  $0 + 1 = 1$ | (32)  $\overline{A + B} = \bar{A} \cdot \bar{B}$ |
| (13)  $1 + 0 = 1$ | (33)  $\overline{A \cdot B} = \bar{A} + \bar{B}$ |
| (14)  $1 + 1 = 1$ | **Also note** |
| (15)  $A + 0 = A$ | (34)  $A + \bar{A}B = A + B$ |
| (16)  $0 + A = A$ | (35)  $A(\bar{A} + B) = AB$ |
| (17)  $A + 1 = 1$ | |
| (18)  $1 + A = 1$ | |
| (19)  $A + A = A$ | |
| (20)  $A + \bar{A} = 1$ | |
| **NOT function** | |
| (21)  $\bar{0} = 1$ | |
| (22)  $\bar{1} = 0$ | |
| (23)  $\bar{\bar{A}} = A$ | |

## COMMUTATIVE LAW

It states that the elements of a function can be arranged in *any* sequence provided the connective is the *same*. Commutative law can also be stated as: 'the *order* in which terms are ANDed or ORed together is unimportant.

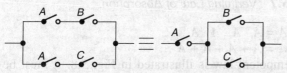

**Fig. 5.2** *Verifying Commutative Law by Switching Analogy.*

**5.1 Verify that the following operations are commutative:**

    (a) AND      (b) OR      (c) XOR

*Solution:*

(a) $A \cdot B = B \cdot A$    Therefore, the AND operation is commutative.

(b) $A + B = B + A$    Therefore, the OR operation is commutative.

(c) $A \oplus B = B \oplus A$    Therefore, the XOR operation is commutative.

## DISTRIBUTIVE LAW

The distributive laws allow the *factoring or multiplying* of expressions. Two distributive laws will be considered.

(a) $A(B + C) = AB + AC$    and

(b) $A + BC = (A + B)(A + C)$

The first statement of the distributive law can be verified by switching analogy and truth table shown in Fig. 5.3. Both of them are self explanatory.

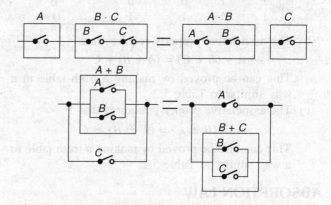

| A | B | C | AB | AC | AB + AC | B + C | A(B + C) |
|---|---|---|----|----|---------|-------|----------|
| 0 | 0 | 0 | 0 | 0 | 0 | 0 | 0 |
| 1 | 0 | 0 | 0 | 0 | 0 | 0 | 0 |
| 0 | 1 | 0 | 0 | 0 | 0 | 1 | 0 |
| 1 | 1 | 0 | 1 | 0 | 1 | 1 | 1 |
| 0 | 0 | 1 | 0 | 0 | 0 | 1 | 0 |
| 1 | 0 | 1 | 0 | 1 | 1 | 1 | 1 |
| 0 | 1 | 1 | 0 | 0 | 0 | 1 | 0 |
| 1 | 1 | 1 | 1 | 1 | 1 | 1 | 1 |

$$AB + AC = A (B + C)$$

This Truth Table Illustrates the First Statement of the Distributive Law: Compare the 0's and 1's in Columns 6 and 8!

**Fig. 5.3** *Verifying the First Statement of the Distributive Law.*

**5.2 Verify the second statement of the distributive law:**

$$A + BC = (A + B) (A + C)$$

*Solution:*

The second statement of the distributive law can be verified by switching analogy and truth table shown in Fig. 5.4. Both of them are self explanatory.

*Note:* This law is extremely useful in the *simplification* of functions and hence of logic circuits. For example in Figs 5.3 and 5.4 one switch contact can be saved by choosing the right-hand circuit in each case.

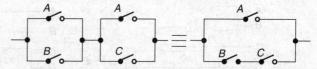

| A | B | C | A + B | A + C | (A + B)(A + C) | BC | A + BC |
|---|---|---|-------|-------|----------------|----|--------|
| 0 | 0 | 0 | 0 | 0 | 0 | 0 | 0 |
| 1 | 0 | 0 | 1 | 1 | 1 | 0 | 1 |
| 0 | 1 | 0 | 1 | 0 | 0 | 0 | 0 |
| 1 | 1 | 0 | 1 | 1 | 1 | 0 | 1 |
| 0 | 0 | 1 | 0 | 1 | 0 | 0 | 0 |
| 1 | 0 | 1 | 1 | 1 | 1 | 0 | 1 |
| 0 | 1 | 1 | 1 | 1 | 1 | 1 | 1 |
| 1 | 1 | 1 | 1 | 1 | 1 | 1 | 1 |

$$(A + B) (A + C) = A + BC$$

**Fig. 5.4** *Verifying the Second Statement of the Distributive Law.*

## ASSOCIATIVE LAW

This law merely states that in any Boolean function containing elements ($A$, $B$, $C$ etc) separated by the *same connective*, it does not matter if some of the elements are considered as a *group*.

(a) $ABC = AB(C) = A(BC) = AC(B)$

(b) $A + B + C = (A + B) + C = A + (B + C)$
$$= (A + C) + B$$

If three switches are connected in series to perform an AND function, or in parallel to perform an OR function, it does not matter if two of them are considered as a group, the circuit is still the same. This is illustrated in Fig. 5.5.

**Fig. 5.5** *Verifying Associative Law.*

*Note:* The associative law does not hold good if elements are connected by *different* connectives.

**5.3 Explain the physical significance of the associative law.**

*Solution:*

When many conditions are to be ANDed or ORed together, the *order* in which the conditions are combined is unimportant. This is illustrated in Fig. 5.6.

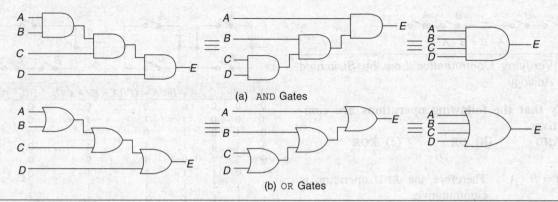

(a) AND Gates

(b) OR Gates

**Fig. 5.6**  *Physical Significance of Associative Law.*

## 5.4 Verify that the following operations are associative:

**(a)** AND          **(b)** OR          **(c)** XOR

*Solution:*

(a) If $A \cdot (B \cdot C) = (A \cdot B) \cdot C$, then the AND operation is associative. This can be proved by making the truth table as given in Table 5.2.

**Table 5.2**

| $A$ | $B$ | $C$ | $(A \cdot B) \cdot C$ | $A \cdot (B \cdot C)$ |
|---|---|---|---|---|
| 0 | 0 | 0 | 0 | 0 |
| 0 | 0 | 1 | 0 | 0 |
| 0 | 1 | 0 | 0 | 0 |
| 0 | 1 | 1 | 0 | 0 |
| 1 | 0 | 0 | 0 | 0 |
| 1 | 0 | 1 | 0 | 0 |
| 1 | 1 | 0 | 0 | 0 |
| 1 | 1 | 1 | 1 | 1 |

(b) The associative property requires that
$$A + (B + C) = (A + B) + C$$
This can be proved by making a truth table in a way similar to Table 5.2.

(c) The associative property requires that
$$A \oplus (B \oplus C) = (A \oplus B) \oplus C$$
This can also be proved by making a truth table in a way similar to Table 5.2.

## ABSORPTION LAW

This law is extremely important for the *elimination of redundant functions* in a system.

(a) $A(A + B) = A$          (b) $A + AB = A$

Figures 5.7(a) and (b) illustrate the law of absorption. In both cases the output is logic 0 when $A$ is 0 and logic 1 when $A$ is 1, *irrespective of the state of B*.

## IDEMPOTENT LAW

This law states that if *a variable is* ANDed *or* ORed *with itself any number of times, the result will always be the original variable.*

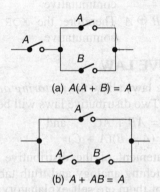

(a) $A(A + B) = A$

(b) $A + AB = A$

**Fig. 5.7**  *Verifying Law of Absorption.*

(a) $A = A \cdot A \cdot A \cdot A \ldots$
(b) $A = A + A + A + A \ldots$

Idempotent law is illustrated in Fig. 5.8. It must be noted that:

(1) Boolean algebra gives a different result to normal algebra (in normal algebra $1 + 1 = 2$, whereas in Boolean algebra $(1 \text{OR} 1 = 1)$ $1 + 1 = 1$.

(2) In Boolean algebra, a variable can have only one of two values, it is either 0 or 1, false or true (*nothing or something*).

| $A$ | $A$ | $A$ | | $A \cdot A \cdot A \ldots$ | $A + A + A \ldots$ |
|---|---|---|---|---|---|
| 0 | 0 | 0 | | 0 | 0 |
| 1 | 1 | 1 | | 1 | 1 |

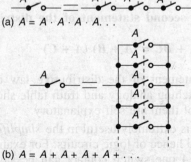

(a) $A = A \cdot A \cdot A \cdot A. \ldots$

(b) $A = A + A + A + A + \ldots$

**Fig. 5.8**  *Verifying Idempotent Law.*

Obviously, if any number of *nothings* are added or multiplied together, the result will also be nothing, whereas if any number of *somethings* are added or multiplied together, the result will also be something.

## 5.5 Verify that the following operations are commutative but not associative.

   (a) NAND          (b) NOR

*Solution:*

(a) Since $AB = BA$, *the* NAND *operation is commutative.* In Table 5.3, the last two columns are not identical i.e.,

$$\overline{A \cdot (\overline{B \cdot C})} \neq \overline{(\overline{A \cdot B}) \cdot C}$$

which means that the NAND *operation is not associative.*

(b) Since $A + B = B + A$, the NOR *operation is commutative.*

By drawing a truth table similar to Table 5.3 it can be verified that $\overline{(\overline{A + B}) + C} \neq \overline{A + (\overline{B + C})}$, which means that *the* NOR *operation is not associative.*

**Table 5.3** *The* NAND *Operation is not Associative.*

| $A$ | $B$ | $C$ | $\overline{A \cdot (\overline{B \cdot C})}$ | $\overline{(\overline{A \cdot B}) C}$ |
|-----|-----|-----|------|------|
| 0 | 0 | 0 | 1 | 1 |
| 0 | 0 | 1 | 1 | 0 |
| 0 | 1 | 0 | 1 | 1 |
| 0 | 1 | 1 | 1 | 0 |
| 1 | 0 | 0 | 0 | 1 |
| 1 | 0 | 1 | 0 | 0 |
| 1 | 1 | 0 | 0 | 1 |
| 1 | 1 | 1 | 1 | 1 |

## LAW OF IDENTITY

The law of identity states that

   $A = A = A$ ... etc.

It does have one *interesting consequence,* which is perhaps not quite so obvious:

   if $A = B$ and $B = C$, then $A = C$

## LAW OF COMPLEMENTATION

This law states that *if a function consists of a variable and its inverse, then the function is a constant.*

   (a) $A\overline{A} = 0$          (b) $A + \overline{A} = 1$

Since an AND gate requires *both* inputs to be logic 1 for a logic 1 output, $A\overline{A}$ is always logic 0, since $A$ and $\overline{A}$ can never be logic 1 simultaneously. This is shown in Fig. 5.9(a).

Since an OR gate requires *only one* input to be logic 1 for a logic 1 output, either $A$ or $\overline{A}$ must be 1 at any time, so the result of $A + \overline{A}$ is always logic 1. This is shown in Fig. 5.9(b).

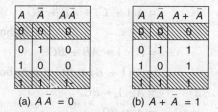

**Fig. 5.9** *Verifying Law of Complementation.*

The switching analogy to verify the law of complementation is illustrated in Fig. 5.10. *Something times nothing equals nothing* ($A\overline{A} = 0$), whereas *nothing plus something equals something* ($A + \overline{A} = 1$).

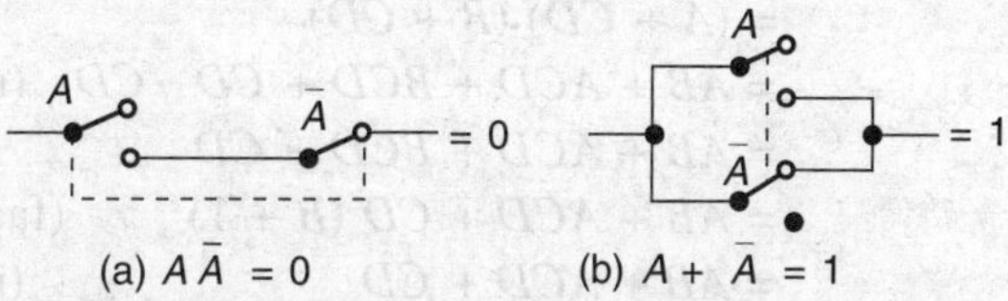

**Fig. 5.10** *Switching Analogy to Verify Law of Complementation.*

## CONNECTION WITH A CONSTANT

Four important relationships that can be used in the *simplification* of Boolean functions are:

1. *Conjunction* (AND and NAND functions) of a variable with *logic 0* always yields a constant ($A \cdot 0 = 0$, and $\overline{A \cdot 0} = 1$).
2. *Conjunction* of a variable with *logic 1* results in the original variable ($A \cdot 1 = A$ and $\overline{A \cdot 1} = \overline{A}$)
3. *Disjunction* (OR, XOR, and NAND functions) of a variable with *logic 0* results in the original variable ($A + 0 = A$ and $\overline{A + 0} = \overline{A}$).
4. *Disjunction* of a variable with *logic 1* results in a constant output ($A + 1 = 1$ and $\overline{A + 1} = \overline{1} = 0$).

## 5.6 Prove that
$$A + \overline{A}B = A + B$$

*Solution:*
$$A + \overline{A}B = (A + AB) + \overline{A}B \quad \text{(rule 30)}$$
$$= (AA + AB) + \overline{A}B \quad \text{(rule 9)}$$
$$= AA + AB + A\overline{A} + \overline{A}B \quad \text{(rule 10)}$$
$$= (A + \overline{A})(A + B) \quad \text{(by factoring)}$$
$$= 1 \cdot (A + B) \quad \text{(rule 20)}$$
$$= A + B \quad \text{(rule 34)}$$
$$A + \overline{A}B = A + B$$

## 5.7 Prove that
$$(A + B)(A + C) = A + BC$$

*Solution:*
$$(A + B)(A + C) = AA + AC + AB + BC$$
$$\text{(distributive law)}$$
$$= A + AC + AB + BC \quad \text{(rule 9)}$$

$$= A(1 + C) + AB + BC$$
$$\text{(distributive law)}$$
$$= A \cdot 1 + AB + BC \qquad \text{(rule 18)}$$
$$= A(1 + B) + BC \quad \text{(distributive law)}$$
$$= A \cdot 1 + BC \qquad \text{(rule 18)}$$
$$= A + BC \qquad \text{(rule 7)}$$
$$(A + B)(A + C) = A + BC \qquad \text{(rule 27)}$$

### 5.8 Prove that

$$A \cdot B + C \cdot D = (A + C)(A + D)(B + C)(B + D)$$

*Solution:*

$$(A + C)(A + D)(B + C)(B + D)$$
$$= (A + CD)(B + CD)$$
$$= AB + ACD + BCD + CD \cdot CD \quad \text{(rule 27)}$$
$$= AB + ACD + BCD + CD \qquad \text{(rule 9)}$$
$$= AB + ACD + CD(B + 1) \qquad \text{(factoring)}$$
$$= AB + ACD + CD \qquad \text{(rule 18)}$$
$$= AB + CD(A + 1) \qquad \text{(factoring)}$$
$$= AB + CD \qquad \text{(rule 18)}$$
$$AB + CD = (A + C)(A + D)(B + C)(B + D)$$

### 5.9 Prove that

$$A(\bar{A} + C)(\bar{A}B + \bar{C}) = 0$$

*Solution:*

$$A(\bar{A} + C)(\bar{A}B + \bar{C}) = (A\bar{A} + AC)(\bar{A}B + \bar{C})$$
$$= (0 + AC)(\bar{A}B + \bar{C}) \quad \text{(rule 10)}$$
$$= AC\bar{A}B + AC\bar{C}$$
$$= A\bar{A}BC + AC\bar{C}$$
$$= 0 \cdot BC + A \cdot 0 \quad \text{(rule 10)}$$
$$= 0$$
Therefore, $\quad A(\bar{A} + C)(\bar{A}B + \bar{C}) = 0$

### 5.10 Simplify the Boolean expression

$$AB + A(B + C) + B(B + C)$$

*Solution:*

$$AB + A(B + C) + B(B + C)$$
$$= AB + AB + AC + BB + BC$$
$$= AB + AB + AC + B + BC \qquad (BB = B, \text{ rule 9})$$
$$= AB + AC + B + BC \quad (AB + AB = AB, \text{ rule 19})$$
$$= AB + AC + B(1 + C)$$
$$= AB + AC + B \qquad (1 + C = 1, \text{ rule 18})$$
$$= AB + B + AC$$
$$= B(A + 1) + AC$$
$$= B + AC \qquad (A + 1 = 1, \text{ rule 17})$$
Therefore, $\quad AB + A(B + C) + B(B + C) = B + AC$

### 5.11 Show that $(A + B)(\bar{A} + C) = AC + \bar{A}B$

*Solution:*

$$(A + B)(\bar{A} + C) = \bar{A}A + AC + \bar{A}B + BC$$
$$= 0 + AC + \bar{A}B + BC(A + \bar{A})$$
$$= AC + \bar{A}B + ABC + \bar{A}BC$$

$$= AC + ABC + \bar{A}B + \bar{A}BC$$
$$= AC(1 + B) + \bar{A}B(1 + C)$$
$$= AC \cdot 1 + \bar{A}B \cdot 1$$
$$= AC + \bar{A}B = \text{R.H.S.}$$

### 5.12 Simplify the expression

$$ABC + \bar{A}\bar{B}\bar{C} + AB\bar{C} + \bar{A}BC$$

*Solution:*

$$ABC + \bar{A}\bar{B}\bar{C} + AB\bar{C} + \bar{A}BC$$
Rearrange $\quad ABC + \bar{A}BC + \bar{A}\bar{B}\bar{C} + AB\bar{C}$
Distributive law $\quad BC(A + \bar{A}) + \bar{A}\bar{B}\bar{C} + AB\bar{C} \quad \text{(rule 26)}$
OR law $\quad BC + \bar{A}\bar{B}\bar{C} + AB\bar{C} \qquad \text{(rule 20)}$
Rearrange $\quad BC + AB\bar{C} + \bar{A}\bar{B}\bar{C}$
Distributive law $\quad B(C + A\bar{C}) + \bar{A}\bar{B}\bar{C} \qquad \text{(rule 26)}$
Distributive law $\quad B(A + C)(C + \bar{C}) + \bar{A}\bar{B}\bar{C} \quad \text{(rule 27)}$
$$B(A + C) + \bar{A}\bar{B}\bar{C}$$

### 5.13 Simplify the Boolean equation $\bar{A}\bar{B}\bar{C} + A\bar{B}\bar{C} + $

$$BC + \bar{A}\bar{B}C + A\bar{B}C$$

*Solution:*

$$\bar{A}\bar{B}\bar{C} + A\bar{B}\bar{C} + BC + \bar{A}\bar{B}C + A\bar{B}C$$

Distributive law $\quad \bar{B}\bar{C}(\bar{A} + A) + BC + \bar{B}C(\bar{A} + A)$
$$\text{(rule 26)}$$
OR law $\quad \bar{B}\bar{C} + BC + \bar{B}C \qquad \text{(rule 20)}$
Distributive law $\quad \bar{B}(\bar{C} + C) + BC \qquad \text{(rule 26)}$
OR law $\quad \bar{B} + BC \qquad \text{(rule 20)}$

### 5.14 Simplify $\bar{A}BC + \bar{B}CD + AC + \bar{A}\bar{B}C\bar{D}$

*Solution:*

$$\bar{A}BC + \bar{B}CD + AC + \bar{A}\bar{B}C\bar{D}$$

OR law $\quad \bar{A}BC + \bar{B}CD(A + \bar{A}) + AC(B + \bar{B})$
$$+ \bar{A}\bar{B}C\bar{D} \qquad \text{(rule 26)}$$
$$\bar{A}BC + A\bar{B}CD + \bar{A}\bar{B}CD + ABC + A\bar{B}C$$
$$+ \bar{A}\bar{B}C\bar{D}$$
Rearrange $\quad \bar{A}BC + ABC + A\bar{B}CD + A\bar{B}C$
$$+ \bar{A}\bar{B}CD + \bar{A}\bar{B}C\bar{D}$$
Distributive law $\quad BC(\bar{A} + A) + A\bar{B}C(D + 1)$
$$+ \bar{A}\bar{B}C(D + \bar{D}) \qquad \text{(rule 26)}$$
OR law $\quad BC + A\bar{B}C + \bar{A}\bar{B}C \qquad \text{(rule 20)}$
Distributive law $\quad BC + \bar{B}C(A + \bar{A}) \qquad \text{(rule 26)}$
OR law $\quad BC + \bar{B}C \qquad \text{(rule 20)}$
Distributive law $\quad C(B + \bar{B}) \qquad \text{(rule 26)}$
OR law $\quad C \qquad \text{(rule 20)}$

## LAW OF DUALISATION (DEMORGAN'S THEOREM)

This is one of the most important laws of Boolean algebra, since *it formulates the relationship between N*

*N*(AND) *and N*(OR) *functions that allows one type of function to be implemented using a different type of gate.*

(a) $\overline{A+B} = \overline{A} \cdot \overline{B}$       (b) $\overline{A \cdot B} = \overline{A} + \overline{B}$

The practical value of these equations is immediately apparent. Equation (a) means that *a* NOR *function can be implemented by inverting the two inputs to an* AND *function.* Equation (b) means that *a* NAND *function can be implemented by inverting the two inputs to an* OR *function.*

Inverting these equations gives two further important relationships:

(c) $A + B = \overline{\overline{A} \cdot \overline{B}}$       (d) $A \cdot B = \overline{\overline{A} + \overline{B}}$

Equation (c) states that an OR *function can be implemented by inverting the inputs to a* NAND *function.* Equation (d) means that an AND *function can be implemented by inverting the two inputs to a* NOR *function.*

The first law states that *the complement of a sum is equal to the product of the complements.* This is stating that the complement of two or more variables ORed is the same as the AND of the complements of each individual variable.

The second law states that the *complement of a product is equal to the sum of the complements.* This is stating that the complement of two or more variables ANDed is the same as the OR of the complements of each individual variable.

A useful general rule for remembering DeMorgan's theorem is as follows:

When the overline extends across a function (e.g. $\overline{A+B}$) then it *inverts the connective.* The inverse of OR is AND and vice versa. The function may then be rewritten using the *inverse connective* and *individual overlines* on the variables. For example:

$$\left.\begin{array}{l} \overline{A \cdot B} = \overline{A} \cdot \overline{B} \\[4pt] \text{'}\overline{\phantom{}}\text{'} = +, \quad \overline{A \cdot B} = \overline{A} + \overline{B} \\[4pt] \overline{A + B} = \overline{A} + \overline{B} \\[4pt] \text{'}\overline{\mp}\text{'} = \cdot, \text{ so } \overline{A + B} = \overline{A} \cdot \overline{B} \end{array}\right\}$$

The *converse* is also quite true.

*Individual overlines on the variables may be replaced by a continuous overline and the inverse connective.*

All possible applications of DeMorgan's theorem to *two variables* are given in Table 5.4.

**Table 5.4**

| OR | ↔ | NAND | AND | ↔ | NOR |
|---|---|---|---|---|---|
| $\overline{A} + \overline{B}$ | | $\overline{A \cdot B}$ | $\overline{A} \cdot \overline{B}$ | | $\overline{A+B}$ |
| $A + \overline{B}$ | | $\overline{\overline{A} \cdot B}$ | $A \cdot \overline{B}$ | | $\overline{\overline{A}+B}$ |
| $\overline{A} + B$ | | $\overline{A \cdot \overline{B}}$ | $\overline{A} \cdot B$ | | $\overline{A+\overline{B}}$ |
| $A + B$ | | $\overline{\overline{A} \cdot \overline{B}}$ | $A \cdot B$ | | $\overline{\overline{A}+\overline{B}}$ |

The truth of DeMorgan's theorem can be demonstrated in several ways.

Using switch contacts, as in Fig. 5.11, the only handicap is that the *inversion of a total function must be illustrated by adding an inverter.*

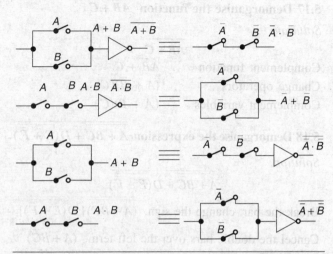

**Fig. 5.11** *Demonstrating the Truth of DeMorgan's Theorem.*

Even so, the results are obvious. For instance, in the first circuit if either switch *A* or switch *B* is closed the input to the inverter is 1 and therefore its output is 0. This is identical to the second circuit, where closing either of the switches breaks the circuit, so that the output becomes 0. These two circuits therefore illustrate the first statement: $\overline{A+B} = \overline{A} \cdot \overline{B}$.

### 5.15 Reduce the expression $A + B\,(\overline{C + \overline{DE}})$.

*Solution:*

$$A + B\overline{(C + \overline{DE})}$$

*Break the line, change the sign.*
First break the line between *D* and *E*

$$A + B\;\overline{(C + \overline{D} + \overline{E})}$$

Next break the line between *C* and *D* and *E*

$$A + B\,(\overline{C}\,DE) = A + B\overline{C}\,DE$$

### 5.16 Reduce the expression $\overline{\overline{AB} + \overline{A} + AB}$.

*Solution:*

$$\overline{\overline{AB} + \overline{A} + AB}$$

Demorganise $\overline{AB}$   $\overline{\overline{A} + \overline{B} + \overline{A} + AB}$       (rule 33)

Reduce       $\overline{\overline{A} + \overline{B} + AB}$       (rule 19)

Reduce       $\overline{\overline{A} + \overline{B} + A}$       (rule 34)

Rearrange $\overline{A + \overline{A} + \overline{B}}$ (rule 25)

Reduce $\overline{1 + \overline{B}}$ (rule 20)

Reduce $\overline{1}$ (rule 22)

Convert $0$

### 5.17 Demorganise the function $\overline{A\overline{B} + C}$.

*Solution:*

$$\overline{A\overline{B} + C}$$

Complement function $A\overline{B} + C$

Change operators $(A + \overline{B})(C)$

Complement variables $(\overline{A} + B)(\overline{C})$

### 5.18 Demorganise the expression $\overline{A + B\overline{C} + D(\overline{E} + \overline{F})}$.

*Solution:*

$$\overline{A + B\overline{C} + D(\overline{E} + \overline{F})}$$

Break the bar, change the sign, $\overline{(A + B\overline{C})}[\overline{D(\overline{E} + \overline{F})}]$

Cancel the double bars over the left term. $(A + B\overline{C})$

$[\overline{D(\overline{E} + \overline{F})}]$.

Break the bar, change the sign. $(A + B\overline{C})[\overline{D(\overline{E} + \overline{F})}]$

Cancel the double bars. $(A + B\overline{C})(\overline{D} + E + F)$

### 5.19 Reduce $\overline{\overline{A\overline{B}} + ABC + A(B + A\overline{B})}$.

*Solution:*

$$\overline{A\overline{B} + ABC + A(B + A\overline{B})}$$

Factorize $\overline{A(\overline{B} + BC) + A(B + A\overline{B})}$

Reduce $\overline{A(\overline{B} + C) + A(B + A)}$

Multiply $\overline{A\overline{B} + AC + AB + AA}$

Reduce $\overline{A\overline{B} + AC + AB + A}$

Factorize $\overline{A\overline{B} + AC + A(B + 1)}$

Reduce $\overline{A\overline{B} + AC + A}$

Demorganise $\overline{A\overline{B}} + \overline{AC}$ $(\overline{A} + B)(\overline{A} + \overline{C}) + \overline{A}$

Multiply $\overline{A}\overline{A} + \overline{A}\overline{C} + \overline{A}B + B\overline{C} + \overline{A}$

Reduce $\overline{A} + \overline{A}\overline{C} + \overline{A}B + B\overline{C} + \overline{A}$

Factorize $\overline{A}(1 + \overline{C}) + \overline{A}B + B\overline{C} + \overline{A}$

Reduce $\overline{A} + \overline{A}B + B\overline{C} + \overline{A}$

Factorize $\overline{A}(1 + B) + B\overline{C} + \overline{A}$

Reduce $\overline{A} + B\overline{C} + \overline{A}$

Reduce $\overline{1 + B\overline{C}}$

Demorganise $\overline{1 + \overline{B} + C}$

Reduce $\overline{1 + \overline{B}}$

Reduce $\overline{1}$

$0$

### 5.20 Prove the following identities using Boolean algebra and DeMorgan's theorems.

(a) $\overline{AB + BC + CA} = \overline{A}\overline{B} + \overline{B}\overline{C} + \overline{C}\overline{A}$

(b) $AB + \overline{AC} + A\overline{B}C(AB + C) = 1$

*Solution:*

(a) $\overline{AB + BC + CA} = \overline{A}\overline{B} + \overline{B}\overline{C} + \overline{C}\overline{A}$

L.H.S. $= \overline{AB + BC + CA}$

$= \overline{AB + (BC + CA)}$

Demorganise $= \overline{AB}\left(\overline{BC + CA}\right)$

Demorganise $= \overline{AB}\left\{\overline{C}(\overline{B + A})\right\}$

$= (\overline{A} + \overline{B})\left\{\overline{C} + (\overline{B + A})\right\}$

Demorganise $= (\overline{A} + \overline{B})(\overline{C} + \overline{B}\overline{A})$

$= \overline{A}\overline{C} + \overline{A}\overline{B}\overline{A} + \overline{B}\overline{C} + \overline{B}\overline{B}\overline{A}$

$= \overline{A}\overline{C} + \overline{A}\overline{A}\overline{B} + \overline{B}\overline{C} + \overline{B}\overline{B}\overline{A}$

Reduce $= \overline{A}\overline{C} + \overline{A}\overline{B} + \overline{B}\overline{C} + \overline{B}\overline{A}$

$= (\overline{A}\overline{B} + \overline{A}\overline{B}) + \overline{B}\overline{C} + \overline{C}\overline{A}$

$= \overline{A}\overline{B} + \overline{B}\overline{C} + \overline{C}\overline{A} =$ R.H.S.

(b) $AB + \overline{AC} + A\overline{B}C(AB + AC) = 1$

L.H.S. $= AB + \overline{AC} + A\overline{B}CAB + A\overline{B}CAC$

$= AB + \overline{AC} + AAB\overline{B}C + AA\overline{B}CC$

$= AB + \overline{AC} + 0 + A\overline{B}C$

$= AB + A\overline{B}C + \overline{AC}$

$= A(B + \overline{B}C) + \overline{AC}$

$= A\left\{B(1 + C) + \overline{B}C\right\} + \overline{AC}$

$= A(B + BC + \overline{B}C) + \overline{AC}$

$= A\{B + C(B + \overline{B})\} + \overline{AC}$

$= AB + AC + \overline{AC}$

$= AB + (AC + \overline{AC})$

$= AB + 1$

$= 1 =$ R.H.S.

**5.21 Simplify the following Boolean function to a minimum number of literals $XY + \bar{X}Z + YZ$.**

*Solution:*

$$XY + \bar{X}Z + YZ = XY + \bar{X}Z + YZ(X + \bar{X})$$
$$= XY + \bar{X}Z + XYZ + \bar{X}YZ$$
$$= XY + XYZ + \bar{X}Z + \bar{X}YZ$$
$$= XY + (1 + Z) + \bar{X}Z(1 + Y)$$
$$= XY + \bar{X}Z$$

**5.22 Find the complement of the functions $F_1 = \bar{A}B\bar{C} + \bar{A}\bar{B}C$ and $F_2 = A(\bar{B}\bar{C} + BC)$.**

*Solution:*

Applying DeMorgan's theorem as many times as necessary, the complements are obtained as follows:

$$\bar{F}_1 = \left(\overline{\bar{A}B\bar{C} + \bar{A}\bar{B}C}\right)$$
$$= (\overline{\bar{A}B\bar{C}})(\overline{\bar{A}\bar{B}C})$$
$$= (A + \bar{B} + C)(A + B + \bar{C})$$
$$\bar{F}_2 = \left[\overline{A(\bar{B}\bar{C} + BC)}\right]$$
$$= \bar{A} + \left(\overline{\bar{B}\bar{C} + BC}\right)$$
$$= \bar{A} + (\overline{\bar{B}\bar{C}}) \cdot (\overline{BC})$$
$$= \bar{A} + (B + C)(\bar{B} + \bar{C})$$

**5.23 Find the complement of the functions $F_1$ and $F_2$ of Problem 5.22 by taking their duals and complementing each literal.**

*Solution:*

1. $F_1 = \bar{A}B\bar{C} + \bar{A}\bar{B}C$
   The dual of $F_1$ is $(\bar{A} + B + \bar{C})(\bar{A} + \bar{B} + C)$
   Complementing each literal:
   $$(A + \bar{B} + C)(A + B + \bar{C}) = \bar{F}_1$$
2. $F_2 = A(\bar{B}\bar{C} + BC)$
   The dual of $F_2$ is: $A + (\bar{B} + \bar{C})(B + C)$
   Complement each literal:
   $$\bar{A} + (B + C)(\bar{B} + \bar{C}) = \bar{F}_2$$

**5.24 Simplify the expression $[A\bar{B}(C + BD) + \bar{A}\bar{B}]C$ as much as possible.**

*Solution:*

$$[A\bar{B}(C + BD) + \bar{A}\bar{B}]C$$
$$(A\bar{B}C + A\bar{B}BD + \bar{A}\bar{B})C$$
$$(A\bar{B}C + 0 + \bar{A}\bar{B})C$$
$$(A\bar{B}C + \bar{A}\bar{B})C$$
$$A\bar{B}CC + \bar{A}\bar{B}C$$
$$A\bar{B}C + \bar{A}\bar{B}C$$
$$\bar{B}C(A + \bar{A})$$
$$\bar{B}C \cdot 1$$
$$\bar{B}C$$

**5.25 Show that using Boolean algebra and DeMorgan's theorems:**

$$\bar{Y}\bar{Z} + \bar{W}\bar{X}\bar{Z} + \bar{W}XY\bar{Z} + WY\bar{Z} = Z$$

*Solution:*

L.H.S. $= \bar{Y}\bar{Z} + \bar{W}\bar{X}\bar{Z} + \bar{W}XY\bar{Z} + WY\bar{Z}$

$$= \bar{Y}\bar{Z} + \bar{W}\bar{X}\bar{Z}(1 + Y) + \bar{W}XY\bar{Z} + WY\bar{Z}$$
$$= \bar{Y}\bar{Z} + \bar{W}\bar{X}\bar{Z} + \bar{W}\bar{X}Y\bar{Z} + \bar{W}XY\bar{Z} + WY\bar{Z}$$
$$= \bar{Y}\bar{Z} + \bar{W}\bar{X}\bar{Z} + \bar{W}Y\bar{Z}(\bar{X} + X) + WY\bar{Z}$$
$$= \bar{Y}\bar{Z} + \bar{W}\bar{X}\bar{Z} + \bar{W}Y\bar{Z} + WY\bar{Z}$$
$$= \bar{Y}\bar{Z} + \bar{W}\bar{X}\bar{Z} + Y\bar{Z}(\bar{W} + W)$$
$$= \bar{Y}\bar{Z} + \bar{W}\bar{X}\bar{Z} + Y\bar{Z}$$
$$= \bar{Y}\bar{Z} + Y\bar{Z} + \bar{W}\bar{X}\bar{Z}$$
$$= \bar{Z}(\bar{Y} + Y) + \bar{W}\bar{X}\bar{Z}$$
$$= \bar{Z} + \bar{W}\bar{X}\bar{Z}$$
$$= \bar{Z} + (1 + \bar{W}\bar{X})$$
$$= \bar{Z} \cdot 1$$
$$= \bar{Z} = \text{R.H.S.}$$

**5.26 Simplify the following expression.**

$$T(A, B, C) = (A + B)\left[\overline{\bar{A}(\bar{B} + \bar{C})}\right] + \bar{A}\bar{B} + \bar{A}\bar{C}$$

*Solution:*

It is necessary to first apply DeMorgan's theorem and multiply out the expression in parentheses.

$$T(A, B, C) = (A + B)(A + BC) + \bar{A}\bar{B} + \bar{A}\bar{C}$$
$$= (A \cdot A + ABC + AB + BBC) + \bar{A}\bar{B} + \bar{A}\bar{C}$$
$$= A + ABC + AB + BC + \bar{A}\bar{B} + \bar{A}\bar{C}$$
$$= A + AB(C + 1) + BC + \bar{A}\bar{B} + \bar{A}\bar{C}$$
$$= A + AB + BC + \bar{A}\bar{B} + \bar{A}\bar{C}$$
$$= A(1 + B) + BC + \bar{A}\bar{B} + \bar{A}\bar{C}$$
$$= A + BC + \bar{A}\bar{B} + \bar{A}\bar{C}$$
$$= A + BC + \bar{B} + \bar{C}$$
$$= A + C + \bar{B} + \bar{C}$$
$$= A + \bar{B} + 1$$
$$= 1$$

**5.27 Prove the following Boolean identity.**

$$ABC + \bar{A}\bar{B}C + \bar{A}BC + AB\bar{C} + \bar{A}B\bar{C}$$
$$= \bar{A}\bar{B} + B(A + C)$$

*Solution:*

L.H.S. $= ABC + \bar{A}\bar{B}C + \bar{A}BC + AB\bar{C} + \bar{A}B\bar{C}$

$$= ABC + \bar{A}\bar{B}C + \bar{A}B\bar{C} + \bar{A}BC + AB\bar{C}$$
$$= ABC + \bar{A}\bar{B}(C + \bar{C}) + \bar{A}BC + AB\bar{C}$$
$$= ABC + \bar{A}\bar{B} + \bar{A}BC + AB\bar{C}$$
$$= \bar{A}\bar{B} + ABC + \bar{A}BC + AB\bar{C}$$
$$= \bar{A}\bar{B} + BC(A + \bar{A}) + AB\bar{C}$$
$$= \bar{A}\bar{B} + BC + AB\bar{C}$$
$$= \bar{A}\bar{B} + B(C + A\bar{C})$$
$$= \bar{A}\bar{B} + B(A + C) = \text{R.H.S.}$$

**5.28 Evaluate**

$$f(W, X, Y, Z) = (WX + \overline{\overline{X}Y})Z + \overline{W\overline{X} + \overline{YZ}} \text{ for }$$
$$W = 1, X = 1, Y = 0, Z = 1.$$

*Solution:*

1. Place parentheses around the *complemented* expressions.

   $$f(W, X, Y, Z) = (WX + (\overline{\overline{X}Y}))Z + (\overline{W\overline{X} + (\overline{YZ})})$$

2. Evaluate the *inner* parenthesized expressions, $(\overline{\overline{X}Y})$ and $(\overline{YZ})$.

   $$\overline{X} = \overline{1} = 0;\ \overline{X}Y = 0.0 = 0;\ \overline{\overline{X}Y} = \overline{0} = 1;$$

   $$YZ = 0.1 = 0;\ \overline{YZ} = \overline{0} = 1$$

3. Evaluate the *outer* parenthesized expressions,

   $$WX = 1 \cdot 1 = 1;\ WX + \overline{\overline{X}Y} = 1 + 1 = 1;$$

   $$W\overline{X} = 1 \cdot 0 = 0;$$

   $$W\overline{X} + \overline{YZ} = 0 + 1 = 1;\ (\overline{W\overline{X} + \overline{YZ}}) = \overline{1} = 0$$

4. Substitute the values of parenthesized expressions into the *remaining* expressions and evaluate the entire function.

   $$f(W, X, Y, Z) = 1 \cdot Z + 0 = 1 \cdot 1 + 0$$
   $$= 1 + 0 = 1$$

**5.29 Evaluate**

$$f(A, B, C, D) = AC + \overline{B(C\overline{D})} + \overline{(A\overline{B} + BC)D}$$
$$\text{for } A = B = 1, C = D = 0.$$

*Solution:*

1. Place parentheses around the *complemented* expressions.

   $$f(A, B, C, D) = AC + (\overline{B(C\overline{D})}) + ((\overline{A\overline{B} + BC})D)$$

2. Evaluate the parenthesized expressions, proceeding from *inner* to *outer* expressions.

   $$C\overline{D} = 0.\overline{0} = 0 \cdot 1 = 0, \quad B(C\overline{D}) = 1 \cdot 0 = 0$$

   $$(\overline{B(C\overline{D})}) = \overline{0} = 1, \quad A\overline{B} + BC = 1 \cdot \overline{1} + 1.0$$
   $$= 1 \cdot 0 + 1 \cdot 0$$
   $$= 0 \cdot 0 = 0$$

   $$(A\overline{B} + BC)0 = 0 \cdot 0 = 0, \quad (\overline{(A\overline{B} + BC)D}) = \overline{0} = 1$$

3. Substitute the values of the parenthesized expressions into the *remaining* expressions and evaluate the entire function.

   $$f(A, B, C, D) = AC + 1 + 1$$
   $$= 1.0 + 1 + 1$$
   $$= 0 + 1 + 1$$
   $$= 1$$

*Note:* Whenever one factor of a *logical product* is 0, the product is 0. Whenever one term of a *logical sum* is 1, the sum is 1.

**5.30 Simplify the expression** $(\overline{A + B}) + \overline{A} \cdot B$ **by constructing a truth table.**

*Solution:*

The *truth table* for the expression may be derived in the usual way.

**Table 5.5**

| $A$ | $B$ | $\overline{A}$ | $\overline{A} \cdot B$ | $\overline{A+B}$ | $(\overline{A+B}) + \overline{A} \cdot B$ |
|---|---|---|---|---|---|
| 0 | 0 | 1 | 0 | 1 | 1 |
| 0 | 1 | 1 | 1 | 0 | 1 |
| 1 | 0 | 0 | 0 | 0 | 0 |
| 1 | 1 | 0 | 0 | 0 | 0 |

An examination of the *last column* shows that

$$(\overline{A+B}) + \overline{A} \cdot B = \overline{A}$$

*Note:* A considerable simplification of the original expression has been achieved. *This method of simplification forms the basis of another method called Karnaugh mapping.*

**5.31 Simplify the expression**

$$X = A \cdot (B + \overline{B} \cdot \overline{C}) + \overline{A} \cdot \overline{B} \cdot C$$
**by constructing a truth table.**

*Solution:*

**Table 5.6**

| A | B | C | $\overline{A}$ | $\overline{B}$ | $\overline{C}$ | $\overline{B} \cdot \overline{C}$ | $\overline{A} \cdot \overline{B} \cdot C$ | $B + \overline{B} \cdot \overline{C}$ | $A \cdot (B + \overline{B} \cdot \overline{C})$ | X |
|---|---|---|---|---|---|---|---|---|---|---|
| 0 | 0 | 0 | 1 | 1 | 1 | 1 | 0 | 1 | 0 | 0 |
| 0 | 0 | 1 | 1 | 1 | 0 | 0 | 1 | 0 | 0 | 1 |
| 0 | 1 | 0 | 1 | 0 | 1 | 0 | 0 | 1 | 0 | 0 |
| 0 | 1 | 1 | 1 | 0 | 0 | 0 | 0 | 1 | 0 | 0 |
| 1 | 0 | 0 | 0 | 1 | 1 | 1 | 0 | 1 | 1 | 0 |
| 1 | 0 | 1 | 0 | 1 | 0 | 0 | 0 | 0 | 1 | 1 |
| 1 | 1 | 0 | 0 | 0 | 1 | 0 | 0 | 1 | 1 | 0 |
| 1 | 1 | 1 | 0 | 0 | 0 | 0 | 0 | 1 | 1 | 0 |

Note, that $X = 1$ for $A = 0, B = 0$ and $C = 1$, i.e. $\overline{A} \cdot \overline{B} \cdot C$ and also when $A = 1, B = 0, C = 1$ i.e. $A \cdot \overline{B} \cdot C$.

$$\therefore \qquad X = \overline{A} \cdot \overline{B} \cdot C + A \cdot \overline{B} \cdot C = \overline{B}C(\overline{A} + A)$$

$$X = \overline{B} \cdot C$$

**5.32 Use DeMorgan's laws to enable the following expressions to be implemented with a *single* logic gate. Use the inputs $A$, $B$, and $C$ rather than $\overline{A}, \overline{B}$ and $\overline{C}$. Apply DeMorgan's laws to the expression and then select one of the following gates to implement it: OR; AND; NOR; NAND.**

(a) $\overline{A} + \overline{B}$ \qquad\qquad (b) $\overline{A} \cdot \overline{B} \cdot \overline{C}$

*Solution:*

(a) By DeMorgan $\overline{\overline{A} + \overline{B}} = A \cdot B$

$\therefore \; \overline{A} + \overline{B} = \overline{A \cdot B}$  (NAND function)

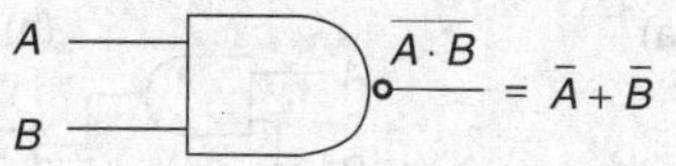

**Fig. 5.12**

(b) By DeMorgan $\overline{\overline{A} \cdot \overline{B} \cdot \overline{C}} = A + B + C$

$\therefore \; \overline{A} \cdot \overline{B} \cdot \overline{C} = \overline{A + B + C}$  (NOR function)

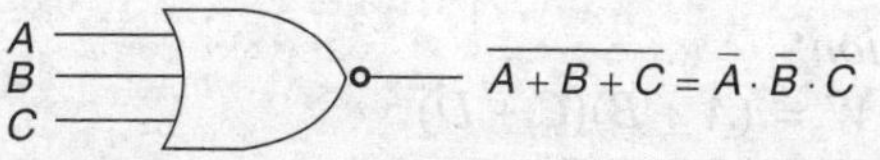

**Fig. 5.13**

**5.33 Verify DeMorgan's law for the Boolean function $A + B = \overline{\overline{A} \cdot \overline{B}}$ by examining truth tables.**

*Solution:*

**Table 5.7**

| $A$ | $B$ | $\overline{A}$ | $\overline{B}$ | $\overline{A} \cdot \overline{B}$ | $\overline{\overline{A} \cdot \overline{B}}$ | $A + B$ |
|---|---|---|---|---|---|---|
| 0 | 0 | 1 | 1 | 1 | 0 | 0 |
| 0 | 1 | 1 | 0 | 0 | 1 | 1 |
| 1 | 0 | 0 | 1 | 0 | 1 | 1 |
| 1 | 1 | 0 | 0 | 0 | 1 | 1 |

Note that $A + B = \overline{\overline{A} \cdot \overline{B}}$, thus verifying one of the forms of DeMorgan's laws.

**5.34 Verify, by examining truth tables, the form of DeMorgan's law that states $A \cdot B = \overline{\overline{A} + \overline{B}}$**

*Solution:*

**Table 5.8**

| $A$ | $B$ | $\overline{A}$ | $\overline{B}$ | $\overline{A} + \overline{B}$ | $\overline{\overline{A} + \overline{B}}$ | $A \cdot B$ |
|---|---|---|---|---|---|---|
| 0 | 0 | 1 | 1 | 1 | 0 | 0 |
| 0 | 1 | 1 | 0 | 1 | 0 | 0 |
| 1 | 0 | 0 | 1 | 1 | 0 | 0 |
| 1 | 1 | 0 | 0 | 0 | 1 | 1 |

Thus $A \cdot B = \overline{\overline{A} + \overline{B}}$

**5.35 Use DeMorgan laws to convert the following expression to both the AND and the OR gate.**

$$\overline{A \cdot B} + \overline{C} \cdot D$$

*Solution:*

(i) To convert to the AND *form* treat $\overline{A \cdot B}$ and $\overline{C} \cdot D$ as *separate whole variables* so that:

$$\overline{A \cdot B} + \overline{C} \cdot D = \overline{\overline{A \cdot B} \cdot \overline{\overline{C} \cdot D}}$$

(ii) To convert to the OR *form*, transform the term $\overline{A \cdot B}$, then transform the term $\overline{C} \cdot D$.

i.e.   $\overline{A \cdot B} = \overline{A} + \overline{B}$

$\overline{C} \cdot D = \overline{C + \overline{D}}$

$\therefore \; \overline{A \cdot B} + \overline{C} \cdot D = \overline{A} + \overline{B} + \overline{C + \overline{D}}$

**5.36 Simplify the expression**

$$\overline{(\overline{A \cdot \overline{B} + \overline{C}})} + (\overline{\overline{A} + \overline{\overline{B} \cdot C}})$$

**resulting from an initial study of a particular design problem, thereby *saving unnecessary logic gates.***

*Solution:*

Using DeMogan's law we see that

$$\overline{\overline{A \cdot \overline{B} + \overline{C}}} = A \cdot \overline{B} \cdot C$$

and that $\overline{\overline{A} + \overline{\overline{B} \cdot C}} = A \cdot \overline{B} \cdot \overline{C}$

Therefore the expression simplifies to

$$A \cdot \overline{B} \cdot C + A \cdot \overline{B} \cdot \overline{C}$$

A further simplification is possible since $A \cdot \overline{B}$ is common to both terms of the expression.

$A \cdot \overline{B} \cdot C + A \cdot \overline{B} \cdot \overline{C} = A \cdot \overline{B}\,(C + \overline{C})$

$\qquad\qquad\qquad = A \cdot \overline{B}$ since $C + \overline{C} = 1$

This is clearly much *simpler than the original.*

**5.37 Using DeMorgan's laws, simplify**

$$\overline{A} + \overline{B} + (\overline{A \cdot \overline{C} + \overline{B}}) + C$$

*Solution:*

$$\overline{A} + \overline{B} + (\overline{A \cdot \overline{C} + \overline{B}}) + C$$

DeMorgan's law applied to the terms in brackets gives:

$$\overline{\overline{A \cdot \overline{C} + \overline{B}}} = A \cdot \overline{C} \cdot B$$

The remainder of the expression is:

$$\overline{A} + \overline{B} + C = \overline{A \cdot B \cdot \overline{C}}$$

The total expression is now:

$$\overline{A \cdot B \cdot \overline{C}} + A \cdot B \cdot \overline{C}$$

which is of the form $\overline{X} + X$, where $X = A \cdot B \cdot \overline{C}$
So clearly the expression always has the value 1.

## BOOLEAN EXPRESSIONS AND LOGIC DIAGRAMS

Boolean algebra is useless unless it can be *translated into hardware.* Similarly, Boolean algebra can be a useful technique for analysing existing circuits *only if hardware can be translated into a Boolean expression.* This capability develops with experience.

*Boolean Algebra to Logic* The easiest way to convert an expression into a logic diagram is to *start with the output and work back toward the input.*

*Logic to Boolean Algebra* The reverse process can be used for converting logic to Boolean algebra. Instead of proceeding from output to input, we *start with the input signals and develop terms until the output is reached.*

In logic, the following precedence rules apply:

1. Consider the NOT operator applied to an expression as putting parentheses around the expression. (Do not bother to put parentheses around a single complemented variable.)

2. Evaluate expressions within parentheses working from inner to outer parentheses in the following order:
   (a) First evaluate NOTs of values from left to right.
   (b) Then evaluate ANDs of pairs of values from left to right.
   (c) Then evaluate ORs of pairs of values from left to right.

3. Substitute the values resulting from evaluations of parenthesized expressions into the remaining expressions and evaluate in the same order, that is:
   (a) First evaluate NOTs from left to right.
   (b) Then evaluate ANDs from left to right.
   (c) Then evaluate ORs from left to right.

**5.38 Write the Boolean equation for each of the logic circuits shown in Fig. 5.14.**

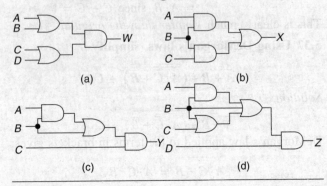

(a)　　　　　　　　　(b)

(c)　　　　　　　　　(d)

**Fig. 5.14**

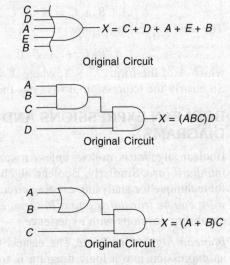

$X = C + D + A + E + B$

Original Circuit

$X = (ABC)D$

Original Circuit

$X = (A + B)C$

Original Circuit

**Fig. 5.16**

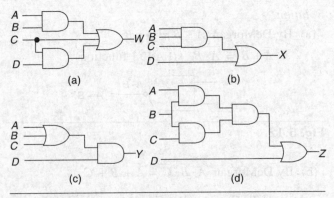

(a)　　　　　　　　　(b)

(c)　　　　　　　　　(d)

**Fig. 5.15**

*Solution:*
   (a) $W = (A + B)(C + D)$
   (b) $X = AB + BC$
   (c) $Y = (AB + B)C$
   (d) $Z = (AB + B) + (B + C))D$

**5.39 Write the Boolean equation for each of the logic circuits shown in Fig. 5.15.**

*Solution:*
   (a) $W = (AB + C) + CD$
   (b) $X = ABC + D$
   (c) $Y = (A + B + C)D$
   (d) $Z = ((AB)(BC)) + D$

**5.40 State the Boolean law that makes each of the equivalent circuits shown in Fig. 5.16 valid.**

*Solution:*
   (a) Commutative law
   (b) Associative law
   (c) Distributive law

**5.41 Write the Boolean equation for the circuits given in Fig. 5.17. Simplify the equations and draw simplified logic circuits.**

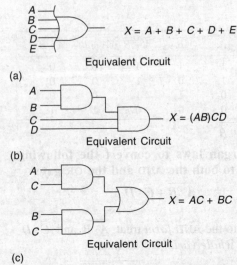

$X = A + B + C + D + E$

Equivalent Circuit

(a)

$X = (AB)CD$

Equivalent Circuit

(b)

$X = AC + BC$

Equivalent Circuit

(c)

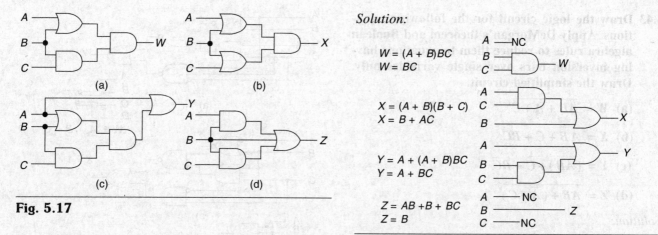

**Fig. 5.17**

*Solution:*

$W = (A + B)BC$
$W = BC$

$X = (A + B)(B + C)$
$X = B + AC$

$Y = A + (A + B)BC$
$Y = A + BC$

$Z = AB + B + BC$
$Z = B$

**Fig. 5.18**   *Solution for Problem 5.41.*

**5.42 Draw the logic circuit for the following equations. Simplify the equations and draw the simplified logic circuits.**

(a)  $V = AC + ACD + CD$
(b)  $W = (BCD + C)CD$
(c)  $X = (B + D)(A + C) + ABD$
(d)  $Y = AB + BC + ABC$
(e)  $Z = ABC + CD + CDE$

*Solution:*

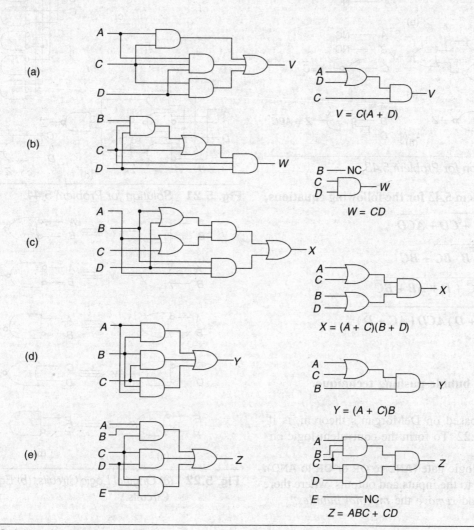

$V = C(A + D)$

$W = CD$

$X = (A + C)(B + D)$

$Y = (A + C)B$

$Z = ABC + CD$

**Fig. 5.19**   *Solution for Problem 5.42.*

**5.43 Draw the logic circuit for the following equations. Apply DeMorgan's theorem and Boolean algebra rules to reduce them to equations having inversion bars over single variables only. Draw the simplified circuit.**

(a) $W = \overline{\overline{AB} + \overline{A} + C}$

(b) $X = \overline{A\overline{B} + C + \overline{BC}}$

(c) $Y = \overline{(AB)} + C + B\overline{C}$

(d) $Z = \overline{AB + (\overline{A} + C)}$

*Solution:*

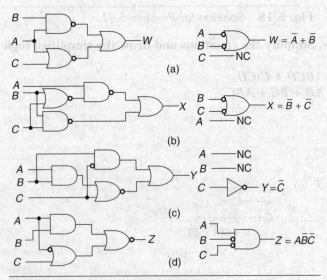

**Fig. 5.20**    *Solution for Problem 5.43.*

**5.44 Repeat Problem 5.43 for the following equations.**

(a) $W = \overline{\overline{AB} + CD} + \overline{AC\overline{D}}$

(b) $X = \overline{\overline{\overline{A} + B} \cdot BC} + \overline{B}C$

(c) $Y = \overline{AB\overline{C} + D} + \overline{A\overline{B}} + B\overline{C}$

(d) $Z = \overline{(C + D)\,\overline{AC D}\,(\overline{A}C + \overline{D})}$

*Solution:*
(See Fig. 5.21).

**5.45 Explain the bubble-pushing technique.**

*Solution:*
Bubble-pushing, based on DeMorgan's theorem, is illustrated in Fig. 5.22. To form the equivalent logic circuit, you must

(a) *Change* the logic gate (AND to OR or OR to AND).

(b) *Add* bubbles to the inputs and outputs, where there were none and *remove* the *original bubbles*.

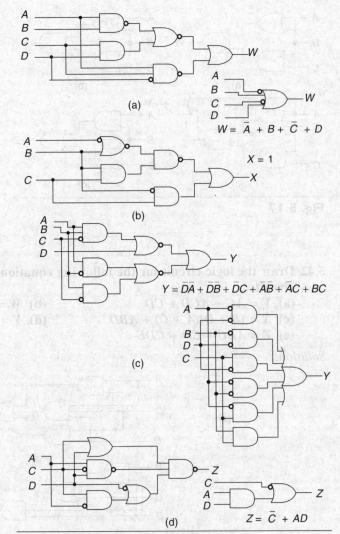

$W = \overline{A} + B + \overline{C} + D$

$X = 1$

$Y = \overline{D}A + \overline{D}B + \overline{D}C + \overline{A}B + \overline{A}C + BC$

$Z = \overline{C} + AD$

**Fig. 5.21**    *Solution for Problem 5.44.*

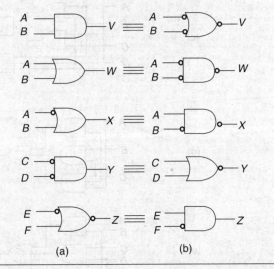

**Fig. 5.22**    *(a) Original Logic Circuits; (b) Equivalent Logic Circuits.*

**5.46 Use the bubble-pushing technique to convert the gates in the Fig. 5.23.**

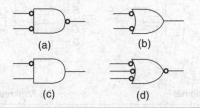

(a)    (b)

(c)    (d)

**Fig. 5.23**

*Solution:*

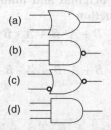

(a)

(b)

(c)

(d)

**Fig. 5.24**   *Solution for Problem 5.46.*

**5.47 Realize the expression $Y = A\bar{B} + \bar{A}B$ using AND, OR, NOR gates.**

*Solution:*

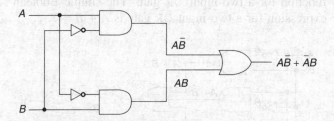

**Fig. 5.25** *Solution for Problem 5.47.*

**5.48 Realise the expression $Y = A\bar{B} + \bar{A}B$ using only NAND gates.**

*Solution:*

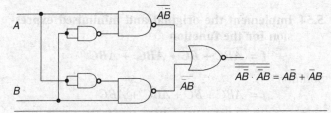

**Fig. 5.26** *Solution for Problem 5.48.*

**5.49 Draw the logic circuit for $Y = A\bar{B} + AB$. Simplify this Boolean equation and the corresponding logic circuit.**

*Solution:*

We have a sum-of-products equation. This implies two AND gates driving an OR gate as shown below.

To simplify the logic circuit, factor the equation as follows:

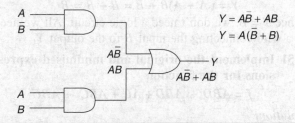

$$Y = A\bar{B} + AB$$
$$Y = A(\bar{B} + B)$$

**Fig. 5.27**   *Solution for Problem 5.49.*

The corresponding logic circuit is shown below. This is simpler because it uses only one AND gate.

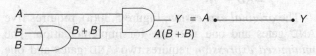

**Fig. 5.27a**   *Simplification of the Original Diagram.*

**5.50 Show the logic circuit for the Boolean equation $Y = (\bar{A} + B)(A + B)$. Simplify the circuit as much as possible using algebra.**

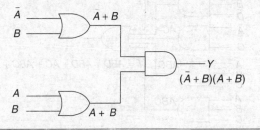

**Fig. 5.28**   *Logic Circuit for $Y = (\bar{A} + B)(A + B)$*

*Solution:*

Figure 5.28 shows the logic circuit for the given Boolean equation. Next, multiply the factors of the given equation to get

$$Y = \bar{A}A + \bar{A}B + BA + BB$$

A variable ANDed with its complement equals zero, so the first term drops out. A variable ORed with itself equals itself, so the last term reduces to $B$. Because of the *commutative law $AB = BA$*. The foregoing simplifications give us the following equation.

$$Y = \bar{A}B + AB + B$$

Figure 5.29 shows the corresponding logic circuit. As you can see, *this circuit is more complicated than the original.*

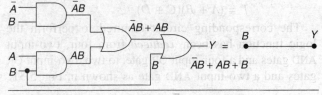

**Fig. 5.29**   *Logic Circuit for $\bar{A}B + AB + B$*

We can also factor the foregoing equation as follows:

$$Y = (\bar{A} + A)B + B = B + B = B$$

Since $Y = B$, we don't need a logic circuit. All we need is a wire connecting the input $B$ to the output $Y$.

## 5.51 Implement the original and minimised expressions for the function

$$f = ABD + AB\bar{D} + \bar{A}C + \bar{A}BC + ABC$$

*Solution:*

$$f = ABD + AB\bar{D} + \bar{A}C + \bar{A}BC + ABC$$
$$= AB(D + \bar{D}) + \bar{A}C + BC(\bar{A} + A)$$
$$= AB + \bar{A}C + BC$$
$$f = AB + \bar{A}C$$

The *original expression*, Figure 5.30(a), requires five AND gates and one OR gate for implementation. The *minimised expression* requires two AND gates and one OR gate, as can be seen in Figure 5.30(b). *The number of literals have been reduced from 14 to 4, and the variable D has been eliminated.*

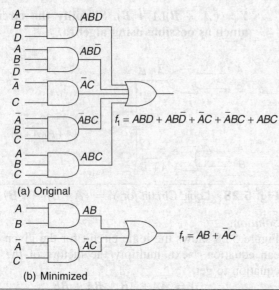

(a) Original

(b) Minimized

**Fig. 5.30** *Implementation of Original and Minimised Expression.*

## 5.52 Implement the original and minimised expression for the function
$$f = A \cdot C + A \cdot D + B \cdot C + B \cdot D$$

*Solution:*

$$f = A \cdot C + A \cdot D + B \cdot C + B \cdot D$$

After simplification,

$$f = (A + B)(C + D)$$

The corresponding circuit required to perform the logic function has been *reduced* from four, two-input AND gates and a four-input OR gate, to two, two-input OR gates and a two-input AND gate as shown in Fig. 5.31.

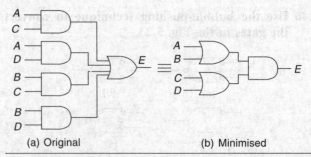

(a) Original

(b) Minimised

**Fig. 5.31** *Implementation of Original and Minimised Expression.*

## 5.53 Implement the original and minimised expression for the function
$$Y = \bar{A} \cdot B + A \cdot \bar{B} + A \cdot B$$

*Solution:*

$$Y = \bar{A} \cdot B + A \cdot \bar{B} + A \cdot B$$

**Table 5.9**

| $A$ | $B$ | $\bar{A}$ | $\bar{B}$ | $\bar{A} \cdot B$ | $A \cdot \bar{B}$ | $A \cdot B$ | $Y = \bar{A} \cdot B + A \cdot \bar{B} + A \cdot B$ |
|---|---|---|---|---|---|---|---|
| 0 | 0 | 1 | 1 | 0 | 0 | 0 | 0 |
| 0 | 1 | 1 | 0 | 1 | 0 | 0 | 1 |
| 1 | 0 | 0 | 1 | 0 | 1 | 0 | 1 |
| 1 | 1 | 0 | 0 | 0 | 0 | 1 | 1 |

The truth table for the Boolean function is the truth function for a two-input OR gate. The simple Boolean expression for a two-input OR gate is $A + B = Y$.

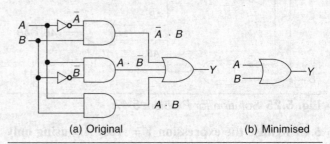

(a) Original

(b) Minimised

**Fig. 5.32** *Implementation of Original and Minimised Expression.*

## 5.54 Implement the original and minimised expression for the function
$$f = \bar{A}\bar{B}C + B\bar{C} + \bar{A}BC + ABC$$

*Solution:*

$$f = \bar{A}\bar{B}C + B\bar{C} + \bar{A}BC + ABC$$
$$= \bar{A}\bar{B}C + B\bar{C} + BC(\bar{A} + A)$$
$$= \bar{A}\bar{B}C + B\bar{C} + BC$$
$$= \bar{A}\bar{B}C + B(\bar{C} + C)$$
$$= \bar{A}\bar{B}C + B$$
$$= \bar{A}C + B$$

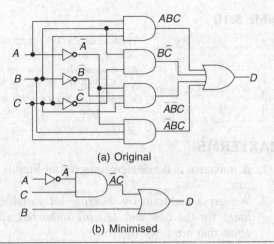

(a) Original

(b) Minimised

**Fig. 5.33**   *Implementation of Original and Minimised Expression.*

## 5.55 Implement the minimised Boolean expression for the function
$$f = B\bar{C}\bar{D} + \bar{A}BD + ABD + BC\bar{D} + \bar{B}CD$$
$$+ \bar{A}\bar{B}\bar{C}D + A\bar{B}\bar{C}D$$

*Solution:*
This can be implemented directly, as in the last example, but would use a large number of gates. Alternatively it may be simplified as follows.

$$f = B\bar{C}\bar{D} + \bar{A}BD + ABD + BC\bar{D} + \bar{B}CD$$
$$+ \bar{A}\bar{B}\bar{C}D + A\bar{B}\bar{C}D$$
$$= BD(A + \bar{A}) + B\bar{D}(C + \bar{C}) + \bar{B}CD + \bar{B}\bar{C}D(A + \bar{A})$$
$$= BD + B\bar{D} + \bar{B}CD + \bar{B}\bar{C}D$$
$$= B(D + \bar{D}) + \bar{B}D(C + \bar{C})$$
$$= B + \bar{B}D$$
$$= B + D$$

This expression can be implemented using a single gate.

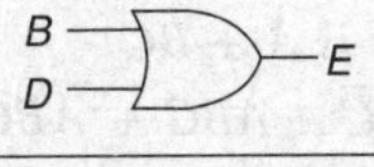

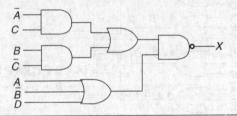

**Fig. 5.34**   *Implementation of Minimised Expression.*

## CANONICAL FORMS

The form of an expression determines how many and which type of logic gates are needed, as well as how they are connected together. *The more complicated the expression, the more complex will be the gate network. It is, therefore, best to simplify an expression as much as possible to get the simplest gate network.* There are two standard or *canonical forms* used to express any combinational logic network: the sum-of-products (*SOP*) form and the product-of-sums (*POS*) form.

## 5.56 Identify each of the following Boolean equations as a produce-of-sums (POS) expression, a sum-of-products (SOP) expression, or both.
(a) $U = A\bar{B}C + BC + \bar{A}C$
(b) $V = (A + C)(\bar{B} + \bar{C})$
(c) $W = A\bar{C}(\bar{B} + C)$
(d) $X = AB + \bar{C} + BD$
(e) $Y = (A\bar{B} + D)(A + \bar{C}D)$
(f) $Z = (A + \bar{B})(BC + A) + \bar{A}B + CD$

*Solution:*
(a) SOP        (b) POS        (c) POS
(d) SOP        (e) POS        (f) POS, SOP

## 5.57 Simplify the circuit shown in Fig. 5.35 down to its SOP form; then draw the logic circuit of the simplified form using a 74LS54 AOI gate.

**Fig. 5.35**   *Original Circuit for Problem 5.57.*

*Solution:*

$$X = \overline{(\bar{A}C + B\bar{C}) \cdot (A + \bar{B} + D)}$$
$$= \overline{\bar{A}C + B\bar{C}} + \overline{A + \bar{B} + D}$$
$$= \overline{\bar{A}C} \cdot \overline{B\bar{C}} + \bar{A}B\bar{D}$$
$$= (A + \bar{C})(\bar{B} + C) + \bar{A}B\bar{D}$$
$$= A\bar{B} + AC + \bar{B}\bar{C} + C\bar{C} + \bar{A}B\bar{D}$$
$$= A\bar{B} + AC + \bar{B}\bar{C} + \bar{A}B\bar{D}  \qquad \text{SOP}$$

The simplified circuit is shown in Fig. 5.36.

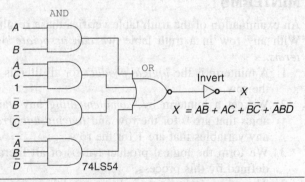

$$X = A\bar{B} + AC + \bar{B}\bar{C} + \bar{A}B\bar{D}$$

**Fig. 5.36**   *Using an AOI IC to Implement the Simplified SOP Equation for Problem 5.57.*

**5.58 Implement the original and minimised expression for the function**

$$f = (A + B + \bar{C})(A + B + C)(A + \bar{B} + C)$$
$$(\bar{A} + \bar{B} + C)$$

*Solution:*

Since $X = X \cdot X$, we can expand $f$ as follows:

$$f = (A + B + C)(A + B + \bar{C})(A + B + C)$$
$$(A + \bar{B} + C)(A + \bar{B} + C)(\bar{A} + \bar{B} + C)$$

| Substitute | $A + B$ | for $(A + B + C)(A + B + \bar{C})$ |
| | $A + C$ | for $(A + B + C)(A + \bar{B} + C)$ |
| and | $B + C$ | for $(A + \bar{B} + C)(\bar{A} + \bar{B} + C)$ |

$$f = (A + B)(A + C)(\bar{B} + C)$$
$$= (A + B)(\bar{B} + C)$$

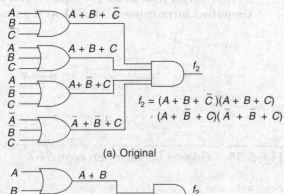

$$f_2 = (A + B + \bar{C})(A + B + C)$$
$$\cdot (A + \bar{B} + C)(\bar{A} + \bar{B} + C)$$

(a) Original

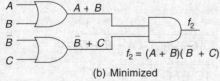

$$f_2 = (A + B)(\bar{B} + C)$$

(b) Minimized

**Fig. 5.37** *Circuit for Original and Minimised Expression.*

*Note: Implementation of minimised expression requires two OR gates and one AND gate instead of four OR gates and one AND gate. Literals have been reduced from 12 to 4.*

## MINTERMS

An examination of the truth table verifies these results: With any row in a truth table *we can associate two terms.*

1. A minterm is the *logical product* for all literals in the row.
2. We get a minterm by *complementing* any variables that are 0 for the row and *leaving unbarred* any variables that are 1 for the row.
3. We form the logical product (AND) of all literals defined by this process.
4. The sum-of-products is known as the minterm form.

**Table 5.10**

| A | B | X |
|---|---|---|
| 0 | 0 | 0 |
| 0 | 1 | 1 |
| 1 | 0 | 1 |
| 1 | 1 | 0 |

Truth table $f(XOR)$ function
$(X = A \oplus B)$
$A = 0$ when $B = 1 \rightarrow \bar{A}B$
$A = 1$ when $B = 0 \rightarrow A\bar{B}$
$X = A\bar{B} + AB = (A + B)(\bar{A} + \bar{B})$
SOP       POS

## MAXTERMS

1. A maxterm is the *logical sum* for all literals in the row.
2. We get a maxterm by *barring* all variables that are 1 for the row and *leaving unbarred* all variables that are 0 for the row.
3. We form the logical sum (OR) of all literals defined by this process.
4. The product-of-sums is known as the maxterm form.

**5.59 Convert $A + B$ to minterms.**

*Solution:*

$$A + B = A(1) + B(1)$$
$$= A(B + \bar{B}) + B(A + \bar{A})$$
$$= AB + A\bar{B} + AB + \bar{A}B$$
$$= AB + A\bar{B} + \bar{A}B$$

Each term in the example contains *all* the letters used: $A$ and $B$. The terms $AB$, $A\bar{B}$, and $\bar{A}B$ are therefore *minterms.*

**5.60 Find the minterms for $A + BC$ and prove that the result is $A + BC$.**

*Solution:*

| Write down the terms | $A + BC$ |
| Insert $X$'s where letters are missing | $AXX, XBC$ |
| Vary all the $X$'s in $AXX$ | $A\bar{B}\bar{C}, A\bar{B}C,$ |
| | $AB\bar{C}, ABC$ |
| Vary all the $X$'s in $XBC$ | $\bar{A}BC, ABC$ |

$$A + BC = A\bar{B}\bar{C} + A\bar{B}C + AB\bar{C} + ABC + \bar{A}BC + ABC$$

*Proof that the result is $A + BC$*

$$A\bar{B}\bar{C} + A\bar{B}C + AB\bar{C} + ABC + \bar{A}BC + ABC$$
$$= A\bar{B}(C + \bar{C}) + AB\bar{C} + BC(\bar{A} + A)$$
$$= A\bar{B} + AB\bar{C} + BC$$
$$= A\bar{B} + B(A\bar{C} + C)$$
$$= A\bar{B} + B(A + C)$$
$$= A\bar{B} + AB + BC$$
$$= A(\bar{B} + B) + BC$$
$$= A + BC$$

## TWO-LEVEL REALISATION

An output function that is 1 for several rows of the truth table is written as a *logical sum* of minterms for all rows for which the functions is 1. This form is the canonical sum-of-products, AND-OR *form*. This realisation is known as two-level realisation. The *first level* consists of AND gates and the *second level* consists of OR gates. The Greek letter $\Sigma$ is used to denote the sum. The decimal expression $\Sigma m$ (1, 2, 4) means that the minterms of rows 1, 2, and 4 are ORed together.

An output function that is 0 for several rows of the truth table is written as a *logical product* of maxterms for all rows for which the function is 0. This form is the canonical product-of-sums OR-AND *form*. This is also a two-level realisation. The *first level* consists of OR gates and the *second level* consists of the AND gate. The Greek letter $\Pi$ is used for the product. The decimal expression $\Pi M$ (0, 6, 7) means that the maxterms of rows 0, 6 and 7 are ANDed together.

### 5.61 Draw a truth table for two variables. Map the minterms and denote the output.

*Solution:*

**Table 5.11** *Two-Variables Truth Table*

| INPUTS | | OUTPUT |
|---|---|---|
| A | B | C |
| 0 | 0 | 0 |
| 0 | 1 | 1 |
| 1 | 0 | 1 |
| 1 | 1 | 1 |

|  | B  0 | 1 |
|---|---|---|
| A | | |
| 0 | $0_0$ | $1_1$ |
| 1 | $1_2$ | $1_3$ |

Two-Variable Map

Each column of the truth table represents a minterm.

1's are placed to indicate that the output *contains* a particular minterm in its sum and 0's when that term is *excluded* from the sum.

$$C = \bar{A}B + A\bar{B} + AB$$
$$C = m_1 + m_2 + m_3$$

$C$ is the sum of minterms 1, 2, and 3.

Another way of representing this relation is to use the Greek letter sigma and an *m* to represent "sum of minterms ..."

$$C = \Sigma m (1, 2, 3)$$

### 5.62 Draw the truth table for three variables showing minterms and maxterms.

*Solution:*

**Table 5.12**

| Row Number | A | B | C | Minterms | Maxterms |
|---|---|---|---|---|---|
| 0 | 0 | 0 | 0 | $\bar{A}\bar{B}\bar{C}$ | $A + B + C$ |
| 1 | 0 | 0 | 1 | $\bar{A}\bar{B}C$ | $A + B + \bar{C}$ |
| 2 | 0 | 1 | 0 | $\bar{A}B\bar{C}$ | $A + \bar{B} + C$ |
| 3 | 0 | 1 | 1 | $\bar{A}BC$ | $A + \bar{B} + \bar{C}$ |
| 4 | 1 | 0 | 0 | $A\bar{B}\bar{C}$ | $\bar{A} + B + C$ |
| 5 | 1 | 0 | 1 | $A\bar{B}C$ | $\bar{A} + B + \bar{C}$ |
| 6 | 1 | 1 | 0 | $AB\bar{C}$ | $\bar{A} + \bar{B} + C$ |
| 7 | 1 | 1 | 1 | $ABC$ | $A + B + C$ |

### 5.63 For any truth table: (a) write the output function that has a 1 output for only one row; (b) write the output functions that has a 0 output for only one row.

*Solution:*

**Table 5.13**

| Row Number | A | B | C | Function $f_1$ |
|---|---|---|---|---|
| 0 | 0 | 0 | 0 | 0 |
| 1 | 0 | 0 | 1 | 0 |
| 2 | 0 | 1 | 0 | 1 |
| 3 | 0 | 1 | 1 | 0 |
| 4 | 1 | 0 | 0 | 0 |
| 5 | 1 | 0 | 1 | 0 |
| 6 | 1 | 1 | 0 | 0 |
| 7 | 1 | 1 | 1 | 0 |

$f_1 = \bar{A}B\bar{C}$

**Table 5.14**

| Row Number | A | B | C | Function $f_2$ |
|---|---|---|---|---|
| 0 | 0 | 0 | 0 | 1 |
| 1 | 0 | 0 | 1 | 1 |
| 2 | 0 | 1 | 0 | 1 |
| 3 | 0 | 1 | 1 | 1 |
| 4 | 1 | 0 | 0 | 1 |
| 5 | 1 | 0 | 1 | 1 |
| 6 | 1 | 1 | 0 | 0 |
| 7 | 1 | 1 | 1 | 1 |

$f_2 = \bar{A} + \bar{B} + C$

### 5.64 Write the sum of products form.

*Solution:*

**Table 5.15**

| Row Number | A | B | C | Function $f_3$ | Minterms with output 1 |
|---|---|---|---|---|---|
| 0 | 0 | 0 | 0 | 0 | |
| 1 | 0 | 0 | 1 | 1 | $\bar{A}\bar{B}C$ |
| 2 | 0 | 1 | 0 | 1 | $\bar{A}B\bar{C}$ |
| 3 | 0 | 1 | 1 | 0 | |
| 4 | 1 | 0 | 0 | 0 | |
| 5 | 1 | 0 | 1 | 1 | $A\bar{B}C$ |
| 6 | 1 | 1 | 0 | 1 | $AB\bar{C}$ |
| 7 | 1 | 1 | 1 | 1 | $ABC$ |

*The sum-of-products form uses the minterms of rows for which the function is 1.*

$$f_3 = \bar{A}\bar{B}C + \bar{A}B\bar{C} + A\bar{B}C + AB\bar{C} + ABC$$

$$= \Sigma m(1, 2, 5, 6, 7)$$

### 5.65 Write the product-of-sums form.

*Solution:*

**Table 5.16**

| Row Number | A | B | C | Function $f_3$ | Minterms with output 0 |
|---|---|---|---|---|---|
| 0 | 0 | 0 | 0 | 0 | $A + B + C$ |
| 1 | 0 | 0 | 1 | 1 | |
| 2 | 0 | 1 | 0 | 1 | |
| 3 | 0 | 1 | 1 | 0 | $A + \bar{B} + \bar{C}$ |
| 4 | 1 | 0 | 0 | 0 | $\bar{A} + B + C$ |
| 5 | 1 | 0 | 1 | 1 | |
| 6 | 1 | 1 | 0 | 1 | |
| 7 | 1 | 1 | 1 | 1 | |

*The product-of-sums form uses the maxterms of rows for which the function is 0.*

$$f_3 = (A + B + C)(A + \bar{B} + \bar{C})(\bar{A} + B + C)$$
$$= \Pi M\,(0, 3, 4)$$

## CONVERTING CIRCUITS TO UNIVERSAL LOGIC

We can simply substitute NANDs for both ANDs and ORs in the AND-OR implementation. Similarly, we can substitute NORs for both ORs and ANDs in the OR-AND implementation. More than two levels may be required. Hence *either* NAND *or* NOR *is a complete set that can express any switching function.* The conversion can easily be accomplished by the following procedure:

1. Draw the circuit in AND-OR-*Invert* (AOI) logic
2. If NAND hardware has been chosen, add a circle to the output of each AND gate on the logic diagram, and provide circles on the inputs to all OR gates.
3. If NOR hardware has been chosen, add a circle to the output of each OR gate on the logic diagram, and provide circles on the inputs to all AND gates.
4. Add or subtract an inverter on each line that received a circle in step 2 or 3.

**5.66 Implement the Boolean expression**
$$D = ABC + A\bar{B}\bar{C} + \bar{A}B\bar{C}$$
**directly; implement the same expression using only NAND gates.**

*Solution:*
The function $D = ABC + A\bar{B}\bar{C} + \bar{A}B\bar{C}$ can be implemented directly as shown in Fig. 5.38.

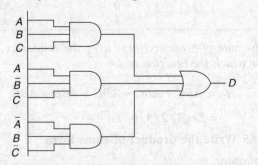

**Fig. 5.38** *Direct Implementation of the Given Function.*

However, from DeMorgan's theorem we know that
$$A + B + C = \overline{\bar{A}\bar{B}\bar{C}}$$

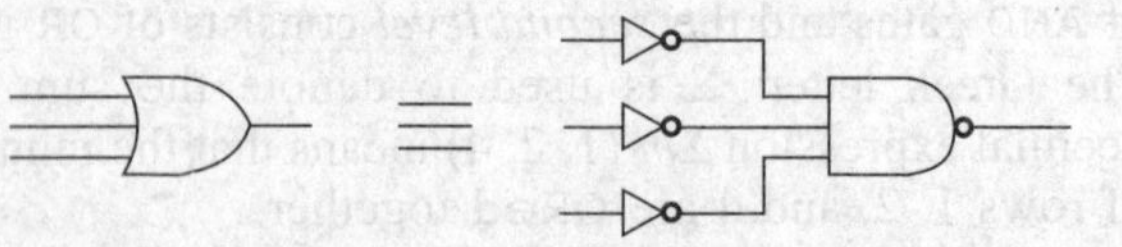

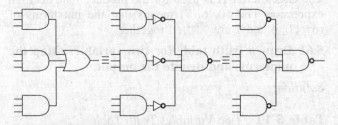

**Fig. 5.39** *Direct Implementation of the Given Function.*

It follows that functions implemented using AND and OR gates may be modified to use only NAND gates, since. (See Fig. 5.40)

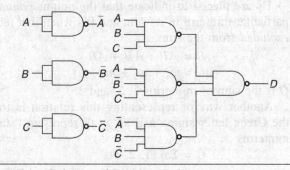

**Fig. 5.40** *Inversion of* AND-OR *to 'NAND Only'.*

*This simplification assumes that inverses of the inputs are available. If this is not the case they can be obtained by using* NAND *gates as inverters. In this way any logic function can be implemented using* only NAND *gates and our example is implemented as shown in Fig. 5.41.*

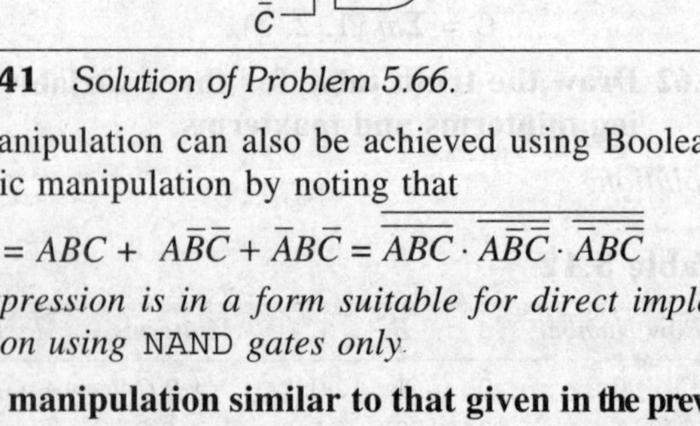

**Fig. 5.41** *Solution of Problem 5.66.*

This manipulation can also be achieved using Boolean algebraic manipulation by noting that

$$D = ABC + A\bar{B}\bar{C} + \bar{A}B\bar{C} = \overline{\overline{ABC} \cdot \overline{A\bar{B}\bar{C}} \cdot \overline{\bar{A}B\bar{C}}}$$

*This expression is in a form suitable for direct implementation using* NAND *gates only.*

**5.67 A manipulation similar to that given in the previous example can be used to implement functions using only NOR gates. Explain. (See Fig. 5.42)**

*Solution:*
The inversions at the front end of this implementation are achieved simply by using the inverted or non-inverted signal as required. Therefore, using the previous example, the solution can be given as shown in Fig. 5.43.

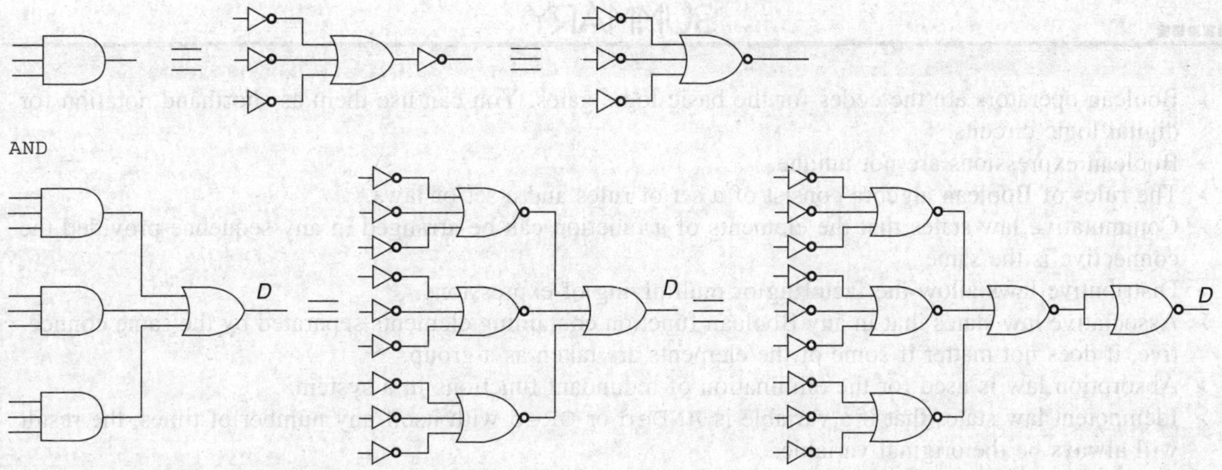

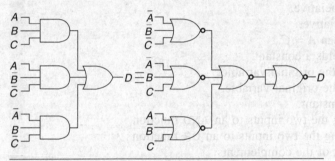

**Fig. 5.42** *Inversion of* AND-OR *to 'NOR Only'*.

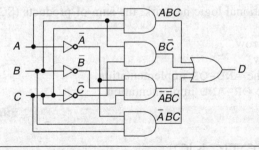

**Fig. 5.43** *Solution for Problem 5.67.*

### 5.68 Simplify and implement the Boolean expression

$$X = \bar{A}\bar{B}C + B\bar{C} + \bar{A}BC + ABC$$

*Solution:*

The expression may be implemented directly as shown in Fig. 5.44.

$$X = \bar{A}\bar{B}C + B\bar{C} + \bar{A}BC + ABC$$

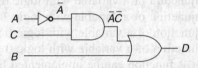

**Fig. 5.44** *Figure for Problem 5.68.*

Alternatively, it can be reduced using Boolean algebra, as follows:

$$
\begin{aligned}
X &= \bar{A}\bar{B}C + B\bar{C} + \bar{A}BC + ABC \\
&= \bar{A}\bar{B}C + B\bar{C} + BC(\bar{A} + A) \\
&= \bar{A}\bar{B}C + B\bar{C} + BC \\
&= \bar{A}\bar{B}C + B(\bar{C} + C) \\
&= \bar{A}\bar{B}C + B \\
&= \bar{A}C + B
\end{aligned}
$$

This can be implemented using only three gates as shown in Fig. 5.45.

**Fig. 5.45** *Implementation of the Simplified Expression.*

### 5.69 Simplify and implement the expression

$$BC\bar{D} + \bar{A}BD + ABD + BC\bar{D} + \bar{B}CD$$
$$+ \bar{A}\bar{B}\bar{C}D + A\bar{B}\bar{C}D$$

*Solution:*

$$
\begin{aligned}
X &= BC\bar{D} + \bar{A}BD + ABD + BC\bar{D} + \bar{B}CD \\
&\quad + \bar{A}\bar{B}\bar{C}D + A\bar{B}\bar{C}D \\
&= BD(A + \bar{A}) + B\bar{D}(C + \bar{C}) + \bar{B}CD \\
&\quad + \bar{B}\bar{C}D(A + \bar{A}) \\
&= BD + B\bar{D} + \bar{B}CD + \bar{B}\bar{C}D \\
&= B(D + \bar{D}) + \bar{B}D(C + \bar{C}) \\
&= B + \bar{B}D \\
&= B + D
\end{aligned}
$$

The expression can be implemented directly using a large number of gates. However, after simplification, the same expression can be implemented using a single gate as shown below.

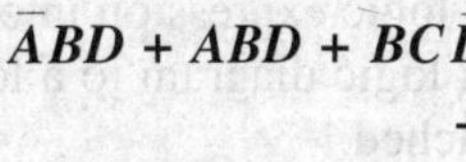

**Fig. 5.46** *Implementation of the Simplified Expression.*

This represents a considerable simplification as compared with the original expression.

# SUMMARY

■■■■■■■

> Boolean operators are the codes for the basic logic gates. You can use them as shorthand notation for digital logic circuits.
> Boolean expressions are not unique.
> The rules of Boolean algebra consist of a set of rules and a set of laws.
> Commutative law states that the elements of a function can be arranged in any sequence provided the connective is the same.
> Distributive laws allow the factoring or multiplying of expressions.
> Associative law states that in any Boolean function containing elements separated by the same connective, it does not matter if some of the elements are taken as a group.
> Absorption law is used for the elimination of redundant functions in a system.
> Idempotent law states that if a variable is ANDed or ORed with itself any number of times, the result will always be the original variable.
> If any number of nothings are added or multiplied together, the result will also be nothing.
> If any number of somethings are added or multiplied together, the result will also be something.
> The NAND operation is commutative and not associative.
> The NOR operation is commutative and not associative.
> Law of identity states that if $A = B$ and $B = C$, then $A = C$.
> Conjunction of a variable with logic 0 always yields a constant.
> Conjunction of a variable with logic 1 results in the original variable.
> Disjunction of a variable with logic 0 results in the original variable.
> Disjunction of a variable with logic 0 yields a constant.
> A NOR function can be implemented by inverting the two inputs to an AND function.
> A NAND function can be implemented by inverting the two inputs to an OR function.
> The complement of a sum is equal to the product of the complements.
> The complement of a product is equal to the sum of the complements.
> To convert a logic expression into a logic diagram, start with the output and work back towards the input.
> To convert a logic diagram to a logic expression start with the input signals and develop terms until the output is reached.
> To use the bubble-pushing technique: change the logic gate (AND to OR or OR to AND) and add bubbles to the input and outputs where there were none, and remove the original bubbles.
> To convert a Boolean expression into a logic diagram, start with the output and go back towards the input.
> To convert a logic diagram into a Boolean expression start with the input signals and develop terms until the output is reached.
> There are two canonical forms to express any combinational logic network: the sum-of-products (SOP) and the product-of-sums (POS).
> A minterm is the logical product for all literals in the row.
> A maxterm is the logical sum for all literals in the row.
> We can substitute NANDs for both ANDs and ORs in the AND-OR implementation.
> We can substitute NORs for both ORs and ANDs in the OR-AND implementation.

■■■■■■■

# REVIEW QUESTIONS

Test your understanding

1. Complete each expression:
   (a) $A + 1 =$    (b) $A \cdot A =$    (c) $B \cdot \bar{B}$    (d) $C + C =$
   (e) $x \cdot 0 =$    (f) $D \cdot 1 =$    (g) $D \cdot 0 =$    (h) $C + \bar{C} =$
2. With the OR operation $1 + 1 = 1$
   $1 + 1 + 1 = ?$
3. With the AND operation $A \cdot A = A$
   $A \cdot A \cdot A = ?$

4. Apply the associative law to the expression $A + (B + C + D)$.
5. Apply the distributive law to the expression $A(B + C + D)$.
6. Draw the truth table for a three-input XOR gate.
7. Write the Boolean expression for a three-input NOR gate.
8. What is the significance of DeMorgan's theorem?
9. Apply DeMorgan's theorems to the following expression:

   (a) $\overline{ABC} + (\overline{\bar{D} + E})$    (b) $\overline{(A + B)C}$    (c) $\overline{A + B + C + \bar{D}E}$

10. How will you implement a NAND function?
11. How will you implement a NOR function?
12. Explain the difference between SOP and POS forms.
13. Give three examples of SOP expressions.
14. Give three examples of POS expressions.
15. Why is the SOP expression used more often?
16. How will you convert a Boolean expression into a logic diagram?
17. How will you convert a logic diagram into a Boolean expression?

18. Draw the logic circuit for the SOP expression $X = \bar{A}C + \bar{A}D + BC + B\bar{D}$. WHat does it signify?

19. Draw the logic circuit for the POS expression $X = (\bar{A} + B)(C + \bar{D})$. What does it signify?

20. Give the pin configuration of AOI IC-74LS54.

21. Use an AOI IC to implement $\bar{X} = \bar{A}C + \bar{A}D + BC + B\bar{D}$.

# SUPPLEMENTARY PROBLEMS

22. Write the output of the given logic circuit.
23. Construct a logic circuit to implement

   $f(A,\ B,\ C,\ D) = (A\bar{B}C) + D + (\overline{A\bar{C}})$

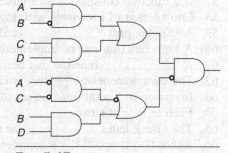

**Fig. 5.47**

24. How will you extract the Boolean expression of a function from its truth table?
25. Simplify the Boolean equation

   $Y = (\bar{A} + B)(A + B)$

Draw the logic circuit of the simplified expression. Compare it with the original circuit. (See Fig. 5.55(a))

26. Show the logic circuit for $Y = A\bar{B} + AB$. Simplify the Boolean equation and the corresponding logic circuit.

27. Simplify the Boolean equation $Y = \bar{A}\bar{B}C + \bar{A}B\bar{C} + A\bar{B}C + AB\bar{C}$, and describe the logic circuit.

28. Implement the function $Y = \overline{AB + CDE + FG + HJK}$ with AOI IC-74LS54.

29. Make the external connections to a 4001 CMOS NOR IC to implement the function $X = \bar{A} + B$.

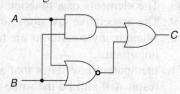

**Fig. 5.48**

30. Extract the Boolean expression for the circuit given in Fig. 5.48.
31. Develop the logic diagram of the Boolean expression

   $C = AB + \overline{\bar{A}\bar{B}} + (A + B)$

# OBJECTIVE TYPE QUESTIONS

## Fill in the Blanks

32. A variable may be ORed or ANDed with itself any number of times and the result will be the _____ variable.

33. A NOR function can be implemented by _____ the inputs to an AND function.
34. A NAND function can be implemented by inverting the inputs to an _____ function.
35. To _____ from Boolean algebra to logic, start with the output and work back toward the input.
36. To convert from logic to Boolean algebra _____ the circuit from input to output until the final expression is obtained.
37. Assertion level refers to the level _____ for an event to occur.
38. DeMorgan's laws are the most commonly used laws of _____ _____.
39. Canonical forms are used to express any _____ logic function.
40. Minterm is a logical _____ for all literals in the row.
41. The sum-of-products is known as the _____ form.
42. Maxterms are _____ to minterms.
43. We can write the output function by _____ maxterms and minterms.
44. We can substitute _____ for both ANDs and ORs in the AND-OR implementation.
45. We can substitute _____ for both ORs and ANDs in the OR-AND implementation.
46. NAND or NOR is a complete set that can express any _____ function.
47. The number of terms in the expression corresponds to the number of _____ _____.
48. The number of _____ in the expression corresponds to the number of inputs.
49. NAND and NOR gates are sometimes referred to as _____ gates.
50. The SOP form is _____ to deal with.
51. The Boolean operators can be considered as _____ for the basic gates.
52. Compound gates can be represented by _____ of the elementary functions.
53. The order in which terms are ANDed or ORed together is _____.
54. The distributive law allows the _____ or multiplying of functions.
55. In any Boolean function containing elements separated by the same connective, it does not matter if some of these elements are considered as a _____.
56. 'Absorption law' is extremely important for the elimination of _____ functions.
57. If a function consists of a variable and its inverse, then the function is a _____.
58. Conjunction of a variable with logic 1 results in the _____ variable.
59. A variable plus _____ is always something.
60. A NOR function can be implemented by inverting the two inputs to an _____ function.
61. A _____ function can be implemented by inverting the two inputs to an OR function.
62. The complement of a product is equal to the _____ of the complements.
63. Inversion of a total function must be illustrated by adding an _____.
64. Each term in the two _____ forms contains each of the binary variables once and only once.
65. The Greek letter _____ is used for the logical product of maxterms.
66. Either NAND or NOR is a complete set that can express any _____ function.
67. A variable in complemented or uncomplemented form is known as a _____.

## True/False Questions

State whether the following statements are True or False.
68. The elements of a function can be arranged in any sequence provided the logical connective is the same.
69. The associative law does not hold if elements are connected by the same connective.
70. When many conditions are to be ANDed or ORed together, the order in which conditions are combined is very important.
71. Idempotent law states that a variable may be ANDed or ORed with itself any even number of times and the result will still be the same variable.
72. If any number of nothings are added or multiplied together the result will also be nothing.
73. Conjunction of a variable with logic 0 always yields a constant.
74. Disjunction of a variable with logic 0 results in a constant output.
75. The complement of a sum is equal to the product of the complements.
76. The Greek letter sigma is used for the logical product of maxterms.
77. Either AND or OR is a complete set that can express any switching function.
78. The simplest Boolean equation results in the simplest array of logic gates for the function.
79. DeMorgan's laws are used to transform a whole expression.
80. Number of literals corresponds to number of inputs.

81. The SOP expression is seldom used because it does not lend itself to the development of truth tables and timing diagrams.
82. Boolean function cannot be simplified by graphical methods.
83. DeMorgan's laws are used to change only part of an expression in order to get the whole expression into a desirable form.
84. A minterm is a logical product of all literals in the row.
85. AND and OR gates are sometimes referred to as universal gates.

## Multiple Choice Questions

86.
Which of the following gates can be used as an inverter?
(a) NAND
(b) AND
(c) NOR
(d) None of the above

87. Which of the following operations is commutative but not associative?
(a) AND
(b) OR
(c) XOR
(d) NAND

88. Which of the following operations is not associative?
(a) NOR
(b) OR
(c) XOR
(d) AND

89. Identify the operation which is commutative but not associative.
(a) OR
(b) NOR
(c) XOR
(d) AND

90. The minterm designator of the term $A\bar{B}C\bar{D}$ is
(a) 8
(b) 9
(c) 10
(d) 11

91. The maxterm designator of the term $\bar{A} + \bar{B} + C + \bar{D}$ is
(a) 11
(b) 2
(c) 13
(d) 10

92. A switching function $f(A, B, C, D) = \bar{A}BCD + \bar{A}B\bar{C}D + \bar{A}\bar{B}CD + A\bar{B}CD + ABCD$ can also be written as
(a) $\Sigma m(1, 3, 5, 7, 9)$
(b) $\Sigma m(3, 5, 7, 9, 11)$
(c) $\Sigma m(3, 5, 9, 11, 13)$
(d) $\Sigma m(5, 7, 9, 11, 13)$

93. A switching function $f(A, B, C) = (A + \bar{B} + C)(A + \bar{B} + \bar{C})(\bar{A} + \bar{B} + C)$ can also be written as
(a) $\Pi M(1, 4, 5)$
(b) $\Pi M(2, 3, 6)$
(c) $\Pi M(0, 2, 3)$
(d) $\Pi M(3, 4, 5)$

94. A switching function $f(A, B, C, D) = \Sigma m(5, 9, 11, 14)$ can be written as
(a) $\bar{A}\bar{B}\bar{C}D + \bar{A}B\bar{C}D + ABC\bar{D} + \bar{A}BCD$
(b) $\bar{A}B\bar{C}D + A\bar{B}\bar{C}D + A\bar{B}CD + ABC\bar{D}$
(c) $\bar{A}\bar{B}\bar{C}D + A\bar{B}CD + AB\bar{C}D + \bar{A}BC\bar{D}$
(d) $\bar{A}BCD + \bar{A}B\bar{C}D + A\bar{B}\bar{C}D + ABCD$

95. The switching function $f(A, B, C, D) = \Pi M(5, 8, 11, 13)$ can also be written as
(a) $AB\bar{C}D + \bar{A}BCD + ABC\bar{D} + A\bar{B}C\bar{D}$
(b) $(A + \bar{B} + C + \bar{D})(A + \bar{B} + \bar{C} + \bar{D})(A + \bar{B} + C + D)(A + B + \bar{C} + D)$
(c) $(\bar{A} + B + \bar{C} + D)(A + \bar{B} + \bar{C} + \bar{D})(A + \bar{B} + C + D)(\bar{A} + \bar{B} + C + \bar{D})$
(d) $ABCD + ABCD + ABCD + ABCD$

96. If the SOP form of a switching function is $f(A, B, C) = \bar{A}\bar{B}C + \bar{A}B\bar{C} + A\bar{B}\bar{C} + ABC$ then the POS form of the function will be
(a) $(\bar{A} + B + C)(A + \bar{B} + C)(A + B + \bar{C})(\bar{A} + B + \bar{C})$
(b) $(\bar{A} + \bar{B} + C)(\bar{A} + B + \bar{C})(A + \bar{B} + \bar{C})(A + B + C)$
(c) $(A + \bar{B} + C)(A + B + C)(\bar{A} + \bar{B} + C)(A + B + \bar{C})$
(d) $(A + \bar{B} + C)(\bar{A} + \bar{B} + \bar{C})(A + \bar{B} + \bar{C})(\bar{A} + B + C)$

97. The dual of the Boolean theorem $A \cdot (B + C) = A \cdot B + A \cdot C$ is
(a) $A + (B \cdot C) = A \cdot B + A \cdot C$
(b) $A \cdot (B + C) = (A + B)(A + C)$
(c) $A + (B \cdot C) = (A + B) \cdot (A + C)$
(d) None of the above

98. $\overline{A \cdot B \cdot C}$ is equivalent to
    (a) $\overline{A} + \overline{B} + \overline{C}$
    (b) $\overline{A \cdot B \cdot C}$
    (c) $A + B + C$
    (d) $A \cdot B \cdot C$

99. $\overline{\overline{A} + \overline{B} + \overline{C}}$ is equivalent to
    (a) $A \cdot B \cdot C$
    (b) $A + B + C$
    (c) $\overline{A \cdot B \cdot C}$
    (d) $\overline{A} + \overline{B} + \overline{C}$

100. The dual of a Boolean function is obtained by
    (a) interchanging all 0s and 1s only
    (b) changing all 0s to 1s only
    (c) changing all 1s to 0s only
    (d) interchanging (i) all 0s and 1s and (ii) '+' and '·' signs

101. In a combinational circuit the outputs at any instant of time depend
    (a) only on inputs present at that instant of time
    (b) only on the past inputs
    (c) only on the past outputs
    (d) on past inputs as well as present inputs

102. A combinational circuit
    (a) never contains memory elements
    (b) always contains memory elements
    (c) may sometimes contain memory elements
    (d) contains only memory elements

103. The SOP form of logical expression is most suitable for designing logic circuits using only
    (a) XOR gates
    (b) AND gates
    (c) NAND gates
    (d) NOR gates

104. The POS form of logical expression is most suitable for designing logic circuits using only
    (a) XOR gates
    (b) NAND gates
    (c) AND gates
    (d) NOR gates

105. The logical expression $Y = AB + AC + BC$ is known as
    (a) standard SOP form
    (b) SOP form
    (c) standard POS form
    (d) POS form

106. The logical expression $Y = (A + B + C)(\overline{A} + C)(\overline{B} + C)(A + \overline{C})$ is known as
    (a) standard SOP form
    (b) SOP form
    (c) standard POS form
    (d) POS form

107. The logical expression $Y = \Sigma m(0, 3, 6, 7, 10, 12, 15)$ is equivalent to
    (a) $Y = \Pi M(0, 3, 6, 7, 10, 12, 15)$
    (b) $\Pi M(1, 2, 4, 5, 8, 9, 11, 13, 14)$
    (c) $\Sigma m(1, 2, 4, 5, 8, 9, 11, 13, 14)$
    (d) $\Sigma m(0, 2, 4, 6, 8, 10, 12, 14)$

108. The logic expression $Y = \Pi M(1, 4, 6, 9, 10, 11, 14, 15)$ is equivalent to
    (a) $\Pi M(0, 2, 3, 5, 7, 8, 12, 13)$
    (b) $\Pi M(0, 2, 3, 4, 5, 6, 12, 13)$
    (c) $\Sigma m(1, 4, 6, 9, 10, 11, 14, 15)$
    (d) $\Sigma m(0, 2, 3, 5, 7, 8, 12, 13)$

109. The minterm corresponding to decimal number 13 is
    (a) $A + B + \overline{C} + D$
    (b) $\overline{A} + \overline{B} + C + \overline{D}$
    (c) $AB\overline{C}D$
    (d) $\overline{A}\,\overline{B}\,\overline{C}\,\overline{D}$

110. The maxterm corresponding to decimal number 15 is
    (a) $ABCD$
    (b) $\overline{A}\,\overline{B}\,\overline{C}\,\overline{D}$
    (c) $A + B + C + D$
    (d) $\overline{A} + \overline{B} + \overline{C} + \overline{D}$

## ANSWERS

1. (a) 1     (b) $A$     (c) 0     (d) $C$     (e) 0     (f) $D$     (g) 0     (h) 1
2. 1                          3. $A$                          4. $A + (B + C + D) = (A + B + C) + D$
5. $A(B + C + D) = AB + AC + AD$

6.

**Table 5.17**　*Solution for Problem 6. Truth Table for a Three-input* XOR *Gate* (A ⊕ B) ⊕ C

| | INPUTS | | OUTPUT |
|---|---|---|---|
| C | B | A | X |
| 0 | 0 | 0 | 0 |
| 0 | 0 | 1 | 1 ✓ |
| 0 | 1 | 0 | 1 ✓ |
| 0 | 1 | 1 | 0 |
| 1 | 0 | 0 | 1 ✓ |
| 1 | 0 | 1 | 0 |
| 1 | 1 | 0 | 0 |
| 1 | 1 | 1 | 1 ✓ |

7. $X = \overline{A + B + C}$.

8. DeMorgan's theorem formulates the relationship between $N$(AND) and $N$(OR) functions that allows one type of function to be implemented using a different type of function.

9. (a) $\bar{A} + \bar{B} + \bar{C} + D\bar{E}$　　　　(b) $\overline{AB} + \bar{C}$　　　　(c) $\overline{ABC} + D + \bar{E}$

10. A NAND function can be implemented by inverting the two inputs to an OR function.

11. A NOR function can be implemented by inverting the two inputs to an AND function.

12. The SOP expression usually takes the form of two or more variables ANDed together, ORed with two more variables ANDed together.
The POS expression usually takes the form of two or more variable ORed together, ANDed with two or more variables ORed together.

13. $X = A\bar{B} + AC + \bar{A}BC$
$X = AC\bar{D} + \bar{C}D + B$
$X = B\bar{C}\bar{D} + A\bar{B}DE + CD$

14. $X = (A + \bar{B}) \cdot (B + \bar{C})$
$X = (B + \bar{C} + \bar{D}) \cdot (BC + \bar{E})$
$X = (A + \bar{C}) \cdot (\bar{B} + E) \cdot (C + B)$

15. Because it lends itself nicely to the development of truth tables and timing waveforms. SOP circuits can also be constructed using a special combinational gate called AND-OR-INVERT (AOI) g.ate.

16. Start with the output and work back towards the input.

17. Start with the input signals and develop terms until the output is reached.

18. AND gates feeding into an OR gate. (See Fig. 5.49)

19. OR gates feeding into AND gate. (See Fig. 5.50)

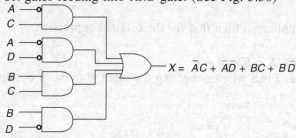

$X = \bar{A}C + \bar{A}D + BC + B\bar{D}$

**Fig. 5.49**　*Solution for Problem 18*

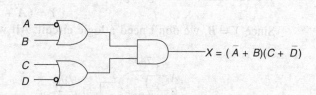

$X = (\bar{A} + B)(C + \bar{D})$

**Fig. 5.50**　*Solution for Problem 19*

20. (See Fig. 5.51)

21. (See Fig. 5.52)

22. (See Fig. 5.53)

23. (See Fig. 5.54)

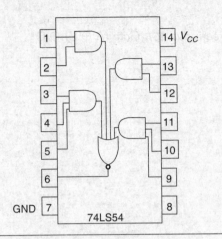

GND [7]      [8]
74LS54

**Fig. 5.51**   *Solution for Problem 20*

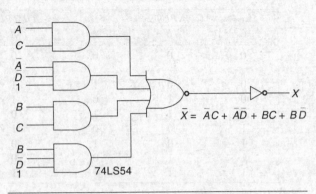

$$\bar{X} = \bar{A}C + \bar{A}D + BC + B\bar{D}$$

74LS54

**Fig. 5.52**   *Solution for Problem 21*

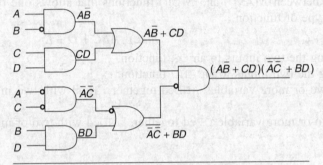

**Fig. 5.53**   *Solution for Problem 22*

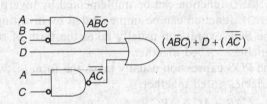

**Fig. 5.54**   *Solution for Problem 23*

24.

**Table 5.18**

| A | B | C |
|---|---|---|
| 0 | 0 | 0 |
| 0 | 1 | 1 |
| 1 | 0 | 1 |
| 1 | 1 | 0 |

*C* is true if *B* is true and *A* is not true, or if *A* is true and *B* is not true.

$$C = (\bar{A} \cdot B) + (A \cdot \bar{B}) = \bar{A}B + A\bar{B} \quad (\text{XOR function})$$

25. Simplified expression $Y = \bar{A}B + AB + B$

The circuit for the simplified expression is more complicated than that for the original expression.
We can factor the forgoing equation as follows

$$Y = (\bar{A} + A)B + B = B + B = B$$

Since $Y = B$, we don't need a logic circuit. All we need is a wire connecting the input *B* to the *Y* output.

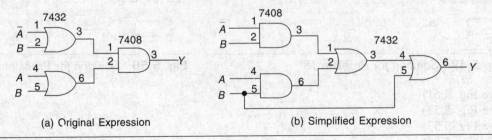

(a) Original Expression          (b) Simplified Expression

**Fig. 5.55**   *Solution for Problem 25.*

26. $Y = A (\bar{B} + B)$
    $= A$
    We don't need a logic circuit. All we have to do is connect a wire between input $A$ and output $Y$.

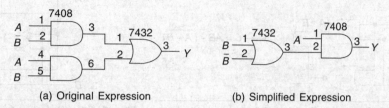

(a) Original Expression    (b) Simplified Expression

**Fig. 5.56** *Solution for Problem 26.*

27. $Y = \bar{C}$ You don't need a logic circuit. All that is required is a wire connecting input $\bar{C}$ to output $Y$.
28. (See Fig. 5.57)

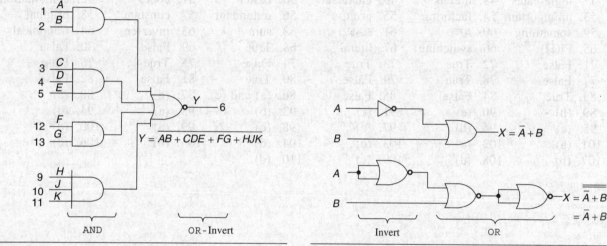

**Fig. 5.57** *Solution for Problem 28.*    **Fig. 5.58** *NOR-NOR circuit for Problem 29.*

29. We will need an inverter and an OR gate to provide the function for $X$. An inverter can be made from a NOR by connecting the inputs, and an OR can be made by inverting the output of a NOR, as shown in Fig. 5.58.

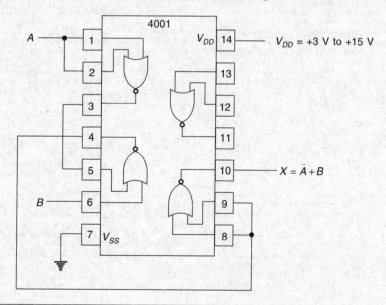

**Fig. 5.59** *Solution for Problem 29 External Connections to a 4001 CMOS IC to Implement* $X = \bar{A} + B$

30. (See Fig. 5.60)
31. (See Fig. 5.61)

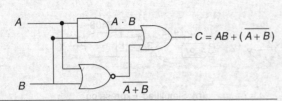

**Fig. 5.60** *Solution for Problem 30*

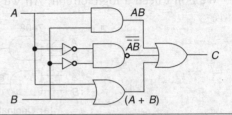

**Fig. 5.61** *Solution for Problem 31*

| | | | | | |
|---|---|---|---|---|---|
| 32. original | 33. inverting | 34. OR | 35. convert | 36. analyse | 37. necessary |
| 38. Boolean algebra | | 39. combinational | | 40. product | 41. minterm |
| 42. complements | | 43. combining | 44. NANDs | 45. NORs | 46. switching |
| 47. logic gates | 48. literals | 49. universal | 50. easier | 51. codes | 52. combinations |
| 53. unimportant | 54. factoring | 55. group | 56. redundant | 57. constant | 58. original |
| 59. something | 60. AND | 61. NAND | 62. sum | 63. inverter | 64. Canonical |
| 65. Pi(Π) | 66. switching | 67. literal | 68. True | 69. False | 70. False |
| 71. False | 72. True | 73. True | 74. False | 75. True | 76. False |
| 77. False | 78. True | 79. False | 80. True | 81. False | 82. False |
| 83. True | 84. False | 85. False | 86. (a) and (c) | 87. (d) | 88. (a) |
| 89. (b) | 90. (c) | 91. (c) | 92. (b) | 93. (a) | 94. (d) |
| 95. (c) | 96. (d) | 97. (c) | 98. (c) | 99. (a) | 100. (d) |
| 101. (a) | 102. (a) | 103. (c) | 104. (d) | 105. (b) | 106. (d) |
| 107. (b) | 108. (d) | 109. (c) | 110. (d) | | |

Chapter

**6**

# Reduction Techniques

## INTRODUCTION

The canonical expressions, two-level circuits, are usually not the most *economical implementation* of the logic functions. There are ways of simplifying or minimising logic functions to achieve economical implementations. *Simplifying* means finding an expression with fewer terms or fewer literals. *Minimising* means finding an expression that is best by some minimisation criteria. Usually, we try to minimise first the *number of terms* in the expression and then the *number of literals*. This classic procedure corresponds to minimising first the *number of logic gates* and then the *number of inputs* in the implementation. There are three methods of minimising:

1. Algebraic simplification (discussed in detail in Chapter 5)
2. Karnaugh map
3. Quine McClusky tables

### 6.1 Find the minterms for $AB + ACD$

*Solution:*

$ABXX$ generates    $AB\bar{C}\bar{D}, AB\bar{C}D, ABC\bar{D}, ABCD$

$AXCD$ generates    $A\bar{B}CD, ABCD$

$AB + ACD = AB\bar{C}\bar{D} + AB\bar{C}D + ABC\bar{D} + ABCD$
$$+ A\bar{B}CD + ABCD$$

### 6.2 Find the minterm designation of $A\bar{B}\bar{C}\bar{D}$.

*Solution:*

Copy original term      $A\bar{B}\bar{C}\bar{D}$
Substitute 1's for *non-barred* letters    1000
and 0's for *barred* letters
Express as decimal subscript of $m$    $m_8$

$$A\bar{B}\bar{C}\bar{D} = m_8$$

### 6.3 Find the minterm designation of $\bar{W}\bar{X}Y\bar{Z}$.

*Solution:*

Copy original term      $\bar{W}\bar{X}Y\bar{Z}$
Convert to binary      0010
Express as decimal subscript of $m$    $m_2$

$$\bar{W}\bar{X}Y\bar{Z} = m_2$$

### 6.4 How will you implement a specified network using logic gates? The block diagram and truth table of the network are given in Fig. 6.1.

*Solution:*

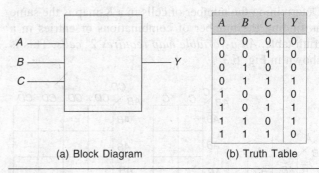

| A | B | C | Y |
|---|---|---|---|
| 0 | 0 | 0 | 0 |
| 0 | 0 | 1 | 0 |
| 0 | 1 | 0 | 0 |
| 0 | 1 | 1 | 1 |
| 1 | 0 | 0 | 0 |
| 1 | 0 | 1 | 1 |
| 1 | 1 | 0 | 1 |
| 1 | 1 | 1 | 0 |

(a) Block Diagram      (b) Truth Table

**Fig. 6.1**

The required function can be described in words by saying that the *output should be 1 if exactly two of the three input signals are 1* and *should be 0 otherwise*. This condition is met by only three combinations of the input signals as shown in the truth table.

The function can be realised by constructing three gate networks to detect each of the combination of the inputs and then ORing the outputs from these three networks.

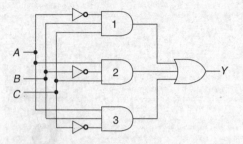

**Fig. 6.2**    *Solution for Problem 6.4.*

## KARNAUGH MAPPING

If the aim is simply to eliminate any redundant terms and obtain the simplest equation to express a given function, then *the graphical methods give quick and positive results*. The graphical method most commonly used is the *Karnaugh map,* also called the *Veitch diagram.*

### 6.5    Explain the significance of Karnaugh mapping.

*Solution:*

A Karnaugh map is similar to a truth table in that it graphically shows the output level of a Boolean equation for each of the possible input variable combinations. A Karnaugh map is simply *a graphical method of applying the laws of complementation and absorption.* Each output level is placed in a separate *cell* (square) of the Karnaugh-map. Karnaugh-maps can be used to simplify equations having two to six different input variables. Solving five-and six-variable Karnaugh-maps is extremely cumbersome; they can be more practically solved using advanced computer techniques.

### 6.6    How will you construct an *n*-variable K-map?

*Solution:*

Determining the number of cells in a K-map is the same as finding the number of combinations or entries in a truth table. *An n-variable map requires $2^n$ cells.* This is shown in Fig. 6.3.

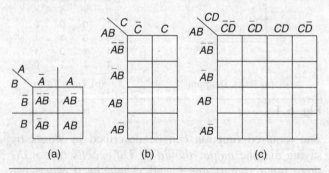

**Fig. 6.3**    *(a) Two-variable K-map (b) Three-variable K-map (c) Four-variable K-maps.*

Each cell in the K-map corresponds to a particular *minterm* (a particular combination of the input variables). In the *two- variable* K-map, for example, the upper left cell corresponds to $\bar{A}\,\bar{B}$ (00), the lower left cell is $\bar{A}B$ (01), the upper right cell is $A\,\bar{B}$ (10) and the lower right cell is $AB$ (11). These four terms represent all possible conjunctions of the two variables and their complements.

### 6.7    What are the basic rules that must be followed when using Karnaugh maps?

*Solution:*

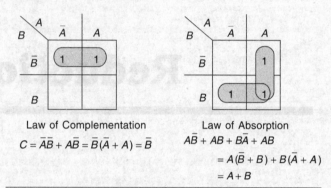

Law of Complementation
$C = \bar{A}\bar{B} + A\bar{B} = \bar{B}(\bar{A} + A) = \bar{B}$

Law of Absorption
$A\bar{B} + AB + B\bar{A} + AB$
$= A(\bar{B} + B) + B(\bar{A} + A)$
$= A + B$

**Fig. 6.4**

The *basic rules* that must be followed when using Karnaugh maps are as follows:

1. *Transform the Boolean equation to be reduced into an SOP expression.*
2. The map is drawn up in such a way that *the terms in adjacent cells differ by only one variable.*
3. The terms in the equation to be simplified are *entered by writing 1's in the appropriate cells in the map.*
4. Where cells that are adjacent horizontally or vertically both contain a 1, *the variable that changes between the cells may be dropped* (by the law of complementation), leaving only the remainder of the term, common to both cells, as part of the final answer. *Whole terms may also disappear by being absorbed.*
5. When all the terms have been simplified, *the final equation is obtained by writing down all the simplified terms and connecting them by disjunction (*OR*).*

## THREE-VARIABLE MAPS

Although the two-variable map illustrates the principle of Karnaugh mapping, it is too trivial to show the full potential and properties of Karnaugh map, nor the procedure for drawing *multivariable maps.* A three-variable Karnaugh map is shown in Fig. 6.5 and consists of *four columns* and *two rows.* Combinations of the first two variables are written down at the head of each column, whilst the two possibilities for the third variable define the two rows. The map could also be drawn the other way, with *two columns* and *four rows* (see Fig. 6.3(b)).

| $AB$ | $\overline{AB}$ | $A\overline{B}$ | $AB$ | $\overline{A}B$ |
|---|---|---|---|---|
| $\overline{C}$ | $\overline{A}\overline{B}\overline{C}$ | $A\overline{B}\overline{C}$ | $AB\overline{C}$ | $\overline{A}B\overline{C}$ |
| $C$ | $\overline{A}\overline{B}C$ | $A\overline{B}C$ | $ABC$ | $\overline{A}BC$ |

**Fig. 6.5**  *A Three-variable Karnaugh Map.*

The rule that *only a one-variable change is allowed* must be followed. The extreme left-hand *column* is taken as being adjacent to the extreme right-hand column and the extreme top *row* is taken as adjacent to the extreme-bottom row. The rule must also be observed between these columns and rows.

**6.8  Reduce the Boolean equation to an SOP expression. Draw a truth table of the SOP expression and then transfer it to a Karnaugh map. Verify your result.**

$$X = \overline{A}(\overline{B}C + \overline{B}\overline{C}) + \overline{A}B\overline{C}$$

*Solution:*
First transform the equation to an SOP expression:

$$X = \overline{A}\overline{B}C + \overline{A}\overline{B}\overline{C} + \overline{A}B\overline{C}$$

Draw a truth table for the SOP expression and transfer to a K-map (Fig. 6.6).

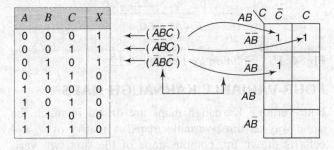

| $A$ | $B$ | $C$ | $X$ |
|---|---|---|---|
| 0 | 0 | 0 | 1 |
| 0 | 0 | 1 | 1 |
| 0 | 1 | 0 | 1 |
| 0 | 1 | 1 | 0 |
| 1 | 0 | 0 | 0 |
| 1 | 0 | 1 | 0 |
| 1 | 1 | 0 | 0 |
| 1 | 1 | 1 | 0 |

**Fig. 6.6**  *Truth Table and Karnaugh Map of the Expression.*

Now encircle adjacent 1's as shown in Fig. 6.7. The simplified equation is obtained by determining which variables remain the same within each loop. $\overline{A}\,\overline{B}$ becomes one of the terms in the SOP expression. The second term in the SOP expression is $\overline{A}\,\overline{C}$. The final

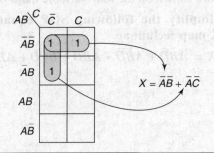

**Fig. 6.7**  *Encircling Adjacent Cells in Karnaugh Map.*

result in SOP format is $X = \overline{A}\,\overline{B} + \overline{A}\,\overline{C}$. This can be verified by algebraic simplification.

**6.9  Simplify the following SOP equation using the Karnaugh map technique.**

$$X = \overline{A}B + \overline{A}\,\overline{B}\,\overline{C} + AB\overline{C} + A\overline{B}\,\overline{C}$$

*Solution:*
Construct an eight-cell K-map (Fig. 6.8) AND fill a 1 in each cell that corresponds to a term in the original equation. $\overline{A}B$ has no $C$ variable. Therefore, $\overline{A}B$ *will fit in two cells:* $\overline{A}B\overline{C} + \overline{A}BC$. Encircle adjacent cells in the *largest group* of two or four or eight. Identify the variables that remain the *same* within each circle and write the final simplified SOP equation by *ORing* them together.

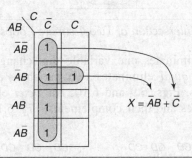

**Fig. 6.8**  *Karnaugh Map* AND *Final Equation for Problem 6.9.*

## LOOPS

The principle of eliminating variables by the law of complementation can be extended beyond two cells. In Fig. 6.9, a 1 appears in every cell of row $C$. Hence, both the variables $A$ and $B$ can be dropped, leaving $C$. Another combination of four cells that eliminates two variables is a square array of $2 \times 2$ cells, Fig. 6.10. Here the variable $B$ changes *horizontally* and is eliminated, while the variable $C$ changes *vertically*, and is eliminated, leaving only $A$ out of these four terms.

| $AB$ | $\overline{A}\overline{B}$ | $A\overline{B}$ | $AB$ | $\overline{A}B$ |
|---|---|---|---|---|
| $\overline{C}$ | | | | |
| $C$ | 1 | 1 | 1 | 1 |

**Fig. 6.9**  *Loops in a Three-variable K-map.*

| $AB$ | $\overline{A}\overline{B}$ | $A\overline{B}$ | $AB$ | $\overline{A}B$ |
|---|---|---|---|---|
| $\overline{C}$ | 0 | 1 | 1 | 0 |
| $C$ | 0 | 1 | 1 | 0 |

**Fig. 6.10**  *A Square Array of $2 \times 2$ Cells.*

To make it easier to see which terms may be grouped together for simplication loops are drawn around them. The *permitted sizes* of loops are any powers of two with the provision that the loop must be either *square or rectangular*. L-shaped or any other shape are not considered as single loops. An array of 3, 5, 6, 7, 9 squares etc. must be made up of two or more smaller loops. It is best to draw the *largest possible loop* in order to obtain the simplest equation. *Intersection of two loops is allowed.* (Fig. 6.11).

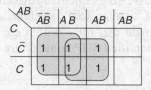

**Fig. 6.11**    *Intersection of Two 4-square Loops.*

A *pair* eliminates one variable that changes form, Fig. 6.4. A *quad* eliminates two variables and their complements, Figs. 6.9 and 6.10. An *octet* eliminates three variables and their complements, Fig. 6.12.

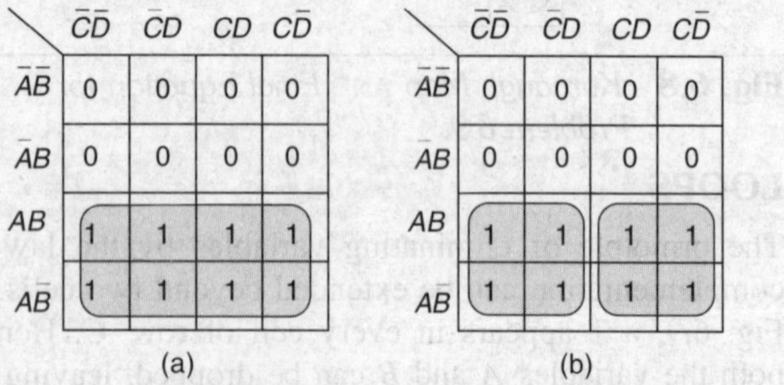

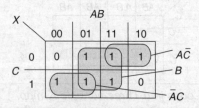

(a)                    (b)

**Fig. 6.12**    *Examples of Octet.*

**6.10 Draw the K-map for the given expression and make the groupings.**

$$\overline{A}B\overline{C} + AB\overline{C} + A\overline{B}\,\overline{C} + \overline{A}\,\overline{B}C + \overline{A}BC + ABC$$

*Solution:*

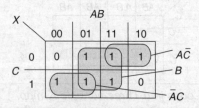

**Fig. 6.13**    *Solution for Problem 6.10.*

**6.11 Draw a three-variable K-map for the expression**

$$F = \overline{A}BC + AB\,(\overline{C} + C)$$

*Solution:*

|     | $\overline{B}C$ | $\overline{B}\overline{C}$ | $BC$ | $B\overline{C}$ |
|-----|-----|-----|-----|-----|
| $\overline{A}$ |     |     | 1   |     |
| $A$ |     |     | 1   | 1   |

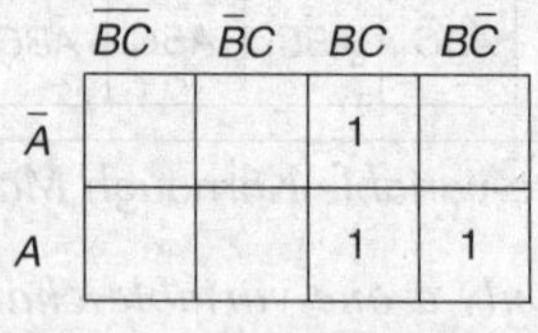

**Fig. 6.14**    *Solution for Problem 6.11.*

Encircle adjacent cells in the largest group of two or four or eight. Identify the variables that remain the same within each circle and write the final SOP equation by ORing them together.

**6.12 Show the factoring or grouping for 1's for the expression**

$$F = \overline{A}BC + AB\,(\overline{C} + C)$$

*Solution:*

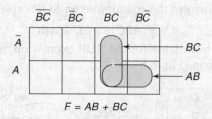

$$F = AB + BC$$

**Fig. 6.15**    *Solution for Problem 6.12.*

## FOUR-VARIABLE KARNAUGH MAPS

Four-variable Karnaugh maps are drawn in much the same way as three-variable maps. A matrix of $4 \times 4$ cells is drawn up, combinations of the first two variables are written at the tops of the columns and combinations of the other variables at the side of the rows.

It should be noted that *as the end columns and top and bottom rows are taken as being adjacent, end-around and four-corner loops are also permitted.* However these possibilities are more pronounced on a larger map. Several possible loops up to eight cells in size are shown on the four-variable maps of Fig. 6.16.

**6.13 Simplify the following SOP equation using K-map technique.**

$$X = A\overline{B}\overline{D} + \overline{A}\,\overline{B}\overline{D} + \overline{A}BD + BCD + AB\overline{C}D$$

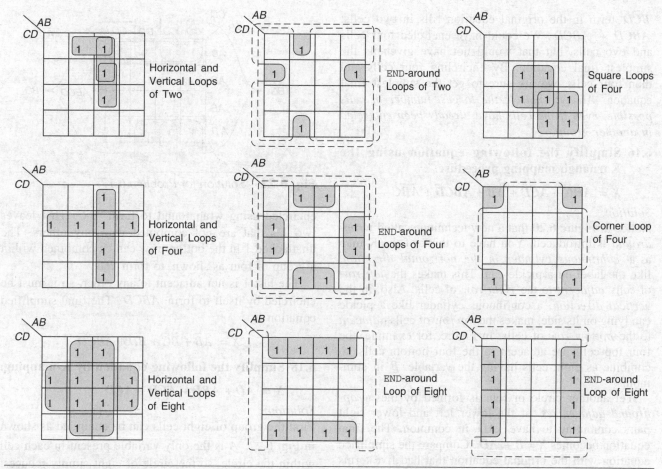

**Fig. 6.16**   *Several Possible Loops upto Eight Cells in Size on Four-Variable Karnaugh Maps.*

*Solution:*

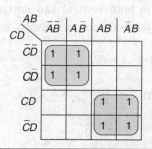

**Fig. 6.17**   *Solution for Problem 6.13.*

Identify the variables that remain the *same* within each circle and write the final simplified SOP equation by ORing them together.

$$X = \bar{B}\,\bar{D} + BD$$

**6.14  Simplify the following equation using Karnaugh mapping procedure:**

$$X = \bar{A}\bar{B}\bar{C}D + A\bar{B}\bar{C}D + \bar{A}\bar{B}C D + AB\bar{C}D$$
$$+ ABC\bar{D} + ABCD$$

*Solution:*
Since there are four different variables in the equation, we need a 16-cell map ($2^4 = 16$) as shown in Fig. 6.18.

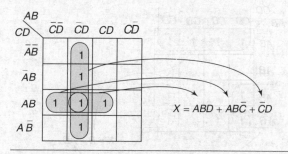

**Fig. 6.18**   *Solution for Problem 6.14.*

**6.15  Solve the following equation using the Karnaugh mapping procedure:**

$$X = B\bar{C}\bar{D} + \bar{A}\bar{B}\bar{C}D + AB\bar{C}D + \bar{A}BCD + ABCD$$

*Solution:*

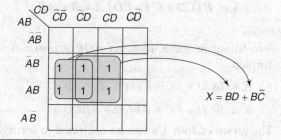

**Fig. 6.19**   *Solution for Problem 6.15.*

$BC\overline{D}$ term in the original equation fills in two cells: $AB\overline{C}\overline{D} + \overline{A}BC\overline{D}$. We could have encircled four cells and two cells, but that would not have given us the simplest final equation. By encircling four cells and then four cells, we are sure to get the simplest final equation. *Always encircle the largest number of cells possible, even if the cells have already been encircled in another group.*

### 6.16 Simplify the following equation using the Karnaugh mapping procedure.

$$X = \overline{A}\overline{B}\overline{C} + A\overline{C}\overline{D} + A\overline{B} + AB\overline{C}\overline{D} + \overline{A}\overline{B}C$$

*Solution:*

Notice in Figure 6.20 that a new technique called *wraparound* is introduced. You have to think of the K-map as a *continuous cylinder in the horizontal direction*, like the label on a pickle can. This makes the *left row* of cells *adjacent* to the *right row* of cells. Also, in the *vertical direction*, a continuous cylinder like a pickle can lying on its side, makes the *top row* of cells *adjacent* to the *bottom row* of cells. In Figure, for example, the four top cells are adjacent to the four bottom cells, to combine as eight cells having the variable $\overline{B}$ in common.

Yet another circle of four is formed by the *wraparound adjacencies* of the lower left and lower right pairs combining to have $A\overline{D}$ in common. The final equation becomes $X = \overline{B} + A\overline{D}$. Compare the simplified equation with the original equation that had five terms in it.

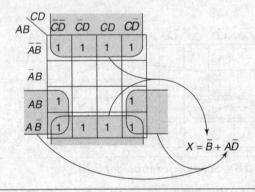

**Fig. 6.20**   *Solution for Problem 6.16.*

### 6.17 Simplify the following equation using K-mapping.

$$X = \overline{B}(CD + \overline{C}) + C\overline{D}(\overline{A} + \overline{B} + AB)$$

*Solution:*

Before filling in the K-map, an *SOP expression* must be formed.

$$X = \overline{B}CD + \overline{B}\overline{C} + C\overline{D}(\overline{A} \cdot \overline{B} + AB)$$

$$= \overline{B}CD + \overline{B}\overline{C} + \overline{A}\overline{B}C\overline{D} + ABC\overline{D}$$

The group of four 1's can be encircled to form $\overline{A}\overline{B}$, as shown in Fig. 6.21. Another group of four can be

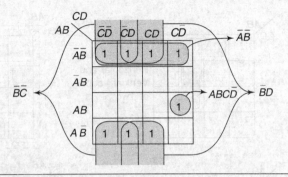

**Fig. 6.21**   *Solution for Problem 6.17.*

encircled using wraparound to form $\overline{B}\,\overline{C}$. That leaves two 1's that are not combined with any others. The unattached 1 in the bottom row can be combined within a group of four as shown, to form $\overline{B}D$.

The last 1 is not adjacent to any other, so it must be encircled by itself to form $ABC\overline{D}$. The final simplified equation is

$$X = \overline{A}\overline{B} + \overline{B}\overline{C} + \overline{B}D + ABC\overline{D}$$

### 6.18 Simplify the following equation by K-mapping.

$$X = \overline{A}D + \overline{A}BD + \overline{A}C\overline{D} + \overline{A}CD$$

*Solution:*

First the group of eight cells can be encircled as shown in Fig. 6.22. $\overline{A}$ is the only variable present in each cell within the circle, so the circle of eight simply reduces. to $\overline{A}$. Notice that larger circles will reduce to four variables in the final equation. Also all four corners are adjacent to each other, because *the K-map can be wrapped around* in both vertical and horizontal directions. Encircling the four corners results in $\overline{B}\overline{D}$. The final equation is

$$X = \overline{A} + \overline{B}\overline{D}$$

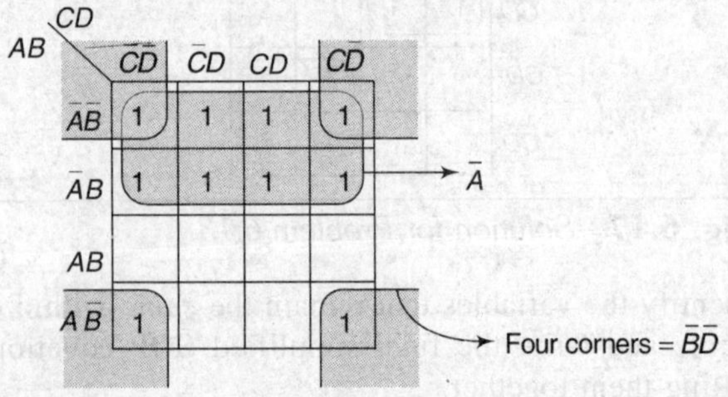

**Fig. 6.22**   *Solution for Problem 6.18.*

### 6.19 Simplify the following equation using the K-mapping procedure.

$$X = \overline{A}B\overline{D} + A\overline{C}\overline{D} + \overline{A}\overline{B}\overline{C} + A\overline{B}\overline{C}D + \overline{A}\overline{B}C\overline{D}$$

*Solution:*

End-around wrapping of the top corners produces $\overline{B}\,\overline{D}$. The group of fours forms $B\overline{C}$. You may be tempted to

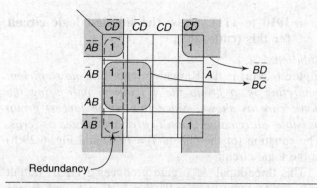

Redundancy

**Fig. 6.23** *Solution for Problem 6.19.*

encircle *CD* group of fours as shown by the dotted line, but that would be *redundant* because each of these 1's is already contained within an existing circle. Therefore, the final equation is

$$X = \overline{B}\overline{D} + B\overline{C}$$

**6.20 Map a four-variable function from the given truth table and simplify.**

*Solution:*

| D | C | B | A | E = f(A, B · C · D) |
|---|---|---|---|---|
| 0 | 0 | 0 | 0 | 0 |
| 0 | 0 | 0 | 1 | 1 |
| 0 | 0 | 1 | 0 | 0 |
| 0 | 0 | 1 | 1 | 0 |
| 0 | 1 | 0 | 0 | 1 |
| 0 | 1 | 0 | 1 | 1 |
| 0 | 1 | 1 | 0 | 1 |
| 0 | 1 | 1 | 1 | 1 |
| 1 | 0 | 0 | 0 | 0 |
| 1 | 0 | 0 | 1 | 1 |
| 1 | 0 | 1 | 0 | 0 |
| 1 | 0 | 1 | 1 | 0 |
| 1 | 1 | 0 | 0 | 1 |
| 1 | 1 | 0 | 1 | 1 |
| 1 | 1 | 1 | 0 | 1 |
| 1 | 1 | 1 | 1 | 1 |

**Fig. 6.24** *Solution for Problem 6.20.*

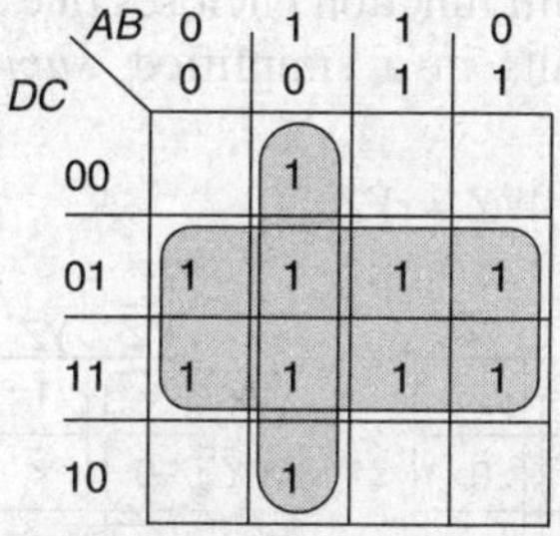

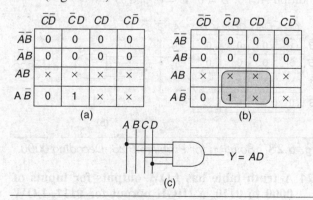

**Fig. 6.25** *Solution for Problem 6.20*

Mapping the function and drawing loops in the usual way immediately obtains the function in its simplest form:

$$X = A\overline{B} + C$$

## DON'T CARE CONDITIONS

There are applications where certain combinations of input variables never occur. As a result, we don't care what the function output is to be for these combinations of the variables because *they are guaranteed never to occur*. These don't care conditions can be used on a map to provide *further simplification* of the function. To distinguish the don't care conditions from 1's and 0's an *X* is used. *The X's may be assumed to be either 0 or 1, whichever gives the simplest expression.* In addition, an *X* need not be used at all if it does not contribute to covering a larger area. In each case, the choice depends only on the simplification that can be achieved.

**6.21 From the table given draw the Karnaugh map with don't cares. Use don't cares to simplify the function. Implement the simplified function (Fig. 6.26).**

| A | B | C | D | Y |
|---|---|---|---|---|
| 0 | 0 | 0 | 0 | 0 |
| 0 | 0 | 0 | 1 | 0 |
| 0 | 0 | 1 | 0 | 0 |
| 0 | 0 | 1 | 1 | 0 |
| 0 | 1 | 0 | 0 | 0 |
| 0 | 1 | 0 | 1 | 0 |
| 0 | 1 | 1 | 0 | 0 |
| 0 | 1 | 1 | 1 | 0 |
| 1 | 0 | 0 | 0 | 0 |
| 1 | 0 | 0 | 1 | 1 |
| 1 | 0 | 1 | 0 | × |
| 1 | 0 | 1 | 1 | × |
| 1 | 1 | 0 | 0 | × |
| 1 | 1 | 0 | 1 | × |
| 1 | 1 | 1 | 0 | × |
| 1 | 1 | 1 | 1 | × |

**Fig. 6.26**

*Solution:*

The output is LOW for all input entries from 0000 to 1000, HIGH for input entry 1001, and an *X* for 1010 through 1111. *These don't cares are like trump cards because you can use them wherever you feel convenient* (Fig. 6.27a).

**Fig. 6.27** *Don't Care Condition.*

Figure 6.27(b) shows the most efficient way to encircle the 1. Notice that *the 1 is included in a quad, the largest group you can find if you visualise the X's as 1's.* After the 1 has been encircled, all the X's outside the quad are visualised as 0's. In this way, the X's are all used to the best possible advantage. You are free to do this because *don't cares correspond to input conditions that never appear.*

The quad of Fig. 6.27(b) results in Boolean equation $Y = AD$. The logic circuit for this is an AND gate, Fig. 6.27(c).

### 6.22 Explain briefly the systematic procedure for using don't care conditions.

*Solution:*
Remember these ideas about don't care conditions:
1. Given the truth table, *draw a Karnaugh map with 0's, 1's and don't cares.*
2. *Encircle the actual 1's on the Karnaugh map in the largest groups you can find by treating the don't-cares as 1's.*
3. After the actual 1's have been included in groups, *disregard the remaining don't cares by visualising them as 0's.*

### 6.23 Suppose the table in Fig. 6.26 has a HIGH output for an input of 0000, LOW outputs for 0001 to 1001, and don't cares for 1010 to 1111. What is the simplest logic circuit with this truth table?

*Solution:*
The truth table has a 1 output only for the input condition 0000. The corresponding fundamental product is $\overline{A}\overline{B}\overline{C}\overline{D}$. Figure 6.28(a) shows the Karnaugh map with a 1 for the fundamental product, 0's for inputs 0001 to 1001, and X's for inputs 1010 to 1111. *In this case, the don't cares are of no help. The best we can do is to encircle the isolated 1, while treating the don't-cares as 0's.* So, the Boolean equation is

$$Y = \overline{A}\overline{B}\overline{C}\overline{D}$$

Figure 6.28(b) shows the logic circuit. The four-input AND gate produces a HIGH output only for the input condition $A = 0$, $B = 0$, $C = 0$, and $D = 0$.

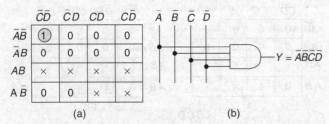

(a)        (b)

**Fig. 6.28** *Solution for Problem 6.23. Decoding 0000.*

### 6.24 A truth table has LOW outputs for inputs of 0000 to 0110, a HIGH output for 0111, LOW outputs for 1000 to 1001, and don't-cares for

**1010 to 1111. Show the simplest logic circuit for this truth table.**

*Solution:*
Figure 6.29(a) is the Karnaugh map. *The most efficient encircling is to group the 1's into a pair using the don't care as shown. Since this is the largest group possible, all remaining don't cares are treated as zeros.* The equation for the pair is $Y = BCD$ and Fig. 6.29(b) is the logic circuit.

This three-input AND gate produces a HIGH output only for an input of $A = 0$, $B = 1$, $C = 1$, and $D = 1$ because the input possibilities range only from 0000 to 1001.

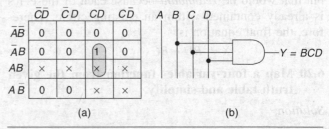

(a)        (b)

**Fig. 6.29** *Solution for Problem 6.24. Decoding 0111.*

### 6.25 Simplify the Boolean function
$$F\ (W, X, Y, Z) = \Sigma m(1, 3, 7, 11, 15)$$
**and the don't-care conditions**
$$d(W, X, Y, Z) = \Sigma m(0, 2, 5)$$

*Solution:*
*The minterms of F are the variable combinations that make the function equal to 1. The minterms of d are the don't–care combinations known never to occur.* The minimisation is shown in Fig. 6.30. The minterms of $F$ are marked by 1's, those of $d$ are marked by X's and the remaining squares are filled with 0's. In (a), the 1's and X's are combined in any convenient manner so as to enclose the maximum number of adjacent cells. *It is not necessary to enclose any or all of the X's, but only those useful for simplifying a term.* One combination that gives a minimum function encloses one X and leaves two out. This results in a simplified *sum-of-products* function:

$$F = \overline{W}Z + YZ$$

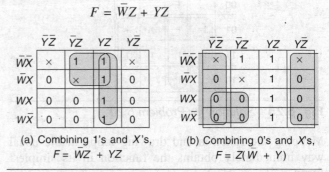

(a) Combining 1's and X's,    (b) Combining 0's and X's,
$F = \overline{W}Z + YZ$          $F = Z(\overline{W} + Y)$

**Fig. 6.30** *Solution for Problem 6.25 with Don't–care Conditions.*

In (b), the 0's Problem are combined with any $X$'s convenient to simplify the complement of the function. The best results are obtained if we enclose the two $X$'s as shown. The complement function is simplified to

$$F' = \bar{Z} + W\bar{Y}$$

Complementing again, we get a simplified *product-of-sums* function:

$$F = Z(\bar{W} + Y)$$

The two expressions obtained in Problem 6.25 give two functions which can be shown to be algebraically equal. This is not always the case when don't-care conditions are involved. As a matter of fact, *if an X is used as 1 when combining the 1's and again as a 0 when combining the 0's, the two resulting functions will not yield algebraically equal answers.*

## FROM TRUTH TABLE TO KARNAUGH MAP

Sometimes even the unsimplified equation of a given function is not available, but a truth table is given. It might appear that it would be necessary to derive an equation from the truth table before inserting it in the Karnaugh map for simplification, but fortunately this is not the case.

It is fairly obvious that *since the truth table and Karnaugh map show all possible combinations of variables, a Karnaugh map can be considered as simply another way of writing a truth table.* Data can thus be transferred directly from a truth table to a Karnaugh map, and the equation is obtained straight from the map in its simplest *minterm form*.

For example, consider a four-variable function containing the term $A \cdot B \cdot \bar{C} \cdot D$. This would be entered on the Karnaugh map as a 1 in the appropriate cell. In the truth table this term is represented by the *input code* 1011 (i.e., a 1 in input column $D$, a 0 in input column $C$, a 1 in input column $B$, and a 1 in input column $A$), and if this term exists in the function a 1 appears in the output column. This means that *where a 1 appears in the output column of a truth table a 1 is entered in the Karnaugh map in the cell that corresponds to that input code.* This procedure can be greatly simplified if, instead of writing the actual terms at the ends of the rows and columns, the combination of logic states that they can assume are written instead (see Fig. 6.31)

| $A\,B$ | 0 | 1 | 1 | 0 |
|---|---|---|---|---|
| $D\,C$ | 0 | 0 | 1 | 1 |
| 0 0 | 0000 | 0001 | 0011 | 0010 |
| 0 1 | 0100 | 0101 | 0111 | 0110 |
| 1 1 | 1100 | 1101 | 1111 | 1110 |
| 1 0 | 1000 | 1001 | 1011 | 1010 |

$$D\bar{C}BA$$

**Fig. 6.31** *Transferring Data from Truth Table to the Map.*

Care must be taken when transferring data from the truth table to the map for several reasons. Firstly, the terms in a Karnaugh map change by only one bit from cell to cell, whereas the input codes of truth tables are commonly written down in a binary sequence, which can change by more than one bit from one code to the next. This means that the terms in the truth table do not appear in the same order as they do in the map.

Secondly, the maps so far considered have had the variables written down in alphabetical order ($A$, $B$, $C$, $D$, ...) since that is how terms are generally written in equations. However, in truth tables codes are generally written in the form (... $D$, $C$, $B$, $A$) since that is the way binary numbers are normally written.

## PRODUCT–OF–SUMS METHOD

With the *sum-of-products* method we start with a *truth table* that summarises the desired input-output conditions. The next step is to *convert* the truth table into an equivalent sum-of-product equation. The final step is to draw the AND-OR network or its equivalent NAND-NAND network.

The *product-of-sums* method is also similar. Given a truth table, you identify the fundamental sums needed for a logic design. Then by ANDing these sums, you get the product-of-sums equation corresponding to the truth table. But there are some differences between the two approaches. *With the sum-of-products method, the fundamental product produces an output 1 for the corresponding input condition. But with the product-of-sums method, the fundamental sum produces an output 0 for the corresponding input condition.*

**6.26 Obtain the product-of-sums equation from the given truth table.**

| $A$ | $B$ | $C$ | $X$ |
|---|---|---|---|
| 0 | 0 | 0 | $0 \rightarrow A + B + C$ |
| 0 | 0 | 1 | 1 |
| 0 | 1 | 0 | 1 |
| 0 | 1 | 1 | $0 \rightarrow A + \bar{B} + \bar{C}$ |
| 1 | 0 | 0 | 1 |
| 1 | 0 | 1 | 1 |
| 1 | 1 | 0 | $0 \rightarrow \bar{A} + \bar{B} + C$ |
| 1 | 1 | 1 | 1 |

**Fig. 6.32**

*Solution:*
*Locate each output 0 in the truth table and write down its fundamental sum.* The first output 0 appears for $A = 0$, $B = 0$, and $C = 0$. The fundamental sum for these inputs is $A + B + C$, because *this produces an output 0 for the corresponding input conditions.*

$$X = A + B + C = 0 + 0 + 0 = 0$$

The second output 0 appears for the input condition of $A = 0$, $B = 1$, and $C = 1$. The fundamental sum for this is $A + \bar{B} + \bar{C}$. Notice that $B$ and $C$ are *comple-*

*mented* because this is the *only way* to get a logical sum of 0 for the given input conditions:

$$X = A + \bar{B} + \bar{C} = 0 + \bar{1} + \bar{1} = 0$$

Similarly, the third output 0 occurs for $A = 1$, $B = 1$, and $C = 0$, therefore, its fundamental sum is $\bar{A} + \bar{B} + C = 0$:

$$X = \bar{A} + \bar{B} + C = \bar{1} + \bar{1} + 0 = 0 + 0 + 0 = 0$$

Notice that each variable is *complemented* when the corresponding input variable is a 1; the variable is *uncomplemented* when the corresponding input variable is a 0. To get the product–of–sums equation, all you have to do is AND *the fundamental sums:*

$$X = (A + B + C)(A + \bar{B} + \bar{C})(\bar{A} + \bar{B} + C)$$

This is the *product–of–sums* equation for the given truth table.

## SIMPLIFICATION

You can simplify with *Boolean algebra.* Alternatively, you may prefer simplification based on the *Karnaugh map.* There are several ways of using the Karnaugh map.

**6.27 Draw the K-map for the truth table in Fig. 6.33. Obtain the sum-of-products equation. Show the corresponding NAND-NAND *circuit.* Draw a complemented map. Obtain the corresponding *product–of–sums* NOR-NOR *circuit* using DeMorgan's theorem.**

| A | B | C | D | Y |
|---|---|---|---|---|
| 0 | 0 | 0 | 0 | 1 |
| 0 | 0 | 0 | 1 | 1 |
| 0 | 0 | 1 | 0 | 1 |
| 0 | 0 | 1 | 1 | 1 |
| 0 | 1 | 0 | 0 | 0 |
| 0 | 1 | 0 | 1 | 0 |
| 0 | 1 | 1 | 0 | 0 |
| 0 | 1 | 1 | 1 | 0 |
| 1 | 0 | 0 | 0 | 0 |
| 1 | 0 | 0 | 1 | 0 |
| 1 | 0 | 1 | 0 | 1 |
| 1 | 0 | 1 | 1 | 1 |
| 1 | 1 | 0 | 0 | 1 |
| 1 | 1 | 0 | 1 | 1 |
| 1 | 1 | 1 | 0 | 1 |
| 1 | 1 | 1 | 1 | 1 |

**Fig. 6.33**

*Solution:*
Draw the K-map in the usual way, Fig. 6.34(a). The encircled groups allow us to write a *sum–of–products* equation:

$$Y = \bar{A}\bar{B} + AB + AC$$

Figure 6.34(b) shows the corresponding NAND-NAND circuits.

To get a *product–of–sums* circuit, begin by complementing each 0 and 1 on the K-map, Fig. 6.35(a). The

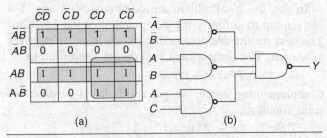

**Fig. 6.34**    *(a) Karnaugh map. (b) Sum–of–products circuit for Y.*

encircled 1's allow us to write the following sum–of–products equation from the *complemented map:*

$$\overline{Y} = \bar{A}B + A\bar{B}\bar{C}$$

*Complementing the K-map is the same as complementing the output of the truth table,* which means the sum–of–products equation for Fig. 6.35(a) is for $\bar{Y}$ instead of $Y$, the complement of the desired output (Fig. 6.35(b)).

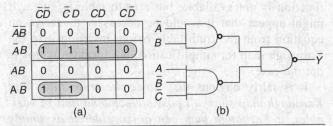

**Fig. 6.35**    *(a) Complemented Map for Fig. 6.34(a).*
            *(b) Sum–of–products Circuit for $\bar{Y}$.*

NAND *gates can be replaced by bubbled* OR *gates;* therefore, we can replace Fig. 6.35(b) by Fig. 6.36(a). *A bus with each variable and its complement is usually available in a digital system.* So instead of connecting $A$ and $B$ to a bubbled OR gate, we connect $A$ and $B$ to an OR gate, as shown in Fig. 6.36(b). In a similar manner $A$, $B$, and $C$ are connected to an OR gate. In short Fig. 6.35(b) is equivalent to Fig. 6.36(a).

The next step is to *slide the bubbles* to the left from the output gate to the input gates. This changes the input OR gate to NOR gates. The final step is to use a NOR gate on the output to produce $Y$ instead of $\bar{Y}$, as shown in Fig. 6.36(d).

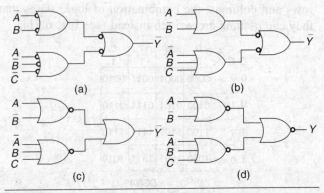

**Fig. 6.36**    *Deriving the Product–of–sums Circuit.*

## DUALITY THEOREM

You don't have to go through every step in changing a complementary NAND-NAND circuit to an equivalent NOR-NOR circuit. Instead you can apply the duality theorem. Given a logic circuit, we can find its *dual* as follows:

1. Change each AND gate to an OR gate.
2. Change each OR gate to an AND gate.
3. *Complement* all input-output signals.

Compare the NOR-NOR circuit of Fig. 6.36(d) with the NAND-NAND circuit of Fig. 6.35(b).

**6.28 Use Karnaugh maps to simplify the following equations:**

(a) $D = AC + \bar{A}C + \bar{C}$

(b) $D = \bar{A}\bar{B}C + A\bar{B}\bar{C} + BC + \bar{A}\bar{B}C + A\bar{B}C$

*Solution:*

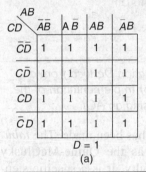

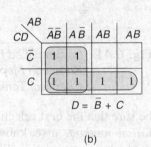

**Fig. 6.37**

**6.29 Use Karnaugh map to simplify the following equations:**

(a) $E = \bar{A}BC + \bar{B}CD + AC + \bar{A}\bar{B}CD$

(b) $E = ABC + BCD + AC + BC$

*Solution:*

**Fig. 6.38** *(a) Solution for Problem 6.29(a).*
*(b) Solution for Problem 6.29(b).*

**6.30 Simplify the given expression by K-mapping:**

$$\bar{A}\bar{B}\bar{C}D + \bar{A}BCD + \bar{A}BC\bar{D} + \bar{A}B\bar{C}\bar{D} + \bar{A}BCD$$
$$+ A\bar{B}\bar{C}\bar{D} + AB\bar{C}\bar{D} + ABC\bar{D} + A\bar{B}CD + A\bar{B}C\bar{D}$$

*Solution:* A group of eight (*octet*) 1's can be factored as shown in Fig. 6.38, because the 1's in the outer columns are *adjacent*. A group of four (*quad*) 1's is formed by the *wraparound adjacency* of cells to pick up the remaining two 1's. The *minimum form* of the original equation is: $X = \bar{D} + BC$

The reduced equation requires one two-input AND gate and one two-input OR gate for implementation.

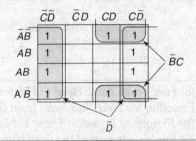

**Fig. 6.39** *Solution for Problem 6.30.*

**6.31 Design a circuit that can be built using an AOI and inverter that will output a HIGH (1) whenever the four-bit hexadecimal input is an odd number from 0 to 9.**

*Solution:*

**Table 6.1** *Hex Truth Table Used to Determine the Equation for Odd Numbers[a] from 0 to 9*

| D | C | B | A | DEC | |
|---|---|---|---|-----|---|
| 0 | 0 | 0 | 0 | 0 | |
| 0 | 0 | 0 | 1 | 1 | $\leftarrow \bar{A}\bar{B}\bar{C}\bar{D}$ |
| 0 | 0 | 1 | 0 | 2 | |
| 0 | 0 | 1 | 1 | 3 | $\leftarrow A\bar{B}CD$ |
| 0 | 1 | 0 | 0 | 4 | |
| 0 | 1 | 0 | 1 | 5 | $\leftarrow A\bar{B}C\bar{D}$ |
| 0 | 1 | 1 | 0 | 6 | |
| 0 | 1 | 1 | 1 | 7 | $\leftarrow ABC\bar{D}$ |
| 1 | 0 | 0 | 0 | 8 | |
| 1 | 0 | 0 | 1 | 9 | $\leftarrow A\bar{B}\bar{C}D$ |

[a]Odd number = $A\bar{B}\bar{C}\bar{D} + ABCD + ABCD + ABC\bar{D} + A\bar{B}\bar{C}D$.

(a)

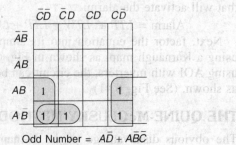

Odd Number = $A\bar{D} + A\bar{B}\bar{C}$
where $A$ = LSB

(b)

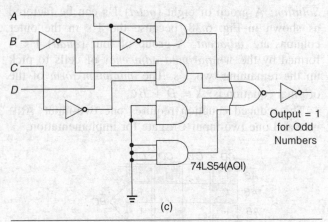

(c)

**Fig. 6.40** *(a) Hex Truth Table Used to Determine the Equation for Odd Numbers[a] from 0 to 9. (b) Simplified Equation Using K-Map. (c) Implementation of the Odd-Number Decoding Using an AOI.*

First build a *truth table* to identify which hex codes from 0 to 9 produce odd numbers. Use the variable $A$ to represent $2^0$ hex input, $B$ for $2^1$, $C$ for $2^2$, and $D$ for $D^3$. Next, reduce this equation to its simplest form by using a *Karnaugh map*. Finally, using an AOI with inverters, the *circuit* can be constructed as shown.

**6.32** **A chemical plant needs a microprocessor-driven alarm system to warn of critical conditions in one of its chemical tanks. The tank has four HIGH/LOW(1/0) switches that monitor temperature ($T$), pressure ($P$), fluid level ($L$), and weight ($W$). Design a system that will notify the microprocessor to activate an alarm when anyone of the following conditions arise:**

1. **High fluid level with high temperature and high pressure.**
2. **Low fluid level with high temperature and low weight.**
3. **Low fluid level with low temperature and high pressure.**
4. **Low fluid level with high temperature and low weight.**

*Solution:*
First, write in Boolean equation form the conditions that will activate the alarm:

$$\text{Alarm} = LTP + \bar{L}TW + \bar{L}\bar{T}P + \bar{L}W\bar{T}$$

Next, factor the equation into its simplest form by using a Karnaugh map, as shown in Fig. 6.41. Finally, using AOI with inverters, the circuit can be constructed as shown. (See Fig. 6.41)

## THE QUINE-McCLUSKY METHOD

The obvious disadvantage of the K-map is that it is essentially a *trial-and-error procedure*, which relies on the ability of human user to recognise certain patterns. For functions of six or more variables, it is difficult to

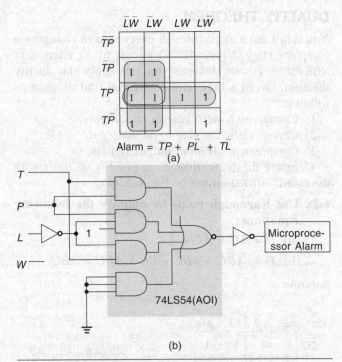

$$\text{Alarm} = TP + P\bar{L} + T\bar{L}$$
(a)

Microprocessor Alarm

74LS54(AOI)

(b)

**Fig. 6.41** *(a) Simplified Equation Derived from a Karnaugh Map. (b) Implementation of the Chemical Tank Using an AOI.*

be sure that the best selection has been made. The *tabulation method*, also known as the Quine-McClusky method overcomes this difficulty. It is a specific step-by-step procedure that is guaranteed to produce a standard-form expression for a function. It can be applied to problems with many variables and has the advantage of being *suitable for machine computation*. However, it is quite tedious for human use and is prone to mistakes.

The tabular method of simplification consists of two parts. The first is to find by an exhaustive search all the terms that are candidates for inclusion in the simplified function. These are called *prime implicants*. The second is to choose among the prime implicants those that give an expression with the least number of literals.

The flow chart for the tabulation method of minimisation is given in Fig. 6.42.

**6.33** **Find out the set of prime-implicants from the switching function given below, obtain the minimal expression using the Karnaugh map.**

$$f(A, B, C, D) = \Sigma(0, 1, 2, 5, 7, 8, 9, 10, 13, 15)$$

*Solution:*
The location of minterms and a four-variable Karnaugh map are given in Figs. 6.43 (a) and (b), respectively.

In the *first step*, adjacent minterms are combined to form the following *sub-cubes of two cells*.

(0, 1), (0, 2), (0, 8), (1, 5), (1, 9), (2, 10), (5, 13), (5, 7), (7, 15), (8, 9), (8, 10), (9, 13), (13, 15)

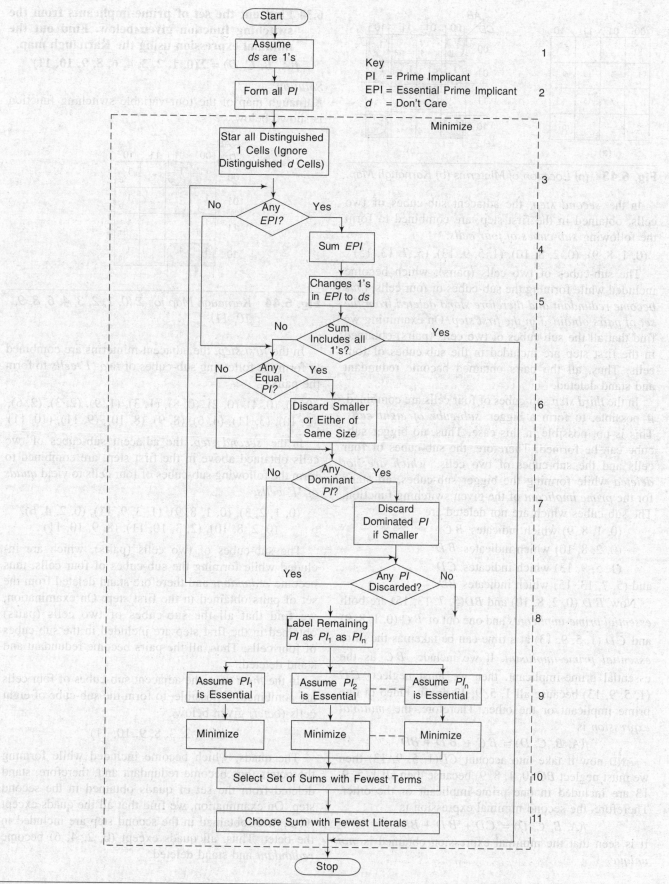

**Fig. 6.42** *Flow Chart for the Tabulation Method of Minimisation Procedure.*

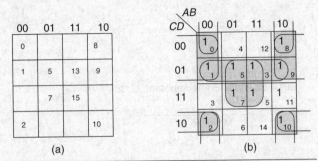

**Fig. 6.43**   *(a) Location of Minterms (b) Karnaugh Map.*

In the *second step*, the adjacent sub-cubes of two cells, obtained in the first step, are combined to form the following *sub-cubes of four cells.*

(0, 1, 8, 9), (0, 2, 8, 10), (1, 5, 9, 13), (5, 7, 13, 15)

The sub-cubes of two cells (pairs), which become included while forming the sub-cubes of four cells, *thus become redundant and therefore stand deleted from the set of pairs obtained in the first step.* On examining we find that all the sub-cubes of two cells (pairs) obtained in the first step are included in the sub-cubes of four cells. Thus, all the pairs obtained become redundant and stand deleted.

In the *third step* sub-cubes of four cells are combined, if possible, to form a bigger *sub-cube of eight cells.* This is not possible in this case. Thus, no bigger sub-cube can be formed. Therefore, the sub-cubes of four cells and the sub-cubes of two cells, *which are not deleted* while forming the bigger sub-cubes, all stand for the *prime implicant* of the given switching function. The sub-cubes which are not deleted are

(0, 1, 8, 9) which indicates $\bar{B}\,\bar{C}$

(0, 2, 8, 10) which indicates $\bar{B}\,\bar{D}$

(1, 5, 9, 13) which indicates $\bar{C}D$

and (5, 7, 13, 15) which indicates $BD$

Now $\bar{B}\,\bar{D}$ (0, 2, 8, 10) and $BD$(5, 7, 13, 15) are both *essential prime-implicants* and one out of $\bar{B}\,\bar{C}$ (0, 1, 8, 9) and $\bar{C}D$ (1, 5, 9, 13) at a time can be taken as the third *essential prime-implicant.* If we include $\bar{B}\,\bar{C}$ as the essential prime-implicant, then we must neglect $\bar{C}D$ (1, 5, 9, 13) because all 1, 5, 9, 13 are included in one prime implicant or the other. Therefore, the *minimal expression* is

$$f(A, B, C, D) = \bar{B}\,\bar{C} + \bar{B}\,\bar{D} + BD$$

AND now if take into account $CD$(1, 5, 9, 13) then we must neglect $BC$ (0, 1, 8, 9) because then all 1, 5, 9, 13 are included in one prime-implicant or the other. Therefore, the second minimal expression is

$$f(A, B, C, D) = \bar{C}D + \bar{B}\,\bar{D} + BD$$

It is seen that the minimal expression obtained is *not unique.*

**6.34 Find out the set of prime-implicants from the switching function given below. Find out the minimal expression using the Karnaugh map.**

$$f(A, B, C, D) = \Sigma(0, 1, 2, 3, 4, 6, 8, 9, 10, 11)$$

*Solution:*

Karnaugh map of the four-variable switching function is shown below

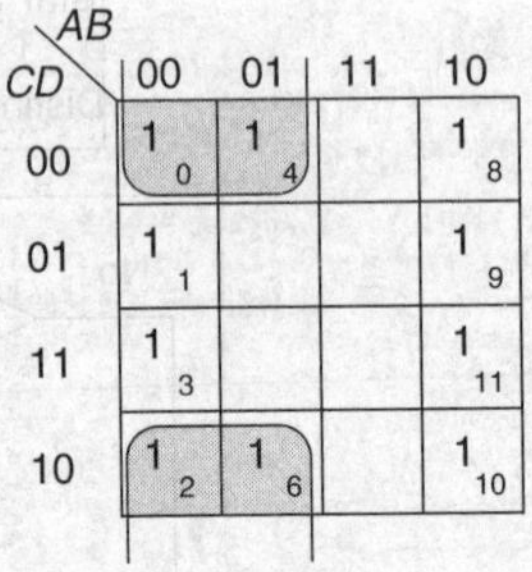

**Fig. 6.44**   *Karnaugh Map for $\Sigma$ (0, 1, 2, 3, 4, 6, 8, 9, 10, 11).*

In the *first step*, the adjacent minterms are combined to form the following sub-cubes of *two '1' cells* to form the pairs.

(0, 1), (0, 4), (0, 2), (0, 8), (1, 3), (1, 9), (2, 3), (2, 6), (2, 10), (3, 11), (4, 6), (8, 9), (8, 10), (9, 11), (10, 11)

In the *second step*, the adjacent sub-cubes of two cells obtained above in the first step, are combined to form the following sub-cubes of four cells to yield *quads of '1' cells.*

(0, 1, 2, 3), (0, 1, 8, 9), (1, 3, 9, 11), (0, 2, 4, 6),
(0, 2, 8, 10), (2, 3, 10, 11), (8, 9, 10, 11)

The sub-cubes of two cells (pairs), which are included while forming the sub-cubes of four cells, thus become *redundant* and therefore stand deleted from the set of pairs obtained in the first step. On examination, we find that all the sub-cubes of two cells (pairs) obtained in the first step are included in the sub-cubes of four cells. Thus, all the pairs become redundant and stand deleted.

In the *third step*, the adjacent sub-cubes of four cells are combined, if possible, to form the sub-cube of eight cells (*octet*) given below.

(0, 1, 2, 3, 8, 9, 10, 11)

The quads, which become included while forming the octets thus become redundant and, therefore, stand deleted from the set of quads obtained in the second step. On examination, we find that all the quads except (0, 2, 4, 6) obtained in the second step are included in the octet. Thus, all quads except (0, 2, 4, 6) become *redundant* and stand deleted.

Since no bigger sub-cubes of 16 cells can be obtained, therefore, the sub-cubes of eight cells (octets), sub-cubes of four cells (quads), and the sub-cubes of two cells, which are not deleted while forming the bigger sub-cubes, all stand for the *prime-implicant* of the given switching function.

The sub-cubes which are not deleted are:

(0, 1, 2, 3, 8, 9, 10, 11) which indicates $\bar{B}$ and (0, 2, 4, 6) which indicates $\bar{A}\bar{D}$.

The above two prime implicants are both *essential prime-implicants*, because prime-implicant $\bar{B}$ contains some minterms or '1' cells viz. 1, 3, 8, 9, 10, 11 which are not included in any other prime-implicant. Similarly, the prime-implicant $AD$ contains some minterms or '1' cells viz. 4 and 6 which are not included in any other prime-implicant.

Thus, the unique minimal expression is given by the sum of these two essential prime implicants as

$$f(A, B, C, D) = \bar{B} + \bar{A}\bar{D}$$

**6.35 Simplify the minimise the following four-variable switching function using the Quine-McClusky tabulation method.**

$$f(A, B, C, D) = \Sigma(0, 1, 2, 3, 4, 6, 8, 9, 10, 11)$$

*Solution:*

The problem is solved by constructing a table (Fig. 6.45) in the three columns, as shown below:

| Index No. | Decimal No. | Column 1 | First Column 2 Reduction | Second Column 3 Reduction |
|---|---|---|---|---|
| | | A B C D | A B C D | A B C D |
| 0 | 0 | 0 0 0 0 ✓ | (0, 1)  0 0 0 – ✓ | (0, 1, 2, 3)  0 0 – – ⎫ |
| | | | (0, 2)  0 0 – 0 ✓ | (0, 2, 1, 3)  0 0 – – ⎬ ✓ |
| 1 | 1 | 0 0 0 1 ✓ | (0, 4)  0 – 0 0 ✓ | (0, 2, 4, 6)  0 – – 0 ⎫ |
| | 2 | 0 0 1 0 ✓ | (0, 8)  – 0 0 0 ✓ | (0, 4, 2, 6)  0 – – 0 ⎬ |
| | 4 | 0 1 0 0 ✓ | (1, 3)  0 0 – 1 ✓ | (0, 8, 1, 9)  – 0 0 – ✓ |
| | 8 | 1 0 0 0 ✓ | (1, 9)  – 0 0 1 ✓ | (2, 3, 10, 11)  – 0 – – ⎫ |
| 2 | 3 | 0 0 1 1 ✓ | (2, 3)  0 0 1 – ✓ | (2, 10, 3, 11)  – 0 1 – ⎬ ✓ |
| | 6 | 0 1 1 0 ✓ | (2, 6)  0 – 1 0 ✓ | (8, 9, 10, 11)  1 0 – – ⎫ |
| | 9 | 1 0 0 1 ✓ | (2, 10)  – 0 1 0 ✓ | (8, 10, 9, 11)  1 0 – – ⎬ ✓ |
| | 10 | 1 0 1 0 ✓ | (4, 6)  0 1 – 0 ✓ | |
| | | | (8, 9)  1 0 0 – ✓ | |
| | | | (8, 10)  1 0 – 0 ✓ | |
| 3 | 11 | 1 0 1 1 | (3, 11)  – 0 1 1 ✓ | |
| | | | (9, 11)  1 0 – 1 ✓ | |
| | | | (10, 11)  1 0 1 – ✓ | |

**Fig. 6.45**

In *column 1*, the minterms are represented in binary form and *written in ascending order according to the number of 1's contained in them*. The minterms have been in four groups separated by horizontal lines. The '0' group and contains 0 number of 1's, first group one 1's, second group two 1's, third group three 1's, and the fourth group contains four 1's, respectively. Their *equivalent decimal numbers* are also written alongside. Any two minterms *differing from each other in one variable only* are combined together like (0, 1), (0, 2), (0, 4), etc. When any two minterms are same in all bit positions except one bit position, then a *check* (✓) is written towards the right side of both these minterms to indicate that these minterms have been used. The pair that results due to this combination is written along with its decimal equivalent in *column 2* of the table. A variable which is eliminated as a result of this *comparison and combination* is replaced by a *dash* (–) in its bit position. For example 0 (= 0000) combines with 1(= 0001) to give the pair (0, 1) = (000–) and minterm

0(= 0000) combines with 2 (= 0010) to form the pair (0, 2) = (00–0) and so on.

Now all the terms in column 2 have three variables. A '0' under the variable indicates that this variable is *complemented*. A '1' under the variable indicates that this variable is in *uncomplemented* form. A ( ) under the variable indicates that the variable is not contained in the term. The comparison and combination procedure is *repeated* for the terms in column 2 to form terms in column 3. The process is *again repeated* for the terms in column 3 to form the following terms:

1. (0, 1, 2, 3, 8, 9, 10, 11) resulting by combination of (0, 1, 2, 3) and (8, 9, 10, 11) or by combination of (0, 8, 1, 9) and (2, 3, 10, 11).
2. (0, 2, 4, 6)

The term (0, 1, 2, 3, 8, 9, 10, 11)

$$= A\,B\,C\,D \text{ stands for } \bar{B}.$$
$$\quad\, – \, 0 \, – \, –$$

The term (0, 2, 4, 6) = $A\,B\,C\,D$ stands for $\bar{A}\bar{D}$.
$$0 \, – \, – \, 0$$

The sum of these two essential prime-implicants gives the minimal expression in SOP form as

$$f(A, B, C, D) = \bar{B} + \bar{A}\bar{D}$$

### 6.36 Simplify and minimise the following four-variable switching function using the Quine-McClusky tabulation method.

$$W\bar{X}\bar{Y}\,\bar{Z} + WX\bar{Y}\,\bar{Z} + \bar{W}XY\bar{Z} + WX\bar{Y}Z$$
$$+ \bar{W}\bar{X}YZ + W\bar{X}\bar{Y}Z + \bar{W}\bar{X}YZ + \bar{W}\bar{X}\bar{Y}\,\bar{Z}$$

*Solution:*
*Step 1* Convert the expression to its *binary form*. The given expression becomes

$$1000 + 1100 + 0110 + 1101 + 0011 + 1001$$
$$+ 0001 + 0000$$

*Step 2* Arrange the binary representations in a table *with a different number of 1's in each section:*

0000
0001
__1000__
1100
0110
0011
__1001__
1101

*Step 3 Perform matches between table entries* Two terms match if they differ exactly in one position. A *new term* is then formed with a *dash* (–) substituted in the position where the two binary values differ. The new terms are then arranged according to Step 2. Of these new terms, *a match occurs if two terms differ exactly in one position and have a dash (–) in the same position*. Again a dash (–) is substituted in the position where the terms differ, and this procedure is repeated until no more matches are found. Terms involving matches are *checked*. All possible matches must be considered. Repeated terms need not be copied. Only terms in different sections need be considered. The unchecked terms are called *prime implicants*, or PIs.

| | | |
|---|---|---|
| ✓ 0000 | | |
| ✓ 0001 | ✓ 000– | |
| ✓ 1000 | ✓ –000 | –00– |
| ✓ 1100 | 00–1 | 1–0– |
| 0110 | ✓ –001 | |
| ✓ 0011 | ✓ 1–00 | |
| ✓ 1001 | ✓ 100– | |
| ✓ 1101 | ✓ 110– | |
| | ✓ 1–01 | |

**Fig. 6.46**

*Step 4* Construct a *prime implicant table* with all minterms listed at the bottom and all prime implicants from the match table along the side. Place *X*'s at the intersections where a prime implicant matches the ca-

nonical term in each binary value; *treat dashes as don't cares*. If a prime implicant agrees with a minterm in each binary position, the PI *covers* the minterm.

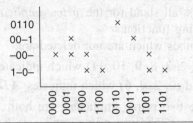

**Fig. 6.47**

*Step 5* Choose a minimal set of prime implicants *so that each minterm is covered*. The logical sum of these is the minimal expression.

$$00{-}1 + {-}00{-} + 1{-}0{-} + 0110$$

or $\quad \bar{W}\bar{X}Z + \bar{X}\bar{Y} + W\bar{Y} + \bar{W}XY\bar{Z}$

### 6.37 Simplify and minimise the following four-variable switching function using the Quine-McClusky tabulation method.

$$f(W, X, Y, Z) = \bar{W}\bar{X}\bar{Y}Z + \bar{W}\bar{X}Y\bar{Z} + \bar{W}\bar{X}Y\bar{Z}$$
$$+ W\bar{X}YZ + WX\bar{Y}\,\bar{Z} + \bar{W}X\bar{Y}Z$$
$$+ \bar{W}\bar{X}YZ + WX\bar{Y}Z + WXYZ$$

*Solution:*

| | | | |
|---|---|---|---|
| ✓ 0000 | ✓ 000– | | 0–01 |
| ✓ 0001 | ✓ 00–0 | 00–– | –011 |
| ✓ 0010 | ✓ 00–1 | | –101 |
| ✓ 0011 | 0–01 | | 110– |
| ✓ 0101 | ✓ 001– | | 11–0 |
| ✓ 1100 | –011 | | 00–– |
| ✓ 1011 | –101 | | |
| ✓ 1101 | 110– | | |
| ✓ 1110 | 11–0 | | |

(a)

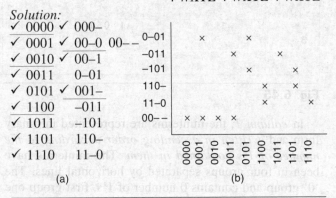

(b)

**Fig. 6.48**

1. Convert the expression to its *binary form*.

$$0000 + 0001 + 0010 + 1011 + 1100 + 0101$$
$$+ 0011 + 1101 + 1110$$

2. Arrange the binary expression with a different number of 1's in each section.

3. Perform matches between table entries.
   Two terms match if they differ exactly in one position.
   Form new terms with a dash(–) substituted in the position where the two binary values differ. Arrange the new terms.
   Perform matches between entries. A match occurs if two terms differ exactly in one position and have a dash (–) in the sample position.

A dash is substituted in the position where the terms differ.

This procedure is repeated until no more matches are found.

Terms involving matches are checked.

4. Construct a prime implicant table. Treat dashes as don't cares.
5. Choose a minimal set of prime implicants so that each minterm is covered.

Choose    00–– + –011 + 11–0 + –101

$$\overline{W}\,\overline{X} + \overline{X}YZ + WX\overline{Z} + X\overline{Y}Z$$

## 6.38 Simplify and minimise the four-variable product-of-sums switching function using the Quine-McClusky tabulation method.

$$f(a, b, c) = (a + \overline{b} + \overline{c}) + (\overline{a} + \overline{b} + c)(\overline{a} + b + c)$$
$$(a + b + \overline{c})(\overline{a} + \overline{b} + \overline{c})$$

*Solution:*

*To minimise a product–of–sums, first complement the expression, then minimise, then complement the result.*

$$\overline{f} = \overline{a}b c + a b \overline{c} + a \overline{b}\,\overline{c} + \overline{a}\,\overline{b}c + abc$$

or    011 + 110 + 100 + 001 + 111

| | | | | |
|---|---|---|---|---|
| ✓ 100 | 1–0 | × | | × |
| ✓ 001 | 0–1 | | × × | |
| ✓ 011 | 0–1 | | | –11 × × |
| ✓ 110 | –11 | 11– | | × × |
| ✓ 111 | 11– | | | |

(a)            (b)

**Fig. 6.49**

There is a choice of two minimal expressions:

(1–0) + (0–1) + (–11)    or (1–0) + (0–1) + (11–)

$\overline{f} = a\overline{c} + \overline{a}c + bc$    or $\overline{f} = a\overline{c} + \overline{a}c + ab$

$f = (\overline{a} + c)(a + \overline{c})(\overline{b} + \overline{c})$    or $f = (\overline{a} + c)(a + \overline{c})(\overline{a} + \overline{b})$

## 6.39 Simplify and minimise the following four-variable switching function using the Karnaugh map and Quine-McClusky tabulation method of minimisation.

$$f(A, B, C, D) = \Sigma(0, 5, 7, 8, 9, 10, 11, 14, 15)$$

*Solution:*

The location of '1' cells on a four-variable Karnaugh map for the given switching function is given in Fig. 6.50.

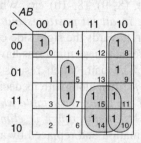

**Fig. 6.50** *Karnaugh Map for* f(A, B, C, D).

By combining the adjacent '1' cells of minterms, the following sub-cubes of two-cells (pairs) and four-cells (quads) are obtained which are not included entirely in any other bigger sub-cube.

| | | |
|---|---|---|
| (0, 8) | which indicates | $\overline{B}\,\overline{C}\,\overline{D}$ |
| (5, 7) | which indicates | $\overline{A}BD$ |
| (8, 9, 10, 11) | which indicates | $A\overline{B}$ |
| (10, 11, 14, 15) | which indicates | $AC$ |

The sum of the above four product terms gives the required minimal SOP expression for the given switching function as

$$f(A, B, C, D) = \overline{B}\,\overline{C}\,\overline{D} + \overline{A}BD + A\overline{B} + AC$$

The same problem is solved again by minimising the given switching function represented by the sum of minterms as

$$f(A, B, C, D) = \Sigma(0, 5, 7, 8, 9, 10, 11, 14, 15)$$

by using the Quine-McClusky tabular method. The table is constructed, as shown, in three columns in Fig. 6.51.

| Index | Column 1 | | Column 2 | | Column 3 | |
|---|---|---|---|---|---|---|
| | Decimal Number | Binary Form A B C D | Decimal Number | First Reduction A B C D | Decimal Number | Second Reduction A B C D |
| 0 | 0 | 0 0 0 0 ✓ | 0, 8 | – 0 0 0 ⓨ | 8, 9, 10, 11 | 1 0 – – ⓥ |
| 1 | 8 | 1 0 0 0 ✓ | 8, 9 | 1 0 0 – ✓ | 10, 11, 14, 15 | 1 – 1 – ⓤ |
| | | | 8,10 | 1 0 – 0 ✓ | | |
| 2 | 5 | 0 1 0 1 ✓ | 5, 7 | 0 1 – 1 ⓧ | | |
| | 9 | 1 0 0 1 ✓ | 9, 11 | 1 0 – 1 ✓ | | |
| | 10 | 1 0 1 0 ✓ | 10, 11 | 1 0 1 – ✓ | | |
| | | | 10, 14 | 1 – 1 0 ✓ | | |
| 3 | 7 | 0 1 1 1 ✓ | 7, 15 | – 1 1 1 ⓦ | | |
| | 11 | 1 0 1 1 ✓ | 11, 15 | 1 – 1 1 ✓ | | |
| | 14 | 1 1 1 0 ✓ | 14, 15 | 1 1 1 – ✓ | | |
| 4 | 15 | 1 1 1 1 ✓ | | | | |

**Fig. 6.51**

In column 1, the minterms are represented in *binary form* and are written in ascending order according to the index. The index indicates the *number of 1's* in the binary form of the minterm. The minterms have been written in four groups separated by horizontal lines. Their *equivalent decimal numbers* are also written alongside.

Any two minterms *differing from each other in one variable* are combined together. This results in formation of pairs (0, 8), (8, 9), (8, 10) etc. When any two minterms are *same in all bit positions but one*, then a *check* (✓) is written towards the right side of both these minterms to indicate that these minterms have been used to form the pairs. The pair which results due to this combination is also written alongwith its decimal equivalent in column 2 of the table. *A variable which is '0' in one minterm and '1' in the other is eliminated* as a result of this combination and replaced by a *dash* (–) in its bit position.

Now all the terms in column 2 have three variables and one dash (–). *Any two pairs of columns differing from each other in one variable only are combined together to form quads of four minterms.* For example, (8, 9) = (100–) is combined with pair (10, 11) = (101–), as they differ only in one position. These combinations result in formation of *quads* (8, 9, 10, 11) and (10, 11, 14, 15). A variable which is '0' in one pair and '1' in the other is eliminated as a result of this combination and is replaced by a dash (–) in its bit position. The quads which result due to this combination are written alongwith their decimal equivalent in column 3. Now any two pairs which are the same in all bit positions but one, are marked with a check (✓) toward their right side in column 2 to indicate that these pairs have been used to form the quads shown in column 3. For (8, 9), (10, 11) are combined (8, 10), (9, 11) are combined, (10, 14) (11, 15) are combined (10, 11), (14, 15) are also combined. The process of combining is repeated to combine quads to form an *octet*, if any. The quads or pairs which are not marked with check (✓), thus cannot be combined and have been marked *u, v, w, x, y*, respectively. Thus, the terms corresponding to *u, v, w, x, y* represent the *prime implicants*.

Construct the prime implicant table to find the *essential prime-implicants* of the function, out of the prime implicants *u, v, w, x, y* found earlier. Construct a table as shown in Fig. 6.52. Each column in this table has a decimal number at the top. This decimal number corresponds to one of the minterms in the canonical SOP form of the given switching function. The columns of the table are named by these decimal numbers in ascending order as shown. Each row of the table corresponds to one of the prime implicants represented by *u, v, w, x, y* on the left.

| Prime Implicants | Minterms | | | | | | | | |
|---|---|---|---|---|---|---|---|---|---|
| | 0 | 5 | 7 | 8 | 9 | 10 | 11 | 14 | 15 |
| u | | | | | | × | × | ⊗ | × |
| v | | | | × | ⊗ | × | × | | |
| w | | | × | | | | | | × |
| x | | ⊗ | × | | | | | | |
| y | ⊗ | | | × | | | | | |

**Fig. 6.52**

Put a cross under each decimal number, which is a term included in the prime implicant represented by that row. For example, for prime implicant *u* which includes 10, 11, 14, 15 we mark a cross under each of these column numbers in that row of prime implicant *u*. For prime implicant *v*, which includes 8, 9, 10, 11 mark a cross under each of these numbers in that row, and so on for prime implicants *w, x, y*, the process is repeated. *Search* all the columns which contain a single *x* i.e. only one cross under them and *mark* a circle around them. Also mark a circle around those prime implicants shown at the left of each of these rows in which the cross has been circled as shown around *u, v, x,* and *y*. These prime implicants, which are circled, represent the *essential prime implicants*.

Switching function $f(A, B, C, D)$

$$= U + V + X + Y$$
$$= (1\text{-}1\text{-}) + (10\text{--}) + (01\text{-}1) + (\text{-}000)$$
$$= AC + A\bar{B} + \bar{A}BD + \bar{B}\bar{C}\bar{D}$$

*which is the same as that found by using Karnaugh map.*

# SUMMARY

> The canonical expressions are usually not the most economical implementation of the logic functions.
> Simplification means finding an expression with fewer terms or literals.
> Minimising means finding an expression that is best by some minimisation criteria.
> The graphical method gives quick and positive results.
> The Karnaugh map is also called the Veitch diagram.
> The permitted sizes of loops are any powers of two with the provision that the loop must either be square or rectangular.
> Don't care conditions are guaranteed never to occur.
> Don't cares are like trump cards because you can use them wherever you feel convenient.

> ➢ A pair eliminates one variable that changes form.
> ➢ A quad eliminates two variables and their complements.
> ➢ An octet eliminates three variables and their complements.
> ➢ End-around and four-corner loops are permitted.
> ➢ A Karnaugh map can be considered as another way of writing a truth table.
> ➢ Every Boolean equation has a dual form obtained by changing OR to AND and AND to OR (0 to 1 and 1 to 0).
> ➢ A sum-of-products equation always results in an AND–OR circuit or its equivalent NAND–NAND circuit.
> ➢ Karnaugh map is a trial-and-error procedure.
> ➢ The tabulation method can be applied to problems with many variables.
> ➢ Each of the basic gates (AND, OR, NAND, NOR) can be used to enable/disable the passage of an input signal to its output.

# REVIEW QUESTIONS

**Test your understanding**

1. Identify each expression as either SOP or POS:
   (a) $X = AB + CD + EF$
   (b) $X = (A + B)(C + D)(E + F)$,
   (c) $X = \bar{A}BC + A\bar{B}C + ABC + \bar{A}B\bar{C}$
2. Determine the logic gate required to implement each of the following terms:
   (a) $ABC$,    (b) $A + B + C$,    (c) $\overline{ABC}$    (d) $\overline{A + B + C}$
3. Write the SOP expression for a circuit with four inputs and an output that is to be HIGH only when input $A$ is LOW at the same time that exactly two other inputs are LOW.
4. If the SOP expression in 3 is implemented using all NAND gates, how many gates are required?
5. A logic designer needs an INVERTER and all that is available is an XOR gate from a 7486 chip. Does he need another chip?
6. Convert $\bar{A}B + C$ to minterms.
7. Convert $AB + \bar{C}D + A\bar{B}C$ to minterms.
8. Find the minterm designations for the following minterms:
   (a) $A\bar{B}C$,    (b) $A\bar{B}C\bar{D}$,    (c) $AB\bar{C}\bar{D}E$
9. How many gate inputs are required for the following equations?
   (a) $W = A\bar{B}C + \bar{A}B + A\bar{C}D$,
   (b) $X = R\bar{S} + R\bar{T}U\bar{V} + RSTUV + TUV$,
   (c) $Y = (A + B + C)(A + \bar{B} + D)(\bar{A} + \bar{C}) + (A + \bar{B} + \bar{C} + D)$
10. Design an SOP circuit that will output a 1 any time the Gray codes 5 through 12, appear at the inputs and a 0 for all other cases.
11. Explain the terms: literal, product term, sum term, and normal term.
12. Draw the truth table for a three-input OR gate. Write the overall expression for the logic function as the sum of minterms.
13. Using NAND gates involves what steps?
14. Draw a pair, a quad, and an octet on K-map.
15. Describe redundancy with the help of an illustration.
16. How many inverters could be formed using a 7400 quad NAND IC?
17. Draw the Karnaugh map for AND and OR functions.
18. What is a Don't care condition?
19. Explain the term looping.
20. Briefly explain the simplification process in a K-map.
21. What is the difference in mapping a POS expression and an SOP expression?
22. What is the standard sum term for a 0 in cell 1011?
23. What is the standard product term for a 1 in cell 0010?
24. What is a prime implicant?

# SUPPLEMENTARY PROBLEMS

25. Suppose a truth table has a LOW output for the first three input conditions: 000, 001 and 010. If all other outputs are HIGH, what is the POS circuit?
26. Draw the SOP circuit for the Karnaugh-map. (See Fig. 6.53)
27. Draw the POS circuit for the Karnaugh-map in problem 26. (See Fig. 6.54)

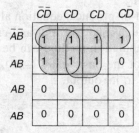

**Fig. 6.53**   $Y = A + BC\overline{D}$.      **Fig. 6.54**   $Y = \overline{A}B + \overline{A}C + \overline{A}D$.

28. Draw the Karnaugh map for the given expression and make the groupings.

$$\overline{A}B\overline{C} + AB\overline{C} + A\overline{B}\overline{C} + \overline{A}\overline{B}C + \overline{A}BC + ABC$$

29. Draw the Karnaugh map for the given expression and make the groupings.

$$\overline{A}\overline{B}\overline{C}\overline{D} + \overline{A}B\overline{C}D + AB\overline{C}D + A\overline{B}\overline{C}D + \overline{A}BCD + ABCD + A\overline{B}CD + ABCD$$

30. Chart on a truth table and map $C = AB + AB$
31. Chart and map the equation $X = ABC + A\overline{B}C + AB\overline{C}$.
32. Chart and map $X = \Sigma m(1, 2, 3, 4, 9, 11, 12, 13, 15)$.
33. Simplify the Boolean expression by K-mapping.

$$Y = AB\overline{C}\overline{D} + \overline{A}BC\overline{D} + \overline{A}BC\overline{D} + ABC\overline{D}$$

34. Simplify the Boolean expression by K-mapping.

$$Y = ABCD + ABCD + ABCD + ABCD$$

35. Simplify the Boolean expression by K-mapping.

$$Y = ABCD + ABCD + ABCD + ABCD$$

36. Find out the minimal expression for the switching function given below by K-map.
$f(A, B, C, D) = \Sigma(1, 3, 6, 7, 9, 13, 14, 15)$.
37. Obtain the minimal expression for the function by using the K-map. (Refer Fig. 6.55)
38. Obtain the minimal POS and SOP expressions for the switching function given below using a four-variable K-map $f(A, B, C, D) = \Pi(3, 4, 6, 7, 11, 12, 13, 14, 15)$ (Refer Fig. 6.56).

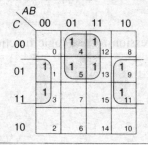

**Fig. 6.55**

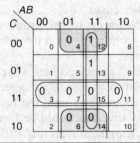

**Fig. 6.56**

39. Find the minimal expression for the Boolean function
$f(W, X, Y, Z) = \Sigma(0, 1, 2, 3, 4, 7, 8, 11, 12, 14, 15)$
40. Minimise the given function by K-mapping: $f(A, B, C, D) = \Pi M(0, 1, 2, 3, 4, 7, 8, 11, 12, 14, 15)$

41. From the given truth table obtain the sum-of-products using K-map AND realise it using NAND gates (refer Fig. 6.57).

| A | B | C | Y |
|---|---|---|---|
| 0 | 0 | 0 | 0 |
| 0 | 0 | 1 | 0 |
| 0 | 1 | 0 | 0 |
| 0 | 1 | 1 | 1 |
| 1 | 0 | 0 | 0 |
| 1 | 0 | 1 | 1 |
| 1 | 1 | 0 | 1 |
| 1 | 1 | 1 | 1 |

**Fig. 6.57**

42. Determine the simplified Boolean equation from the truth table given in Fig. 6.58.

| A | B | C | D | Y |
|---|---|---|---|---|
| 0 | 0 | 0 | 0 | 1 |
| 0 | 0 | 0 | 1 | 1 |
| 0 | 0 | 1 | 0 | × |
| 0 | 0 | 1 | 1 | × |
| 0 | 1 | 0 | 0 | 1 |
| 0 | 1 | 0 | 1 | 1 |
| 0 | 1 | 1 | 0 | × |
| 0 | 1 | 1 | 1 | × |
| 1 | 0 | 0 | 0 | × |
| 1 | 0 | 0 | 1 | × |
| 1 | 0 | 1 | 0 | × |
| 1 | 0 | 1 | 1 | × |
| 1 | 1 | 0 | 0 | 1 |
| 1 | 1 | 0 | 1 | 1 |
| 1 | 1 | 1 | 0 | × |
| 1 | 1 | 1 | 1 | × |

**Fig. 6.58**

## OBJECTIVE TYPE QUESTIONS

**Test your understanding**

### Fill in the Blanks

43. Karnaugh mapping requires that you reduce the equation to a _____ format.
44. A Karnaugh map is similar to a _____.
45. Karnaugh mapping is a graphical method of applying the laws of _____ and absorption.
46. An *n*-variable requires _____ cells.
47. Adjacent cells in a Karnaugh must not differ by _____ one variable.
48. The variable that _____ between the cells is dropped.
49. The permitted sizes of loops are any power of _____.
50. The loops must be either rectangular or _____.
51. The _____ of two loops is allowed.
52. End-around and _____ loops are permitted.
53. A larger loop is defined by _____ variables.
54. Don't care conditions never _____ as long as the system is working properly.
55. You can let a _____ condition either 1 or 0.
56. A quad eliminates two variables and their _____.
57. An octet eliminates _____ variables and their complements.
58. With the POS method, the _____ sum produces an output 0 for the corresponding input condition.
59. Complementing the Karnaugh map is the same as complementing the _____ of the truth table.

60. NAND gates can be replaced by _____ OR gates.
61. Karnaugh map depends on the ability of the human user to recognise certain _____.
62. A logic function can be expressed in two _____ forms.
63. Simplifying an expression means finding an expression with _____ terms or literals.
64. Don't care conditions can be used on a map to provide further _____ of the function.

### True/False Questions

State whether the following statements are True or False.

65. The process of unreducing a Boolean expression is called expansion.
66. The Karnaugh map method of simplification starts with converting the Karnaugh map to a truth table.
67. Every Boolean equation has a dual form obtained by changing AND to OR, OR to AND, 0 to 1, and 1 to 0.
68. In a Karnaugh map you cannot eliminate the variable that changes form.
69. You can eliminate the variable that appears in both complemented and uncomplemented form.
70. A quad eliminates two variables and their complements.
71. An octet eliminates four variables and their complements.
72. System complexity and size are indirectly related to the complexity of the corresponding logic expressions and equations.
73. Most common, for a large number of variables, is the K-map.
74. Adjacent cells represent minterms which differ by at least one variable.
75. The minterm represented by a cell is determined by the binary assignments of the variables for that cell.
76. Many logic gates combine two or more of the basic logic functions.
77. A single NAND gate performs an OR operation on its uncomplemented input terminals.
78. A single NOR gate performs an AND operation on its complemented input terminals.
79. The Quine-McClusky tabular method of minimisation is especially useful for functions with several variables but it cannot be programmed for a computer.
80. Complex functions can be constructed by successively applying operators to functions.
81. Precedence rules are not needed to specify unambiguously the order in which operators should be applied.
82. The Quine-McClucky approach is algorithmic.

### Multiple Choice Questions

83. Karnaugh map is used to
    (a) minimise the number of flip-flops in a digital circuit
    (b) to design gates
    (c) to minimise the number of gates in only a digital circuit
    (d) to minimise the number of gates and fan-in requirements of the gates in a digital circuit.
84. The SOP form of logical expression is most suitable for designing logic circuits using only
    (a) XOR gates      (b) NOR gates
    (c) NAND gates     (d) AND gates
85. The POS form of logical expression is most suitable for designing logic circuits using only
    (a) XOR gates      (b) NOR gates
    (c) NAND gates     (d) OR gates
86. Total number of cells in the Karnaugh map of a switching function $(A, B, C)$ consisting of only three variables is
    (a) 4          (b) 8          (c) 10          (d) 12
87. The Karnaugh map method of minimisation of switching functions is very convenient and effective, if the number of variables in the switching function is
    (a) 8          (b) 4          (c) 5          (d) 6
88. The minimised expression for the given K-map is (See Fig. 6.59)

    (a) $\bar{B}C\bar{D} + \bar{B}\bar{C}D + \bar{C}D$

    (b) $\bar{B}\bar{D} + \bar{C}D$

    (c) $\bar{A}BCD + A\bar{B}CD + AB\bar{C} + \bar{A}B\bar{C}$

    (d) $\bar{C}D + A\bar{B}C + \bar{A}BCD + A\bar{B}C$

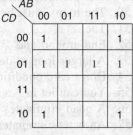

| CD\AB | 00 | 01 | 11 | 10 |
|-------|----|----|----|----|
| 00    | 1  |    |    | 1  |
| 01    | 1  | 1  | 1  | 1  |
| 11    |    |    |    |    |
| 10    | 1  |    |    | 1  |

**Fig. 6.59**

89. The minimised expression for the given K-map is (See Fig. 6.60)

(a) $\bar{A}B\bar{C}D + \bar{A}CD + \bar{A}B\bar{C}\bar{D}$

(b) $\bar{A}B\bar{C}D + \bar{A}CD + \bar{A}BC$

(c) $B\bar{C}\bar{D} + CD + \bar{A}BC$

(d) $B\bar{C}\bar{D} + CD + BC$

90. The minimised expression for the given K-map is (See Fig. 6.61)

(a) $\bar{A} \cdot (A + B)$

(b) $\bar{A} + B$

(c) $\bar{A} \cdot B$

(d) $(\bar{A} + \bar{B})(\bar{A} + B)(A + B)$

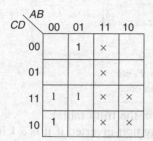

**Fig. 6.60**

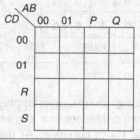

**Fig. 6.61**

91. The minimised expression for the given K-map is (See Fig. 6.62)

(a) $(C + D)(\bar{C} + \bar{D})(A + \bar{B})$

(b) $(\bar{B} + C + D)(A + \bar{B} + C)(A + B + \bar{C} + \bar{D})(\bar{A} + \bar{B} + \bar{C} + \bar{D})$

(c) $(\bar{B} + C + D)(A + \bar{B} + C + D)(A + B + \bar{C} + \bar{D})(A + B + \bar{C} + \bar{D})$

(d) $(\bar{A} + B + C)(\bar{A} + B + C + \bar{D})(A + B + \bar{C} + D)(\bar{A} + \bar{B} + \bar{C} + \bar{D})$

92. The number of cells in a six-variable K-map is

(a) 4

(b) 16

(c) 32

(d) 64

93. In the given K-map, the values of *P, Q, R,* and *S* are, respectively (See Fig. 6.63).

(a) 10, 11, 10, 11

(b) 10, 11, 11, 10

(c) 11, 10, 10, 11

(d) 11, 10, 11, 10

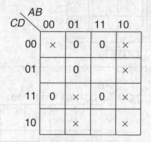

**Fig. 6.62**

**Fig. 6.63**

94. In K-map simplification, a group of eight adjacent ones leads to a term with

(a) one literal less than the total number of variables

(b) two literals less than the total number of variables

(c) three literals less than the total number of variables

(d) four literals less than the total number of variables

# ANSWERS

1. (a) SOP,       (b) POS,       (c) SOP.

2. (a) 3-input AND,    (b) 3-input OR,    (c) 3-input NAND,    (d) 3-input NOR.

3. $\bar{A}\bar{B}\bar{C}D + \bar{A}B\bar{C}D + \bar{A}BC\bar{D}$.

4. Eight.

5. No. The available XOR gate can be used as an Inverter by connecting one of its inputs to a constant HIGH.

6. $\bar{A}\bar{B}C + \bar{A}B\bar{C} + \bar{A}BC + A\bar{B}\bar{C} + ABC$

7. $\bar{A}\bar{B}\bar{C}D + \bar{A}B\bar{C}\bar{D} + \bar{A}BCD + \bar{A}BC\bar{D} + A\bar{B}\bar{C}\bar{D} + A\bar{B}C\bar{D} + AB\bar{C}\bar{D} + ABC\bar{D} + ABCD$

8. (a) 5,              (b) 10,             (c) 25.

9. (a) 11,           (b) 18,             (c) 16.

10. $B\bar{C} + BD + AC\bar{D}$

11.

| Term | Definition |
|------|-----------|
| Literal | Variable or its complement ($A$, $\bar{A}$, $B$, $\bar{B}$, etc.) |
| Product term | Series of literals related by AND, e.g., $A\bar{B}D$, $AC\bar{D}E$, etc. |
| Sum term | Series of literals related by OR, e.g.; $\bar{A} + B + \bar{C} + D + \bar{E} + F$, etc. |
| Normal term | Product or sum term in which no variable appears more than once. |

12. (1) A minterm is generated for each column in which a 1 appears in the truth table.
    (2) The minterm contains each input variable in turn; the input being non-inverted if it is a 1 in the truth table and inverted if it is a 0.

13. Using NAND gates involves the following steps:
    1. Start with a minterm (sum-of-products) Boolean expression.
    2. Draw the AND-OR logic diagram using AND, OR, and NOT symbols.
    3. Substitute NAND symbols for each AND and OR symbol, keeping all connections the same.
    4. Substitute NAND symbols with all inputs tied together for each inverter.
    5. Test the logic containing all NAND gates to determine if it generates the proper truth table.

14.

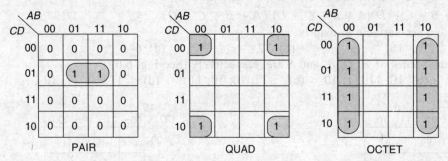

**Fig. 6.64**

15. While forming groups, overlapping of groups is allowed i.e. two redundant (not allowed) groups can have one or more 1's in common. At the same time redundancy is not allowed i.e. a group whose all 1's are overlapped by other groups. (See Fig. 6.65)

16. 4

17. (See Fig. 6.66)

18. An input condition for which there is no specific required output condition i.e. we are free to make it 0 or 1.

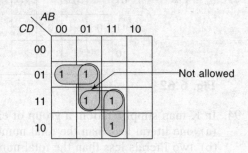

**Fig. 6.65**

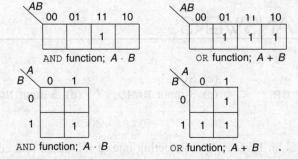

**Fig. 6.66** *Solution for Problem 17.*

19. The expression for output $X$ can be simplified by properly combining those squares in the K-map which contain 1's. The process for combining these 1's is called looping.

20. When a variable appears in both complemented and uncomplemented form within a loop, that variable is eliminated from the expression. Variables that are the same for all squares of the loop must appear in the final expression.

21. In mapping a POS expression, 0's are placed in cells whose value makes the standard sum term zero, and in mapping an SOP expression 1's are placed in cells having the same values as the product terms.

22. 0 in 1011 cell: $\bar{A} + B + \bar{C} + \bar{D}$.

23. 1 in the 0010 cell: $\bar{A}\bar{B}C\bar{D}$

24. A tabular reduced term incapable of being reduced further.

25. (See Fig. 6.67)

26. (See Fig. 6.68)

27. (See Fig. 6.69)

28. (See Fig. 6.70)

29. (See Fig. 6.71)

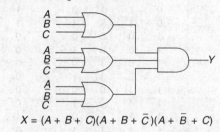

$X = (A + B + C)(A + B + \bar{C})(A + \bar{B} + C)$

**Fig. 6.67**  *Solution for Problem 25*

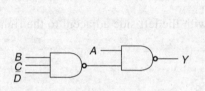

**Fig. 6.68**  *Solution for Problem 26.*

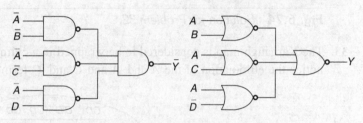

**Fig. 6.69**  *Solution for Problem 27.*

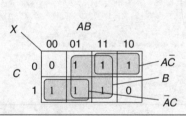

**Fig. 6.70**  *Solution for Problem 28.*

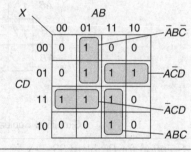

**Fig. 6.71**  *Solution for Problem 29.*

30.

| INPUTS | | OUTPUT |
|---|---|---|
| A | B | C |
| 0 | 0 | 1 |
| 0 | 1 | 0 |
| 1 | 0 | 1 |
| 1 | 1 | 0 |

(a) Charting

$\bar{A}\bar{B}$ is $m_0$.
$A\bar{B}$ is $m_2$.

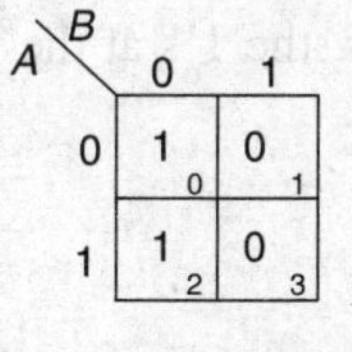

B

| A | 0 | 1 |
|---|---|---|
| 0 | 1 (0) | 0 (1) |
| 1 | 1 (2) | 0 (3) |

(b) Mapping

**Fig. 6.72**  *Solution for Problem 30.*

31.

| INPUTS | | | OUTPUT |
|---|---|---|---|
| A | B | C | X |
| 0 | 0 | 0 | 1 |
| 1 | 0 | 1 | 1 |
| 1 | 0 | 0 | 1 |

(a) Charting

$ABC$ is $m_7$
$A\bar{B}C$ is $m_5$
$A\bar{B}\bar{C}$ is $m_4$

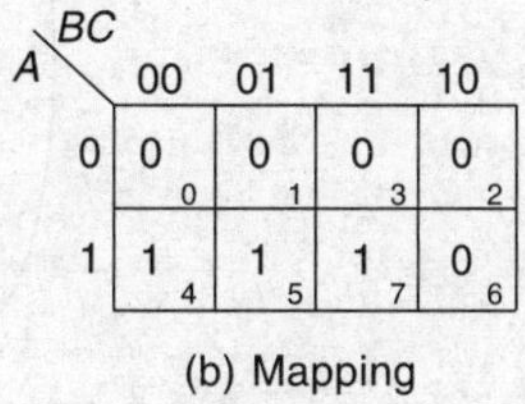

BC

| A | 00 | 01 | 11 | 10 |
|---|---|---|---|---|
| 0 | 0 (0) | 0 (1) | 0 (3) | 0 (2) |
| 1 | 1 (4) | 1 (5) | 1 (7) | 0 (6) |

(b) Mapping

**Fig. 6.73**  *Solution for Problem 31.*

32.

| INPUTS | | | | OUTPUT |
|---|---|---|---|---|
| A | B | C | D | E |
| 0 | 0 | 0 | 0 | 0 |
| 0 | 0 | 0 | 1 | 0 |
| 0 | 0 | 1 | 0 | 0 |
| 0 | 0 | 1 | 1 | 0 |
| 0 | 1 | 0 | 0 | 1 |
| 0 | 1 | 0 | 1 | 1 |
| 0 | 1 | 1 | 0 | 1 |
| 0 | 1 | 1 | 1 | 1 |
| 1 | 0 | 0 | 0 | 0 |
| 1 | 0 | 0 | 1 | 0 |
| 1 | 0 | 1 | 0 | 0 |
| 1 | 0 | 1 | 1 | 0 |
| 1 | 1 | 0 | 0 | 0 |
| 1 | 1 | 0 | 1 | 0 |
| 1 | 1 | 1 | 0 | 1 |
| 1 | 1 | 1 | 1 | 0 |

(a) Charting

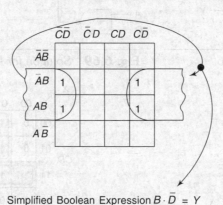

(b) Mapping

**Fig. 6.74** *Solution for Problem 32.*

33. The Karnaugh map is considered to be wrapped in a cylinder, with the left side adjacent to the right side. Also notice the elimination of the $A$ and $\bar{A}$ and $C$ and $\bar{C}$ terms.

Simplified Boolean Expression $B \cdot \bar{D} = Y$

**Fig. 6.75** *Solution for Problem 33.*

34. The K-map is considered to be a horizontal cylinder. In this way the four 1's can be looped. (See Fig. 6.76)
35. The K-map is considered to be a ball. In this way, the 1's at the four corners can be enclosed in a single loop. (See Fig. 6.77).

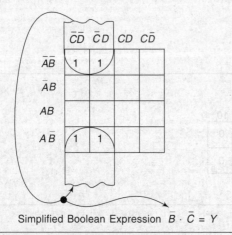

Simplified Boolean Expression $\bar{B} \cdot \bar{C} = Y$

**Fig. 6.76** *Solution for Problem 34.*

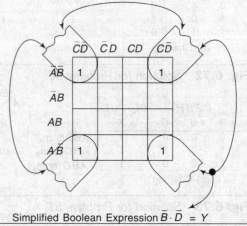

Simplified Boolean Expression $\bar{B} \cdot \bar{D} = Y$

**Fig. 6.77** *Solution for Problem 35.*

36. $f(A, B, C, D) = \bar{A}\bar{B}D + A\bar{C}D + BC$

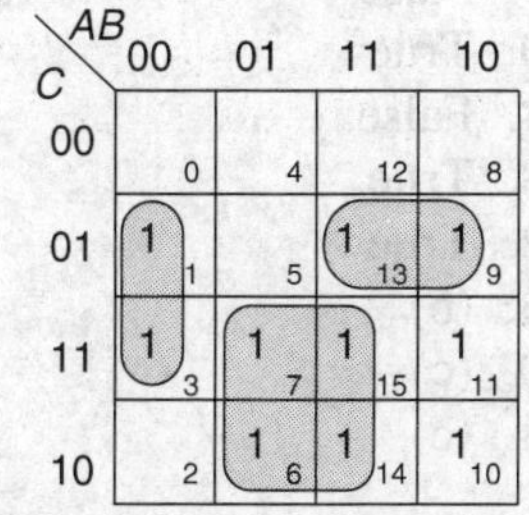

**Fig. 6.78** *Solution for Problem 36.*

37. $f(A, B, C, D) = B\bar{C} + \bar{B}D$

38. POS, $f(A, B, C, D) = (\bar{A}+\bar{B})(\bar{B}+D)(\bar{C}+D)$; SOP, $f(A, B, C, D) = \bar{B}\bar{C}+\bar{B}\bar{D}+\bar{A}\bar{C}D$

39. $f(W, X, Y, Z) = \bar{W}\bar{X} + \bar{X}\bar{Z} + \bar{W}\bar{Y}\bar{Z} + W\bar{X}\bar{Y} + WXYZ$ (See Fig. 6.79)

40. $f(A, B, C, D) = (A + B)(C + D)(\bar{C}+\bar{D})(\bar{A}+\bar{B}+\bar{C})$ (See Fig. 6.80)

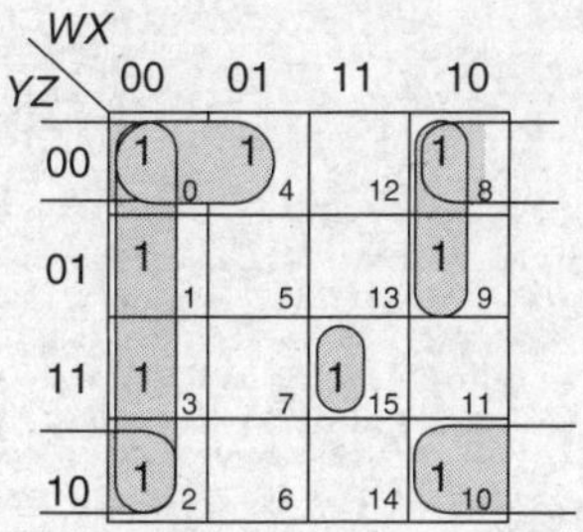

**Fig. 6.79** *Solution for Problem 39.*

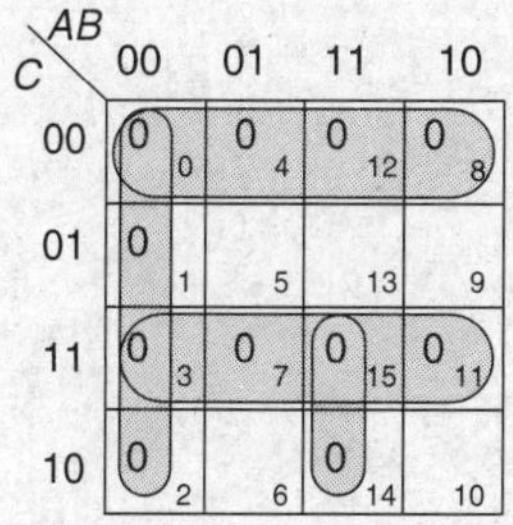

**Fig. 6.80** *Solution for Problem 40.*

41. SOP expression $Y = AB + BC + AC$

$$\bar{Y} = \overline{AB+BC+AC}$$

$$= \overline{AB}\cdot\overline{BC}\cdot\overline{AC}$$

$$Y = \overline{\overline{A}\cdot\overline{BC}\cdot\overline{AC}}$$

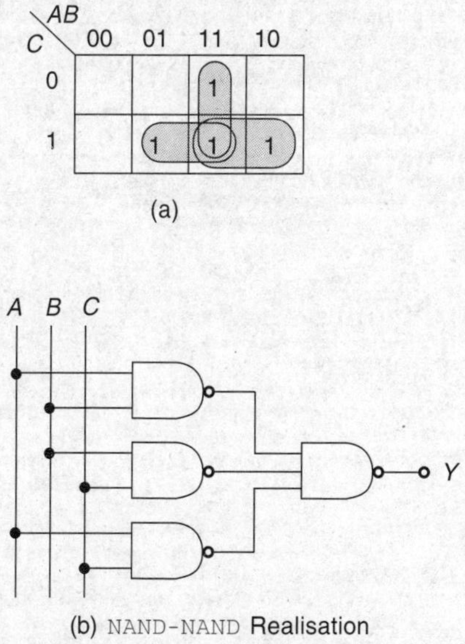
(a)
(b) NAND-NAND Realisation

**Fig. 6.81** *Solution for Problem 41.*

42. Minimised expression

$Y = \bar{A}\bar{B} + BD + AB + \bar{C}\bar{D}$

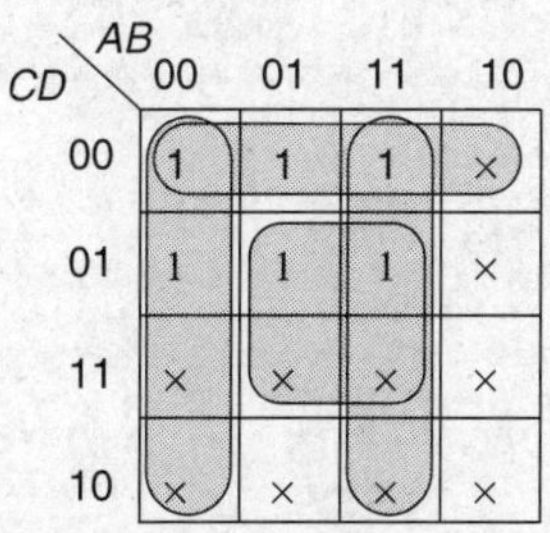

**Fig. 6.82** *Solution for Problem 42.*

| | | | |
|---|---|---|---|
| 43. SOP | 44. Truth table | 45. Complementation | 46. $2^n$ |
| 47. More than | 48. Changes | 49. Two | 50. Square |
| 51. Intersection | 52. Four corner | 53. Fewer | 54. Occur |
| 55. Don't care | 56. Complements | 57. Three | 58. Fundamental |

| | | | |
|---|---|---|---|
| 59. Output | 60. Bubbled | 61. Patterns | 62. Canonical |
| 63. Minimum | 64. Simplification | 65. True | 66. False |
| 67. True | 68. False | 69. True | 70. True |
| 71. False | 72. False | 73. False | 74. False |
| 75. True | 76. True | 77. False | 78. True |
| 79. False | 80. True | 81. False | 82. True |
| 83. (d) | 84. (c) | 85. (b) | 86. (b) |
| 87. (b) | 88. (b) | 89. (d) | 90. (c) |
| 91. (a) | 92. (d) | 93. (d) | 94. (c) |

# Pulse and Switching Devices

## INTRODUCTION

Digital signals are composed of two *well-defined voltage levels*. For most of the circuits these voltage levels will be 0 V (GND) and +3 to +5V. These are called *TTL voltage levels* because they are used with transistor-transistor logic family of ICs. A TTL signal could be generated manually by using a *mechanical switch*. One problem with a mechanical switch is *contact bounce*. To cure this problem mechanical switches are sometimes *debounced*. Many of the mechanical logic switches are debounced with *latch* circuits. Latches are sometimes called `flip-flops`.

An *electromechanical relay* can also be used for switching, accomplished by *making* and *breaking* a connection between two electrical conductors. An electro-mechanical relay has contacts like a manual switch, but it is *controlled by external voltage* instead of being operated manually.

Manual switches and electromechanical relays have limited application in today's digital electronic circuits. *Most digital systems are based on semiconductor technology, which uses diodes and transistors*. A diode and a transistor can also operate as a simple ON/OFF switch. Each device has its own limitations.

### 7.1 One problem with a mechanical switch is contact bounce. How is it overcome?

*Solution:*
As the blade of the single-pole, double-throw (SPDT) switch in Fig. 7.1(a) is moved up and down, it produces the *digital waveform* shown at the right. At time period $t_1$, the voltage is 0 V, or LOW. At $t_2$, the voltage is +5 V, or HIGH. At $t_3$, the voltage is again 0 V, or LOW, and at $t_4$, it is again +5 V, or HIGH.

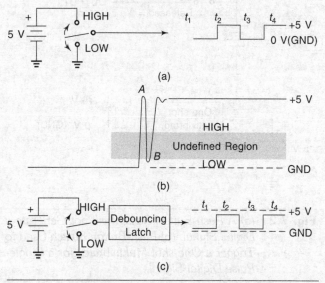

**Fig. 7.1** *(a) Generating a Digital Signal with a Switch. (b) Waveform of Contact Bounce Caused by a Mechanical Switch. (c) Adding a Debouncing Latch to a Simple Switch to Condition the Digital Signal.*

One problem with a mechanical switch is *contact bounce*. When the switch *toggles* from LOW to HIGH, the waveform first goes directly from LOW to HIGH (see A in Fig. 7.1(b)) but then, because of contact bounce, drops to LOW and then back to HIGH again. Although this happens in a very short time, digital circuits are fast enough to see this as a LOW, HIGH, LOW, HIGH waveform. There is actually a range of voltages that are defined HIGH and LOW. The *undefined region* between HIGH and LOW causes trouble in digital circuits and should be avoided (see Fig. 7.1(b)).

Mechanical switches are sometimes debounced. A block diagram of a *debounced logic switch* is shown in Fig. 7.1(c). The switch has been debounced with a *latch circuit* (sometimes called `flip-flop`). The output of the latch during time period $t_1$ is *LOW but not quite 0 V*. During time $t_2$ the output of the latch is *HIGH but not quite +5 V*. Likewise $t_3$ is LOW and $t_4$ is HIGH. The latch is also called a *bistable multivibrator*.

### 7.2 What type of signal does a push-button switch generate?

*Solution:*
A push-button switch can be used to make a digital signal. When the button is pressed a HIGH is generated at the output, Fig. 7.2(a). When the push-button is released, however, the voltage at the output is *undefined*. There is an open-circuit between the power supply and the output. This would not work properly as a logic switch.

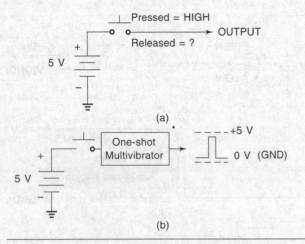

(a)

(b)

**Fig. 7.2** *(a) A Push-Button Switch will not Generate a Digital Signal. (b) Push-Button Switch Used to Trigger a One-shot Multivibrator for a Single-Pulse Digital Signal.*

Figure 7.2(b) shows the push-button switch connected to a one-shot multivibrator circuit. For each press of the push-button, a single short, positive pulse is output from the *one-shot* circuit. The pulse width of the output is determined by the design of the multivibrator, and not by how long you hold down the push-button. The one-shot is also called a *monostable multivibrator*.

### 7.3 What is the significance of a free-running multi-vibrator in digital logic circuits?

*Solution:*
A *free-running multivibrator* oscillates by itself without the need for external switching or an external signal.

The block diagram of a free-running multivibrator, also known as an *astable multivibrator* is shown in Fig. 7.3. The free-running multivibrator (MV) generates a continuous series of TTL level pulses. The output alternately goes LOW and HIGH.

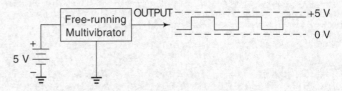

**Fig. 7.3** *Free-Running Multivibrator Generates a String of Digital Pulses.*

## PULSE WAVEFORMS

A single *positive pulse* is generated when the voltage (or current) goes from its normally LOW level to HIGH level and then back to its LOW (level). A single *negative pulse* is generated when the voltage (or current) goes from its normally HIGH level to its LOW level and back to its HIGH level.

### 7.4 What are the characteristics of an ideal pulse?

*Solution:*
The pulse in Fig. 7.4 has two edges; a leading edge and a trailing edge. For a positive pulse, the *leading edge* is a positive-going transition (rising edge), and the *trailing edge* is a negative-going transition (falling edge). The pulses in Fig. 7.4 are *ideal* because the rising and falling edges change instantaneously (in zero time). *Actually, these transitions never occur instantaneously.* However, for most digital work we can assume ideal pulses.

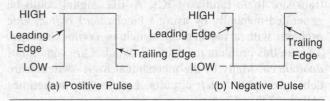

(a) Positive Pulse          (b) Negative Pulse

**Fig. 7.4** *Ideal Pulse Characteristics.*

### 7.5 What are the characteristics of non-ideal pulses?

*Solution:*
A *non-ideal pulse* is shown in Fig. 7.5. The time required for the pulse to go from its LOW level to its HIGH level is called the *rise time* ($t_r$). The time required for the pulse to go from its HIGH level to its LOW level is called the *fall time* ($t_f$). It is common to measure rise time from 10% of the pulse amplitude to 90% of the pulse amplitude and to measure the fall time from 90% to 10% of the pulse amplitude. This is because of

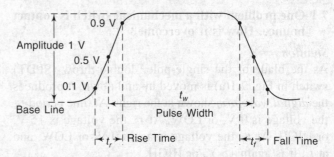

**Fig. 7.5** *Non-Ideal Pulse Characteristics.*

*non-linerarities* that commonly occur near the bottom and top of the pulse, as illustrated in Fig. 7.5.

The *pulse width* ($t_w$) is a measure of the duration of the pulse and is defined as the time between 50% points on the rising and falling edges, as indicated in Fig. 7.5.

### 7.6 Differentiate between periodic and non-periodic pulses.

*Solution:*

A *periodic pulse waveform* is one that repeats itself at a fixed time interval called the *period* ($t_p$). The *frequency* of the pulse is the rate at which it repeats itself and is measured in pulses per second (pps) or Hertz (Hz).

$$f = 1/t_p \qquad \text{(pulse repetition rate)}$$
$$t_p = 1/f \qquad \text{(period)}$$

An important characteristic of a periodic pulse waveform is its *duty cycle* defined as the ratio of the pulse width ($t_w$) to the period ($t_p$) expressed as a percentage.

$$\text{Duty cycle} = (t_w/t_p) \times 100$$

A *non-periodic pulse waveform* does not repeat itself at fixed intervals and may be composed of pulses of differing pulse widths and/or differing time intervals between the pulses. Both waveforms are shown in Fig. 7.6.

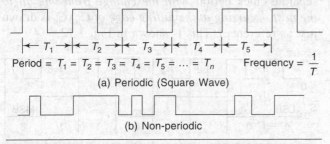

Period = $T_1 = T_2 = T_3 = T_4 = T_5 = \ldots = T_n$    Frequency = $\dfrac{1}{T}$

(a) Periodic (Square Wave)

(b) Non-periodic

**Fig. 7.6** *Periodic and Non-periodic Pulse Waveforms.*

### 7.7 What is the frequency of a clock waveform whose period is 2 microseconds?

*Solution:*

$$f = \frac{1}{t_p} = \frac{1}{2\,\mu s}$$
$$f = \frac{10^6}{2} = 0.5 \text{ MHz}$$

### 7.8 If the frequency of a pulse waveform is 4.17 MHz, what is its period?

*Solution:*

$$t_p = 1/f$$
$$= 1/4.17 \times 10^6$$
$$= 0.240\ \mu s.$$

### 7.9 Determine the duty cycle of the waveform in Fig. 7.7.

*Solution:*

$$t_w = 1 \text{ ms and } t_p = 10 \text{ ms}$$

$$\text{Duty cycle} = \frac{t_w}{t_p} \times 100 = 10\%$$

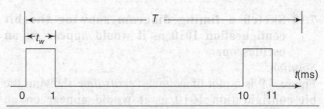

**Fig. 7.7** *For P7.9.*

## CLOCK WAVEFORM TIMING

A free-running clock will generate a continuous series of pulses. Most digital signals require *precise timing*. Special clock and timing circuits are used to produce clock waveforms to *trigger* the digital signals at precise intervals. Astable, monostable, and bistable multi-vibrators can all be wired using *discrete components*. Because of their superior performance, ease of use, and low cost, the *integrated circuit* (IC) form of these components (Fig. 7.8) is preferred. A schematic diagram for a practical free-running clock circuit is shown in Fig. 7.8(a). This clock circuit produces a *low-frequency* (10 to 20 Hz) TTL output. The heart of the circuit is a common *555 timer IC*. A typical breadboard wiring of the circuit is sketched in Fig. 7.8(b). Pin 1 on the IC is immediately counterclockwise from the *notch* or dot.

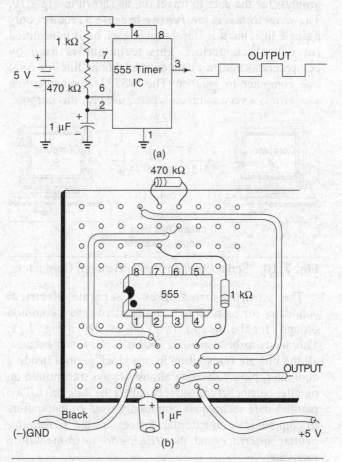

**Fig. 7.8** *(a) Schematic Diagram of a Free-running Clock using a 555 Timer IC. (b) Wiring the Free-running Clock Circuit on Solderless Breadboard.*

**7.10 Sketch a timing diagram showing the bit configuration 1010 as it would appear on an oscilloscope.**

*Solution:*

Figure 7.9 is a plot of *voltage versus time* showing the bit configuration 1010 as it would appear on an oscilloscope. The LSB comes first in time. *In this case the LSB is transmitted first.* The MSB could have been transmitted first as long as the system on the receiving end knows which method is used.

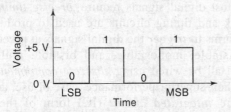

**Fig. 7.9**    *Typical Digital Signal.*

## SERIAL AND PARALLEL REPRESENTATION

Binary information can be transmitted from one location to another either in serial or parallel format. The *serial format* uses a single electrical conductor (and a common ground) for the data to travel on, as shown in Fig 7.10. The serial format is *inexpensive* because it requires only a single line, but it is *slow* because each bit is transmitted for one clock period. This technique is used by computers to transmit data over telephone lines or from one computer to another. The *RS232 communication standard* is a very common scheme used for this purpose.

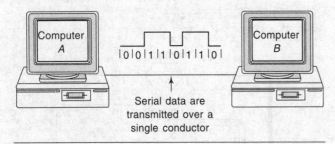

**Fig. 7.10**    *Serial Communication Between Computers.*

The *parallel format* uses a separate electrical conductor for each bit to be transmitted (and a common ground) for the data to travel on, as shown Fig. 7.11. This tends to be *expensive*, but it is very *fast* because all the bits are transmitted in one clock period. Inside a computer, binary data are almost always transmitted on parallel channels (collectively called the *data bus*). Two parallel data techniques commonly used by computers to communicate to external devices are the *Centronics printer interface* and the *IEEE-488* instrumentation interface.

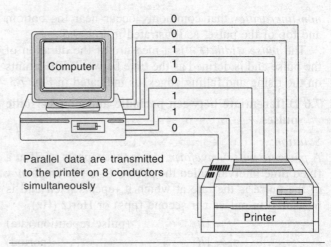

**Fig. 7.11**    *Parallel Communication between a Computer and a Printer.*

**7.11 Sketch the serial representation of the binary number 01101100.**

*Solution:*

The serial representation, $S_o$, is shown with respect to some clock waveform, $C_p$, and its *LSB is drawn first*. Each bit from the given binary number occupies a separate clock period *with the change from one bit to the next occurring at the falling edge of $C_p$ ($C_p$ is drawn just as reference)*. This is shown in Fig. 7.12.

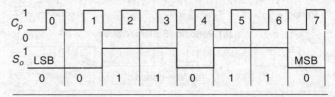

**Fig. 7.12**    *Serial Representation of a Binary Number.*

**7.12 Sketch the parallel representation of the binary number 01101100. Explain.**

*Solution:*

Figure 7.13 represents the same number in parallel representation. If the clock period were 2 μs, it would take 2 μs × 8 = 16 μs to transmit the number in serial and 2 μs × 1 = 2 μs to transmit the same 8-bit number in parallel. Thus *when the speed is important, parallel transmission is preferred over serial transmission.*

**7.13 Sketch the serial and parallel representation of the 4-bit binary number 0111. If the clock frequency is 5 MHz, find the time to transmit, using each method.**

*Solution:*

Figure 7.14 illustrates the representation of the 4-bit number 0111.

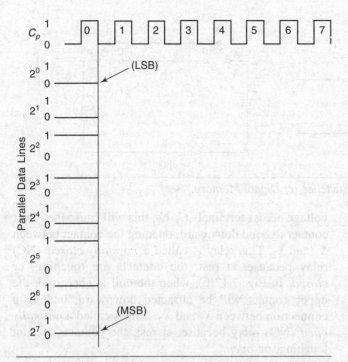

**Fig. 7.13** *Parallel Representation of a Binary Number.*

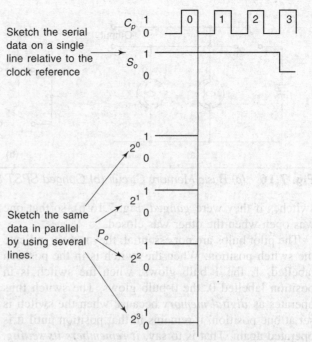

**Fig. 7.14** *Serial and Parallel Representation of a Binary Number.*

$$t_p = \frac{1}{f} = \frac{1}{5 \times 10^6} = 0.2 \ \mu s$$

$$t_{serial} = 4 \times 0.2 = 0.8 \ \mu s$$

$$t_{parallel} = 1 \times 0.2 = 0.2 \ \mu s$$

**7.14 Sketch the serial and parallel representations (least significant digit first) of the hexadecimal number 4 A. Assume a 4-bit parallel system and a clock frequency of 4 kHz. Also what is the state of the serial line 1.2 ms into the transmission?**

*Solution:*

$$4A_{16} = 0100\ 1010_2$$

$$t_p = \frac{1}{4 \times 10^3} = 0.25 \ ms$$

Therefore, *the incremental time of each falling edge increases by 0.25 ms.* Because each period is 0.25 ms, 1.2 ms, will occur within the 0 period of the number 4, which on the $S_o$ line, is a 0 logic state. (See Fig. 7.15)

## SWITCHES IN ELECTRONIC CIRCUITS

A switch is any mechanical device by which two (or more) electrical conductors may be conveniently *connected or disconnected*. The simplest form of switch consists of two strips of spring metal on which electrical contacts are mounted. A lever or push-button controls whether the switch is *open* (contacts separated) or *closed* (contacts touching).

**7.15 Illustrate and explain how switches can operate as digital memory.**

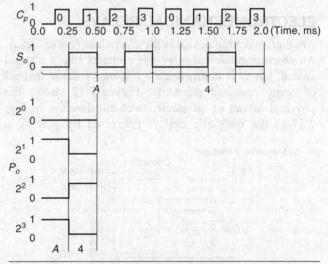

**Fig. 7.15** *Serial and Parallel Representation of the Hexadecimal Number $4A_{16}$ ($0100\ 1010_2$).*

*Solution:*

In fact, the basic digital circuit is a single pole double through (SPDT) switch. By itself, the switch forms a single bit of *memory* circuit. If the switch is in one position, current is through one pole, and in the opposite position through the other. The *live pole* indicates the position of the switch, or to use digital jargon *stores* the position.

By adding a battery to supply power and two pilot bulbs to indicate which pole has the current, we arrive at the circuit shown in Fig. 7.16(a). It would also be possible to use two single pole single throw (SPST)

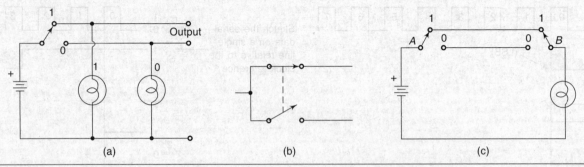

**Fig. 7.16**    *(a) Basic Memory Circuit (b) Ganged SPST Switches (c) Digital Memory.*

switches if they were *ganged*, Fig. 7.16(b), so that one was open when the other was closed.

The pilot bulbs are not essential, they merely indicate the switch position. When the switch is in the position labelled, 1, the 1 bulb glows, when the switch is in position labelled 0, the 0 bulb glows. The switch thus operates as *digital memory* because when the switch is set at one position, it remains in that position until it is operated again. That is to say, *it remembers its setting*. Toggle, or rocker, switches are widely used in digital equipment to *remember* instructions from the operator to the equipment.

## ELECTROMECHANICAL RELAYS

Another switching device is the *electromechanical relay*. An electromechanical relay has contacts like a manual switch, but *it is controlled by external voltage* instead of being operated manually. Figure 7.17 shows the physical layout of an electromechanical relay. In Fig. 7.17(a) the magnetic coil is energised by placing a

voltage across terminals $C_1$-$C_2$; this will cause the lower contact to bend downward, opening the contact between $X_1$ and $X_2$. This relay is called a *normally closed* (NC) relay because, at rest, the contacts are touching, or *closed*. In Fig. 7.17(b), when the coil is energised, the upper contact will be attracted downward, making a connection between $X_1$ and $X_2$. This is called a *normally open* (NO) relay because, at rest, the contacts are not touching, or *open*.

### 7.16 Discuss the main features of electromechanical relays.

*Solution:*

A relay provides *total isolation* between the triggering source applied to $C_1$-$C_2$ and the output $X_1$-$X_2$. This total isolation is sometimes important in many digital applications and it is a feature that certain semiconductor switches (such as diodes, transistors, and integrated circuits) cannot provide. Also *rated currents* of the contacts are normally much higher than those for *semiconductor switches*.

The position of the relay contacts when the coil is not energised is known as the *normal position*. A relay may have *both* normally open (NO) and normally closed (NC)contacts as in Fig. 7.18(a). In Fig. 7.18(b) we have a simple relay circuit for controlling a light bulb. The light will be lit if relay *A* OR relay *B* is energised AND relay *C* is NOT energised.

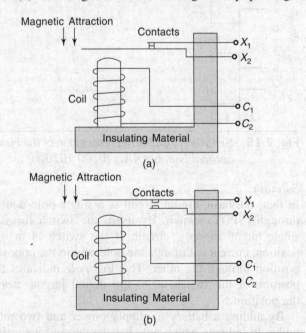

**Fig. 7.17**    *Physical Representation of an Electro-mechanical Relay: (a) Normally Closed (NC) Relay, (b) Normally Open (NO) Relay.*

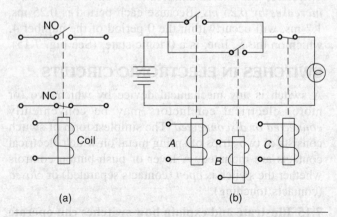

**Fig. 7.18**    *Typical Relay Symbols and Relay Logic Circuit.*

While relays are *far too slow* for use in the "main frame" of a digital computer, they are still useful for various *auxiliary functions* in peripheral equipment. The *bilateral* nature of relay circuits gives rise to some special problems.

Systems requiring *complex* relay switching schemes are generally implemented using *programmable logic controllers* (PLCs). PLCs are microprocessor based systems that are programmed to perform complex logic operations usually to *control* electrical processes in manufacturing and industrial facilities. They use a programming technique called *ladder logic* to monitor and control several processes, eliminating the need for individually wired relays. PLC® is a registered trademark of Allen-Bradley Corporation.

**7.17 Draw the timing diagram for the circuit shown in Fig. 7.19 given the $C_p$ waveform.**

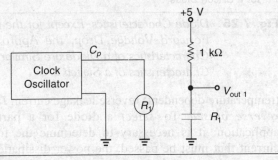

**Fig. 7.19**

*Solution:*

When $C_p$ is LOW, the $R_1$ relay coil is de-energised, the $R_1$ contacts are open, $I_{1\ k\Omega} = 0$ A, $V_{1\ k\Omega} = 0$ V, and $V_{out\ 1} = 5$ V.

When $C_p$ is HIGH, the $R_1$ coil is energised, the $R_1$ contacts are closed, and $V_{out\ 1} = 0$.

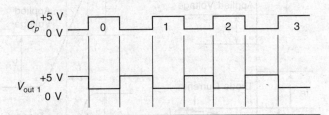

**Fig. 7.20**  *Solution for Problem 7.17.*

**7.18 With the help of a diagram, discuss the use of relay as a shorting switch in an electric circuit.**

*Solution:*

The +5 V source is used to energise the relay coil and the +12 V source is supplying the external electric circuit. When the switch SW in Fig. 7.21(a) is closed, *the relay coil will become energised, causing the relay contacts to open,* which will make $V_{out\ 1}$ change from 0 V to 6 V with respect to ground. The voltage divider equation is used to calculate $V_{out}$.

$$V_{out} = \frac{12\ V \times 5\ k\Omega}{5\ k\Omega + 5\ k\Omega} = 6\ V$$

When the switch in Fig. 7.21(b) is closed, *the relay coil becomes energised, causing the relay contacts to close,* changing $V_{out\ 2}$ from 6 V to 0 V.

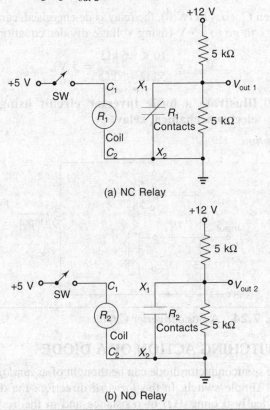

**Fig. 7.21**  *(a) NC Relay Used in a Circuit, (b) NO Relay Used in a Circuit.*

**7.19 Replace the 5 V battery and switch in problem 7.18 with a clock oscillator and use a timing diagram to analyse the results.**

*Solution:*

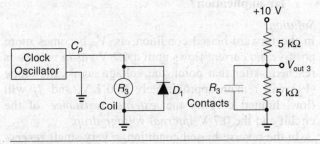

**Fig. 7.22**  *Relay used in a Digital Circuit.*

The relay coil is *triggered* by the clock waveform $C_p$. The diode, $D_1$, is placed across the relay coil to *protect* it from arcing each time the relay coil is de-energised. Timing diagrams are very useful for comparing waveforms relative to time. When the clock goes HIGH (1) the relay is energised, causing $V_{out\ 3}$ to go LOW(0).

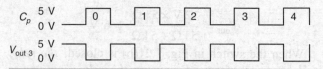

**Fig. 7.23**   *Solution for Problem 7.19.*

When $C_p$ goes LOW(0), the relay is de energised, causing $V_{out\,3}$ to go to +5 V (using voltage divider equation

$$V_{out\,3} = \frac{10\,V \times 5\,k\Omega}{5\,k\Omega + 5\,k\Omega} = 5\,V).$$

**7.20 Illustrate a basic inverter circuit using an electromechanical relay.**

*Solution:*

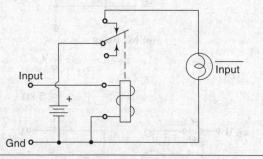

**Fig. 7.24**   *A Basic Inverter Circuit.*

## SWITCHING ACTION OF A DIODE

The semiconductor diode can be thought of as *analogous* to a simple switch. In the *forward* direction, the diode is ideally 0 ohms ($\Omega$) of resistance and in the *reverse* direction, infinite resistance. A switch has similar characteristics, 0 $\Omega$ when *closed* and infinite resistance when *open*. However, *the diode is not an ideal device in either the forward or reverse direction.*

**7.21 Describe the operation of a diode in both forward and reverse directions. What would you consider when selecting a diode for a particular application?**

*Solution:*

In the forward-biased condition, as $V_F$ becomes more positive, no current flows until a 0.7 V *cut-in voltage* is reached. After that point, the voltage across the diode ($V_F$) will remain approximately at 0.7 V, and $I_F$ will flow, limited only by the *external resistance* of the circuit and the 0.7 V *internal voltage drop*.

In the reverse-biased condition, a very small *reverse current* flows. When the voltage goes sufficiently negative, a phenomenon known as *Zener breakdown* occurs, and the reverse current increases sharply. *In normal switching circuit applications, diodes are never operated in the Zener range.*

Diode characteristics can be ignored in many applications. The device is assumed to have a constant voltage drop $V_F$ when *forward biased* and a constant

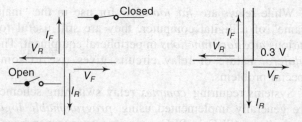

(a) Switch and Ideal Diode     (b) Approximate Characteristics
    Characteristic                     for a Germanium Diode

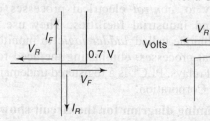

(c) Approximate Characteristics   (d) Reverse Characteristic
    for a Silicon Diode

**Fig. 7.25**   *Diode Characteristics. Except for the Device Forward Voltage Drop, the Approximate Characteristics of a Diode are Similar to the Characteristics of a Switch.*

(temperature dependent) reverse leakage current $I_S$ when *reverse biased*. To *select* a diode for a particular application, it is necessary to determine the forward current that must be passed, the power dissipation, the reverse voltage and the maximum reverse leakage current that can be tolerated. Another item that must be considered is the required *operating frequency* of the diode.

**7.22 What happens when a diode is switched from ON to OFF?**

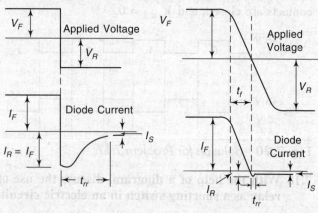

(a) $I_R$ with very Fast Reverse     (b) $I_R$ Minimized by Making
    Bias                                    $t_f \gg t_{rr}$

**Fig. 7.26**   *A Diode Switching from ON to OFF Conducts in Reverse for a Time Known as the Reverse Recovery Time $t_{rr}$. If the Fall Time of the Forward Current is Made Much Larger than $t_{rr}$, the Reverse Current can be Minimised.*

*Solution:*
The effect of a *sudden change* from forward bias to reverse bias is illustrated in Fig. 7.26(a). *Instead of switching* OFF *sharply when the input becomes negative, the diode initially conducts in reverse.* The reverse current $I_R$ is at first equal to $I_F$; then it falls off to reverse leakage current $I_S$. At the instant of reverse bias there are charge carriers crossing the junction depletion region, and these must be removed. This removal of charge carriers constitutes the reverse current $I_R$. The *reverse recovery time* $t_{rr}$ is the time required for the reverse current to fall to $I_S$. *Typical values of* $t_{rr}$ *for switching diodes range from 4 ns to 50 μs.*

If the diode forward current is reduced to a very small level before the device is reverse biased, then the initial level of reverse current will also be very small. Even when there is a large forward current, the reverse current can be kept very small if the forward current is reduced slowly. This means that for *minimum reverse current, the fall time of forward current should be much longer than the diode reverse recovery time.* (see Fig. 7.26(b)).

When a diode is switched ON (from reverse bias to forward bias), there is a finite *turn-on time.* However, the turn-on time is so small as compared to the reverse recovery time that it is usually neglected.

**7.23 Determine if the silicon diodes shown in the Fig. 7.27 are forward biased or reverse biased.**

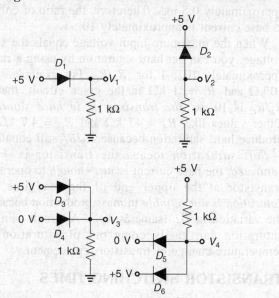

**Fig. 7.27**

*Solution:*
$D_1$ is forward biased.    $D_2$ is reverse biased.
$D_3$ is forward biased.    $D_4$ is reverse biased.
$D_5$ is forward biased.    $D_6$ is reverse biased.

**7.24 Determine $V_1$, $V_2$, $V_3$, and $V_4$ (with respect to ground) for the circuits in Fig. 7.27.**

*Solution:*
$V_1$: $D_1$ is forward biased, dropping 0.7 V across its terminals.
Therefore $V_1 = (5.0 - 0.7)$ V $= 4.3$ V
$V_2$: $D_2$ is reverse biased. No current will flow through the 1 kΩ resistance, so $V_2 = 0$ V.
$V_3$: Because $D_4$ is reverse biased (open), it has no effect on the circuit. $D_3$ is forward biased, dropping 0.7 V, making $V_3 = 4.3$ V.
$V_4$: $D_6$ is reverse biased (open), so it has no effect on the circuit. $D_5$ is forward biased, so it has 0.7 V on its anode side, which is +0.7 V above the 0 V ground level, making $V_4 = +0.7$ V.

## SWITCHING ACTION OF A TRANSISTOR

The *bipolar transistor* is a very commonly used switch in digital electronic circuits. It is a three-terminal semiconductor component that allows an input signal at one of its terminals to cause the other two terminals to become a *short* or an *open* circuit. The transistor is most commonly made of *silicon* that has been altered into an *n*-type material and *p*-type material.

Three distinct regions (Fig. 7.28) make up a bipolar transistor, *emitter, base* and *collector.* They can be a combination of *p-n-p* type material or *n-p-n* type material *bonded together as a three-terminal device.*

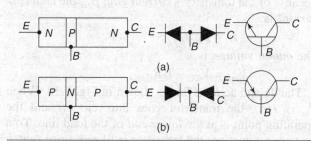

**Fig. 7.28** *Bipolar Transistor Symbols (a) npn (b) pnp.*

In an electronic circuit, the *input signal*(1 or 0) is usually applied to the base of the transistor, which causes the collector-emitter junction to become a short or an open circuit. The *rules of transistor switching* are:

1. In the *n-p-n transistor,* applying a positive voltage from base-to-emitter causes the collector-to-emitter junction to short. This is called *turning the transistor ON.* Applying a negative voltage or 0 V from base-to-emitter causes the collector-to-emitter junction to open. This is called *turning the transistor OFF.*

2. In a *p-n-p transistor* applying a negative voltage from base-to-emitter turns it *ON.* Applying a positive voltage or 0 V from base-to-emitter turns it *OFF.*

**7.25 How can a transistor be used as a switch? Show the current voltage relations in a common-emitter circuit. What is the significance of the load line?**

*Solution:*

The simplest way to use a transistor is as a *switch*, meaning that we operate it at either *saturation* or *cut off* but nowhere else along the load line. When saturated, the transistor is like a *closed switch*. When cut off, it's like an *open switch*. This is *two-state operation*, because only two points on the load line are used.

In the figure below a common-emitter circuit is shown. A simplified drawing of the same circuit is also given.

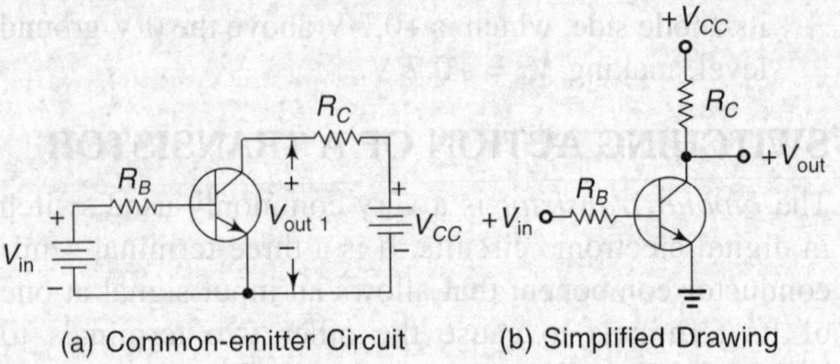

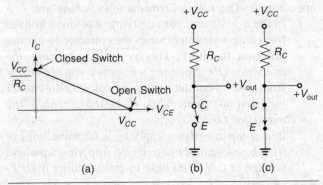

(a) Common-emitter Circuit     (b) Simplified Drawing

**Fig. 7.29**  *For P7.25.*

The *base current* $I_B$ is given by

$$I_B = \frac{V_{in} - V_{BE}}{R_B}$$

Because of the transistor's *current gain* $\beta_{dc}$, the *collector current* is

$$I_C = \beta_{dc} I_B$$

The *output voltage* is

$$V_{out} = V_{CC} - I_C R_C$$

The dc and ac *load line* is shown in Fig. 7.30. When $V_{in}$ is zero, the transistor goes into *cut off* and the operating point is at the *lower end* of the load line. To a first approximation, the transistor is like an *open switch* between the collector and the emitter. On the other hand, when $V_{in}$ is large, the transistor goes into *saturation* and the operating point is at the *upper end* of the load line. Ideally, the transistor is like a *closed switch*.

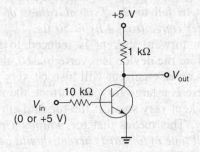

**Fig. 7.30**  *(a) Load Line (b) Cut Off (c) Saturation.*

### 7.26 Illustrate, with example, the difference between hard saturation and soft saturation.

*Solution:*

*Hard saturation* means the transistor has sufficient base current to be saturated *under all operating conditions*. To get hard saturation, the designer makes $I_{C,sat}$ approximately 10 times the value of $I_{B, sat}$. A ratio of 10 : 1 is low enough for almost any transistor to remain saturated, despite temperature extremes, transistor replacement, supply-voltage changes, etc.

**Fig. 7.31**

For example, in Fig. 7.31, the input voltage, in the CE configuration, may be either 0 V or +5 V. When $V_{in}$ is zero, the transistor cuts off and $V_{out}$ equals +5V. When $V_{in}$ is +5 V, the transistor goes into *hard saturation* and $V_{out}$ is approximately zero. $I_{C, sat}$ is ideally 5 mA. Ignoring the $V_{BE}$ of the transistor, $I_{B, sat}$ is approximately 0.5 mA. Therefore, the ratio of collector to base current is approximately 10 : 1.

When the maximum input voltage equals the supply voltage, you can get hard saturation by using a ratio of approximately 10 : 1 for $R_B/R_C$. For example, $R_B =$ 10 kΩ and $R_C = 1$ kΩ in the given circuit, the ratio $R_B/R_C$ is 10, so *the transistor is in hard saturation*. Other values like $R_B = 47$ kΩ and $R_C = 4.7$ kΩ also produce hard saturation because $R_B/R_C$ still equals 10.

*Soft saturation* means the transistor is *barely saturated*, the base current is *just enough* to operate the transistor at the upper end of the load line. *Soft saturation is not reliable* in mass production because of the variation in $\beta_{dc}$ (same as $h_{FE}$). A circuit using soft saturation can easily come out of saturation with temperature change or transistor replacement.

### TRANSISTOR SWITCHING TIMES

One very important characteristic of a switching transistor is the *speed* with which it can be turned ON and OFF. Consider Fig. 7.32 where the time relationship between collector current and base current is shown. When the inputs current $I_B$ is applied, the transistor does not switch ON immediately. *The time between*

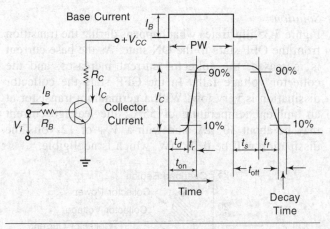

**Fig. 7.32** *Transistor Switching Times.*

*application of the base current and commencement of collector current is termed the delay time, $t_d$.* The delay time is defined as the time required for $I_C$ to reach 10% of its final value, after $I_B$ has commenced. Even when the transistor begins to switch ON, a final time elapses before $I_C$ reaches its maximum level. The *rise time, $t_r$* is defined as the time it takes for $I_C$ to go from 10% to 90% of its maximum level. The *turn-on time, $t_{on}$* for the transistor is the sum of $t_d$ and $t_r$.

$$t_{on} = t_d + t_r$$

Similarly, a *transistor cannot be switched* OFF *instantaneously.* The *turn-off time $t_{off}$* is composed of a storage time $t_s$ and a fall-time $t_f$. The *storage time* results from the fact that the collector-base junction is forward biased when the transistor is in saturation. Charge carriers crossing a forward biased junction are *trapped* (stored) in the depletion region when the junction is reverse biased. These charge carriers must be withdrawn or *made to recombine* with charge carriers of an opposite type before the collector current begins to fall. The storage time $t_s$ is defined as the time between $I_B$ switch-off and $I_C$ falling to 90% of its maximum level. The *fall time $t_f$* is the time required for $I_c$ to fall from 90% to 10% of its maximum. A further quantity, the *decay time $t_d$* is sometimes included in the turn-off time. This is the time required for $I_C$ to go from its 10% level to $I_{CO}$. Usually, this is not an important quantity, since the transistor is regarded as being OFF when $I_C$ falls to the 10% level. The turn-off time $t_{off}$ of the transistor is the sum of $t_s$ and $t_f$.

$$t_{off} = t_s + t_f$$

To conclude, *saturating and then cutting off a transistor cannot be done instantaneously. This problem can be overcome by never allowing the transistor to go into saturation.* Emitter-coupled logic is biased so that it is in the *active region* at all times and therefore has very small propagation delay times.

Faster operation generally means greater computing power, so there is a continual search for faster and faster

logic circuits. The development of faster circuits is the domain of electronic circuit engineer, not the logic designer, and the actual speed of the electronics is of only indirect interest to the logic designer. However, *the qualitative nature of the transitions and delays in logic circuits plays an important role in the logic theory of sequential circuits.*

### 7.27 Describe in detail the switching action of a transistor.

*Solution:*
Figure 7.33(a) illustrates a circuit incorporating a conventional switch with mechanically operated contacts.

Figure 7.33(b) shows a corresponding arrangement in which the current through the load $R_L$ is controlled by a transistor.

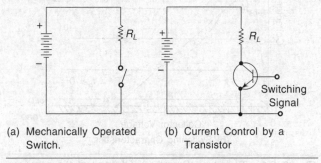

(a) Mechanically Operated Switch.

(b) Current Control by a Transistor

**Fig. 7.33** *Switching Action of a Transistor.*

With a reverse voltage applied to the base of the transistor, only the very small collector to base leakage current can flow through the transistor, and so there will be almost zero load current, the full battery voltage appearing across the transistor. If the base voltage is made positive, the collector to emitter impedance will fall and the load current can now flow through the transistor and load resistance; the voltage across the transistor falling to almost zero.

*In practically all switching applications the transistor is used in the common-emitter configuration since the high current gain allows large collector current to be switched by means of a relatively small base current.*

In addition to the OFF state and the ON state, the *transition* through which the transistor must pass, in going from one to the other, is important. Consider the circuit in Fig. 7.34(a) and the collector characteristics of Fig. 7.34(b). The load line corresponding to the load resistance $R_L$ is shown on the characteristics.

With the base current at zero, collector current will be the collector-to-emitter leakage current $I_{CEO}$. If a reverse voltage is applied to the base, the collector current is reduced to the collector-to-base leakage current $I_{CBO}$. This current is very small-with silicon planar transistors, of the order of 1 nano ampere- giving an OFF impedance above 1,000 MΩ. *When the base-emitter*

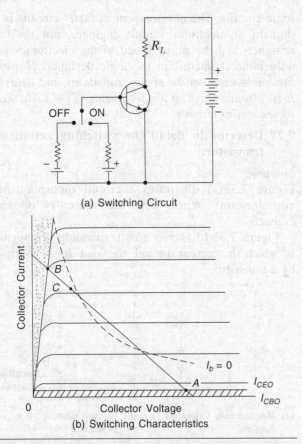

**Fig. 7.34**    *Transistor Switching Characteristics.*

*junction of the transistor is reverse biased the transistor is said to be cut off* and is then in the shaded region of Fig. 7.34(b). With the load resistance $R_L$, the operating point will be at $A$.

As the base current is increased, the collector current increases, and the operating point moves along the loadline and eventually reaches point $B$. Then further increase of base current will not result in any more increase of collector current and *the transistor is said to be saturated or bottomed.* The collector-to-emitter voltage will have fallen to a very low value, known as the collector saturation voltage $V_{CE(\text{sat})}$. In this condition the resistance between the collector and emitter of the transistor is very low-only a few ohms. As the collector voltage falls to the low $V_{CE(\text{sat})}$, the collector junction becomes forward biased. Thus *in the* ON *condition both junctions of the transistor are forward biased* and the current flowing through the load resistance will be $(V_{CC} - V_{CE(\text{sat})})/R_L$ or approximately $V_{CC}/R_L$ which is independent of the base current. The saturation region is shown dotted in Fig. 7.34(b).

**7.28 What happens during the transition when a transistor is switched from the OFF state to the ON state?**

*Solution:*
Figure 7.35 illustrates what happens during the transition from the OFF state to the ON state. As the base current is increased, the collector current increases, and the collector voltage falls. In the OFF state the collector dissipation is very low. With a germanium transistor at an ambient temperature of 55°C, the leakage current may be about 30 μA, and with a $V_{CE}$ of 12 volts the dissipation will be 0.36 mW, which is negligible.

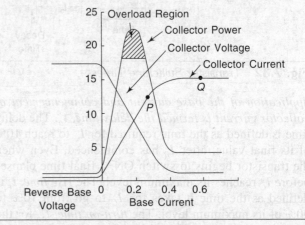

**Fig. 7.35**    *Transistor Characteristics.*

As the collector current increases from the OFF state the transistor dissipation increases as shown in Fig. 7.35. It passes through a maximum point and falls to a low value again as saturation is reached. At its maximum value the power dissipation may be in excess of the rating of the transistor and it would not be possible to operate the transistor permanently in that condition. *To ensure the most satisfactory operation from the power dissipation view point the base signal must be sufficient to drive the transistor into saturation very quickly so that the mean power dissipated is kept low.* Referring to Fig. 7.34, the base current should be larger than that needed to take the operating point to $B$ to ensure that the transistor is driven into saturation. The effective current gain will then be lower than the small signal current gain. At the point $P$, Fig. 7.35, in the active transistor region, the small gain may be near about 40. If the base current is increased to the point $Q$ to ensure saturation, the effective gain will only be about 25.

**7.29 Sketch the waveform at $V_{\text{out}}$ in the circuit shown, given the input signal $C_p$. (See Fig. 7.36)**

*Solution:*
When $C_p = 0$ V, the transistor is OFF and $I_C = 0$ A. Therefore,

$$V_{\text{out}} = 5 \text{ V} - (0 \text{ A} \times 2k\Omega) = 5 \text{ V}$$

When $C_p = +5$ V, the transistor is ON and the collector is shorted directly to ground. Therefore,    $V_{\text{out}} = 0$ V.

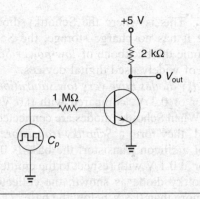

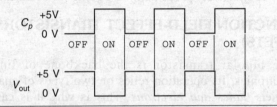

**Fig. 7.36**

**Fig. 7.37** *Solution for Problem 7.29.*

**7.30 Sketch the waveform at $V_{out}$ in the circuit shown, given the input signal, $C_p$.**

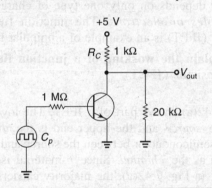

**Fig. 7.38**

*Solution:*

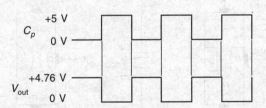

**Fig. 7.39** *Solution for Problem 7.30.*

When $C_p = 0$ V, the transistor is OFF. From voltage divider formula, we have

$$V_{out} = \frac{5 \text{ V} \times 20 \text{ k}\Omega}{20 \text{ k}\Omega + 1 \text{ k}\Omega} = 4.76 \text{ V}$$

When $C_p = +5$ V, the transistor is ON and the collector is shorted to ground, making $V_{out} = 0$ V. Notice the *difference* in $V_{out}$ as compared to Problem 7.29 in which there is no *load resistor* connected to $V_{out}$.

**7.31 One basic function of TTL (transistor-transistor logic) integrated circuit is as a complementary switch. Explain with the help of an example.**

*Solution:*
One basic function of TTL is as an *inverter*. The inverter is used to take a digital level at its input and *complement* it to its opposite state at its output (1 becomes 0, 0 becomes 1). Figure 7.40 illustrates how a common-emitter connected transistor can be used to perform the same function.

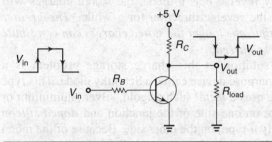

**Fig. 7.40**

When $V_{in}$ equals 1 (+5 V), the transistor is 'turned on' (*saturation*), and $V_{out}$ equals 0 (0 V). When $V_{in}$ equals 0 (0 V), the transistor is 'turned off' (*cut off*) and $V_{out}$ equals 1 (approximately 5 V), assuming that $R_L$ is much greater than $R_C (R_L \gg R_C)$.

**7.32 In Problem 7.31 assume that $R_C = 1$ k$\Omega$, $R_L = 10$ k$\Omega$, and $V_{in} = 0$, calculate $V_{out\ 1}$. If $R_L$ decreases to 1 k$\Omega$ by adding more loads in parallel, calculate $V_{out\ 2}$.**

*Solution:*

$$V_{out\ 1} = \frac{5 \text{ V} \times 10 \text{ k}\Omega}{1 \text{ k}\Omega + 10 \text{ k}\Omega} = 4.55 \text{ V}$$

$$V_{out\ 2} = \frac{5 \text{ V} \times 1 \text{ k}\Omega}{1 \text{ k}\Omega + 1 \text{ k}\Omega} = 2.5 \text{ V}$$

The decrease in $V_{out}$ (from 4.55 V to 2.5 V), by adding more loads in parallel, is called *loading effect*.

## THE SCHOTTKY DIODE

For some applications it may be desirable to arrange that the transistor does not go into saturation. This can be done either by *limiting* the value of the base current drive, or by *clamping*. The arrangement is then called a *non-saturating switch*, and care must be taken that the power rating of the transistor is not exceeded. The solution to this problem is the *Schottky diode*.

**7.33 Explain the role played by charge storage in switching diodes.**

*Solution:*
When a small-signal diode is switched ON (forward biased), electrons from the *n*-region *diffuse* across the junction and travel into the *p*-region before recombi-

nation occurs. Similarly holes from the *p*-region *diffuse* across the junction and travel into the *n*-region before recombination occurs.

The greater the *life time,* the farther the charge carriers can travel before recombination occurs. The greater the *forward current,* the larger the number of charges that cross the junction. *This temporary storage of free electrons and holes is referred to as charge storage.*

When you switch a diode from ON to OFF, charge storage creates a problem. This is because if you suddenly reverse bias a diode, the stored charges will flow in the reverse direction for a while. *The greater the life time, the longer the stored charges can contribute to reverse current.*

The solution to this charge storage problem is a special purpose device called a Schottky diode. This type of diode uses a *metal* such as gold, silver, aluminium or platinum on one side of the junction and *doped silicon* (typically *n*-type) on the other side. Because of the metal on one side of the junction, *the Schottky diode has no depletion layer.* The lack of a depletion layer means that there are no stored charges at the junction.

### 7.34 Explain the working of a Schottky diode and Schottky transistor.

*Solution:*
When a Schottky diode is unbiased free electrons on the *n*-side are in *smaller* orbits than are the free electrons on the metal side. This difference in orbit size is called the *Schottky barrier,* approximately 0.3 V. When the diode is forward biased, free electrons on the *n*-side can gain enough energy to travel in *larger* orbits. Because of this, free electrons can cross the junction and enter the metal, producing a large forward current. *Since the metal has no holes, there is no charge storage and no reverse recovery time.* Schottky diode, sometimes called a *hot-carrier diode,* can switch off faster than an ordinary diode. The symbol for Schottky diode is a rectangular S as shown in Fig. 7.41.

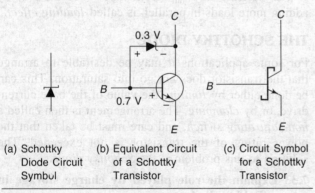

(a) Schottky Diode Circuit Symbol   (b) Equivalent Circuit of a Schottky Transistor   (c) Circuit Symbol for a Schottky Transistor

**Fig. 7.41** *Schottky Diode and Transistor.*

The most important application of Schottky diodes is in digital computers. *The speed of computers depends on how fast their diodes and transistors can turn on*

*and off'.* This is where the Schottky diode comes in. Because it has no charge storage, the Schottky diode has become the backbone of *low-power Schottky TTLs,* a group of widely used digital devices.

*Schottky diodes have very low saturation voltages,* of the order of 0.3 V, compared with 0.6 V for diffused diodes. When Schottky diodes are connected as shown in Fig. 7.41, they form a *Schottky transistor.* During saturation of a silicon transistor, the base is 0.7 V and the collector at 0.1 V with respect to the emitter. By placing the Schottky diode as shown, the collector cannot be driven more than 0.3 V below the base. *Thus, the transistor is effectively prevented from going into saturation.*

## JUNCTION FIELD-EFFECT TRANSISTORS (JFETS)

The bipolar transistor is the backbone of linear electronics. Its operation relies on two types of charge carriers *holes and electrons.* This is why it is called *bipolar.* For most linear applications, the bipolar transistor is the best choice.

There are some applications in which the *unipolar* transistor is better suited. The operation of a unipolar transistor depends on only one type of charge carrier, *either holes or electrons.* The junction field-effect transistor (JFET) is an example of a unipolar transistor.

### 7.35 Explain the working of a junction field-effect transistor (JFET).

*Solution:*
Figure 7.42(a) shows part of a JFET. The lower end is called the *source* and the upper end is the *drain.* The piece of semiconductor between the source and the drain is known as the *channel.* Since *n*-material is used for the JFET in Fig. 7.42(a), the majority carriers are free electrons.

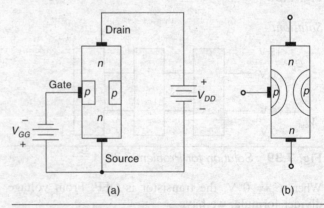

**Fig. 7.42** *The Junction Field-effect Transistor: (a) Normal; Bias Voltages (b) Depletion layer.*

By doping two *p* regions in the sides of the channel, we get the *n*-channel JFET of Fig. 7.42(b). Each of these *p* regions is called a *gate.* When the manufacturer connects a separate external lead to each gate, the device is called a *dual-gate* JFET. If the gates are internally connected by the manufacturer, the device is called a *single-gate* JFET.

The normal polarities for biasing an *n*-channel JFET are also shown in the illustration. The idea is to apply a negative voltage between the gate and the source. Since the gate is reverse biased, only a very small reverse current flows in the gate lead. The more negative the gate voltage is, the smaller the current.

The name *field-effect* is related to the depletion layers around each *p-n* junction. Figure 7.42(b) shows these depletion layers. Free electrons moving between the source and the drain must flow through the *narrow channel* between depletion layers. The size of these depletion layers determines the *width* of the conducting channel. The more negative the gate voltage is, the *narrower* the conducting channel becomes, because the depletion layers get closer to each other. Therefore, *the gate voltage controls the current that flows between the source and the drain.*

### 7.36 What is the difference between a JFET and a bipolar transistor?

*Solution:*

The key difference between a JFET and a bipolar transistor is that the gate of a JFET is *reverse-biased,* whereas the base of a transistor is *forward biased.* This crucial difference means *the JFET is a voltage-controlled device* because the input voltage alone controls the output current. *The bipolar transistor is a current-controlled device,* because the input current controls the output current.

### 7.37 (a) Draw the schematic symbols of a JFET.
###      (b) Draw the drain curves of an *n*-channel JFET.

*Solution:*

(a) Figure 7.43(a) shows the schematic symbol of a JFET. The thin vertical line in Figure 7.43(b) is the channel. The source and drain connect to this line. The gate arrow points towards the *n*-material and away from the *p*-material. *A p-channel JFET is the complement of an n-channel JFET.*

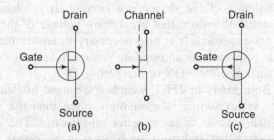

**Fig. 7.43**

(b) Drain curves of a JFET (Fig. 7.44) resemble collector curves of a bipolar transistor. The highest

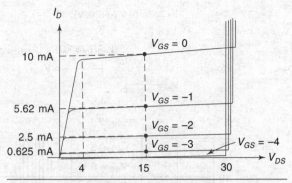

**Fig. 7.44** *Drain Curves of an* n-Channel *JFET.*

curve is for $V_{GS} = 0$. When the gate voltage is zero, the gate is effectively shorted to the source. This is called the *shorted-gate* condition. The *pinch-off voltage* is the drain voltage above which drain current becomes almost constant for the shorted-gate condition. When the drain voltage equals $V_p$, the conducting channels almost touch and further increases in drain voltage produce only a very slight increase in drain current. In Fig. 7.44, $V_p = 4$ V. The *shorted-gate drain current, $I_{DSS}$* (Drain-to-Source with shorted gate), is a close approximation for the drain current anywhere in the active region for the shorted-gate condition. $I_{DSS}$ is the maximum drain current with normal operation of a JFET. All other gate voltages are negative and result in less drain current. When $V_{GS} = V_{GS(OFF)}$ (*Gate Source cut off voltage*), the depletion layers touch, cutting off the drain current. In Fig. 7.44. $V_p = 4$ V and $V_{GS} = -4$ V.

$$V_p = -V_{GS(OFF)}$$

The drain current rises rapidly in the *saturation region* but then levels off in the *active region*. Between voltages $V_p$ and $V_{DS(max)}$, the drain current is almost constant. When the drain voltage is too large, the JFET breaks down. The active region is along the almost horizontal part of the curve. In this region the JFET acts like a constant-current source. The main advantage of JFET amplifiers is *high input resistance*, while the main disadvantage is *low voltage gain*.

### 7.38 For the circuit given, determine the output voltage ($V_{out}$) for the input voltage ($V_{in}$) of (a) –5 V, (b) 0 V. The output characteristics of the JFET are given. (See Fig. 7.45)

*Solution:*

Load line for $V_{DD} = 20$ V and $R_D = 5$ k$\Omega$ is drawn on the output characteristics of the JFET as shown.

(a) When the input voltage $V_{in} = -5$V, the JFET is operating at point *A,* where $I_D \approx 0$ and $V_{out} \approx V_{DD} = 20$ V. This corresponds to the switch in the OFF *state.*

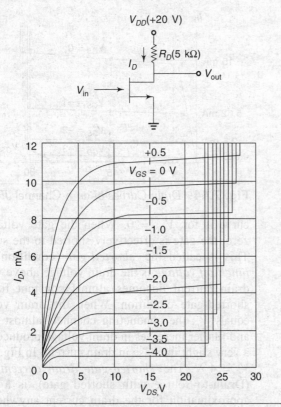

**Fig. 7.45**    *Output Characteristics of an* n-*Channel JFET.*

(b) When $V_{in} = 0$ V, the JFET is operating at point *B*, where $I_D \approx 3.8$ mA and $V_{out} = 1$ V. This corresponds to the switch in the ON *state*.

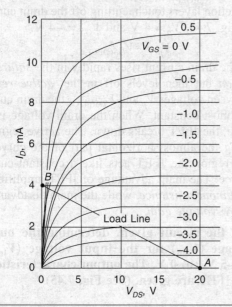

**Fig. 7.46**    *Solution for P7.38. Output Characteristics of JFET.*

## SWITCHING ACTION OF JFETS

The analog switch is one of the main applications of a JFET. *An analog switch either transmits or blocks an analog input voltage.* This analog voltage may be as simple as a sine wave or as complex as speech and music. *The idea behind a JFET analog switch is to use only two points on the load line: cut off and saturation.* When the JFET is *cut off* it's like an open switch. When it is *saturated,* it's like a closed switch.

### 7.39 Explain the switching action of a JFET.

*Solution:*

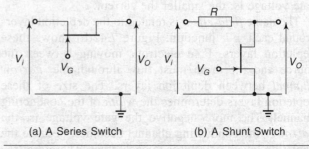

(a) A Series Switch          (b) A Shunt Switch

**Fig. 7.47**    *Junction Field-effect Transistor as an Analog Switch.*

Figure 7.47(a) shows a JFET being used as a *series switch*. When the device is turned ON, the resistance between the input and output is small. Provided the resistances of the source and destination are larger compared with the *ON resistance* of the FET, the device will resemble a *short circuit*.

When the device is turned OFF, the resistance between the source and destination will be equal to the *OFF resistance* of the FET. Provided this is large compared with the resistance within the circuit, this will represent an *open circuit*. Because of the many orders of magnitude difference between the ON and OFF resistances of the FET it is usually easy to satisfy these conditions, allowing the FET to be used as a very efficient switch.

Figure 7.47(b) shows an FET used as a *shunt switch*. Here the series resistance *R* is chosen to be large compared with $R_{ON}$ and small compared with $R_{OFF}$. The potential divider produces an output voltage close to $V_i$ when the device is turned OFF and close to zero when it is turned ON.

*Care must be taken to ensure that the operating conditions of the device are correct.* It is obviously essential to ensure that breakdown voltage of the gate is not exceeded. It is also necessary to ensure that the gate is taken to an appropriate voltage to turn the device either *completely* ON or *completely* OFF.

Both kinds of JFET switches are used in industry. The series switch is used more often than the shunt switch because it has a *better on-off ratio*. The series switch either transmits or blocks an ac signal. *The switching is not perfect in a shunt switch.* When the switch is open, all the input voltage reaches the output. But when the switch is closed, a small amount of the input still reaches the output.

FET circuits in digital applications usually adopt a two-state, or *binary*, arrangement in which all signals are constrained to be within one of two voltage ranges, one range representing one state (for example, the OFF *state*), and the other representing a second state (for example, the ON *state*). These ranges are often referred to as 'logical 0' and 'logical 1'.

# MOSFETS

FETs are probably the simplest forms of transistor to understand and are widely used in both analog and digital applications. *They are characterised by very high input resistances, low power requirements and small physical dimensions.* These characteristics combine to make them ideal for the construction of very high density, such as that used in *Very Large-Scale Integrated* (VLSI), circuits. There are two main forms of field-effect transistors namely the *junction-gate* FET and the *insulated-gate* FET, which is known by a variety of names including the MOSFET.

The *metal-oxide semiconductor FET* or MOSFET, has a source, gate, and drain. Unlike a JFET, however, *the gate is insulated from the channel.* Because of this, we can apply positive voltages as well as negative voltages to the gate. In either case, negligible gate current flows.

## 7.40 Briefly describe the structure of a MOSFET.

*Solution:*

There is an *n*-region with a *source* and *drain*, Fig. 7.48(a). A positive voltage applied across the drain, source terminals forces free electrons to flow from the source to the drain. Unlike the JFET, the MOSFET has a single *p*-region, Fig. 7.48(b), called the *substrate*. This *p*-region reduces the channel between the source and

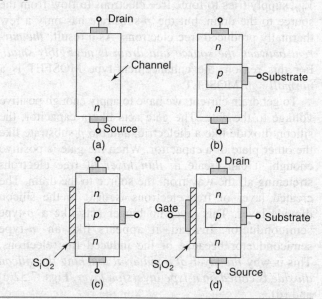

**Fig. 7.48** *MOSFET Structure (a) n-Channel (b) Adding the Substrate (c) Adding the Silicon Dioxide ($S_iO_2$) (d) Adding the Gate.*

the drain so that only a small passage remains at the left side of Fig. 7.48(b). Free electrons flowing from the source to the drain must pass through this *narrow channel.*

A thin layer of *silicon dioxide* ($S_iO_2$) is deposited over the left side of the channel, as shown in Fig. 7.48(c). This material acts as an *insulator.* Finally, a metallic gate is deposited on the insulator, Fig. 7.48(d). Because the gate is insulated from the channel, a MOSFET is also known as an *insulated-gate FET (IGFET).*

## 7.41 Explain the operation of a depletion mode MOSFET?

*Solution:*

In an *n*-channel MOSFET the gate voltage controls the resistance of the *n*-channel. But since the gate is insulated from the channel, we can apply either a positive or a negative voltage to the gate. Figure 7.49(a) shows a negative voltage. This voltage repels free electrons and tries to push them back to the source. This means that *a negative voltage depletes the flow between the source and the drain.*

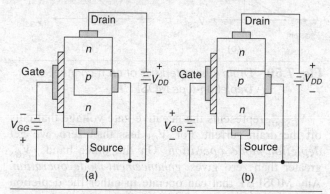

**Fig. 7.49** *(a) Negative Gate Voltage (Depletion Mode).*
*(b) Positive Gate Voltage (Enhancement Mode).*

The more negative the voltage is, the smaller the current through the channel. Enough negative voltage on the gate cuts off the current between the source and the drain. Therefore, with *negative* gate voltage the action of a MOSFET is similar to that of a JFET. Because the action depends on depleting the charges in the channel, *negative gate operation is known as the depletion mode.*

A positive voltage applied to the gate *enhances* the conductivity of the channel. The more positive the gate voltage, the greater the conduction from source to drain. *Operating a MOSFET with a positive gate voltage is known as the enhancement mode.* This is shown in Fig. 7.49(b).

Because of the insulating layer, negligible current flows in either mode of operation. *The input resistance of the gate is incredibly high.* The device in Fig. 7.49 is an *n*-channel MOSFET. *The complementary device is a p-channel MOSFET.*

**7.42 Draw the drain characteristics and symbols of a depletion-type MOSFET.**

*Solution:*

Figure 7.50 illustrates the drain curves of an *n*-channel depletion-type MOSFET.

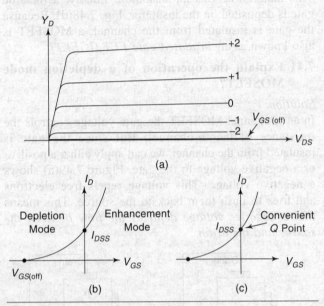

(a)

(b)    (c)

**Fig. 7.50**    *Drain Characteristics of an n-channel Depletion-type MOSFET.*

$V_{GS(off)}$ represents the negative gate voltage that cuts off the drain current. For $V_{GS}$ less than zero, we get *depletion-mode operation*. On the other hand, $V_{GS}$ greater than zero gives *enhancement-mode operation*. Any MOSFET that can operate in either the depletion or the enhancement mode is called a *depletion-type* MOSFET. Since this type of MOSFET has drain current with zero gate voltage, it is also called a *normally on* MOSFET.

Figure 7.51 shows the schematic symbol for a *normally-on MOSFET*. The *gate* appears like a capacitor on the gate cuts off the current between the source and the drain. Therefore some negative voltage.

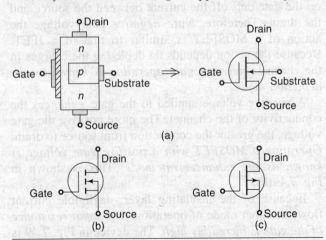

**Fig. 7.51**    *Depletion Type MOSFET Symbols: (a) n-Channel with Substrate Lead (b) n-Channel device (c) p-Channel Device.*

plate. Just to the right of the gate is a thin vertical line that represents the *channel*. The *drain* lead comes out of the top of the channel and the *source* connects to the bottom. *The arrow on the substrate points to the n-material.* Therefore the device is an *n*-channel MOSFET.

**7.43 Draw the structure, drain characteristics and symbols of an enhancement-type MOSFET.**

*Solution:*

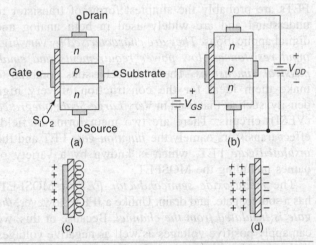

**Fig. 7.52**    *Enhancement Type MOSFET: (a) Structure (b) Normal Bias (c) Creation of Negative Ions (d) Creation of n-Type Inversion Layer.*

Figure 7.52 (a) illustrates an enhancement-type MOSFET. Notice that *the substrate extends all the way to the silicon dioxide.* Because of this, there no longer is an *n*-channel between the source and the drain. Figure 7.52(b) shows the normal biasing polarities. When $V_{GS} = 0$, the $V_{DD}$ supply tries to force free electrons to flow from the source to the drain, but the *p*-substrate has only a few thermally produced free electrons. As a result, *the current between the source and drain is negligibly small.* For this reason, the enhancement-type MOSFET is a *normally off* MOSFET.

To get drain current, we have to apply enough positive voltage to the gate. The gate acts like a capacitor, the silicon dioxide like a dielectric, and the *p* substrate like the other plate of a capacitor. When the gate is positive enough, it can create a *thin layer* of free electrons stretching all the way from the source to the drain. The created layer of free electrons is next to the silicon dioxide layer. This layer no longer acts like a *p*-type semiconductor. Instead, it appears like an *n*-type semiconductor because of the induced free electrons. This is why *the layer of p-material touching the silicon dioxide is called an n-type inversion layer,* Figs. 7.52(c) and (d).

The minimum gate-source voltage that creates the *n*-type inversion layer is called the *threshold voltage,* designated $V_{GS(th)}$. When the gate voltage is *less than* this voltage, no current flows from the source to the drain. But when the gate voltage is *greater than* this voltage, an *n*-type inversion layer connects the source to the drain, and we get a current.

Figure 7.53 shows a set of drain curves for an enhancement type MOSFET. The lowest curve is the $V_{GS(th)}$ curve. When $V_{GS}$ is *less than* $V_{GS(th)}$, the drain current is ideally zero and the MOSFET is OFF. When $V_{GS}$ is *greater than* $V_{GS(th)}$, drain current appears. The larger $V_{GS}$ is, the greater the drain current. The symbol for enhancement type MOSFET, Fig. 7.54, has a broken channel line to indicate the *normally* OFF (NO) condition. In the case of a *p*-channel MOSFET, the threshold voltage is negative and the current is in a direction opposite to that of an *n*-channel device.

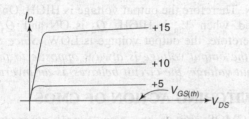

**Fig. 7.53** *Drain Curves for an Enhancement Type MOSFET.*

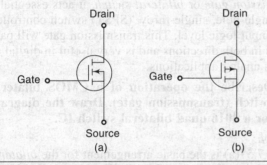

**Fig. 7.54** *For P7.43 Enhancement Type MOSFET Symbols. (a) n-Channel (b) p-Channel.*

## SWITCHING ACTION OF A MOSFET

Computers use integrated circuits with thousands of transistors. These integrated circuits work remarkably well, despite transistor tolerances and changes in temperature. This is because of *two-state design,* using only two points on the load line of each transistor. When used in this way, the transistor acts like a switch rather than a current source. Circuits using transistor switches are called *switching* circuits, *digital* circuits or *logic* circuits. On the other hand, circuits using transistor current sources are called *linear* circuits, *analog* circuits, etc.

### 7.44 What is the significance of MOSFETs?

*Solution:*
The *enhancement-type* MOSFET has had its greatest impact in digital circuits. One reason is its *low power consumption.* Another is the *small amount of space* it

takes on a chip (integrated circuit). A manufacturer can put many more enhancement-type MOSFETs on a chip than bipolar transistors. This is the reason enhancement-type MOSFETs are used in *large-scale integration* (LSI) for microprocessors, memories, and other devices requiring thousands of devices on a chip.

### 7.45 Describe the difference between an active load and a passive load.

*Solution:*
Figure 7.55(a) shows a MOSFET driver and a *passive load* (resistor $R_D$). In this switching circuit when $V_{in}$ is LOW, the MOSFET is cut off and $V_{out}$ equals the supply voltage. On the other hand, when $V_{in}$ is HIGH, the MOSFET conducts heavily and $V_{out}$ drops to a low value. In this circuit, $V_{in}$ is either LOW or HIGH and *the MOSFET acts like a switch that is either ON or OFF.*

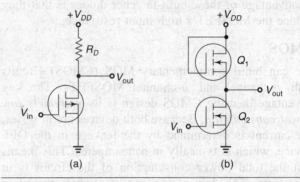

**Fig. 7.55** *MOSFET Driver: (a) Passive Load (b) Active Load.*

Resistors take up much more area than MOSFETS. For this reason, *resistors are rarely used in MOS integrated circuits.* Fig. 7.55 (b) shows another switching circuit with a MOSFET driver $Q_2$ and an *active load* $Q_1$. Because of the drain-feedback bias, $Q_1$ is always conducting. By deliberate design the upper MOSFET has an ON resistance at least ten times greater than that of the lower MOSFET. $Q_1$ *acts like a resistor, and* $Q_2$ *acts like a switch.*

Using a MOS driver and MOS load leads to much smaller integrated circuits because MOSFETs take less room on a chip than resistors. This is why *MOS technology dominates in computer applications; it allows you to get many more circuits on a chip.*

### 7.46 Differentiate between an PMOS and an NMOS.

*Solution:*
One of the first semiconductor techniques used to build *digital ICs* was *p*-channel MOS technology. In this approach *p*-channel enhancement-type MOSFETS act like switches and active loads. But *p*-channel MOS has a big disadvantage; its carriers are holes instead of free electrons. Holes move more slowly than free electrons, which means that *the switching speed of a p-channel device is less than that of an n-channel device. Because*

*of its greater speed, n-channel technology dominates in memory and microprocessor applications.* Circuits using n-channel MOSFETS are often called *NMOS* circuits, the letters being an abbreviation of *N*-channel Metal Oxide Semiconductor. Similarly circuits based on *p*-channel devices are referred to as *PMOS* circuits.

### 7.47 What type of protection is provided to MOSFETs and why?

*Solution:*

MOSFETs are shipped with a *wire ring* around the leads. *The ring is removed only after the MOSFET is connected in the circuit.* The newer MOSFETs are protected by *build-in zener diodes* in parallel with the gate and the source. The zener voltage is less than $V_{GS(max)}$ rating. In this way, the zener diode breaks down before any damage occurs to the thin insulating layer. The disadvantage of these built-in zener diodes is that they reduce the MOSFET's high input resistance.

## CMOS

We can build complementary MOS (CMOS) circuits with *p*-channel and *n*-channel MOSFETs. The key advantage in using CMOS design is its *extremely low power consumption*. Because both devices are in series, the current is determined by the leakage in the OFF device, which is typically in nanoamperes. This means that the total power consumption of the circuit is in nanowatts. This low power consumption is the main reason why CMOS circuits are popular in pocket calculators, digital wrist watches and satellites.

### 7.48 Explain the working of a CMOS inverter.

*Solution:*

$Q_1$ is a *p*-channel device and $Q_2$ an *n*-channel device. This circuit (Fig. 7.56(a)) is analogous to the class-B push-pull bipolar amplifier in Fig. 7.56(b). *When one device is ON, the other is OFF, and vice versa.*

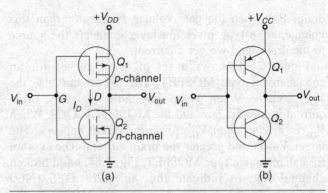

**Fig. 7.56** *(a) CMOS Inverter (b) Bipolar Equivalent.*

For instance, when $V_{in}$ is LOW, $Q_2$ is OFF but $Q_1$ is ON. Therefore the output voltage is HIGH. On the other hand, when $V_{in}$ is HIGH, $Q_2$ is ON and $Q_1$ is OFF. Therefore, the output voltage is LOW. *Since the phase of the output voltage is always opposite to that of the input voltage, the circuit behaves as an inverter.*

## SWITCHING ACTION OF CMOS

A CMOS switch has *very small quiescent power dissipation*. Because of this CMOS switches have become very popular in logic circuits known as the *transmission gate* or *bilateral switch*, it acts essentially as a single-pole, single-throw (SPST) switch controlled by an input logic level. This transmission gate will pass signals in both directions and is very useful in digital as well as analog applications.

### 7.49 Describe the operation of a CMOS bilateral switch (transmission gate). Draw the diagram for a 4016 quad bilateral switch IC.

*Solution:*

Figure 7.57(a) is the basic arrangement for the *bilateral switch*. It consists of a P-MOSFET and an N-MOSFET *inparallel* so that *both* polarities of input voltage can be switched. The CONTROL input and its inverse are used

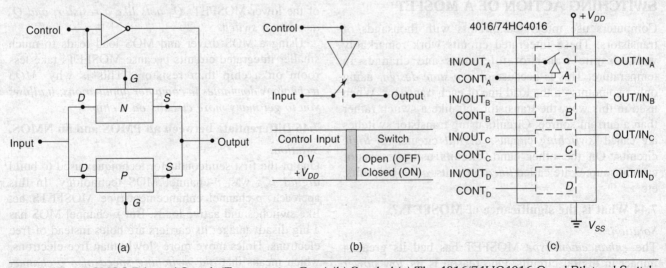

| Control Input | Switch |
|---|---|
| 0 V | Open (OFF) |
| +$V_{DD}$ | Closed (ON) |

**Fig. 7.57** *(a) CMOS Bilateral Switch (Transmission Gate) (b) Symbol (c) The 4016/74HC4016 Quad Bilateral Switch.*

to turn the switch on (closed) and off (open). When the CONTROL is HIGH, both MOSFETs are turned ON and the switch is closed. When the CONTROL is LOW, both MOSFETs are turned OFF and the switch is open. Ideally, this circuit operates like an electromechanical relay. In practice, it is not a perfect short circuit when the switch is closed; the switch resistance $R_{on}$ is typically 200 Ω. In the open state, the switch resistance $R_{off}$ is very large, typically $10^{12}$ Ω, which for most purposes is an open circuit. The *symbol* in Fig. 7.57(b) is used to represent the bilateral switch.

This circuit is called a bilateral switch because *the input and output terminals can be interchanged.* The signals applied to the switch inputs can be either digital or analog signals, *provided they stay within the limits of 0 to $V_{DD}$ volts.*

Figure 7.57(c) shows the traditional logic diagram for a 4016 quad bilateral switch IC, which is also available in the 74HC series as a 74HC4016. The IC contains four bilateral switches that operate as described above. *Each switch is independently controlled by its own control input.* For example, the ON/OFF status of the top switch is controlled by input $CONT_A$. *Since the switches are bidirectional, either switch terminal can serve as input or output,* as the labeling indicates.

# SUMMARY

- ➢ One problem with a mechanical switch is contact bounce.
- ➢ Mechanical switches are sometimes debounced with a latch, called a `flip-flop`.
- ➢ The latch is also called a bistable multivibrator.
- ➢ For a positive pulse the leading edge is a positive-going transition (rising edge).
- ➢ In ideal pulses the transitions occur instantaneously.
- ➢ In non-ideal pulses the transitions are not instantaneous because of nonlinearities that occur near the bottom and top of the pulse.
- ➢ Pulse width is a measure of the duration of the pulse.
- ➢ Duty cycle is the ratio of the pulse width to the period expressed as a percentage.
- ➢ A nonperiodic pulse waveform does not repeat itself at fixed intervals.
- ➢ Most digital signals require precise timing.
- ➢ Serial format is inexpensive but it is slow.
- ➢ Parallel format is expensive but it is fast.
- ➢ The RS232 communication standard is a very common scheme for serial transmission of data over telephone lines or from one computer to another.
- ➢ Centronics printer interface and IEEE-488 instrumentation interface are commonly used by computers to communicate to external devices.
- ➢ The SPDT switch forms a single bit of memory circuit.
- ➢ An electromechanical relay has contacts like a manual switch, but it is controlled by external voltage instead of being operated manually.
- ➢ A relay provides total isolation between the triggering source and the output.
- ➢ The rated currents of relay contacts are normally much higher than those for semiconductor devices.
- ➢ Relays are far too slow for use in the main frame of a computer; they are used for various auxiliary functions in peripheral devices.
- ➢ Systems requiring complex relay switching schemes are generally implemented using PLCs.
- ➢ The semiconductor diode is analogous to a simple switch.
- ➢ In normal switching circuit applications, diodes are never operated in the Zener range.
- ➢ When used as a switch, we operate the transistor at either saturation or cutoff.
- ➢ Soft saturation means that the transistor is barely saturated; it is not reliable.
- ➢ Hard saturation means the transistor has a sufficient base current to be saturated under all operating conditions.
- ➢ The Schottky diode has no depletion layer, and hence no stored charges at the junction.
- ➢ The Schottky diode forms the backbone of low-power Schottky TTLs.
- ➢ The JFET is a unipolar device; it is also a voltage-controlled device.
- ➢ The junction transistor is a bipolar device; it is a current-controlled device.
- ➢ The JFET can be used either as a series switch or as a shunt switch.
- ➢ JFET series switch is used more often; it has a better on-off ratio.
- ➢ MOS technology dominates in computer applications; it allows you to get many more circuits on a chip.
- ➢ Since CMOS switches are bilateral, either switch terminal can serve as input or output.

# REVIEW QUESTIONS

1. What type of logic, positive or negative, is used in digital systems?
2. Which system requires more electrical conductors, serial or parallel?
3. Which system is faster, serial or parallel?
4. How does a mechanical switch differ from an electromechanical relay?
5. What is the range of reverse recovery time for switching diodes?
6. How can a transistor be operated as a switch?
7. Explain the disadvantage of using *p*-channel MOS.
8. What are the applications of CMOS?
9. Why does the MOS technology dominate the area of microprocessors, memory, and other LSI devices?
10. What is the key advantage of CMOS?
11. Explain the term active load.
12. What are complementary devices?
13. Why is a CMOS switch called bilateral?
14. What does a CMOS bilateral switch consist of?
15. Draw the symbol of a CMOS bilateral switch.

# SUPPLEMENTARY PROBLEMS

16. Determine the period of a clock waveform whose frequency is:
    (a) 2 MHz        (b) 500 kHz        (c) 4.27 MHz        (d) 17 MHz
17. Determine the frequency of a clock waveform whose period is:
    (a) 2 μs        (b) 100 μs        (c) 0.75 ms        (d) 1.5 μs
18. (a) How long will it take to transmit the $33_{10}$ in serial if the clock frequency is 3.7 MHz? Transmit the number as an 8-bit binary number.
    (b) Is the serial line HIGH or LOW at 1.21 μs?
19. Draw the timing diagram for $V_{out1}$, $V_{out2}$, and $V_{out3}$ in the given Fig. 7.58.

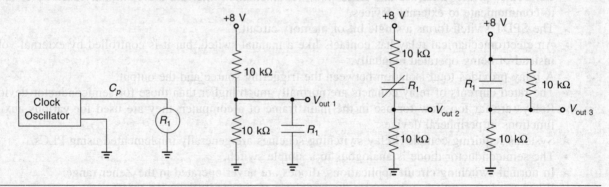

**Fig. 7.58** *For Problem 19*

20. Determine $V_1$, $V_2$, $V_3$, $V_4$, $V_5$, $V_6$ and $V_7$ in the given circuit.
21. In Fig. 7.59, if the anodes of any of the diodes $D_{11}$, $D_{12}$, or $D_{13}$ is connected to +5 V instead of 0 V, what happens to $V_7$?

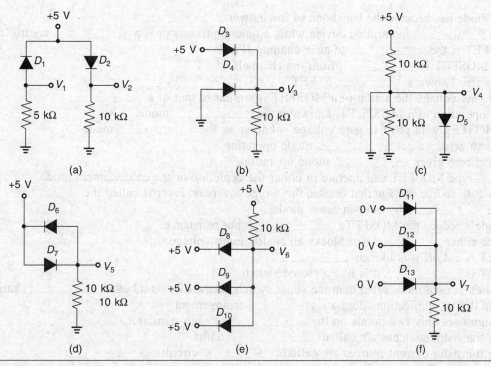

**Fig. 7.59**  *For Problem 20.*

# OBJECTIVE TYPE QUESTIONS

Test your understanding

## Fill in the Blanks

22. Digital signals respond to the digital _____ and not the actual voltage levels.
23. To forward bias a diode the anode is made more _____ than the cathode.
24. When the input current $I_B$ is applied, the transistor does not switch ON _____.
25. The time between application of base current and commencement of collector current is termed as the _____ time.
26. The rise time is defined as the time it takes for $I_C$ to go from _____ to 90% of its maximum level.
27. $t_{on}$ = _____.
28. A transistor cannot be switched on _____.
29. The speed and delay problems are overcome by never allowing the transistor to go into _____.
30. Faster operation generally means greater _____ power.
31. In the ON condition both junctions of the transistor are _____.
32. In the ON condition current flowing through the transistor is _____ of base current.
33. In the OFF state the collector dissipation is _____.
34. In the ON state the collector dissipation is _____.
35. For satisfactory operation, from the power dissipation view point, the base signal must be _____ to drive the transistor into saturation.
36. If the transistor does not go into saturation, the arrangement is called a _____ switch.
37. The greater the _____ the farther the charge carriers can travel before recombination occurs.
38. The greater the forward current the _____ the number of charges that cross the junction.
39. The greater the life time the _____ the stored charges contribute to the reverse current.
40. $t_{rr}$ is the time it takes for reverse current to drop _____ of the forward current.
41. The Schottky diode has no _____ layer.
42. There is no charge _____ at the junction of a Schottky diode.
43. The Schottky barrier is approximately _____.
44. Schottky diode is sometimes called a _____ diode.
45. The symbol for Schottky diode is a _____.

46. The Schottky diode has become the backbone of low-power _____.
47. The JFET is a _____ controlled device while a junction transistor is a _____ controlled device.
48. A *p*-channel JFET is the _____ of an *n*-channel JFET.
49. The gate of a MOSFET is _____ from the channel.
50. A MOSFET is also known as _____ FET.
51. With negative gate voltage the action of a MOSFET is similar to that of a _____.
52. Negative gate operation of a MOSFET is known as the _____ mode.
53. Operating a MOSFET with positive gate voltage is known as the _____ mode.
54. For $V_{GS}$ less than zero, we get _____ mode operation.
55. $V_{GS}$ greater than zero gives _____ mode operation.
56. A _____ type MOSFET can operate in either the depletion or the enhancement mode.
57. The minimum gate-source voltage that creates the *n*-type inversion layer is called the _____ voltage.
58. MOSFETs are _____ by built-in zener diodes.
59. Protection diode's reduce the MOSFETs _____ input resistance.
60. An FET switch either _____ or blocks an analog input voltage.
61. When the JFET is cut off it is like an _____.
62. When the JFET is _____ it is like a closed switch.
63. The series switch is used more often than the shunt switch because it has a better _____ ratio.
64. FET circuits in digital application adopt a _____ arrangement.
65. Two-state design uses only two points on the _____ of each transistor.
66. Circuits using transistor switches are called _____ circuits.
67. Circuits using transistor current sources are called _____ circuits.
68. Resistors are rarely used in _____ integrated circuits.

## True/False Questions

State whether the following statements are True or False.

69. A pulse has two edges: a leading edge and a lagging edge.
70. The pulse width is a measure of the duration of the pulse.
71. The serial format is expensive.
72. The diode is an ideal device in either direction.
73. A transistor can be operated in three configurations.
74. Schottky diodes are used to prevent saturation.
75. In practically all switching applications the transistor is used in CB configuration.
76. The speed and delay problems are overcome by allowing the transistor to go into saturation.
77. The JFET is a bipolar device.
78. Positive gate operation is known as depletion mode.
79. When a JFET is cut off, it is like a closed switch.
80. An ideal pulse waveform is the complement of a non-ideal pulse waveform.
81. The serial system requires more electrical conductors.
82. The range of reverse recovery time for switching diodes is from 4 to 50 ns.
83. When the manufacturer connects a separate external lead to each gate, the device is called a dual-gate JFET.
84. The drain current levels off in the active region and the JFET acts like a constant-current source.
85. FETs have moderate input resistance.
86. The key advantage of CMOS is its low power consumption.
87. MOSFETs have low input resistance.
88. Zero bias works with enhancement type MOSFET.
89. Complementary devices are identical in every way except their supply and input voltage polarities.
90. PMOS is faster than NMOS.
91. The Schottky diode has no depletion layer.
92. The JFET can be operated only as a series switch.

## Multiple Choice Questions

93. Active devices used in digital circuits generally operate as
    (a) amplifiers        (b) switches        (c) rectifiers        (d) waveform generators
94. The devices commonly used for making digital circuits are
    (a) mechanical switches              (b) relays
    (c) vacuum tubes                     (d) semiconductor devices

95. The time required to switch a *p-n* junction from ON to OFF is equal to
    - (a) zero
    - (b) storage time
    - (c) switching time
    - (d) transition time

96. The storage time of a *p-n* junction
    - (a) decreases with increased reverse-bias voltage
    - (b) decreases with increased forward-bias voltage
    - (c) increases with increased reverse-bias voltage
    - (d) increases with increased forward-bias voltage

97. Faster switching of a *p-n* junction requires
    - (a) a large current in the reverse direction
    - (b) zero current in the reverse direction
    - (c) reverse saturation current in the reverse direction
    - (d) none of the above

98. The maximum operating frequency of a diode used as a switch
    - (a) depends on the diode characteristics and switching voltages
    - (b) depends only on switching voltages
    - (c) depends only on diode characteristics
    - (d) none of the above

99. For fastest switching operation, it is preferred to use
    - (a) normal *p-n* junction diodes
    - (b) vacuum diodes
    - (c) zener diodes
    - (d) Schottky diodes

100. The Schottky diode is a
    - (a) metal-semiconductor junction
    - (b) *p-n* junction
    - (c) MOS device
    - (d) vacuum device

101. The switching speed of a Schottky diode
    - (a) is lower than that of a *p-n* junction diode.
    - (b) is the same as that of a *p-n* junction diode.
    - (c) is higher than that of a *p-n* junction diode.
    - (d) may be lower than or higher than that of a *p-n* junction diode.

102. The most commonly used configuration of a transistor used as a switch is
    - (a) CB
    - (b) CC
    - (c) CE
    - (d) CB or CC

103. The delay in the switching mode operation of a *p-n* junction diode is mainly due to
    - (a) excess minority charge stored in the junction when forward biased.
    - (b) metallic contacts.
    - (c) different doping levels on the two sides of the junction.
    - (d) none of the above.

104. A junction transistor used as a switch, switches between
    - (a) cut-off and saturation regions.
    - (b) cut-off and active regions.
    - (c) active and saturation regions.
    - (d) none of the above.

105. A BJT with $h_{FE} = 200$, $I_B = 10\ \mu A$ and $I_C = 4$ mA is operating in
    - (a) active region
    - (b) cut-off region
    - (c) saturation region
    - (d) (a) or (c)

106. *n-p-n* transistors are preferred over *p-n-p* transistors for digital applications because
    - (a) they consume less power.
    - (b) of the requirements of positive logic system.
    - (c) the mobility of electrons is higher than that of holes.
    - (d) none of the above.

107. In switching applications CE configuration is preferred because
    - (a) it requires low voltage or low current.
    - (b) it requires only one power supply.
    - (c) it has negligible $I_{CEO}$.
    - (d) it is easy to understand.

108. When a BJT is turned OFF, the transistor comes to the OFF state
    - (a) as soon as the input signal is reversed.
    - (b) as soon as the power is switched OFF.
    - (c) after excess charge stored in the base region is removed.
    - (d) as soon as the input signal is removed.

109. When used as a switch, a Schottky transistor switches between
    - (a) cut-off and active regions.
    - (b) cut-off and saturation regions.
    - (c) active and saturation regions.
    - (d) different operating points in the active region.

110. Schottky transistors are preferred over normal transistors in digital applications because of their
     (a) higher propagation delay          (b) lower propagation delay
     (c) higher power dissipation           (d) lower power dissipation
111. Higher switching speed is possible in Schottky transistors over normal transistors because
     (a) the transistor is not allowed to go to cut-off.
     (b) the transistor is not allowed to go to saturation.
     (c) the transistor operates in cut-off and saturation regions.
     (d) the transistor operates in active and saturation regions.
112. For an *n*-channel enhancement mode MOSFET, the drain current
     (a) decreases with increase in drain voltage     (b) decreases with decrease in drain voltage
     (c) increases with increase in gate voltage       (d) decreases with increase in gate voltage
113. For a MOSFET, the gate current
     (a) is dependent on drain current               (b) is negligibly small
     (c) is independent of gate voltage              (d) increases with increase in gate voltage
114. *n*-channel MOS devices are preferred over *p*-channel MOS devices for digital applications because of
     (a) higher mobility of electrons than that of holes
     (b) lower power dissipation
     (c) higher power dissipation
     (d) none of the above

# ANSWERS

1. Positive logic is preferred
2. Parallel
3. Parallel
4. An electromechanical relay is controlled by external voltage instead of being operated manually.
5. 4 ns to 50 ns
6. By operating it at either saturation or cut off but no where else along the load line.
7. The switching speed of a *p*-channel device is less than that of an *n*-channel device
8. Pocket calculators, digital wrist watches and satellites
9. It takes less space on a chip and allows you to get many more circuits on a chip.
10. Extremely low power consumption
11. An active load is a transistor that acts as a load for another transistor.
12. *p*-MOS and *n*-MOS are complementary devices
13. Because it passes signals in both directions.
14. A *p*-MOSFET and an *n*-MOSFET in parallel with a control input and its inverse.
15. See text
16. (a) 0.5 μs          (b) 2 μs          (c) 0.234 μs          (d) 58.8 ns
17. (a) 500 kHz         (b) 10 kHz        (c) 1.33 kHz          (d) 0.667 MHz
18. (a) 2.16 μs         (b) LOW

19.

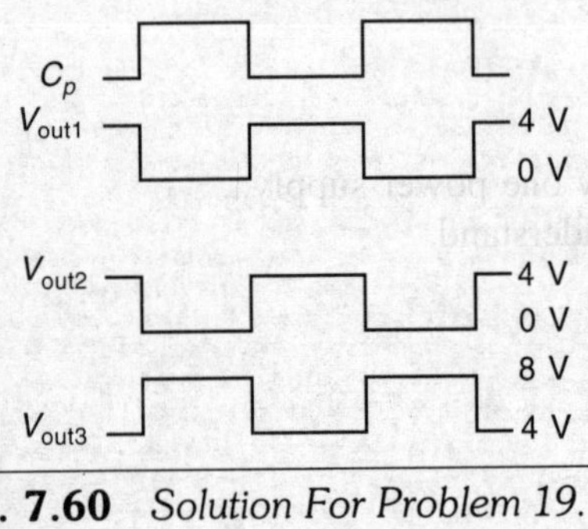

**Fig. 7.60**   *Solution For Problem 19.*

20. $V_1 = 0$ V, $V_2 = 4.3$ V
    $V_3 = 4.3$ V, $V_4 = 0$ V, $V_5 = 4.3$ V
    $V_6 = 5.0$ V, $V_7 = 0$ V
21. The diode will conduct raising $V_7$ to 4.3 V (OR)

| | | | |
|---|---|---|---|
| 22. state | 23. positive | 24. immediately | 25. delay |
| 26. 10% | 27. $t_d + t_r$ | 28. instantaneously | 29. saturation |
| 30. computing | 31. forward biased | 32. independent | 33. very low |
| 34. low | 35. sufficient | 36. non-saturating | 37. life time |
| 38. larger | 39. longer | 40. 10% | 41. depletion |
| 42. storage | 43. 0.3 V | 44. hot-carrier | 45. rectangular |
| 46. Schottky TTL | 47. voltage; current | 48. complement | 49. insulated |
| 50. insulated-gate | 51. JFET | 52. depletion | 53. enhancement |
| 54. depletion | 55. enhancement | 56. depletion | 57. threshold |
| 58. protected | 59. high | 60. transmits | 61. open |
| 62. saturated | 63. ON-OFF | 64. two-state | 65. load line |
| 66. digital | 67. analog | 68. MOS | 69. True |
| 70. True | 71. False | 72. False | 73. True |
| 74. True | 75. False | 76. False | 77. False |
| 78. False | 79. False | 80. False | 81. False |
| 82. True | 83. True | 84. True | 85. False |
| 86. True | 87. False | 88. False | 89. True |
| 90. False | 91. True | 92. False | 93. (b) |
| 94. (d) | 95. (c) | 96. (a) | 97. (a) |
| 98. (a) | 99. (d) | 100. (a) | 101. (c) |
| 102. (c) | 103. (a) | 104. (b) | 105. (c) |
| 106. (c) | 107. (a) | 108. (c) | 109. (a) |
| 110. (b) | 111. (b) | 112. (c) | 113. (b) |
| 114. (a) | | | |

# Wave Shaping

## INTRODUCTION

The waveforms obtained from digital circuits using active devices are called *primary waveforms*. The process of obtaining a desired waveform from a given waveform by suitable operations is called *wave-shaping* and the circuits used for this purpose are called *wave-shaping circuits*.

Wave shaping can be classified as linear wave shaping and non-linear wave shaping. In *linear wave shaping* the signal passes through linear systems and circuits like integrators and differentiators (named for the mathematical operations of integration and differentiation). In *non-linear wave shaping* the signal passes through non-linear systems and circuits like clippers, clampers etc. (rejection of positive or negative spikes or both).

## CAPACITOR CHARGE AND DISCHARGE RATES

When a capacitor is charged from a d.c. voltage source through a resistor, the *instantaneous level* of capacitor voltage may be calculated at any given time. There is a definite relationship between the *time constant* of an RC circuit and the time required for the capacitor to charge to approximately 63% and 99% of the input voltage. Also, an important relationship exists between the time constant of a circuit and the *rise time* of the output voltage from the circuit. Depending on the *arrangement of the RC circuit,* it may be employed as an integrator or a differentiator.

**8.1 Establish the relation between charge and discharge of a capacitor through a resistor. What is the significance of CR time constant?**

*Solution:*
In the circuit in Fig. 8.1, the capacitor $C$ is uncharged. The circuit conditions immediately after the switch $S$ is closed in position 1, are $Q = 0$, $V_C = 0$, $V_R = E$, and the *charging current* is $I_C = \dfrac{E}{R}$ (maximum value).

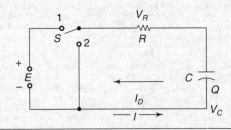

**Fig. 8.1**    *Charge and Discharge of a Capacitor Through a Resistor.*

$Q$ is the charge, measured in coulombs, that initially must be zero because a capacitor can neither charge nor discharge instantaneously. Since no voltage can appear across the capacitor until time has elapsed after the switch is closed in position 1, *the capacitor must initially behave as a short circuit*. The *time constant* of the circuit is CR seconds where $C$ is measured in farads and $R$ in ohms. After a time interval of CR seconds from the instant $S$ is closed in position 1, the circuit conditions, as shown in Fig. 8.2, are

$$Q = 63.2\% \text{ of } CE \text{ coulombs}$$
$$V_C = 63.2\% \text{ of } E$$
$$V_R = 36.8\% \text{ of } E$$
$$I_C = 36.8\% \text{ of } \frac{E}{R}$$

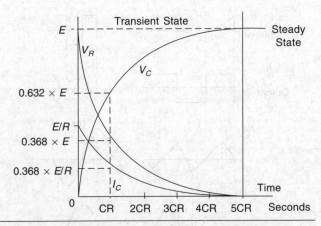

**Fig. 8.2**   *Charging a Capacitor Through a Resistor.*

You can find the order of time constant value from Table 8.1. Following an interval of 2CR seconds from the instant *S* is closed in position 1, the capacitor has acquired 86.5% of its final charge, CE coulombs, and the voltage across the capacitor is 0.865E. After 3CR and 4CR seconds, the charge percentages are respectively 95.0% and 98.2%. *After 5 CR seconds, the circuit is assumed to have reached its steady state conditions which are $Q = CE$, $V_C = E$, $V_R = 0$, and $I_C = 0$. The fully charged capacitor behaves as an open circuit.*

**Table 8.1**   *CR Time Constants*

| C | R | Time Constant CR |
|---|---|---|
| farads | ohms | seconds |
| μF | ohms | microseconds |
| μF | kΩ | milliseconds |
| μF | MΩ | seconds |
| pF | ohms | picoseconds |
| pF | kΩ | nanoseconds |
| pF | MΩ | microseconds |

## 8.2 Express the mathematical relations during charging and discharging of the capacitor during transient state.

*Solution:*

The following equations refer to the *charging* of the capacitor during the transient state.

$$\left\{ \begin{array}{l} Q = CE(1 - e^{-t/CR}), \ V_C = E(1 - e^{-t/CR}) \\ I_C = \dfrac{E}{R} \ e^{-t/CR} \ \text{and} \ V_R = E \ e^{-t/CR} \end{array} \right. \quad (8.1)$$

where $e = 2.7183$ and is the base of natural logarithms.

If *S* is now switched to position 2, Fig. 8.1, the initial conditions are

$$Q = CE, \ V_C = E, \ V_R = -E,$$

and the *discharging current* $I_D = -\dfrac{E}{R}$.

The *negative signs* for the values of $V_R$ and $I_D$ indicate that the *polarity* of the voltage drop across the resistor, $V_R$, has *reversed* because the discharge current, $I_D$, is in

the opposite direction to the previous charging current, $I_C$; $I_D$ and $V_R$ are therefore shown below the time axis in Fig. 8.3. After an interval equal to one time constant (CR seconds), the conditions are

$$Q = 36.8\% \text{ of CE}$$
$$V_C = 36.8\% \text{ of } E$$
$$V_R = 36.8\% \text{ of } (-E)$$
$$I_D = 36.8\% \text{ of } (-E/R)$$

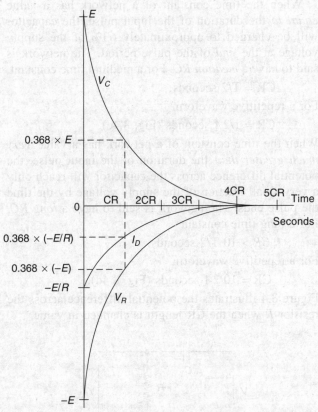

**Fig. 8.3**   *Discharge of a Capacitor Through a Resistor.*

Following an interval of 2CR seconds from the instant *S* is switched to position 2, the capacitor's charge has fallen to 13.5% of CE coulombs; the capacitor therefore has lost 86.5% of its initial charge. After 3CR seconds, the percentages for the capacitor's remaining charge are respectively 5.0% and 1.8%. The equations for the transient *discharge* state are

$$\left\{ \begin{array}{l} Q = CEe^{-t/CR}, \ V_C = Ee^{-t/CR} \\ I_D = -\dfrac{E}{R} \ e^{-t/CR} \ \text{and} \ V_R = -Ee^{-t/CR} \end{array} \right. \quad (8.2)$$

*After 5CR seconds, the capacitor is assumed to have fully discharged,* and all circuit quantities are zero. The capacitor is now completely discharged. $Q = 0$ C, $V_C = V_R = 0$ V, $I_D = 0$ A.

## 8.3 Differentiate between short *RC*, medium *RC*, and long *RC*.

*Solution:*

When the time constant of a network has a value *very much less* than the duration of the input pulse, the capacitor will be charged to the supply voltage a long time *before* the pulse ends. The network is said to have a *short RC*. If the pulse duration is *T/2* seconds, for short time constant

$$CR < T/20 \text{ seconds.}$$

When the input signal is a repetitive waveform, its periodicity is

*T* = 1/f seconds and CR = 1/20 f seconds (Fig. 8.4b).

When the time constant of a network has a value *equal to* the duration of the input pulse, the capacitor will be charged to approximately 63% of the supply voltage at the *end* of the pulse period. The network is said to have a *medium RC*. For a medium time constant.

$$CR = T/2 \text{ seconds.}$$

For a repetitive waveform

$$CR = 1/2 \text{ f seconds (Fig. 8.4c).}$$

When the time constant of a network has a value *very much greater than* the duration of the input pulse, the potential difference across the capacitor will reach only a very small fraction of the supply voltage by the time the pulse ends. The network is said to have a *long RC*. For a long time constant

$$CR > 10 \text{ } T/2 \text{ seconds.}$$

For a repetitive waveform

$$CR = 10/2 \text{ f seconds (Fig. 8.4d).}$$

Figure 8.4 illustrates the potential difference across the resistor *R* when the CR length is changed in value.

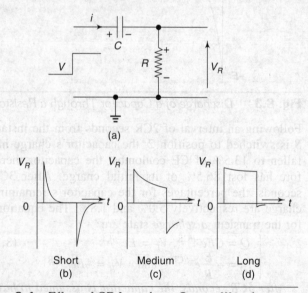

**(a)**

**Short (b)**    **Medium (c)**    **Long (d)**

**Fig. 8.4**    *Effect of CR Length on Output Waveform.*

## INTEGRATORS

An integrator is used as a *wave shaper* in many special applications. *The integrator has a long time constant and the output is taken across a capacitor.* Integrated waveforms are shown in Fig. 8.5.

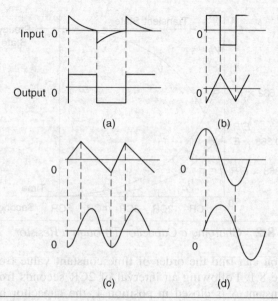

**(a)**    **(b)**

**(c)**    **(d)**

**Fig. 8.5**    *Integrated Waveforms.*

**8.4 Describe the operation of an integrator with a square wave input.**

*Solution:*

Integration is a *summation* of area. An integrator produces an output voltage which is proportional to the area enclosed by the input waveform. Figure 8.6 shows an *RC* circuit with a square wave input and with the output voltage taken across the *capacitor*. The shape of the output (capacitor) voltage is dependent upon the relationship between the time constant (*RC*) and the pulse width (PW).

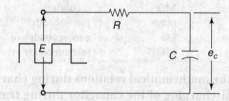

**Fig. 8.6**    *Integrating Circuit with Square Wave Input.*

1. When $RC \leq PW/10$ the capacitor is charged to 99.3% of the input voltage after time $t = 5 \ RC$. Let $RC = PW/10$, then $e_c \approx E$ at $t = PW/2$.

   In this case, the output voltage *roughly approximates* the square wave input. If *RC* is made smaller than one-tenth of PW, then the output even closely resembles the square wave input. This is shown in Fig. 8.7(a).

2. When $RC = PW$, the settled waveform has an amplitude which is less than 63.2% of the input voltage after time $t = RC$. Under these conditions, *the waveform of the capacitor voltage begins to approach a triangular shape*. This is shown in Fig. 8.7(b).

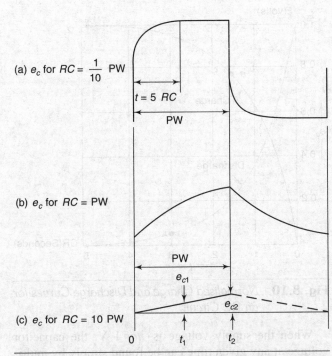

(a) $e_c$ for $RC = \frac{1}{10}$ PW

$t = 5\,RC$

PW

(b) $e_c$ for $RC = $ PW

PW

$e_{c1}$

$e_{c2}$

(c) $e_c$ for $RC = 10$ PW

$0 \qquad t_1 \qquad t_2$

**Fig. 8.7** *Output Waveforms for Various RC and PW Relationships. The Circuit behaves as an Integrator only when RC is Equal to or Greater than 10 PW.*

3. When $RC \geq 10\ PW$, the $RC$ circuit, as arranged in Fig. 8.6 is referred to as an *integrator*. The capacitor voltage waveform is shown in Fig. 8.7(c). To understand how the circuit integrates, it is necessary to calculate the voltage output levels in relation to time.

$$e_{c2} = E - Ee^{-1/10} \text{ (at time } t_2) \approx 0.1\ E$$
$$e_{c1} = E - Ee^{-1/20} \text{ (at time } t_1) \approx 0.05\ E$$

This result shows that after time $t_1$, $e_{c1} \approx 0.05\ E$, and after time $t_2 = 2t_1$, $e_{c2} = 0.1\ E = 2e_{c1}$. *The capacitor voltage increases almost linearly.* It is observed from Fig. 8.7(c) that

(a) When the *pulse width* is doubled, the output voltage is doubled.
(b) The *charging rate* is linear for $RC \geq 10$ PW.
(c) The *output amplitude* is directly proportional to the pulse width.
(d) The *charging rate* increases in proportion to the input voltage.
(e) The *output voltage* is proportional to the pulse area (PA).

$$e_c \propto \text{PA} \times \text{PW}$$

An *integrating circuit* is an *RC* circuit with the output taken across the capacitor and $RC \geq 10$ PW.

**8.5 Calculate the levels of capacitor voltage $e_c$ in the circuit given in Fig. 8.8 at 2 ms intervals from the instant the switch $S$ is closed. Plot a graph of $e_c$ versus time. $E = 10$ V, $C = 4\ \mu F$, and $R = 1\ k\Omega$.**

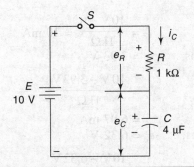

**Fig. 8.8**

*Solution:*

Since $E_0 = 0$, equation $e_c = E(1 - e^0)$ may be used to calculate $e_c$.

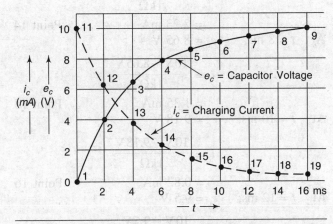

**Fig. 8.9** *Capacitor Voltage and Current Plotted Versus Time for an RC Circuit.*

Charging current $i_c$ is initially a maximum when the capacitor voltage $e_c$ is zero. As $e_c$ increases exponentially, $i_c$ decreases exponentially.

At $t = 0$, $\quad e_c = E(1 - e^0) = 0$ V $\qquad$ Point 1
At $t = 2$ ms, $\quad e_c = 10$ V $[1 - e^{-2ms(1\ k\Omega \times 4\ \mu F)}]$
$\qquad\qquad\qquad = 3.93$ V $\qquad\qquad\qquad\qquad$ Point 2
At $t = 4$ ms, $\quad e_c = 10$ V $[1 - e^{-4ms(1\ k\Omega \times 4\ \mu F)}]$
$\qquad\qquad\qquad = 6.32$ V $\qquad\qquad\qquad\qquad$ Point 3
At $t = 6$ ms, $\qquad e_c = 7.77$ V $\qquad\qquad\qquad$ Point 4
At $t = 8$ ms, $\qquad e_c = 8.65$ V $\qquad\qquad\qquad$ Point 5
At $t = 10$ ms, $\qquad e_c = 9.18$ V $\qquad\qquad\qquad$ Point 6
At $t = 12$ ms, $\qquad e_c = 9.5$ V $\qquad\qquad\qquad$ Point 7
At $t = 14$ ms, $\qquad e_c = 9.7$ V $\qquad\qquad\qquad$ Point 8
At $t = 16$ ms, $\qquad e_c = 9.82$ V $\qquad\qquad\qquad$ Point 9

**8.6 Determine the instantaneous levels of charging current in the circuit shown in Fig. 8.8 at 2 ms time intervals from the instant that switch $S$ is closed. Plot a graph showing $i_c$ versus time.**

*Solution:*

$$i_c = \frac{E - e_c}{R}$$

At    $t = 0$,        $i_c = \dfrac{10\,V - 0}{1k\Omega} = 10$ mA        Point 11

At    $t = 2$ ms,     $e_c = 3.93$ V

$$i_c = \dfrac{10\,V - 3.93\,V}{1k\Omega}$$

$= 6.07$ mA        Point 12

At    $t = 4$ ms,     $e_c = 6.32$ V

$$i_c = \dfrac{10\,V - 6.32\,V}{1k\Omega}$$

$= 3.68$ mA        Point 13

At    $t = 6$ ms,     $e_c = 7.77$ V

$$i_c = \dfrac{10\,V - 7.77\,V}{1k\Omega}$$

$= 2.23$ mA        Point 14

At    $t = 8$ ms,     $e_c = 8.65$ V

$$i_c = \dfrac{10\,V - 8.65\,V}{1k\Omega}$$

$= 1.35$ mA        Point 15

At    $t = 10$ ms,    $e_c = 9.18$ V

$$i_c = \dfrac{10\,V - 9.18\,V}{1k\Omega}$$

$= 0.82$ mA        Point 16

At    $t = 12$ ms,    $e_c = 9.5$ V

$$i_c = \dfrac{10\,V - 9.5\,V}{1k\Omega}$$

$= 0.5$ mA        Point 17

At    $t = 14$ ms,    $e_c = 9.7$ V

$$i_c = \dfrac{10\,V - 9.7\,V}{1k\Omega}$$

$= 0.3$ mA        Point 18

At    $t = 16$ ms,    $e_c = 9.82$

$$i_c = \dfrac{10\,V - 9.82\,V}{1k\Omega}$$

$= 0.18$ mA        Point 19

**8.7 What is the significance of normalised charge and discharge curves for an *RC* circuit. How will you use these curves for circuit calculations?**

*Solution:*

Normalised charge and discharge curves are drawn in Fig. 8.10. These curves can be employed to *graphically* solve many problems. The *normalised curves* are plotted for the case of $E = 1$ V, $C = 1$ F, and $R = 1$ $\Omega$. *For these values, the capacitor voltage can be determined at any given time t after commencement of charge or discharge.*

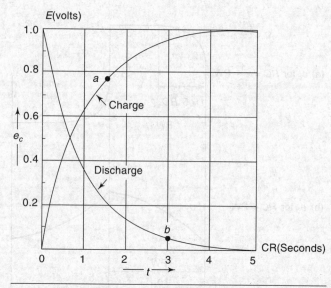

**Fig. 8.10**    *Normalised Charge and Discharge Curves for an RC Circuit.*

When the supply voltage is *not* 1 V, the capacitor voltage at any given time can be found simply by multiplying the voltage from the graph by the value of $E$. For example, when $t = 2$ s, on the charge curve, $e_c = 0.86$ V. If, instead of 1 V, $E = 5$ V, then

$$e_c = 0.86 \times 5\ V = 4.3\ V$$

Similarly, when $C$ and $R$ are not 1 F and 1 $\Omega$, respectively, the time at any instant is multiplied by $RC$. For example, if $C = 1$ $\mu$F and $R = 1$ k$\Omega$ when $e_c = 0.5$ V

$$t = 0.7 \times 1\ k\Omega \times 1\ \mu F = 0.7\ ms$$

**8.8 Using the normalised charge and discharge curves in Fig. 8.10, determine**

**(a) $e_c$ at 1 ms starting from $e_c = 0$ V, when $R = 1$ kΩ, $C = 1$ μF, and $E = 10$ V.**

**(b) $e_c$ at 6 ms from full charge when $R = 20$ kΩ, $C = 0.1$ μF, and $E = 12$ V.**

*Solution:*

(a) Each second on the *time scale* becomes

$$t = RC = 1\ k\Omega \times 1\ \mu F = 1\ ms$$

Each volt on the *voltage scale* becomes

$$e = E \times 1\ V = 10\ V$$

At   $t = 1.5$ ms (point *a* on the *charge curve*),

$$e_c = 10\ V \times 0.78$$
$$= 7.8\ V$$

(b) Each second on the *time scale* becomes

$$t = RC = 20\ k\Omega \times 0.1\ \mu F = 2\ ms$$

Each volt on the *voltage scale* becomes

$$e = E \times 1\ V = 12\ V$$

At   $t = 6$ ms (point *b* on the *discharge curve*)

$$e_c = 12\ V \times 0.05 = 0.6\ V$$

**8.9 The circuit shown in Fig. 8.11 has the following pulse inputs applied:**
**(a) $E = 10$ V, PW = 1 ms; (b) $E = 10$, PW = 2 ms; (c) $E = 20$ V, PW = 1 ms.**
**Calculate the level of $e_c$ at the end of each pulse. The initial charge on $C$ is assumed to be zero. Show that $e_c \propto$ PA $\times$ PW.**

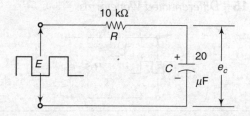

**Fig. 8.11**

*Solution:*
(a) $e_c = E - (E - E_0)e^{-t/RC}$
$e_{c(a)} = 10 \text{ V} - (10 \text{ V} - 0)e^{-1\text{ms}/(10 \text{ k}\Omega \times 20 \ \mu\text{F})}$
$\approx 50$ mV
This is shown as output (a) in Fig. 8.12.
(b) $e_{c(b)} = 10 \text{ V} - (10 \text{ V} - 0)e^{-2\text{ms}/(10 \text{ k}\Omega \times 20 \ \mu\text{F})}$
$\approx 100$ mV
This is shown as output (b) in Fig. 8.12.
(c) $e_{c(c)} = 20 \text{ V} - (20 \text{ V} - 0 \text{ V})e^{-1\text{ms}/10 \text{ k}\Omega \times 20 \ \mu\text{F}}$
$\approx 100$ mV
This is shown as output (c) in Fig. 8.12.

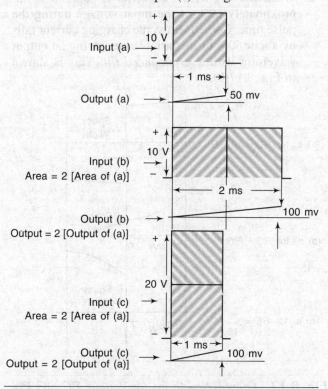

**Fig. 8.12** *Integration of Pulses with* Different Amplitudes and Widths. *In All Cases the Final Output Voltage (Capacitor Voltage) is* Directly Proportional to the Area Under the Pulse.

*Alternate Solution* Since the charging current remains *constant* during the input pulse width, this problem can also be solved as

$$e_c = \frac{It}{C} = \frac{E}{R} \times \frac{t}{C}$$

(a) $e_{c(a)} = \dfrac{10 \text{ V} \times 1 \text{ ms}}{10 \text{ k}\Omega \times 20 \ \mu\text{F}} = 50$ mV

$e_{c(b)} = \dfrac{10 \text{ V} \times 2 \text{ ms}}{10 \text{ k}\Omega \times 20 \ \mu\text{F}} = 100$ mV

$e_{c(c)} = \dfrac{20 \text{ V} \times 1 \text{ ms}}{10 \text{ k}\Omega \times 20 \ \mu\text{F}} = 100$ mV

1. When the *pulse width* is doubled, the output voltage is doubled.
2. When the *pulse amplitude* is doubled, the output voltage is doubled.
3. The *output voltage* is proportional to the pulse area i.e.,

$$e_c \propto \text{PW} \times \text{PA}. \qquad (8.3)$$

**8.10 Illustrate the steps involved in the integration of a sine wave.**

*Solution:*
The integrator output is *zero* when the sine wave input is at its *peak level*. Therefore, although a sine wave commences at zero and goes positive, the instant at which the peak level commences to decrease (shown as $t_x$ in Fig. 8.14) is taken as the *starting point* to determine the output waveform.

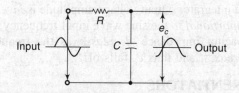

**Fig. 8.13** *Integrator with a Sine Wave Input.*

The sine wave input is *divided into sections of equal widths*. The height of each section corresponds approximately to the instantaneous sine wave amplitude. Thus, *the sine wave is represented by a series of pulses of varying amplitudes*.

The *first* pulse causes a *linear increase* in capacitor voltage from $t_x$ to $t_1$. This produces output voltage $\Delta e_1$. The *second* pulse, from $t_1$ to $t_2$ also produces a linear increase in capacitor voltage. However, the pulse amplitude is now smaller, so the *rate of increase* in capacitor voltage is reduced. Thus $\Delta e_{c2}$ is less than $\Delta e_{c1}$. Similarly, the *third* and *fourth* pulses produce *linear voltage increases at decreasing rates*. Since pulse *five* is negative, it causes the capacitor voltage to *decrease* by a small amount. Pulses five and four are equal in amplitude, so the decrease in amplitude of $e_c$ due to

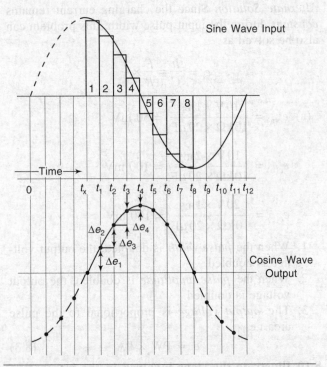

Sine Wave Input

Time →

Cosine Wave Output

$\Delta e_2$  $\Delta e_4$  $\Delta e_3$  $\Delta e_1$

**Fig. 8.14**   *Sine Wave Divided into* Equal-Width Pulses *to Show How it is* Integrated *to Give a* Negative Cosine Waveform.

five is equal to the increase $\Delta e_{c4}$ produced by pulse four. Negative pulses *six, seven* and *eight* linearly decrease the capacitor voltage.

We see that

1. Integration of the sine wave input produces *a negative cosine wave output.*
2. The integrator output voltage amplitude is *inversely proportional to* the sine wave input frequency. The capacitor impedance *decreases* as the frequency *increases,* and thus $e_c$ falls off.

## DIFFERENTIATORS

Differentiation is a measure of rate of change. *A differentiating circuit produces an output voltage which is proportional to the rate of change of the input.* When the output from an *RC* circuit is taken across *R,* the output voltage is the differential of the input. A differentiator is used to produce a *peaked waveform* for timing or synchronizing purposes using a square or rectangular shaped input. *The differentiator has a short time constant and the output is taken across a resistor.* Differentiated waveforms are shown in Fig. 8.15.

**8.11 Describe the operation of a differentiator with a square wave input.**

*Solution:*
Figure 8.16 shows an *RC* circuit with a square wave input and with the output voltage taken across the resistor. The shape of the output (resistor) voltage is depen-

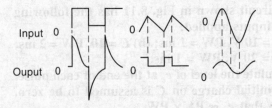

Input  0

Ouput  0

0     0     0     0

**Fig. 8.15**   *Differentiated Waveforms.*

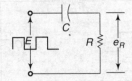

$E$     $C$     $R$  $e_R$

**Fig. 8.16**   *Differentiating Circuit with a Square Wave Input.*

dent upon the relationship between the time constant (*RC*) and the pulse width (PW).

1. When $RC \geq 10\ PW$, the capacitor charges very little during the pulse time, and the charging current falls only a small amount from its initial level. This is shown in Fig. 8.17(a). $e_R$ remains *almost constant,* the capacitor is discharged and $i_c$ is a negative quantity. The resistor voltage is now negative and remains nearly constant during the discharge time.
2. When $RC = PW$, the capacitor is charged to approximately 60% of the input voltage during the pulse time. Consequently, the charging current falls by about 60% of its initial value, giving an output waveform with a *pronounced tilt.* This is shown in Fig. 8.17(b).

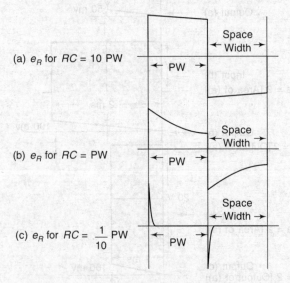

(a) $e_R$ for $RC = 10\ PW$          Space Width          PW

(b) $e_R$ for $RC = PW$          Space Width          PW

(c) $e_R$ for $RC = \frac{1}{10}\ PW$          Space Width          PW

**Fig. 8.17**   *Output Waveforms for Various RC and PW Relationships. The Circuit behaves as a Differentiator only when RC is Less than or equal to 10 PW.*

3. When $RC \leq 1/10 \ PW$, the capacitor is charged very rapidly. Only a *brief pulse* of current is necessary to charge and discharge the capacitor at the beginning and end of the pulse period.

The resultant waveform of resistor voltage is *a series of positive and negative spikes* at the leading and lagging edges, respectively, of the pulse. This is shown in Fig. 8.17(c). At the *leading edge* of the input pulse, the input voltage is changing rapidly in a positive direction. At the *trailing edge* of the input pulse, the input voltage is changing rapidly in a negative direction. During both the pulse width and space width, the input voltage does not change at all. Thus, the positive and negative spikes indeed represent a differentiated square wave.

## 8.12 What happens when a ramp voltage is applied to the input of a differentiator circuit?

*Solution:*

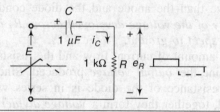

**Fig. 8.18** *Ramp Voltage Applied to the Input of a Differentiating Circuit.*

When a ramp voltage is applied to the input of a differentiating circuit *the resultant output is a constant d.c. voltage level.*

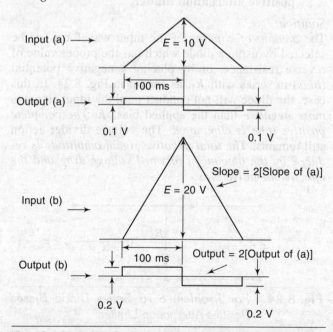

**Fig. 8.19** *Differentiation of Ramp Voltages with Different Rates of Change. In Each Case the Circuit Output (Resistor) Voltage is Directly Proportional to the Rate of Change of the Ramp Voltage.*

While the input voltage continuously increases, the capacitor cannot become completely charged. Hence, *the instantaneous capacitor voltage is always slightly less than the instantaneous input voltage.* This small difference in $E$ and $e_c$ is developed across $R$, giving a constant level of charging current, and thus a constant level of $e_R$. While the ramp *increases positively,* the capacitor is charged with the polarity, positive on the left, negative on the right, and $i_c$ produces a positive level of $e_R$. When the ramp goes *negative,* $i_C$ is reversed, and consequently $e_R$ is negative.

## 8.13 For input waveforms, (a) and (b) in Fig. 8.19, calculate the levels of the outputs from the differentiating circuits.

*Solution:*
At the end of the input ramp, $e_c \approx E_{\max}$. Since the charging current is constant
 (a) For the 10 V ramp.

$$I = \frac{CE_{\max}}{t} = \frac{1\,\mu\text{F} \times 10\,\text{V}}{100\,\text{ms}} = 0.1 \text{ mA}$$

and $e_R = I \times R = 0.1 \text{ mA} \times 1 \text{ k}\Omega = 0.1$ V
This is the output (a), as shown in Fig. 8.19.
 (b) For the 20 V ramp.

$$I = \frac{CE_{\max}}{t} = \frac{1\,\mu\text{F} \times 20\,\text{V}}{100\,\text{ms}} = 0.2 \text{ mA}$$

and $e_R = I \times R = 0.2 \text{ mA} \times 1 \text{ k}\Omega = 0.2$ V
This is the output(b), as shown in Fig. 8.19.

The rate of change of the 10 V ramp is 10 V/100 ms, that is 0.1 V/ms. For the 20 V ramp, the rate of change is 0.2 V/ms. Thus, *the differentiated output doubles when the rate of change of input voltage is doubled.*

## 8.14 Explain the steps involved in the differentiation of a sine wave.

*Solution:*

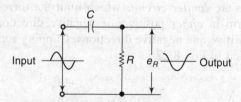

**Fig. 8.20** *Differentiator with a Sine Wave Input.*

Although the input sine wave commences at zero volts and goes positive, the output waveform is investigated by starting at the positive peak of the input at time $t_x$.

At the peak of the sine wave, the rate of change of the voltage is zero. Thus, the differentiated output voltage is zero. At time $t_1$, the sine wave amplitude is decreasing, producing a negative rate of change. Consequently, the differentiated output voltage is $-e_1$. At times $t_2$ and $t_3$, the negative rate of charge increases and finally becomes maximum at $t_4$. The differentiated

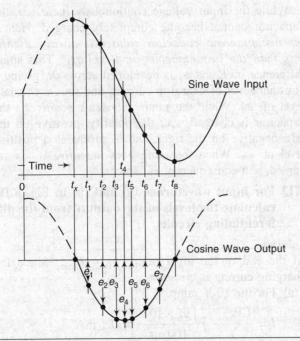

**Fig. 8.21**   *When a Sine Wave is Differentiated, Each Instantaneous Output Level is Directly Proportional to the Instantaneous Rate of Change of the input. This Results in a Cosine Wave Output.*

output, therefore, increases negatively through $-e_2$ and $-e_3$ to $-e_4$. Beyond $t_4$, the negative rate of change decreases progressively to zero at $t_8$. Extending the waveform shows the differential of a sine wave to be a cosine wave. The differentiator output voltage is proportional to the input sine wave frequency. The capacitor impedance decreases as the input frequency increases, and thus $e_R$ grows.

## CLIPPERS

Clippers are *limiter circuits* which limit the travel of a waveform in *either* positive *or* negative direction, *or* both positive and negative directions. Clipping action is illustrated in Fig. 8.22.

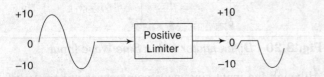

**Fig. 8.22**   *Clipper Action.*

### 8.15 Describe the working of a series diode positive-alternation limiter.

*Solution:*
*Series limiters* may be used to *limit* either the positive or negative excursion of the waveform. A typical cir-

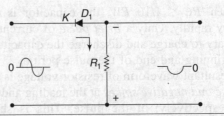

**Fig. 8.23**   *Series Diode Positive-alternation Limiter.*

cuit used to limit the *positive half-cycle* of the waveform is shown in Fig. 8.23.

Diode $D_1$ is connected *in series* between the input and output, with $R_1$ serving as the load resistor. When a *positive* input is applied between $D_1$ cathode and ground, the cathode is made more positive than the anode, and the diode does not conduct. The reverse resistance of the diode will not allow any signal to pass to the load. When the input signal is *negative,* the cathode is more negative than the anode and the diode conducts. *The polarity of the voltage developed across $R_1$ is negative with respect to ground.*

The amount of current flow and the resistance value determine the *output voltage* produced. Since the forward resistance of the diode is in series with $R_1$ to ground, together they form a *voltage divider,* and with the output voltage taken across $R_1$ always less than the input voltage. Also, *since the load resistor is not frequency selective the output waveform has the same phase as the original signal.*

### 8.16 Describe the working of a series diode biased positive alternation limiter.

*Solution:*
The *amount of clipping* of the input waveform can be selected by using a diode which has the proper value of reverse resistance, or by placing a negative potential (*bias*) in series with $R_1$, as shown in Fig. 8.24. In this case, the diode will not conduct until the input signal is *more negative* than the applied bias, E. *The complete positive lobe is eliminated.* The voltage divider action still remains. *The total negative signal amplitude is reduced by the amount of forward voltage drop and the effective negative bias.*

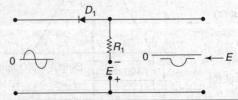

**Fig. 8.24**   *For Problem 8.16 Series Diode Biased Positive Attenation Limiter.*

The same circuit can be used for negative clipping by *reversing* the polarity of the diode, and *also* of the bias voltage (if used).

**8.17 Describe the operation of a parallel, positive-diode limiter.**

*Solution:*

Similar to their series counterparts, *parallel limiters* may be used to limit (or clip) either the negative or positive half-cycle of the input waveform.

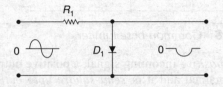

**Fig. 8.25** *Parallel Limiter.*

A parallel, positive diode limiter is shown in Fig. 8.25. Diode $D_1$ conducts only during the *positive* portion of the input signal. Since $R_1 >> R_F$, practically the *entire* input voltage drops across $R_1$, while comparatively a *very small* voltage drops across $D_1$. When the input signal goes *negative,* the diode does not conduct. A small reverse current still flows through $D_1$, and a small portion of the input voltage is dropped across $R_1$. The amount of reverse resistance depends on the characteristics of the diode selected.

**8.18 Describe the operation of a parallel biased positive-peak limiter.**

*Solution:*

A *parallel, biased positive diode limiter* is shown in Fig. 8.26. Diode $D_1$ conducts only during the *positive* portion of the input signal. Since the value of $R_1$ is very large compared to the forward resistance of the diode, practically the entire value of the input voltage drops across $R_1$, while comparatively a very small voltage drops across $D_1$. When the input signal goes *negative*, the diode does not conduct. A small reverse current still flows through $D_1$ and a small portion of the input voltage is dropped across $R_1$. The amount of reverse resistance of the diode depends on the characteristics of the diode selected.

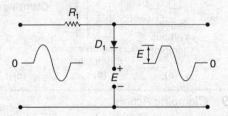

**Fig. 8.26** *Parallel, Biased Positive-peak Limiter.*

A parallel, positive peak limiter may also be used to limit only the peaks of the positive waveform, while allowing a given value of the positive signal to pass through the circuit to the output. This may be achieved by applying a *biasing voltage,* having a value equal to

the value of the positive signal to be passed by the circuit, to the cathode of the diode, as shown in Fig. 8.26. When connected in this manner, with the cathode of $D_1$ connected to the *positive* terminal of the d.c. bias source, the cathode of the diode is held more positive than the anode by the value of *E*. As long as the positive half cycles of the input voltage remain *less positive than E,* the diode remains cut off because its cathode is positive with respect to the anode and the output voltage is equal to the input voltage minus the voltage developed by the reverse resistance of the diode. Since all of the negative half cycles of the input voltage are less positive than *E,* these also cause the diode to remain cut off. When the input signal increases to a value which exceeds *E,* the anode becomes positive with respect to the cathode, and *the diode begins to conduct, and continues conducting as long as the input remains more positive than E.*

**8.19 Explain the working of a biased, double-diode positive and negative peak limiter.**

*Solution:*

The *parallel, double-diode limiter* is used when it is necessary to limit a portion of *both* the positive and negative half-cycles of the waveform, and allow the remainder of the signal to pass without modification. This limiter is used *to square off the peaks of an applied signal,* to obtain a rectangular waveform from a sine wave signal, or to *eliminate* the negative or positive portion of a waveform and *clip* the other portion.

The circuit of a parallel, biased, double-diode negative- and positive-peak limiter is shown in Fig. 8.27. Diode $D_1$ limits the *positive half-cycle* of the input and diode $D_2$ limits the *negative half-cycle.* Separate supplies $E_1$ and $E_2$ bias their respective diodes. Resistor $R_1$ is the input load. $E_1$ and $E_2$ voltages reverse bias the diodes. Therefore, when no signal is applied at the input, they do not conduct.

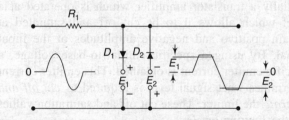

**Fig. 8.27** *Biased, Double-Diode Positive and Negative Peak Limiter.*

As the sine wave signal is applied at the input and begins increasing in a positive direction, both diodes remain cut off due to the bias, and the positive half of the reproduced *ramp* at the output begins. The output continues to follow the input signal until a point is reached where the signal becomes more positive than the positive bias applied to the cathode of $D_1$. At this point, $D_1$ anode becomes more positive than the cathode, and $D_1$ conducts. When $D_1$ conducts, it provides a low resistance path for forward current to ground, and *shunts* the output through the diode, instead of the external load. It is at this point that the waveform is *flattened*. The output voltage is *slightly higher* than the diode bias.

As the input signal reaches its positive peak and begins decreasing towards zero, it again reaches a level which is less than $E_1$, diode $D_1$ again cuts off and the input is again faithfully reproduced at the output (negative going *ramp*). The input signal swing continues in the negative direction, and when its amplitude becomes more negative than $E_2$, the cathode of $E_2$ is made more negative than its anode, and $D_2$ conducts, repeating the action which occurred on the positive half-cycle (*flattened bottom*). The input then reaches the negative peak and begins decreasing toward zero. As it becomes less negative than $E_2$, $D_2$ ceases conducting, and the remainder of the input signal is reproduced at the output.

The *amount of clipping* which takes place at the output is dependent to a certain extent on the *type of diodes* selected, but primarily upon *the value of bias*. As $E_1$ is made more positive, *less* clipping occurs on the *positive half-cycle,* and as it is made less positive, *more* clipping occurs. By the same token, as $E_2$ is made more negative, *less* clipping occurs on the *negative half-cycle,* and as it becomes less negative, *more* clipping occurs.

## 8.20 Describe the operation of a common-base limiter.

*Solution:*

A *common-base limiter* is used in semiconductor circuits when it is desired to limit the amplitude of a *relatively small input signal* to a definite negative and positive output level. The common-base limiter is essentially a transistor amplifier which is operated at a level which allows it to be cut off and saturated at certain positive and negative amplitudes of the input signal. By using a specific emitter-to-base voltage, a specific emitter current is obtained. This emitter current determines what signal level is required to *cut off and saturate* the limiter. These cut off and saturation values are the *limiting levels.*

$C_1$ and $R_1$, Fig. 8.28, form a network that couples the signal to transistor $Q_1$. Bias supply $V_{EE}$ determines the emitter-base bias voltage.

The value of $R_1$ in conjunction with the bias supplied by $V_{EE}$ determines the emitter current. Collector load resistor $R_2$ and collector supply $V_{CC}$ establish the collector current. Capacitor $C_2$ couples the output of $Q_1$ to the following stage.

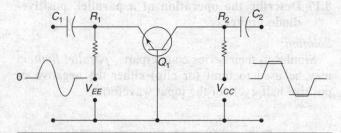

**Fig. 8.28** *Common-base Limiter.*

For a *positive* incoming signal, a positive output voltage is obtained and it is *semi-square upto cut off.* For any further increase in signal voltage, beyond cut off, there is no change in output voltage and *it stays constant for any variation of input signal voltage well beyond cut off.*

For a *negative* incoming signal, a negative output voltage is obtained, and it is *semi-square upto saturation.* Any further increase in signal voltage does not affect the collector current or voltage at the collector, *since the transistor has already attained saturation.*

*It is at these levels of saturation and cut off that the output voltage is limited.* To achieve limiting it is necessary to supply a large-amplitude signal. *Between* the limits of cut off and saturation, the circuit acts as a conventional amplifier. *Beyond* these limits the peaks are cut off and the waveform is effectively squared off.

## CLAMPERS

*Clampers,* also referred to as *d.c. restorers* and *base line stabilizers,* are used in electronic circuits *to hold either amplitude extreme of a waveform to a given reference level.* Clamping action is illustrated in Fig. 8.29. The clamper does not affect the shape of the waveform.

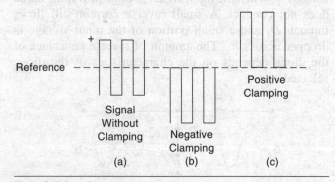

**Fig. 8.29** *Clamping Action.*

## 8.21 Describe the operation of an unbiased negative clamper.

*Solution:*

To effect clamping, the semiconductor diode is operated as a switch controlled by the polarity of the input waveform. In the direction of *forward conduction,* it passes the signal, but in the direction of *reverse conduction* it is in effect an open circuit and blocks the signal. In addition to the inherent disadvantage of a relatively *low reverse resistance*, the semiconductor diode also has a *capacitive effect* which varies with applied voltage. When a semiconductor diode is used as a d.c. restorer at video and higher frequencies, the shunting capacitance may affect the waveform of the signal.

Since the diode may be connected to operate on positive or negative signals and may also be biased positively or negatively, *four basic circuit variations of the diode clamp exist*. Operation of these four basic configurations is practically identical, the major differences being in the polarities of the diode and the bias supplies.

The *unbiased diode clamper* is usually employed as a shunt across the resistor portion of an *RC* coupling circuit. By providing a low resistance path during *conduction periods* and a high resistance path during *nonconduction periods,* the diode provides *different charge and discharge times* for the coupling capacitor. When the positive portion of the input waveform causes the diode to conduct, clamping is produced.

The schematic of a basic *unbiased negative clamp* is shown in Fig. 8.30. $C_1$ is the coupling capacitor of an *RC* coupling network. $R_1$ is the input resistor of the network and determines the *long time constant* of the

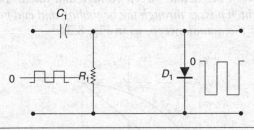

**Fig. 8.30**  *Negative Clamper-unbiased.*

circuit. Clamping diode $D_1$, connected in shunt with $R_1$ determines the *short time constant* of the circuit. When a *positive-going* input signal is applied, it causes $D_1$ to conduct, and $C_1$ is quickly charged to the input potential. Since the output is taken across $R_1$, which is effectively shorted by the conducting diode, *little or no output appears for the positive portion of any applied signal.* During the negative-going portion of the input signal (the trailing edge falling to zero), $D_1$ does not conduct; consequently, *the negative portion of the input signal appears as the output across $R_1$.* This circuit acts to effectively *shift* the entire waveform in a negative direction by holding the positive peak of the input signal to the zero level. Therefore, *the input waveform can only appear as a negative output. The positive portion is eliminated by the clamping diode.* If the circuit is to be used as a positive clamp, the polarities of the diode and the output waveform are *reversed.*

## 8.22 Describe the working of a negative-biased negative-clamper.

*Solution:*

In Fig. 8.31 $C_1$ and $R_1$ form an *RC* coupling network and determine the *long time constant* associated with the circuit. Diode $D_1$, during the period of its conduction, together with $C_1$, determines the *short time constant* associated with the circuit. The *bias supply* alters the reference level from zero to a level equal to the bias.

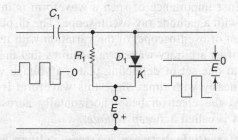

**Fig. 8.31**  *Negative-biased Negative-clamper.*

When the circuit is initially energised, *with no signal applied to the input,* the diode begins conducting because of the negative potential applied to its cathode. As $D_1$ conducts, $C_1$ begins charging, and when its charge is equal to the bias supply, the diode cuts off, since its anode and cathode potentials are not equal. The voltage at the output at this time is equal to the bias voltage, *E.*

*When a signal is applied*, the voltage increases almost instantly. Capacitor $C_1$ cannot change its charge immediately and the anode of $D_1$ suddenly becomes more positive than its cathode and $D_1$ begins conducting. Because $C_1$ cannot change its charge immediately, the entire input voltage is developed across the diode. The output, taken across the diode, increases in a positive direction. The conducting state of $D_1$ provides a *very short time constant* for the capacitor, and $C_1$ rapidly charges to the new voltage. As $C_1$ charges, the voltage drop across $D_1$ decreases, and reaches the *reference level,* when $C_1$ is fully charged.

The output remains at this voltage until *the input swings negative.* Again, $C_1$ cannot change its charge immediately, but this time the diode cannot conduct, because its anode is negative with respect to its cathode. The entire input voltage, therefore, is developed across $R_1$, and the output voltage swings in a negative direction from reference level. Because the diode is not conducting, $R_1$ provides a *long time constant* for $C_1$ and the capacitor begins charging very slowly to the input signal level.

At this time, *the input again swings positive*, bringing $D_1$ into conduction. This sudden rise also produces an increase in the output. Because of the *short time constant* provided by $D_1$, the capacitor quickly charges again to the reference level and remains there until the input swings negative, when the cycle repeats.

By *reversing* the diode, the circuit can be converted into a *negatively biased positive diode clamper.* The entire output waveform will then be clamped *above* the negative bias voltage level instead of below it as in the negative clamper in Fig. 8.31.

## SWEEP CIRCUITS

A *linear time-base generator* is one that provides an output waveform, a portion of which exhibits a linear variation of voltage or current with time. An application of first importance of such a waveform is in connection with a cathode ray oscilloscope. The display on the screen of oscilloscope, of the variation with respect to time of an arbitrary waveform, requires that there be applied to one set of deflecting plates a voltage which varies linearly with time. Since this waveform is used to *sweep* the electron beam horizontally across the screen, it is called a *sweep voltage.*

### 8.23 Differentiate between a sweep voltage and a sawtooth voltage.

*Solution:*
The typical form of a time-base voltage is shown in Fig. 8.32. Here it appears that the voltage starting from some initial value, increases linearly with time to a maximum value, after which it *returns* again to its initial value. The time required for the return to the initial value is called the *return time,* the *restoration time,* or the *flyback time.*

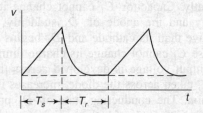

**Fig. 8.32**   *A General Sweep Voltage. The Sweep Time is $T_s$ and the Return Time is $T_r$.*

In some cases, a restoration time is desired which is very short in comparison with the time occupied by the linear portion of the waveform. If it should happen that the restoration time is extremely short and that a new linear voltage is initiated at the instant the previous one is terminated, then the waveform will appear as in Fig. 8.33.

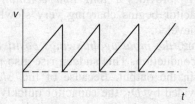

**Fig. 8.33**   *A Sawtooth Voltage Waveform.*

This figure suggests the designation *sawtooth generator* or *ramp generator.* It is customary to refer to waveforms of the type shown in Figs 8.31 and 8.32 as *sweep waveforms* even in applications not involving the deflection of an electron beam.

### 8.24 Express deviations from linearity in sweep voltages and the correlations among them.

*Solution:*
Generators of time-base signals do not provide sweep voltages that are *precisely linear.* Moreover, a nominally linear sweep may be *distorted* in the course of transmission through a coupling network. The three most useful ways of expressing the *deviation from linearity,* and the correlations among them, are as follows:

1. *The Slope or Sweep-Speed Error, $e_s$:* In case of a *general-purpose cathode ray oscillograph,* an important requirement of the sweep is that *sweep speed* must be constant. A reasonable definition of the *deviation from linearity* is

$$\frac{\text{difference in slope at beginning and end of sweep}}{\text{initial value of slope}}$$

2. *The Displacement Error $e_d$:* In connection with other *timing applications,* a more important criterion of linearity is the *maximum difference between the actual sweep voltage and linear sweep which passes through the beginning and end points of the actual sweep,* as in Fig. 8.34.

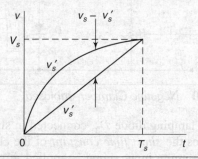

**Fig. 8.34**   *Relating to the Definition of Displacement Error.*

Here we may define

$$e_d = \frac{(v_s - v_s')\,\text{max}}{V_s}$$

3. *The Transmission Error, $e_t$:* If a ramp voltage is transmitted through a *high-pass RC network,* the output falls away from the input as indicated in Fig. 8.35.

The transmission error is defined as the *difference between the input and output divided by the input.* Thus, with reference to Fig. 8.35, we have (at time $t = T_s$)

$$e_t = \frac{V_s' - V_s}{V_s'}$$

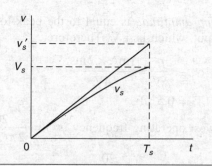

**Fig. 8.35** *Relating to the Definition of Transmission Error.*

If the deviation in linearity is small, so that the sweep voltage may be approximated by the sum of a linear and quadratic term in $t_1$ then

$$e_d = \frac{1}{8} e_s = \frac{1}{4} e_t$$

# MILLER INTEGRATORS AND BOOT STRAP RAMP GENERATORS

Miller integrators and bootstrap ramp generators produce *nearly linear output ramps*

### 8.25 Describe the operation of a Miller integrator.

*Solution:*

The Miller integrator utilizes the *Miller effect* to generate a linear ramp. In the circuit of Fig. 8.36(a), a square wave input supplies charging current, *alternatively positive and negative,* to $C_1$. The non-inverting input terminal of the op-amp is grounded by a resistance $R_2$ (equal to resistance $R_1$). Because the non-inverting terminal is grounded, the inverting input terminal is always very close to ground level. Thus the input voltage appears across $R_1$ and the input current is simply $V_i/R_1$, which remains constant.

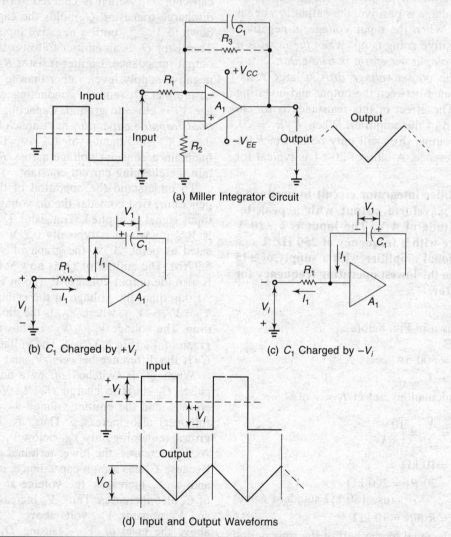

(a) Miller Integrator Circuit

(b) $C_1$ Charged by $+V_i$

(c) $C_1$ Charged by $-V_i$

(d) Input and Output Waveforms

**Fig. 8.36** *Miller Integrator Circuit. A Symmetrical Square Wave Input Charges the Capacitor Linearly, First with One Polarity and then with Reverse Polarity. This Produces a Triangular Wave Output.*

If the input current $I_1$ is much greater than the input bias current of the amplifier, then $I_1$ will not flow into the amplifier. Instead, effectively all of $I_1$ flows through capacitor $C_1$. For a *positive* input voltage, $I_1$ flows into $C_1$, charging it positively on the left side and negatively on the right side, Fig. 8.36(b). In this case, the output voltage becomes negative, because the positive terminal, that is, the left terminal, of the capacitor is held at the virtual ground level of the inverting input terminal. A *negative* input voltage produces a flow of current out of $C_1$, Fig. 8.36(c). Thus, the capacitor is charged negatively on the left side and positively on the right side. Now the output becomes positive, because the negative terminal of the capacitor is held at virtual ground.

Since $I_1$ is a *constant quantity* (+ or −), and since effectively all of $I_1$ flows through the capacitor, $C_1$ is charged linearly. Thus, *the output voltage changes linearly, providing either a positive or negative ramp.* When the input voltage is positive, the output is a negative going ramp. When the input voltage is negative, the output is a positive going ramp. *When the input is a square wave, the output waveform is triangular.*

To minimise the *output voltage drift*, a large resistance $R_3$ is connected between the output and inverting input terminals. The effect of this resistance is to *cut down* the d.c. gain of the amplifier. When $R_3/R_1 = 20$, for example, the output drift will only be 20 times the input voltage difference. A ratio of 20 : 1 is typical for $R_3/R_1$.

**8.26 Design a Miller integrator circuit to produce a triangular waveform output with a peak-to-peak amplitude of 4 V. The input is a ±10 V square wave with a frequency of 250 Hz. Use a 741 operational amplifier with a supply of ±15 V. Calculate the lowest operating frequency for the integrator.**

*Solution:*
The circuit is shown in Fig. 8.36(a).
From Appendix C
$$I_{B(max)} = 500 \text{ nA}$$
$$I_1 \gg I_{B(max)}$$
For convenient calculations, select $I_1 = 1$ mA.

$$R_1 = \frac{V_i}{I_1} = \frac{10\,V}{1\,mA}$$
$$= 10 \text{ k}\Omega$$

Select    $R_3 = 20\,R_1 = 200 \text{ k}\Omega$
(use 180 kΩ standard value)
$$R_2 = R_3 \| R_1 \approx 10 \text{ k}\Omega$$

The *ramp length* is equal to one-half of the time period of the input, which is $1/(2\,f)$, or

$$t = \frac{1}{2 \times 250\,Hz} = 2 \text{ ms}$$

The *ramp amplitude* is equal to the peak-to-peak voltage output, which is 4 V. Therefore,

$$C_1 = \frac{It}{\Delta V} = \frac{1\,mA \times 2\,ms}{4\,V}$$
$$= 0.5 \ \mu F$$

The lowest operating frequency is: $f = \dfrac{20}{2\pi C_1 R_3}$

$$f = \frac{20}{2\pi \times 0.5\,\mu F \times 180 \text{ k}\Omega}$$
$$= 35 \text{ Hz}$$

**8.27 Describe the operation of a transistor bootstrap ramp generator.**

*Solution:*
The circuit of a transistor *bootstrap ramp generator* is shown in Fig. 8.37(a). The ramp is generated across capacitor $C_1$, which is charged via resistance $R_1$. The discharge transistor $Q_1$ holds the capacitor voltage $V_1$ down to $V_{CE(sat)}$ until a negative input pulse is applied. Transistor $Q_2$ is an emitter follower that provides a low output impedance. Emitter resistor $R_E$ is connected to a negative supply level, rather than to ground. This is to ensure that $Q_2$ remains conducting when its base voltage $V_1$ is close to ground. Capacitor $C_3$, known as the *bootstrapping capacitor,* has a much higher capacitance than $C_1$. The function of $C_3$, as will be shown, is to maintain a constant voltage across $R_1$, and thus maintain the charging current constant.

To understand the operation of the bootstrap ramp generator, first consider the dc voltage levels before an input signal is applied. Transistor $Q_1$ is *on*; its voltage is $V_{CE(sat)}$, which is typically 0.2 V. This level is indicated as point $A$ on the graph of voltage $V_1$ in Fig. 8.37(b). The emitter of $Q_2$ is now at $(V_1 - V_{BE2})$, which is also the output voltage, $V_o$ (point $B$ on the $V_o$ graph). At this time, the voltage at the cathode of diode $D_1$ is $V_K = V_{CC} - V_{D1}$, where $V_{D1}$ is the diode forward voltage drop. The voltage $V_{CC} - V_{D1}$ is shown at point $C$ on the graph of $V_K$ (Fig 8.37(b)). The voltage across capacitor $C_3$ is the difference between $V_K$ and $V_o$.

When $Q_1$ is switched *off* by a negative-going input pulse, $C_1$ starts to charge via $R_1$. Voltage $V_1$ now increases, and the emitter voltage $V_o$ of $Q_2$ (the emitter follower) also increases. Thus, as $V_1$ grows, $V_o$ also grows, remaining only $V_{BE}$ below $V_1$. [See Fig. 8.37(b)]. As $V_o$ increases, the lower terminal of $C_3$ is *pulled up*. Because $C_3$ has a high capacitance, it retains its charge, and, as $V_o$ increases, the voltage at the upper terminal of $C_3$ also increases. Thus, $V_K$ increases as $V_1$ increases, and $V_K$ remains $V_{C3}$ volts above $V_o$. (In fact, $V_K$ goes above the level of $V_{CC}$, causing $D_1$ to be reverse biased.) The constant voltage across $C_3$ maintains the voltage $V_{R1}$ constant across $R_1$. Therefore, the charging current through $R_1$ is held constant, and consequently, $C_1$ charges linearly, giving a linear output ramp.

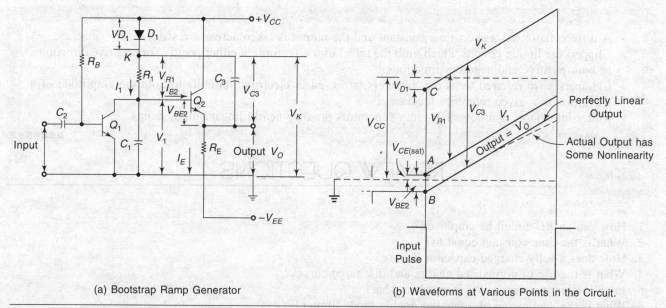

(a) Bootstrap Ramp Generator

(b) Waveforms at Various Points in the Circuit.

**Fig. 8.37**    *A Transistor Bootstrap Ramp Generator is Basically a Simple RC Ramp Generator (as in Figure 8.37) with the Addition of Emitter Follower Q₂, Diode D₁, and Bootstrapping Capacitor C₃. These Components maintain a Constant Voltage Across R₁ and thus Produce a linear Output Ramp.*

During the ramp time, $D_1$ is reverse biased as already explained, and the charging current through $R_1$ is provided by capacitor $C_3$. If $C_3$ has a very high capacitance, and $I_1$ is small, then $C_3$ will discharge by only a very small amount. When the input pulse is removed and $C_1$ is discharged rapidly by $Q_1$, $V_o$ drops to its initial level. Also, $V_K$ drops, allowing $D_1$ to become forward biased. At this time, a current pulse through $D_1$ replaces the small charge lost from $C_3$. The circuit is then ready to generate another output ramp.

In addition to producing a very linear output ramp, another advantage of the bootstrap generator is that *the amplitude of the ramp can approach the level of the supply voltage*. Note that the output ramp amplitude may be made *adjustable* over a fixed time period by making $R_1$ adjustable.

The broken line on the graph of output voltage [Fig. 8.37(b)] shows that, instead of being perfectly linear, the output may be slightly nonlinear. If the difference between the actual output and the ideal output is 1% of the output peak voltage, then the ramp may be said to have 1% *nonlinearity*. Some nonlinearity results from the slight discharge of $C_3$ that occurs during the ramp time. Another source of nonlinearity is the $Q_2$ base current $I_{B2}$. As the capacitor voltage grows, $I_{B2}$ increases. Since $I_{B2}$ is part of $I_1$, the capacitor charging current decreases slightly as $I_{B2}$ increases. Thus, the charging current does not remain perfectly constant, and consequently, the ramp is not perfectly linear. *The design of a bootstrap ramp generator begins with a specification of ramp linearity*. This dictates the charging current and the capacitance of $C_3$. The percentage of nonlinearity usually is allocated in equal parts to $\Delta I_{B2}$ and $\Delta V_{C3}$.

Note that the preceding reasoning about ramp linearity assumes that there is no significant leakage current through the capacitors. This requires that the capacitors not be electrolytic.

# SUMMARY

> The process of obtaining a desired waveform from a given waveform by suitable operations is called waveshaping.
> In linear waveshaping the signal passes through linear systems and circuits like integrators and differentiators.
> In non-linear waveshaping the signal passes through non-linear systems and circuits like clippers and clampers.
> The time constant of a circuit is CR seconds (C is in Farads and R in ohms).
> After 5 time constants, the circuit is assumed to have reached its steady state conditions.
> An integrator has a long time constant and the output is taken across a capacitor.

> ➤ A differentiator has a short time constant and the output is taken across a resistor.
> ➤ Clippers are limiter circuits which limit the travel of a waveform in either positive or negative directions, or both positive and negative directions.
> ➤ Clampers, also referred to as d.c. restorers, are used in electronic circuits to hold the amplitude of a waveform to a given reference level.
> ➤ Miller integrators and bootstrap ramp generators produce nearly linear output ramps.

# REVIEW QUESTIONS

**Test your understanding**

1. How can an *RC* circuit be employed?
2. What is the time constant equal to?
3. How does a fully charged capacitor behave?
4. What is the use of normalised charge and discharge curves?
5. In an integrating circuit, *RC* is equal to what?
6. What is the application of a parallel double-diode limiter?
7. Where is a common-base limiter used?
8. What is the speciality of clampers?
9. Give one application of sweep circuits.
10. List the deviations from linearity.

# SUPPLEMENTARY PROBLEMS

**Test your understanding**

11. The capacitor in Fig. 8.38 is initially discharged. How long after the switch is moved from position 2 to position 1 will it take the capacitor to reach 4 V?
12. Assume that the capacitor in Fig. 8.38 is initially charged to 4 V. How long after the switch is moved from position 2 to position 3 will it take for the voltage to drop to 2 V?

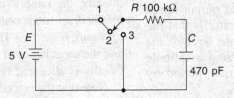

**Fig. 8.38** *For Problem 12.*

13. A capacitor of 10 μF capacitance is charged through a 1 MΩ non-inductive resistance by a battery of EMF 10 volts. Find the time constant of the circuit and the time taken for the capacitor to charge to 90% of its supply voltage.
14. The negative series clipping circuit is to have an input of $E = \pm50$ V. The output current from the circuit is to be $I_L = 20$ mA and the negative output voltage is not to exceed –0.5 V. Calculate the value of $R_1$, and specify the diode in terms of forward current, power dissipation, and peak inverse voltage. The reverse leakage current can be taken as 5 μA. (See Fig. 8.39)
15. A negative shunt clipper is to have an output voltage of 9 V and an output current of approximately 1 mA. If the input voltage is ±10 V, calculate the value of $R_1$ and the diode forward current. (See Fig. 8.40)

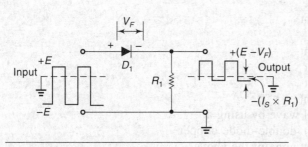

**Fig. 8.39** *For Problem 14.*

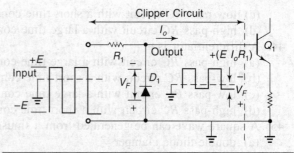

**Fig. 8.40** *For Problem 15.*

# OBJECTIVE TYPE QUESTIONS

## Fill in the Blanks

16. The voltage on a charging capacitor will increase _____ (faster/slower) if its series resistance is increased.
17. The output of an integrator is taken across a _____.
18. The differentiator has a _____ time constant.
19. Clampers hold either amplitude _____ of a waveform to a given reference level.
20. The capacitor charges at an _____ rate toward the value of $E$ source.
21. A discharging capacitor can be thought of as charging to a _____ voltage.
22. The rise time is defined as the time taken for the potential difference to rise from _____ of the applied signal voltage.
23. Integration is a _____ of area.
24. When $RC$ = PW, the waveform of capacitor voltage begins to approach a _____ shape.
25. If $RC$ is _____ than or equal to 10 PW, the $RC$ circuit is referred to as an _____.
26. If the output of an $RC$ circuit is taken from across the resistor the $RC$ circuit is referred to as a _____.
27. A differentiating circuit produces an output voltage which is proportional to the _____ of the input.
28. The parallel double-diode limiter is used to _____ the peaks of an applied voltage.
29. The clamper is also known as a _____.
30. Follow-the-leader action is called _____.

## True/False Questions

State whether the following statements are True or False.
31. A 1 μF capacitor with a 10 kΩ resistor will have the same charging rate as a 10 μF with a 1 kΩ series resistor.
32. The integrator has a short time constant.
33. The output of a differentiator is taken across a capacitor.
34. Clippers are limiter circuits which limit the travel of a waveform in either or both directions.
35. A capacitor is 99% charged after a time equal to 4 $RC$.
36. Depending on the arrangement of the $RC$ circuit, it may be employed as a differentiator or an integrator.
37. If $RC$ is made greater than one-tenth of PW, then the output closely resembles the square-wave input.
38. If the output of an $RC$ circuit is taken from across the capacitor the $RC$ circuit is referred to as a differentiator.
39. A negative limiter can be changed to a positive limiter by changing the polarity of the bias voltage but not that of the diode.
40. It is more important to keep $R_i$ large in the bootstrapping circuit than in the Miller circuit.
41. Pulse transformers are used to change the impedance level of a pulse.
42. Pulse transformers are used to integrate a pulse.

## Multiple Choice Questions

43. An integrator is a
    (a) low-pass $RC$ circuit with a large time constant
    (b) high-pass $RC$ circuit with a large time constant

    (c) low-pass *RC* circuit with a short time constant

    (d) high-pass *RC* circuit with a large time constant

44. A differentiator is a

    (a) high-pass *RC* circuit with a large time constant

    (b) low-pass *RC* circuit with a short time constant

    (c) low-pass *RC* circuit with a large time constant

    (d) high-pass *RC* circuit with a short time constant

45. A square wave can be generated from a sinusoidal wave by using a

    (a) double-diode clamper         (b) double-diode clipper

    (c) transistor clipper             (d) none of the above

46. A clamping circuit is also called a

    (a) limiter         (b) dc restorer        (c) stabiliser       (d) amplitude selector

47. The amplifier used in the Miller voltage sweep should have a gain of

    (a) $-\infty$          (b) $+1$            (c) $+\infty$         (d) $-1$

48. The amplifier used in the bootstrap voltage sweep should have a gain of

    (a) $+1$          (b) $+\infty$         (c) $-1$          (d) $-\infty$

# ANSWERS

1. Depending on the arrangement of the *RC* circuit, it may be employed as an integrator or a differentiator.
2. CR seconds
3. as an open circuit.
4. The capacitor voltage can be determined at any given time *t* after commencement of charge or discharge.
5. $RC \geq 10$ PW
6. It is used to square off the peaks of an applied signal.
7. It is used to limit the amplitude of a relatively small input signal to a definite negative or positive output level.
8. Clampers do not affect the shape of the waveform.
9. To sweep the beam horizontally across the screen of a scope.
10.   1. Slope or sweep-speed error.
      2. Displacement error   3. Transmission error.

| | | | |
|---|---|---|---|
| 11. 75.6 μs | 12. 32.6 μs | 13. 10 s; 23 s | |
| 14. $R_1 = 100$ kΩ; $I_F = 20.5$ mA; $P_{R1} = 2.5$ mW; $P_{D1} = 14.35$ mW; PIV = $-50$ V. | | | |
| 15. $R_1 = 1$ kΩ; $I_F = 9.3$ mA | 16. slower | 17. capacitor | 18. short |
| 19. extreme | 20. exponential | 21. lower | 22. 10% to 90% |
| 23. summation | 24. triangular | 25. greater, integrator | 26. differentiator |
| 27. rate of change | 28. square off | 29. d.c. restorer | 30. bootstrapping |
| 31. True | 32. False | 33. False | 34. True |
| 35. False | 36. True | 37. False | 38. False |
| 39. False | 40. True | 41. True | 42. False |
| 43. (a) | 44. (d) | 45. (b) | 46. (b) |
| 47. (a) | 48. (a) | | |

# Logic Families

## INTRODUCTION

The various approaches to digital logic design are called logic families. Many different types of logic families exist and depending on the *application*, circuits in a particular piece of equipment may be selected from one or more of these families.

Integrated-circuit logic gates (small-scale integration, *SSI*), combinational logic circuits (medium-scale integration, *MSI*), and microprocessor systems (large-scale integration and very large scale integration, *LSI* and *VLSI*) are readily available from several manufacturers through distributors and electronic parts suppliers. Basically, there are three *commonly used families* of digital IC logic: transistor-transistor logic (*TTL*), complementary metal oxide semiconductor (*CMOS*) and emitter-coupled logic (*ECL*). Within each family, several *subfamilies* (or series) of logic types are available with *different ratings.*

### 9.1 Describe the numbering system for digital ICs.

*Solution:*

Fortunately, the different manufactures of digital ICs have standardised a *numbering scheme* so that basic part numbers will be the same regardless of the manufacturer. The *prefix* of the part number, however, will differ because it is the manufacturer's abbreviation. For example, a typical TTL part number might be S74F08N. The 7408 is the *basic number* used by all manufacturers for a quad AND gate. The *F* stands for the FAST TTL subfamily and the *S* prefix is the manufacturer's code for Signetics, National Semiconductor uses the prefix DM, and Texas Instruments uses the prefix SN. The *N* suffix at the end

of the part number is used to specify the package type. *N* is used for the *plastic dual-in-line* (DIP), *W* is used for *ceramic flatpack*, *D* is used for the *surface mounted SO plastic package.* The best sources of information on available package styles and their dimensions are the manufacturers *data manuals.*

### 9.2 Briefly describe the characteristics of TTL and CMOS.

*Solution:*

The most important characteristics of TTL and CMOS are that *TTL gates switch very fast,* while *CMOS has very low power dissipation.* Other characteristics of logic gates are supply voltage, input and output voltage levels, input and output current levels, noise immunity and the number of gate inputs that can be supplied by one gate output. *Usually, a single type of logic gate is used throughout a logic system, but sometimes different types of logic gates have to be interfaced.*

### 9.3 Draw the logic family tree. What are the primary circuit differences?

*Solution:*

Figure 9.1 is a family tree of the *most common logic families and their derivatives,* complete with circuit details, showing how they differ. *Bipolar devices* are junction devices in which the majority current flow is across the junction: as with diodes and transistor. *MOS* metal oxide silicon-devices operate in a different way, dependent upon the *field effect,* and the majority current flow stays within the different semiconductor types, apart from minute leakage currents. Of the two major logic types, *TTL* is more widely used, because it is much more tolerant towards the handler; *special precautions*

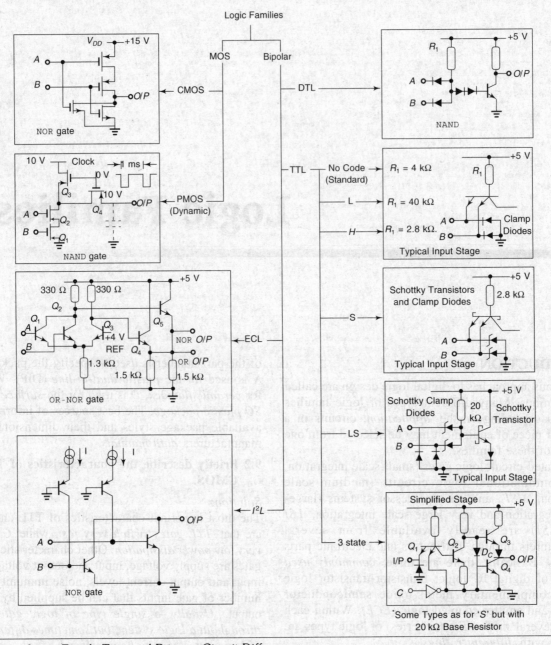

**Fig. 9.1** *Logic Family Tree and Primary Circuit Differences.*

must be taken when handling *MOS devices* to prevent damaging them by stray electrostatic fields. The particular advantage of the latter type is its low power consumption, and wide supply voltage tolerance.

## LOGIC SPECIFICATIONS

Specific information about the *operating characteristics* of a particular IC family can be obtained from *data sheets* published by the manufacturer. A typical data sheet is divided into three main sections: (1) recommended operating conditions; (2) electrical characteristics; and (3) switching characteristics.

### 9.4 Describe data sheet parameters.

*Solution:*

Parameters of the data sheet are given below:

1. $V_{CC}$: The dc voltage that supplies power to the device. *Below* the specified minimum, reliable operation cannot be guaranteed. *Above* the specified maximum, damage to the device may occur.

2. $I_{OH}$: The maximum output current that the gate can *source* to a load and operate reliably when the output is at HIGH level. *By convention, the current out of a terminal is assigned a negative value.* Figure 9.2(a) illustrates this parameter.

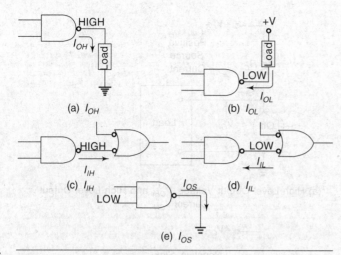

**Fig. 9.2** *Illustrating Data Sheet Parameters.*

3. $I_{OL}$: The minimum output current that the gate can *sink* and operate reliably when the output is at LOW level. *By convention, current into a terminal is assigned a positive value.* Figure 9.2(b) illustrates this parameter.

4. $V_{IH}$: The value of input voltage that can be accepted as a HIGH level by the gate.

5. $V_{IL}$: The value of input voltage that can be accepted as a LOW level by the gate.

6. $V_{OH}$: The value of HIGH level output voltage that the gate produces.

7. $V_{OL}$: The value of LOW level output voltage that the gate produces.

8. $I_{IH}$: The value of input current for a HIGH level input voltage, Fig. 9.2(c).

9. $I_{IL}$: The value of input current for a LOW level input voltage, Fig. 9.2(d).

10. $I_{OS}$: The output current when the gate output is shorted to ground and with input conditions that establish a HIGH level output, Fig. 9.2(e).

11. $I_{CCH}$: The total current from the $V_{CC}$ supply when all gate outputs are at the HIGH level.

12. $I_{CCL}$: The total current from the $V_{CC}$ supply when all gate outputs are at the LOW level.

## PROPAGATION DELAY TIME

This parameter is a result of the limitation on switching speed or frequency at which a logic gate can operate. The terms low speed and high speed, applied to logic circuits refer to the propagation delay time. *The shorter the propagation delay, the higher the speed of the circuit and the higher the frequency at which it can operate.*

### 9.5 What is the significance of propagation delay time, $t_p$?

*Solution:*

Propagation delay time, $t_p$, of a logic gate is *the time interval between the application of an input pulse and*

*the occurrence of the resulting output pulse.* There are two different measurements of propagation delay time associated with a logic gate that apply to all the types of basic gates:

$t_{PHL}$: the time between a *specified* reference point on the input pulse and a *corresponding* reference point on the resulting output pulse, with the output changing *from the HIGH level to the LOW level (HL).*

$t_{PLH}$: the time between a *specified* reference point on the input pulse and a *corresponding* reference point on the resulting output pulse, with the output changing *from the LOW level to the HIGH level (LH).*

### 9.6 Show the propagation delay times of the inverter in Fig. 9.3(a).

*Solution:*

The propagation delay times $t_{PHL}$ and $t_{PLH}$ are indicated in Fig. 9.3(b). In this case, *the delays are measured between the 50% points of the corresponding edges of the input and output pulses.* The values of $t_{PHL}$ and $t_{PLH}$ *are not necessarily equal* but in many cases they are the same. The propagation delay time specified on the logic gate data sheets is usually the *average* of $t_{PHL}$ and $t_{PLH}$.

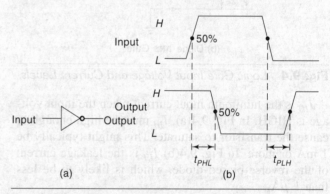

**Fig. 9.3(b)** *Solution for Problem 9.6.*

### 9.7 Illustrate and explain 'input and output' voltages and 'input and output' currents.

*Solution:*

$V_{IH(min)}$ is the minimum high-input voltage regarded as *the minimum voltage required to represent a logic 1 input level.* If, for example, an input of 2 V or higher will cause the output of a given type of gate to change state, but any level less than 2 V may not change the output, then (in this case) $V_{IH(min)} = 2$ V. In Fig. 9.4(a)

$$V_{IH(min)} = V_{BE} + I_{IH} R_B$$

where input current $I_{IH}$ is *large enough* to drive the transistor into saturation.

$V_{IL(max)}$ is the maximum low-input voltage regarded as the maximum voltage required to represent a logic 0 input level. For the circuit of Fig. 9.4(a) $V_{IL(max)}$ must be much less than $V_{BE}$ level that biases the transistor ON. With silicon transistors, $V_{IL(max)}$ might be around 0.2 V.

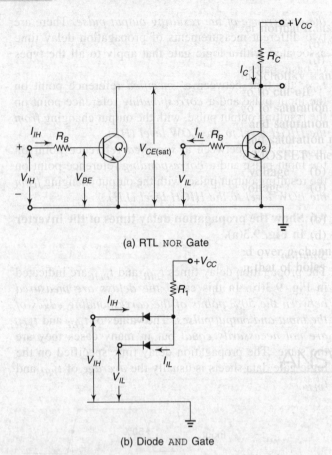

(a) RTL NOR Gate

(b) Diode AND Gate

**Fig. 9.4**    *Logic Gate Input Voltage and Current Levels.*

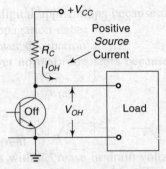

(a) High Level Output Voltage $V_{OH}$, and High Level Output Current $I_{OH}$.

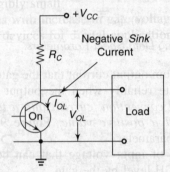

(b) Low level output voltage $V_{OL}$, and low level output current $I_{OL}$

**Fig. 9.5**    *Logic Gate Output Voltage and Current Levels.*

$I_{IH}$ is the minimum input current when the input voltage is HIGH. In Fig. 9.4(a), $I_{IH}$ must be high enough to cause the transistor to saturate. This might typically be 1 mA or more. In Fig. 9.4(b) $I_{IH}$ is the leakage current of the reverse-biased diode, which is likely to be less than 1 $\mu$A.

$I_{IL}$ is the maximum input current when the input voltage is LOW. In Fig. 9.4(a), $I_{IL}$ occurs when $Q_2$ is OFF. Thus, it is a junction leakage current with a level less than 1 $\mu$A. In Fig. 9.4(b), $I_{IL}$ is the current through a forward-biased diode, so it might typically be 1 mA. *This current actually flows out of the input terminal.* In data sheets it will be listed as a *negative quantity*.

$V_{OH(\text{min})}$ is the minimum high-output voltage from a gate, or logic 1 output level. In Fig. 9.5(a)

$$V_{OH} = V_{CC} - I_{OH} R_C$$

where $I_{OH}$ is the output current, $V_{OH(\text{min})}$ must be larger than $V_{IH(\text{min})}$.

$V_{OL(\text{max})}$ is the maximum low-output voltage from a gate, or logic 0 output level. In Fig. 9.5(b), $V_{OL(\text{max})}$ would equal the transistor saturation voltage, which is typically around 0.2 V. For any given type of logic gate driving another similar gate, the maximum logic 0 output voltage must be equal to or less than the maximum logic 0 input voltage.

$I_{OH}$ is the high-level output current when the gate output voltage is HIGH. It is a *positive* quantity; the current flows *out of* the gate output terminal, as shown in Fig. 9.5(a). In this case, the gate is said to *source* the output current, and the gate output may be termed a *current source*.

$I_{OL}$ is the low-level output current when the gate output voltage is LOW. It is a *negative* quantity; the current flows *into* the output terminal, as shown in Fig. 9.5(b). In this case, the gate is said to *sink* this current, and the gate output may be termed a *current sink*.

## NOISE IMMUNITY

With careful design, digital systems can be made *nearly noise-free*. Few of the components in digital systems are intrinsically noisy enough to produce *erroneous transitions* from HIGH to LOW and LOW to HIGH. The principal hazards are *capacitive couplings* to other digital waveforms that might switch suddenly (a specific problem in *closely packed circuits*), *improperly shielded power-line transients,* or *transmission-line effects* in which pulses are "reflected" from the input of one gate and can return to the output of a previous gate to induce a transition. In TTL logic, where the current pulses during a gate transition can be large, it is possible for the small resistance in the *bus wires* used to distribute power to cause a momentary drop in the local power supply voltage, thereby causing an error. It is recommended, therefore, that *capacitors between the supply and ground be distributed throughout digital circuits to provide local reservoirs of stored energy that can supply the transient switching circuits.*

**9.8 Explain in detail the significance of noise margins of a gate.**

*Solution:*

The region between $V_{IL(max)}$ and $V_{IH(min)}$ is identified as an *indeterminate range*. This is shown in Fig. 9.6. If any voltage between these two levels is applied as an input to a gate, the output of the gate is *unpredictable.*

The difference between $V_{OL(max)}$ and $V_{IL(max)}$ is referred to as the *low-state noise margin* for the gate. The difference between $V_{OH(min)}$ and $V_{IH(min)}$ is referred to as the *high-state noise margin*. Both of these noise margins are illustrated in Fig. 9.6.

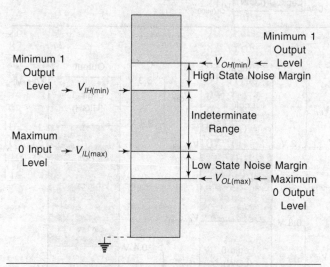

**Fig. 9.6** *Each Logic Gate has a Maximum Logic 0 Input Voltage and a Minimum Logic 1 Input Voltage. Any voltage that Falls within the Indeterminate Range between These Two Levels Might Produce Unwanted Gate Triggering.*

Noise spikes with amplitudes greater than either noise margin may drive a gate into the indeterminate range, possibly producing *unwanted triggering.*

Clearly, many factors are involved in the noise immunity for a given type of logic gate. Instead of trying to rate the noise immunity of each type of gate in terms of voltage levels, switching time, and impedance, *noise immunity is usually described as poor, fair, good, or excellent.*

$$V_{NH} = V_{OH(min)} - V_{IH(min)} \text{ and } V_{NL} = V_{IL(max)} - V_{OL(max)}$$

**9.9 The propagation delay times for a 74LS08 AND gate (Fig. 9.7) are $t_{PLH}$ = 15 ns, $t_{PHL}$ = 20 ns and**

**for a 7402 NOR gate they are $t_{PLH}$ = 22 ns, $t_{PHL}$ = 15 ns. Sketch $V_{out1}$ and $V_{out2}$ showing the effects of propagation delay. Assume 0 ns for rise and fall times.**

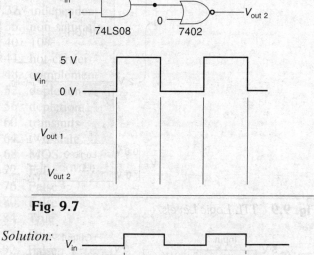

**Fig. 9.7**

*Solution:*

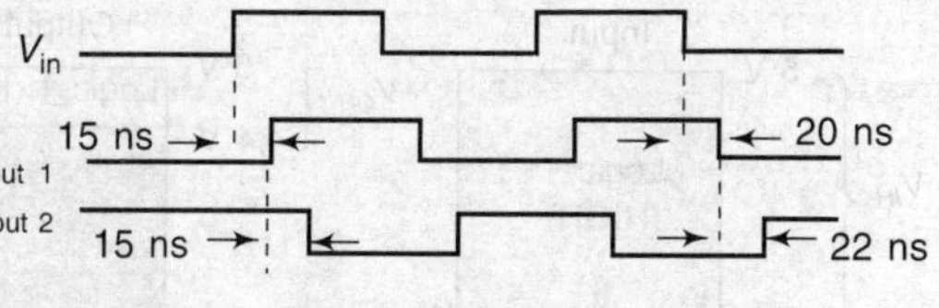

**Fig. 9.8** *Solution for Problem 9.9.*

## SUPPLY VOLTAGE AND POWER DISSIPATION

Most integrated circuit logic gates are designed to operate with a supply of 5 V. Some types of gates use a *higher* supply voltage and one type (CMOS) can operate with a supply voltage as *low* as 1 V. Where a $V_{CC}$ of 5 V is specified, the actual voltage must usually be within ±0.25 of 5 V for *reliable gate operation.*

Where a logic circuit is to operate with a *battery power supply,* it must use gates with the lowest possible power dissipation to minimise the current drain on the battery. Current drain is less important for a logic system with *ac power supply,* but even in this case the heat generated by a large number of gates can present a problem. *In general, high power dissipation is accepted with gates that must switch very fast.* Typical power dissipations range from 10 to 25 mW per gate, depending upon the gate circuitry.

## SPEED/POWER PRODUCT

The speed power product is sometimes specified by the manufacturer as a *figure of merit* of a logic circuit based on the product of the propagation delay time and the power dissipation at a *specified frequency.*

## 9.10 Illustrate TTL and CMOS logic levels.

*Solution:*

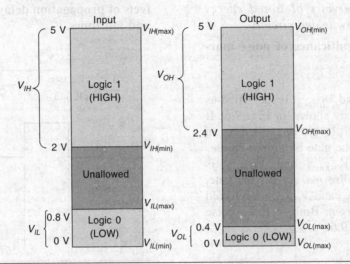

**Fig. 9.9** *TTL Logic Levels.*

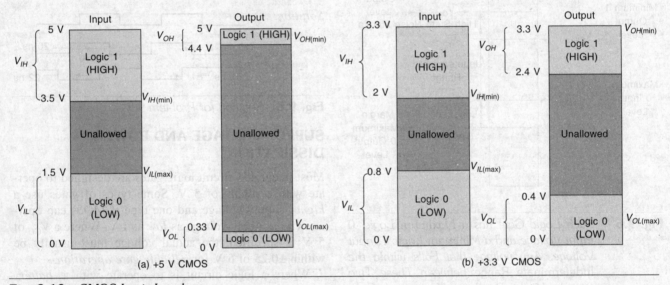

**Fig. 9.10** *CMOS Logic Levels.*

## 9.11 Determine the HIGH-level and LOW-level noise margins for TTL and CMOS by using the information in Figs 9.9 and 9.10.

*Solution:*

| For TTL | | For 5 V CMOS | |
|---|---|---|---|
| $V_{IH(min)} = 2$ V | $V_{IL(max)} = 0.8$ V | $V_{IH(min)} = 3.5$ V | $V_{IL(max)} = 1.5$ V |
| $V_{OH(min)} = 2.4$ V | $V_{OL(max)} = 0.4$ V | $V_{OH(min)} = 4.4$ V | $V_{OL(max)} = 0.33$ V |
| $V_{NH} = V_{OH(min)} - V_{IH(min)}$ $= 2.4 - 2$ V $= 0.4$ V | | $V_{NH} = V_{OH(min)} - V_{IH(min)}$ | $= 4.4$ V $- 3.5$ V $= 0.9$ V |
| $V_{NL} = V_{IL(max)} - V_{OL(max)}$ $= 0.8$ V $- 0.4$ V $= 0.4$ V | | $V_{NL} = V_{IL(max)} - V_{OL(max)}$ | $= 1.5$ V $- 0.33$ V $= 1.17$ V |

*A TTL gate is immune to upto 0.4 V of noise for both the HIGH and LOW input states.*

**9.12 Illustrate the effects of input noise on gate operation.**

*Solution:*

If, for example, noise voltage causes the input of a 5 V *CMOS gate* to drop below 3.5 V in the HIGH state, the input is in the unallowed region and operation is unpredictable. Thus, the gate may interpret the fluctuation below 3.5 V as a LOW level, as illustrated in Fig. 9.11(a). Similarly, if noise causes a gate input to go above 1.5 V in the LOW state, an uncertain condition is created, as illustrated in Fig. 9.11(b).

**9.13 A certain gate has a propagation delay of 5 ns, $I_{CCH} = 1$ mA and $I_{CCL} = 2.5$ mA with a dc supply of 5 V. Determine the speed-power product.**

*Solution:*

$$P_D = V_{CC}\left(\frac{I_{CCH} + I_{CCL}}{2}\right) = 5\,\text{V}\left(\frac{1\,\text{mA} + 2.5\,\text{mA}}{2}\right)$$

$$= 8.75\ \text{mW}$$

$$\text{SPP} = (5\ \text{ns})\,(8.75\ \text{mW})$$

$$= 43.75\ \text{pJ}$$

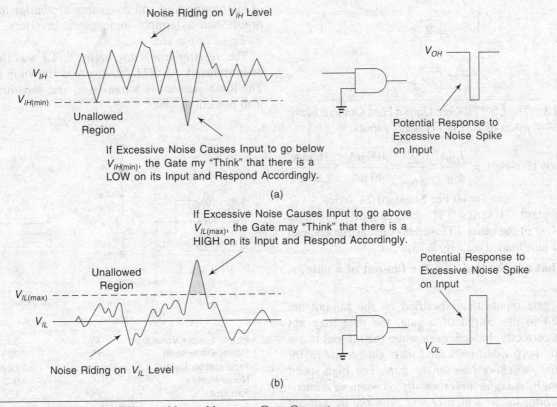

**(a)**

**(b)**

**Fig. 9.11**   *Illustration of the Effects of Input Noise on Gate Operation.*

## FAN-IN AND FAN-OUT

Fan-in and fan-out are terms that are used when gates are connected together into a gate circuit. The *fan-in* of a gate is equal to the maximum number of gate outputs which can be connected to it and used as inputs. A gate with a fan-in of three, for example, could be connected so that upto three gate outputs provide its input voltages. Another way of saying this is that three gates could be used to drive this gate. *In any logic configuration, the number N of inputs is called the fan-in.* This is shown in Fig. 9.12.

The *fan-out* of a gate is a much more important quantity, equal to the maximum number of inputs that can be connected to the output of a gate. A gate with a fan-out of 10, for example, means that up to 10 inputs of other gates could be connected to the one output, and reliable operation still obtained. *In any logic configura-*

*tion, the number M of outputs is called the fan-out.* This is shown in Fig. 9.12.

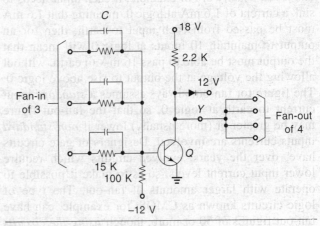

**Fig. 9.12**   *Fan-in and Fan-out.*

### 9.14 Elaborate the term unit load. Give examples.

*Solution:*

Fan-out is specified in terms of unit loads. *A unit load for a logic gate equals one input to a like circuit.* For example, a unit load for a 7400 NAND gate equals one input to another logic gate in the standard 7400 series (not necessarily a NAND gate).

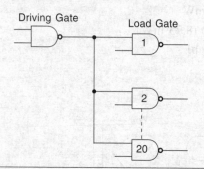

**Fig. 9.13** *The LS TTL Gate Output Fans Out to a Maximum of 20 LS TTL Gate Inputs.*

$$\text{Unit loads (fan-out)} = \frac{I_{OH}}{I_{IH}} = \frac{I_{OL}}{I_{IL}} = \frac{400\,\mu A}{40\,\mu A} = \frac{16\,mA}{1.6\,mA}$$

$$= 10 \text{ For Standard 74 series}$$

A standard 74 series TTL gate can drive 10 unit loads. Most of the other TTL series, such as the LS, can drive 20 unit loads (see Fig. 9.13).

### 9.15 What are the limits on the fan-out of a gate?

*Solution:*

If more gate inputs than specified by the fan-out are connected to the output of a gate, the gate may not function correctly. Indeed, even when the fan-out is not exceeded, *each additional load at a gate tends to increase the switching time of the gate.* For high-speed operation, *IC manufacturers usually recommend a maximum loading factor which is less than the dc fan-out capability of the gate.*

The *limits* on the fan-out of a gate are caused by the currents which flow when the inputs have to be held at one level, usually 0. For example, if each input needs to sink a current of 1.6 mA at logic 0, meaning that 1.6 mA must be passed from each input to earth, then for an output to maintain 10 inputs at logic 0 will mean that the output must be able to pass 16 mA to earth, without allowing the voltage at the output to rise above logic 0. The figure for fan-out always assumes a *standard* input current to earth at logic 0, so that the fan-out figure may be greater or (more usually) lower if *non-standard* inputs currents are involved. Designers of gate circuits have, over the years, evolved circuits which require lower input current levels, so as to make it possible to operate with larger amounts of fan-out. The type of logic circuits known as CMOS, for example, can have fan-out figures of 50 or more, though *using the circuits*

*with large amounts of fan-out will have the effect of limiting the speed with which gates can be operated.* CMOS means Complementary Metal Oxide Semiconductor—a variety of field-effect transistor integrated circuit.

### 9.16 What does the term logic family signify? Explain resistor-transistor logic (RTL)

*Solution:*

Digital ICs are categorised according to how their gates are interconnected. They may be placed in *logic families,* each logic family having in common *a certain type of interconnection* and consisting of *similar logic functions,* such as simple logic gates, inverters, registers, flip-flops etc.

The *resistor-transistor logic* (RTL) was the first to be introduced. An *RTL NOR gate* is shown in Fig. 9.14. The logic element is a transistor, and resistors connect it to preceding gates.

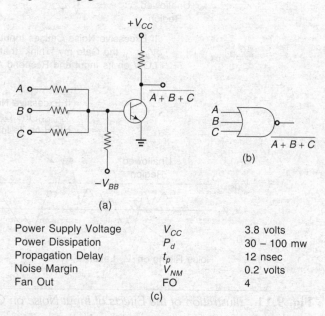

| | | |
|---|---|---|
| Power Supply Voltage | $V_{CC}$ | 3.8 volts |
| Power Dissipation | $P_d$ | 30 – 100 mw |
| Propagation Delay | $t_p$ | 12 nsec |
| Noise Margin | $V_{NM}$ | 0.2 volts |
| Fan Out | FO | 4 |

(c)

**Fig. 9.14** *RTL-NOR gate: (a) Schematic, (b) Symbol, (c) Specifications.*

Because of the few components required, RTL circuits are simple and reliable. Also, these circuits have relatively low power consumption and are inexpensive. *Disadvantages* of the RTL family are: their slow switching speeds because of their tendency to be driven deep into saturation, and their poor drive capability compared to other logic families.

A *positive input* at A, OR B, OR C will drive the transistor into conduction, increasing the voltage drop across the collector resistor and decreasing the positive output voltage. The transistor in this gate is driven by a heavy base current when any input is a logic-1 (positive voltage). In fact, it is made to operate in the *saturation mode,* where further increases in collector voltage would produce no further increase in collector current. Ordinarily, the gate would be made to drive other gates. *The number of gates it drives in a given application is the fan-out.* There is a limit to the fan-out, since *the more the gates that must be driven, the more the current that must be supplied.* The fan-out is an important specification of digital ICs. For a given load, a gate with a fan-out of five can drive five circuits with a fan-in load of one, or one circuit with a fan-in load of five.

### 9.17 Explain diode-transistor logic. Give its specifications.

*Solution:*

The next logic family that was introduced was diode-transistor logic (DTL). The purpose of the input resistors in Fig. 9.14 is to *isolate* the inputs from one another. If diodes are used instead of resistors, we have DTL, Fig. 9.15.

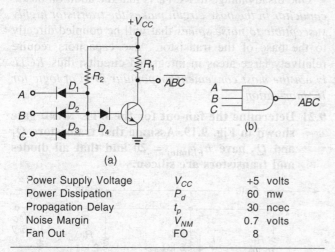

| Power Supply Voltage | $V_{CC}$ | +5 | volts |
| Power Dissipation | $P_d$ | 60 | mw |
| Propagation Delay | $t_p$ | 30 | ncec |
| Noise Margin | $V_{NM}$ | 0.7 | volts |
| Fan Out | FO | 8 | |

**Fig. 9.15** *DTL NAND Gate; (a) Schematic; (b) Symbol*

The circuit shown is essentially a diode AND circuit with a transistor inverter to provide the NAND function. *The diodes provide much better input isolation than resistors.* Although the gates in the DTL family can switch states faster than the gates in the RTL family, *the diodes place a limit on the switching speed due to the charge stored in their junctions.* A logic family designed to get around this problem is TTL (transistor-transistor logic) family.

Diode-transistor logic can be purchased with either 6 or 2 kΩ load resistors. This allows the designer to vary his power dissipation. However, lower power dissipation using the 6 kΩ resistor also introduces greater propagation delays. DTL was the first development in *custom-made logic devices;* for most purposes it has been superseded by TTL.

The DTL family is probably the easiest logic to use, and is also the cheapest form of logic available for *medium-speed applications.*

### 9.18 Briefly explain high-threshold logic. Give its specifications.

*Solution:*

There are occasions where digital circuits must operate in an environment which produces very high noise signals. For operation in such surroundings, there is available *a type of DTL gate which possesses a high threshold to noise immunity.* This type of gate is called a high-threshold logic (HTL) gate, Fig. 9.16.

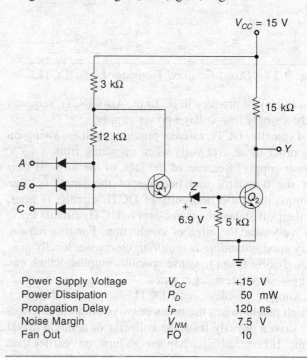

| Power Supply Voltage | $V_{CC}$ | +15 | V |
| Power Dissipation | $P_D$ | 50 | mW |
| Propagation Delay | $t_P$ | 120 | ns |
| Noise Margin | $V_{NM}$ | 7.5 | V |
| Fan Out | FO | 10 | |

**Fig. 9.16** *High Threshold Logic (HTL).*

In order for output transistor $Q_2$ to conduct, the emitter of $Q_1$ must rise to a potential of one $V_{BE}$ drop plus the fixed zener voltage of 6.9 V, for a total of about 7.5 V. The low level for the gate remains at 0.2 V, but the high level is about 15 V. With the input of 0.2 V, the base of $Q_1$ is at 0.9 V and $Q_2$ is off. The noise signal must be greater than 7.5 V to change the state of $Q_2$. With all inputs at 15 V, output transistor $Q_2$ is saturated. The noise signal must be greater than 7.5 V (in the negative direction) to turn the transistor off. Thus, the noise margin is 7.5 V for both voltage levels.

### 9.19 Explain direct-coupled transistor logic.

*Solution:*

Logic gates can be made by direct interconnection of transistors. This type of logic is called direct-coupled transistor logic (DCTL) and was one of the first types of logic made into integrated circuits. Typical NAND and NOR gates using DCTL circuits are shown in Fig. 9.17. The DCTL gate is simple to make, needing few parts,

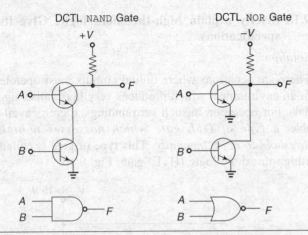

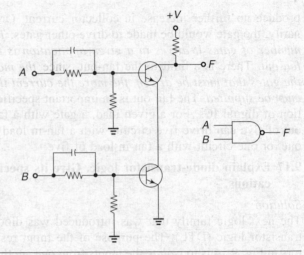

**Fig. 9.17**  *Direct-Coupled Transistor Logic (DCTL).*

and is easy to produce in IC form. Also, DCTL requires only a single low-voltage power supply.

Typically, DCTL circuits provide a voltage swing on the order of several volts when operating from a +3 V power supply. Because of the lack of the turn-off bias for the transistor and because of the small voltage swings, the noise immunity of DCTL circuits is poor. In their off states, the transistors in DCTL circuits operate very near the edge of conduction. For this reason, *very good grounding is required;* otherwise, locally generated noise is apt to cause spurious outputs, which can trigger subsequent logic gates.

Another problem with DCTL is *current hogging,* which results when the bases of two or more transistors are driven directly from the collector of a single driver stage. If one transistor happens to turn 'on' earlier than the others, the output transistor might be clamped to a value that is insufficient to turn 'on' the other transistors. *Because of this current hogging characteristic, the drive capability of DCTL is quite limited. Also, in order to minimise current hogging, transistors must be carefully selected to have very nearly identical turn-on voltages.*

### 9.20 Explain resistor-capacitor-transistor logic (RCTL).

*Solution:*
The RTL transistor switching circuits suffer from slow switching speeds because of their tendency to draw excessive base current. This base current drives the transistor into the saturation region, resulting in an *accumulation of stored charge*. The time required to remove the stored charge as the transistor attempts to change states is called the *storage delay time*. One method of reducing storage delay time is to add up a *speed-up capacitor* in parallel with the base resistor, as shown in Fig. 9.18. *The speed-up capacitor stores the charge instead of the transistor, thus allowing the transistor to switch out of saturation faster.* When a resistor and capacitor are used in this manner, the resulting logic circuit is called resistor-capacitor-transistor logic (RCTL).

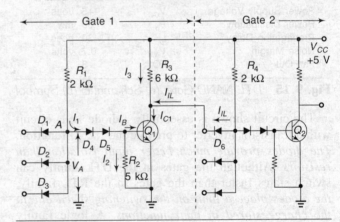

**Fig. 9.18**  *Resistor-Capacitor-Transistor Logic (RCTL).*

One disadvantage to RCTL is that the addition of *the capacitor in the base circuit makes the transistor highly susceptible to noise spikes* that will be coupled directly to the base of the transistor. Also capacitors require relatively large areas in integrated circuits; thus *RCTL is not the most convenient or popular form of logic for IC fabrication.*

### 9.21 Determine the fan-out for the DTL NAND gate shown in Fig. 9.19. Assume that transistors $Q_1$ and $Q_2$ have $h_{FE(min)} = 20$ and that all diodes and transistors are silicon.

**Fig. 9.19**  *One Diode Transistor Logic (DTL) NAND Gate Driving Another Similar Gate. The Gate Fan-out may be Calculated from a Knowledge of the Low-level Input and Output Currents, $I_{IL}$ and $I_{OL}$.*

*Solution:*

$$I_2 = \frac{V_{BE1}}{R_2} = \frac{0.7 \text{ V}}{5 \text{ k}\Omega} = 140 \text{ } \mu\text{A}$$

$$V_A = V_{F4} + V_{F5} + V_{BE1}$$
$$= 0.7 \text{ V} + 0.7 \text{ V} + 0.7 \text{ V}$$
$$= 2.1 \text{ V}$$

$$I_1 = \frac{V_{CC} - V_A}{R_1} = \frac{5\,V - 2.1\,V}{2\,k\Omega} = 1.45\ mA$$

$$I_B = I_1 - I_2 = 1.45\ mA - 140\ \mu A$$
$$= 1.31\ mA$$

$$I_{C1} = h_{FE}\,I_B = 20 \times 1.31\ mA$$
$$= 26.2\ mA$$

$$I_3 = \frac{V_{CC} - V_{CE\,(sat)}}{R_3} = \frac{5\,V - 0.2\,V}{6\,k\Omega} = 0.8\ mA$$

The maximum low-level output current is

$$I_{OL} = I_{C1} - I_3 = 26.2\ mA - 0.8\ mA = 25.4\ mA$$

With $Q_2$ off, the unit load is

$$I_{IL} = \frac{V_{CC} - V_{F6}}{R_4} = \frac{5\,V - 0.7\,V}{2\,k\Omega}$$
$$= 2.15\ mA$$

$$\frac{I_{OL}}{I_{IL}} = \frac{25.4\ mA}{2.15\ mA} = 11.8$$

Fan-out = 11

### 9.22 What is the function of an expander gate?

*Solution:*

Lead $C$ in Fig. 9.20(a) is called an *expander* circuit. If lead $E$ of Fig. 9.20(b) is connected to lead $C$, the gate will become a six-input gate. *This allows a great deal of versatility in design.*

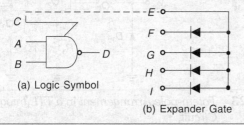

(a) Logic Symbol

(b) Expander Gate

**Fig. 9.20** *Expander Gate.*

## TRANSISTOR-TRANSISTOR LOGIC (T²L OR TTL)

Diode-transistor logic was used in early *small-scale integration* SSI components. The next stage in the development of logic circuits was to introduce a new kind of *multi-emitter transistor* thereby minimising the number of chip interconnections, saving space, and simplifying the manufacturing requirements. Because the input diodes were replaced by transistors, these devices became to be known as transistor-transistor logic (TTL or T²L)

### 9.23 What is the significance of TTL? Give the specifications of TTL.

*Solution:*

By far, the *most widely used* digital logic family today is the TTL, familiar to us in the form of the *7400 series* devices. The basic 7400 series encompasses just about *all levels of integration*—small-scale integration SSI gates, expanders, `flip-flops`; medium-scale integration *MSI* counters, registers, decoders; and to an extent, large-scale integration *LSI* in some of the memory circuits. Pioneered by *Texas Instruments,* the 7400 TTL line is now available from virtually all manufacturers of digital logic.

| | | | |
|---|---|---|---|
| Power Supply | $V_{CC}$ | +5 | volts |
| Power Dissipation | $P_d$ | 100 | mw |
| Propagation Delay | $t_p$ | 15 | nsec |
| Noise Margin | $V_{NM}$ | 0.4 | volts |
| Fan Out | FO | 10 | |

The list of *available functions* numbers about 300 and is still expanding. This is perhaps the biggest virtue of the 7400 logic—*the large number of functions available.* A second virtue is the fact that a great many of them are also available in low power, high speed, the super-high speed Schottky and low-power Schottky versions. *This allows one to optimise a particular performance parameter with a minimum of change merely by substituting an equivalent device for high speed or low power.* All 7400 families can be intermixed if loading considerations are taken into account.

### 9.24 Describe the basic circuitry of a three-input TTL gate.

*Solution:*

In TTL logic, the input signals are applied directly to transistor emitters. In Fig. 9.21(a), the output transistor $Q_2$ is controlled by the voltage at the collector terminal

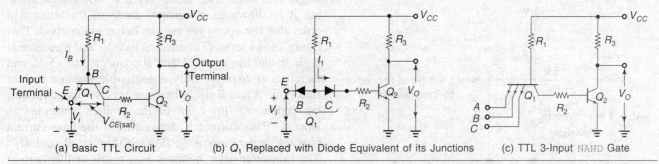

(a) Basic TTL Circuit

(b) $Q_1$ Replaced with Diode Equivalent of its Junctions

(c) TTL 3-Input NAND Gate

**Fig. 9.21** *Basic Circuitry of a TTL Gate-Signal-inputs are Applied to the Emitter Terminals of a Saturated Transistor. The Junctions of this Transistor behave like two Diodes in DTL Gate. A Multiemitter Transistor is employed to Provide Several Input Terminals.*

of transistor $Q_1$. When the input terminal is grounded, sufficient base current $I_B$ flows to keep $Q_1$ in saturation. The collector voltage of $Q_1$ is $V_{CE(sat)}$ above ground. Typically $V_{CE(sat)}$ is 0.2 V, which is not high enough to bias $Q_2$ on. Therefore, when the input voltage is LOW, $Q_2$ is off and the output level is HIGH.

If a positive voltage is applied to the input terminal, $Q_1$ remains in saturation ($I_B$ is still large enough) and $Q_1$ collector voltage goes to $V_i + V_{CE(sat)}$. Depending upon the actual level of input voltage, sufficient base current can be supplied to $Q_2$ to drive it into saturation, causing the output to switch LOW. Figure 9.21(b) shows $Q_1$ *replaced* by diodes representing the base-emitter and collector-base junctions. This arrangement is similar to that of a DTL circuit. The input voltage could easily be made large enough to reverse bias the base-emitter junction of $Q_1$. When this occurs, the collector-base junctions of $Q_1$ remains forward biased, and current $I_1$ flows to saturate the output transistor.

Figure 9.21(c) shows a *basic three-input TTL circuit*. $Q_1$ is seen to be a transistor with three emitter terminals. This is fabricated easily in intergrated circuit form. The three emitters are the input terminals to the gate. For $Q_1$ collector to rise above $V_{CE(sat)}$ input A AND input B AND input C must be HIGH positive levels. Because of this, and because the output level goes from HIGH to LOW, the circuit is a NAND gate.

**9.25 Describe how the problem of a variable load is overcome by the totem-pole arrangement.**

*Solution:*

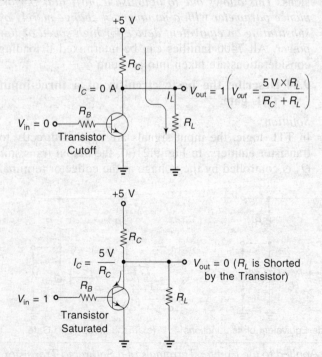

**Fig. 9.22**   *Common-emitter Calculations.*

The 1-level output of an inverter is very dependent on the size of the load resistor, $R_L$, which can typically vary by a factor of 10. This is only for the case when the transistor is cut-off ($V_{out} = 1$), but when the transistor is saturated ($V_{out} = 0$), the transistor collector current will be excessive if $R_C$ is very small ($I_C = 5$ V/$R_C$). This is shown in Fig. 9.22.

Therefore, it seems that when the transistor is *cut-off* we want $R_C$ to be *small* to ensure that $V_{out}$ is close to 5 V. But when the transistor is *saturated,* we want $R_C$ to be *large* to avoid excessive collector current. This idea of needing a variable $R_C$ resistance is accommodated by the TTL integrated circuit, Fig. 9.23. It uses another transistor, $Q_4$, in place of $R_C$ to act like a variable resistance. $Q_4$, is cut-off (*acts like a high $R_C$*) when the output transistor, $Q_3$, is saturated, and when $Q_4$ is saturated (*acts like a low $R_C$*) then $Q_3$ is cut-off. In other words, *when one transistor is ON, the other is OFF*. This combination of $Q_3$ and $Q_4$ is often referred to as *totem-pole arrangement.*

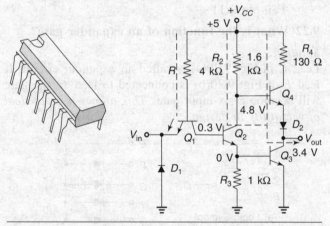

**Fig. 9.23**   *Totem-pole Arrangement in a TTL Integrated Circuit.*

**9.26 Discuss and illustrate TTL ratings.**

*Solution:*

By diffusing a number of separate emitter $n$-types into the base $p$-type of the input transistor shown as $Q_1$ in Fig. 9.24, the *same* logic inputs can be derived within a single transistor. The diode $D_1$ is a *distributed diode* but it is shown as a separate diode in this circuit in order that the operation may be better understood. This figure shows input C connected to 0 V, and therefore at *logic 0,* and the inputs A and B connected to +5 V, and therefore at *logic 1*. Only a negligible leakage current flows into A and B since these are reverse-biased diodes, but current $I_b$ flows out of the emitter connected to input C. This current is derived from the base current plus the larger current $I_a$, flowing through $R_1$ and $D_1$. The input transistor bottoms as a result of this current and the collector of $Q_1$ is at about +0.2 V, i.e. the saturation level for the collector-emitter.

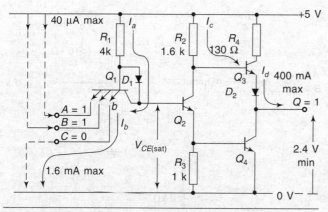

**Fig. 9.24 A** *TTL Gate with One Input LOW.*

This condition cuts-off $Q_2$ and allows current $I_C$ to flow through $R_2$, so biasing $Q_3$ into conduction, and allowing the larger emitter current $I_d$ to flow through $D_2$ and *out* at $Q$. This causes $Q$ to be HIGH, i.e. at *logic 1*. The characteristics of the standard 7400 series of TTL gate specifies that the maximum HIGH level current which can be drawn from the output ($I_{OH}$) is 400 $\mu$A. Since the maximum HIGH level input current ($I_{IH}$) for any gate connected to an output is specified at 40 $\mu$A, this allows up to 10 input gates to be connected to an output. The output voltage level in the HIGH state ($V_{OH}$) is specified as 2.4 V minimum, which means that *a logic 1 output should always be equal to or greater than this voltage.*

Figure 9.25 shows the same gate with all inputs HIGH. Now no current flows out of the emitters of $Q_1$,

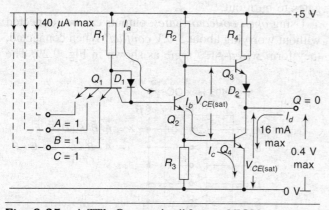

**Fig. 9.25** *A TTL Gate with all Inputs HIGH.*

and the current $I_a$ diverts to form the base current of $Q_2$. Emitter current $I_b$, comprising both $I_a$ and current drawn through $Q_2$ collector, flows as base current $I_c$, through $Q_4$. This causes $Q_4$ to switch hard on, and current $I_d$, flows *into* the output $Q$. The transistor bottoms to give an output equal to $V_{CE(sat)}$ for $Q_4$, thereby producing a *logic 0*. With $Q_2$ bottomed in this condition, diode $D_2$ ensures that $Q_3$ is cut-off.

The characteristics of the 7400 series gates in this condition specify that the maximum LOW level output

current ($I_{OL}$) is 16 mA. Since the maximum LOW level input current ($I_{IL}$) for any gates connected to an output is 1.6 mA, this allows upto 10 gates to be connected to any output. Thus, for any logic conditions, *this series of devices allows a fan out of 10,* i.e. 10 inputs may be connected to any output. The specifications also state that the maximum low level output voltage ($V_{OL}$) shall be +0.4 V.

### 9.27 Discuss TTL noise margins.

*Solution:*
In order to provide *safety margins* within the specifications, the input requirements are made to *overlap* the output guaranteed levels to provide a *noise margin* of at least 0.4 V. Figure 9.26 depicts TTL noise margins.

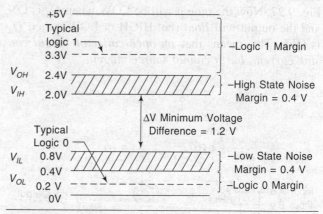

**Fig. 9.26** *TTL Noise Margins.*

The output HIGH level is guaranteed to be at least +2.4 V, but input gates accept a logic 1 above +2.0 V to provide a HIGH state noise margin of 0.4 V. The output LOW level is guaranteed to be +0.4 V or less, but input gates accept a logic 0 below + 0.8 V, again ensuring a LOW state noise margin of 0.4 V. The minimum voltage difference between logic states must therefore be at least 1.2 V, and *typical logic 1 and logic 0 levels are +3.3 V and +0.2 V, respectively.*

### 9.28 How will you connect unused gate inputs and outputs?

*Solution:*
Whilst multiemitter transistors provide a load for each emitter in the HIGH state, they do not do so in the LOW state. Thus, if several inputs *to the same logic gate* are tied together, they only appear as a single LOW level load to the driving gate, since the current flowing *out* of the inputs is simply *shared* between the various emitters.

In the HIGH state each separate junction contributes its own leakage current. Unused inputs on gates can often be conveniently tied to neighbouring inputs. *All inputs should be taken either HIGH or LOW.*

Unused inputs on AND *and* NAND *gates* should be tied HIGH, and on OR *and* NOR *gates* should be tied to ground. Also the outputs of unused gates on an IC should be forced HIGH to reduce the $I_{CC}$ supply current and thus reduce power dissipation. To do this, tie AND *and* OR inputs HIGH, and tie NAND *and* NOR inputs LOW.

**9.29  Is there any alternative to the totem-pole arrangement in the output stage of a TTL gate?**

*Solution:*
Instead of using a totem-pole arrangement in the output stage of a TTL gate, yet another arrangement, called the *open-collector* (OC) *output* is available. With the totem-pole output stage, for a LOW output the lower transistor is ON and the upper transistor is OFF, and vice versa for a HIGH output. *With the open-collector output the upper transistor is removed*, as shown in Fig. 9.27. Now the output will be LOW when $Q_4$ is ON and the output will *float* (not HIGH or LOW) when $Q_4$ is OFF. This means that *an open-collector output can sink current, but it cannot source current.*

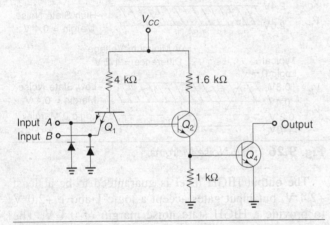

**Fig. 9.27**   *TTL* NAND *with an Open-collector Output.*

To get an OC output to produce a HIGH, an external resistor, called a *pull-up resistor*, must be used, as shown in Fig. 9.28. Now when $Q_4$ is OFF (open) the output is approximately 5 V (HIGH) and when $Q_4$ is ON (short) the output is approximately 0 V (LOW).

The optimum size for a pull-up resistor depends on the size of the output's load and the leakage current through $Q_4$ ($I_{OH}$) which is OFF. Usually a good size for a pull-up resistor is 10 kΩ. 10 kΩ is *not too small* to allow excessive current to flow when $Q_4$ is ON and it is *not too large* to cause an excessive voltage drop across itself when $Q_4$ is OFF.

Open-collector buffer/driver ICs are available for output loads requiring large sink currents, such as displays, relays, or motors. *The term buffer/driver signifies the ability to provide high output currents to drive heavy loads.* Typical ICs of this type are the 7406 OC inverter buffer/driver and the 7407 OC buffer/driver. They are each capable of sinking upto 40 mA, which is 10 times greater than the 4 mA capability of the standard 7404 inverter.

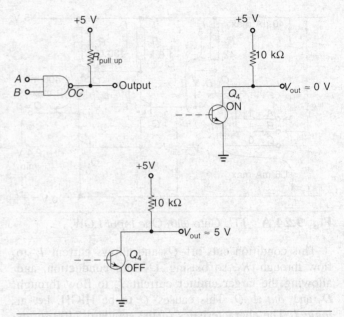

**Fig. 9.28**   *Using a Pull-up Resistor with Open-collector Output.*

**9.30  When and where do we use open-collector operation?**

*Solution:*
The main use of the open-collector gates is when the outputs from two or more gates or other devices have to be *tied* together. Using the regular *totem-pole output gates*, if a gate having a HIGH output (5 V) is connected to another gate having a LOW output (0 V), you would have a *direct short circuit* causing either or both gates to burn out.

Using *open-collector gates*, outputs can be connected without worrying about *5-0 V conflict*. When connected, they form *wired-*AND *logic* as shown in Fig. 9.29. The

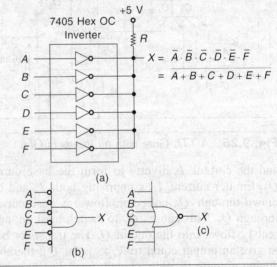

**Fig. 9.29**   *(a) Wired-*AND *Connections to a Hex OC Inverter to form a Six-input* NOR *Gate; (b)* AND *Gate Representation; (c) Alternative* NOR *Gate Representation.*

7405 IC has six open-collector inverters in a single package. By *tying* their outputs together, as shown in Fig. 9.29(a), we have in effect ANDed *all the inverters*. The outputs of all six inverters must be floating (all inputs must be LOW) to get a HIGH output ($X = 1$ if $A = 0$ AND $B = 0$ AND $C = 0$, and so on). If any of the inverter output transistors ($Q_4$) turn 'on', the output will go LOW. The result of this wired-AND connection in the six-input NOR function is shown in Fig. 9.29(c). The advantage of the wired-AND arrangement available with open-collector TTL is that *it can be substituted in place of a logic gate.*

### 9.31 Write the Boolean equation at the output of Fig. 9.30(a).

*Solution:*

The outputs of all three gates in either circuit must be floating in order to get a HIGH output at $X$. Using Fig. 9.30(b)

$$X = \overline{A}\overline{B} \cdot (\overline{C} + \overline{D}) \cdot EF$$

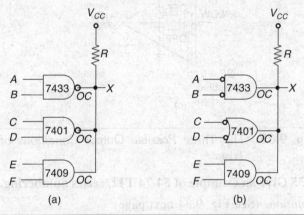

**Fig. 9.30** *Wired-ANDing of Open-collector Gates (a) Original Circuit, (b) Alternative Gate representations used for Clarity.*

### 9.32 A wired-AND circuit is to drive the inputs of five TTL gates. Determine a suitable pull-up resistor.

*Solution:*

When the output is LOW, the maximum input current to each driven gate is

$$I_{IL(\max)} = 1.6 \text{ mA}$$

Total load (input) current

$$= 5 \times I_{IL(\max)} = 5 \times 1.6 \text{ mA}$$
$$= 8 \text{ mA}$$

Assuming only one wired-AND gate is 'on'

$$I_R = I_{OL(\max)} - I_L = 16 \text{ mA} - 8 \text{ mA}$$
$$= 8 \text{ mA}$$
$$V_R = V_{CC} - V_{OL(\max)} = 5 \text{ V} - 0.4 \text{ V}$$
$$= 4.6 \text{ V}$$

$$R = \frac{V_R}{I_R} = \frac{46 \text{ V}}{8 \text{ mA}}$$
$$= 575 \ \Omega \text{ (use 680 } \Omega \text{ standard value)}$$

## TRISTATE LOGIC

Conventional logic gates have two possible output states, namely 0 and 1. *Under some circumstances it is convenient to have a third state corresponding to a high impedance condition, when the output is allowed to float.* Under these circumstances the voltage at the output will be determined by whatever circuitry is connected to it. Circuits with this property are called three-state logic gates. *The output of the gate is 'enabled' or 'disabled' by a control input,* which is usually given the symbol $C$ on simple gates. In more complicated circuits this control signal is often referred to as the *output enable* line.

### 9.33 Describe tristate logic (TSL). Draw and explain the circuit of a TSL NAND gate.

*Solution:*

Figure 9.31 shows how three-state function is represented in a circuit symbol. Figure 9.31(a) shows a non-inverting buffer with an *active-high* control input (i.e., the output is enabled if $C = 1$); Fig. 9.31(b) shows the symbol for a similar gate with an *active-low* control input (i.e. the output is enabled if $C = 0$). The first of these could represent one of the gates in a 74126, and the second gate in a 74125. Both devices contain six such gates.

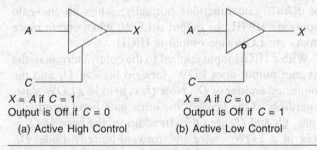

**Fig. 9.31** *Symbolic Representation of three-state Logic Gates.*

The output circuit of a three-state gate resembles that of a totem-pole device with the addition of extra components to turn both output transistors OFF to disable the output. This allows the output to float, independent of the other gate inputs. Since, when enabled, the output resembles the conventional totem-pole arrangement, *the use of three-state techniques does not incur the speed penalty associated with open collector circuits.*

Figure 9.32 shows the circuit arrangement and logic symbol for a TSL NAND gate. Note that the control input terminal goes to an inverter. The output of the inverter is connected to one emitter on transistor $Q_1$ and to the base of $Q_3$ via a diode.

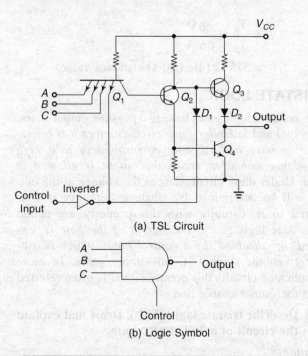

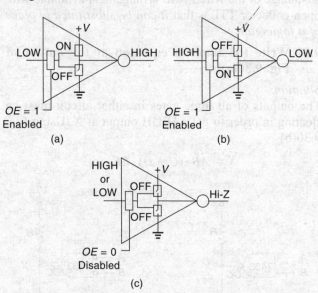

**Fig. 9.32**    *Tristate TTL (TSL) Circuits have a third Output State. In Addition to being HIGH or LOW, the Output may be Placed in a High-impedance State. This is Accomplished by Setting Transistors $Q_3$ and $Q_4$ in an OFF Condition.*

When the control input is LOW, the inverter output is HIGH. This reverse biases $D_1$ and provides a HIGH input to the connected emitter of $Q_1$. In this condition the NAND gate functions normally; when all the gate inputs are HIGH, the output is LOW; when one or more inputs are LOW, the output is HIGH.

With a HIGH input applied to the control terminal, the inverter output goes LOW, forward biasing $D_1$ and the connected emitter of $Q_1$. Now $Q_1$ is held in a LOW state, regardless of the level of the other gate input terminals. Thus, $Q_2$ and $Q_4$ are OFF. In addition, the base of $Q_3$ is held in a LOW  state by (forward-biased) diode $D_1$. Consequently, $Q_3$ is OFF. Both output transistors $Q_3$ and $Q_4$ are OFF, and the output terminal offers a high impedance to all circuits connected to it. This condition is the *third state* of the TSL circuit: *the output of a TSL gate may be HIGH or LOW, or have a high output impedance.*

TSL gates are used in logic systems where the output of several gates are connected in parallel to a single input of another circuit. *All gates are usually maintained in the high output impedance state and are sampled, or switched on briefly, one at a time, by the control signals applied in sequence.* This avoids the possibility of the output of one gate short-circuiting another gate output.

Yet another aspect of the TSL gate is that circuit *input impedance* also becomes HIGH when the gate is placed in its HIGH *output impedance* state.

Tristate logic is used in circumstances where a number of gates share a common output line. This technique is common in computers and other digital systems where data from several sources has to be routed via a single data highway or *bus*.

**9.34 Illustrate the three-output conditions of tristate?**

*Solution:*
The three possible output conditions of tristate are shown in Fig. 9.33.

**Fig. 9.33**    *The Three Possible Output Conditions of Tristate.*

**9.35 Give an example of 54-74 TTL series numbering.**

*Solution:* (See Fig. 9.34 next page)

## EMITTER-COUPLED LOGIC (ECL)

One major limitation on the switching speed of logic circuits is the *storage time* of the saturated transistors. The storage time is the time required to drive a transistor out of saturation, that is, to reverse the forward bias on a collector-base junction. In *emitter-coupled logic*, also called the *current-mode logic*, the transistors are maintained in an *unsaturated* condition. This eliminates the transistor storage time and results in logic gates which switch very fast indeed.

**9.36 How does emitter-coupled logic operate? What are its specifications?**

*Solution:*
In Fig. 9.35, causing $A$ to go HIGH will drive the $Q_2$ collector LOW, causing both the base and emitter of $Q_1$ to go LOW, outputting a LOW  on the NOR lead. At the same time, the $Q_4$ emitter will go HIGH, tending to cut it off, and the $Q_5$ base will go HIGH  as will the $Q_5$ emitter, and, consequently, the OR output. $D_1$ and $D_2$

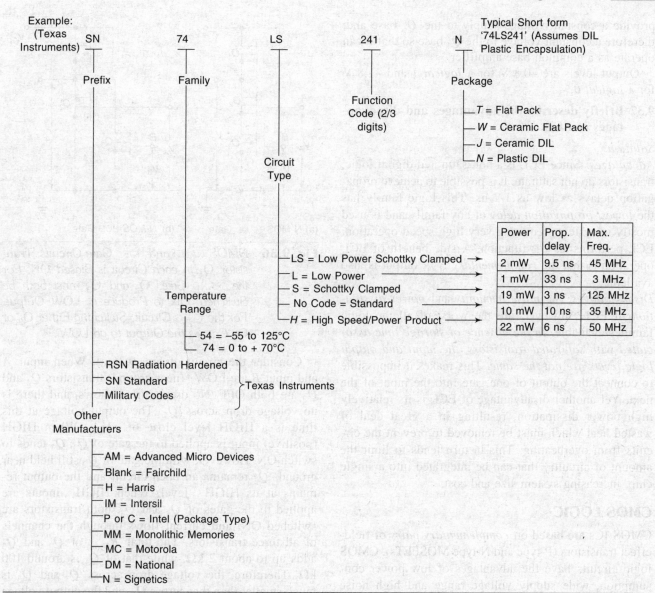

**Fig. 9.34**   *Example of 54/74 Series Numbering.*

| Power | Prop. delay | Max. Freq. |
|---|---|---|
| 2 mW | 9.5 ns | 45 MHz |
| 1 mW | 33 ns | 3 MHz |
| 19 mW | 3 ns | 125 MHz |
| 10 mW | 10 ns | 35 MHz |
| 22 mW | 6 ns | 50 MHz |

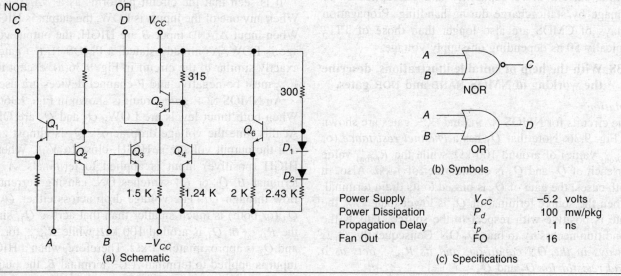

| Power Supply | $V_{CC}$ | −5.2 volts |
|---|---|---|
| Power Dissipation | $P_d$ | 100 mw/pkg |
| Propagation Delay | $t_p$ | 1 ns |
| Fan Out | FO | 16 |

(c) Specifications

**Fig. 9.35**   *Emitter-coupled Logic (ECL).*

provide a constant voltage supply to the $Q_6$ base and, therefore a constant voltage to the $Q_4$ base so that it can operate as a common base amplifier.

Output levels are −0.8 V for a *logical 1* and −1.8 V for a *logical 0*.

### 9.37 Briefly describe the advantages and disadvantages of ECL.

*Solution:*

*Advantages:* Since ECL is a non-saturated digital logic, transistors do not saturate. It is possible to achieve propagation delays as low as 1-2 ns. This logic family has the *lowest propagation delay* of any family and is used mostly in systems requiring very high-speed operation. ECL performs an OR function. A side benefit of ECL operation is that the *complementary* NOR output is also available.

*Disadvantages:* The *noise immunity* and *power dissipation* of ECL, however, are the worst of all the logic families available. *In the absence of storage time associated with saturated transistors, the input and output logic levels are not the same.* This makes it impossible to connect the output of one gate into the input of the next. Yet another disadvantage of ECL is its relatively high power dissipation, resulting in a great deal of wasted heat which must be removed to prevent the circuits from overheating. This in turn tends to limit the amount of circuitry that can be integrated into a single chip, increasing system size and cost.

## CMOS LOGIC

CMOS ICs are based on *complementary pairs* of field-effect transistors (P-type and N-type MOSFETs). CMOS logic circuits have the advantages of low power consumption, wide supply voltage range and high noise immunity, but suffer from such disadvantages as low output current drive capability and susceptibility to damage by static charge during handling. Propagation delays of CMOS are also longer than those of TTL, typically 50 ns depending on supply voltage.

### 9.38 With the help of suitable illustrations, describe the working of NMOS NAND and NOR gates.

*Solution:*

The circuits for NMOS NAND and NOR gates are shown in Fig. 9.36. Note that $Q_1$ has a *channel resistance* (or $R_{D(on)}$ value) of around 100 kΩ, while the $R_{D(on)}$ value for each of $Q_2$ and $Q_3$ is on the order of 1 kΩ. Also, in both cases, the gate of $Q_1$ is biased to its drain terminal. When the source terminal of $Q_1$ is lower than $V_{DD}$, the gate is positive with respect to the source. This is the condition necessary to bias $Q_1$ ON. Consequently, $Q_1$ is *always in the ON condition, and its $R_{D(on)}$ acts as a load resistor for $Q_2$ and $Q_3$.*

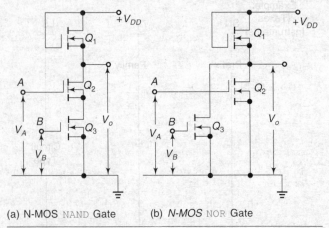

(a) N-MOS NAND Gate    (b) *N-MOS* NOR Gate

**Fig. 9.36**    *NMOS* NAND *and* NOR *Gate Circuits. Transistor* $Q_1$ *in each Circuit is Biased ON. For the* NAND *Gate,* $Q_2$ *and* $Q_3$ *must both be Switched ON to Produce a LOW Output. For the* NOR *Circuit, Switching Either* $Q_2$ *or* $Q_3$ *Causes the Output to go LOW.*

Consider the circuit of Fig. 9.36(a). When input $A$ and input $B$ are LOW (near ground) transistors $Q_2$ and $Q_3$ are both OFF. No drain current flows, and there is no voltage drop across $Q_1$. The output voltage at this time is a HIGH level close of $+V_{DD}$. When HIGH (positive) input is applied to the gate of $Q_3$, $Q_3$ tends to switch ON. However, with the gate of $Q_2$ still held near ground, $Q_2$ remains an open circuit and the output remains at its HIGH level. When HIGH inputs are applied to the gates of $Q_2$ and $Q_3$, both transistors are switched ON, and current flows through the channels of all three transistors. The total $R_{D(on)}$ of $Q_2$ and $Q_3$ adds up to about 2 kΩ, while that of $Q_1$ is around 100 kΩ. Therefore, the voltage drop across $Q_2$ and $Q_3$ is much smaller than that across $Q_1$, and the output voltage is now at a LOW level.

It is seen that the circuit performs as a *NAND gate*. When any one of the inputs is LOW, the output is HIGH. When input $A$ AND input $B$ are HIGH, the output voltage is LOW. As already stated, a PMOS NAND gate is exactly similar to the circuit in Fig. 9.36(a), except that $V_{DD}$ must be negative and P-channel devices are used.

An NMOS NOR *gate* circuit is shown in Fig. 9.36(b). When both input levels are LOW, $Q_2$ and $Q_3$ are OFF. At this time the voltage drop across $Q_1$ is almost zero and the output voltage is HIGH, close to $V_{DD}$. When a HIGH (positive) input is applied to terminals $A$ OR terminal $B$, $Q_2$ or $Q_3$ switches ON, causing current to flow through $Q_1$. The voltage drop across either $Q_2$ or $Q_3$ (or both) is much smaller than that across $Q_1$, since the $R_{D(on)}$ of $Q_1$ is around 100 kΩ, while $R_{D(on)}$ for $Q_2$ and $Q_3$ is approximately 1 kΩ. Therefore, when a HIGH input is applied to terminal $A$ OR terminal $B$, the output voltage goes to a LOW level. A PMOS NOR gate is exactly similar to the circuit of Fig. 9.36(b), except that $V_{DD}$ must be a negative quantity and P-channel devices are used.

### 9.39 Discuss the specifications of PMOS, NMOS, and CMOS logic gates.

*Solution:*
PMOS and NMOS logic gates typically use a *supply* of 10 V, but can operate with lower or higher supply voltages. Using a 5 V supply, *power dissipation* is approximately 0.25 mW per gate, and *noise margin* is 1.5 V. Because there is no input current to MOSFET devices, there should be no limit to dc fan-out for PMOS and NMOS logic gates. But gate inputs do have capacitance, and each additional gate input connected as a gate output terminal slows down the switching speed of the gate. A *fan-out* of 50 is considered a normal maximum. *Propagation delay time* is around 50 ns for NMOS and 100 ns for PMOS. The relatively large switching time is due to the high output resistance, approximately 2 kΩ, which is 20 times the typical $R_o$ of 100 Ω for TTL. For a given load capacitance (typically, 15 pF is used when testing for $t_r$), an NMOS gate will be 20 times slower than TTL.

Although the integrated circuit fabrication process for CMOS is more complicated than that for PMOS or NMOS, CMOS has the very important advantage that *its power dissipation per gate is much less than that for any other logic family.* (integrated injection logic can be an exception to this). Other advantages are: (1) operation from supply voltages as low as 1 V, (2) fan-out in excess of 50, and (3) excellent noise immunity.

### 9.40 Explain the working of CMOS NAND and NOR gates. Give its specifications.

*Solution:*
Consider the CMOS NAND gate shown in Fig. 9.37(a). The *parallel-connected* transistors $Q_1$ and $Q_2$ are P-channel MOSFETs and the *series-connected* devices $Q_3$ and $Q_4$ are N-channel MOSFETs. When input terminals *A* and *B* are grounded, the gates of $Q_1$ and $Q_2$ are negative with respect to the source terminals. Therefore, $Q_1$ and $Q_2$ are biased ON. Also the gates of $Q_3$ and $Q_4$ are at the same potential as the device source terminals, and consequently $Q_3$ and $Q_4$ are OFF. Depending on the actual load current and the values of $R_{D(on)}$, there will be a small voltage drop along the channels of $Q_1$ and $Q_2$. Thus, the output voltage $V_o$ is close to the level of the supply voltage.

When a HIGH positive input voltage (equal to 0.7 $V_{DD}$ or greater) is applied to terminal *B*, $Q_4$ is biased ON and $Q_2$ is biased OFF. However, with terminal *A* still grounded, $Q_3$ remains OFF, $Q_1$ is still ON, and the output voltage remains at $V_o \approx V_{DD}$. When HIGH inputs are applied to terminal *A* AND terminal *B*, both

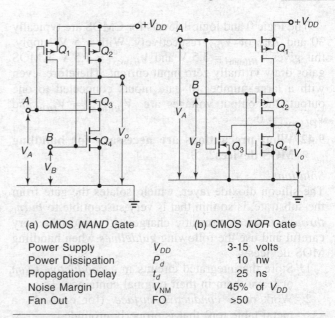

| | | |
|---|---|---|
| (a) CMOS *NAND* Gate | (b) CMOS *NOR* Gate | |

| | | | |
|---|---|---|---|
| Power Supply | $V_{DD}$ | 3-15 | volts |
| Power Dissipation | $P_d$ | 10 | nw |
| Propagation Delay | $t_d$ | 25 | ns |
| Noise Margin | $V_{NM}$ | 45% of $V_{DD}$ | |
| Fan Out | FO | >50 | |

**Fig. 9.37** *CMOS,* NAND *and* NOR *gate circuits.*

P-channel devices ($Q_1$ and $Q_2$) are biased OFF, and both N-channel MOSFETs ($Q_3$ and $Q_4$) are biased ON. The output now goes to $V_o \approx 0$ V.

The circuit of a *CMOS NOR gate* is shown in Fig. 9.34(b). Once again two P-channel devices ($Q_1$ and $Q_2$) and two N-channel devices ($Q_3$ and $Q_4$) are employed. When both inputs are at ground level, $Q_3$ and $Q_4$ are biased OFF, and $Q_1$ and $Q_2$ are ON. In this condition there is about a 10 mV drop from drain to source terminals in P-channel transistors, and $V_o$ is very close to $V_{DD}$. When terminal *A* has a HIGH positive input, $Q_1$ switches OFF and $Q_3$ switches ON. The series combination of $Q_1$ and $Q_2$ is now open circuited, and the output is shorted to ground via $Q_3$. Similarly, if terminal *A* remains grounded, and terminal *B* has a HIGH input applied, $Q_2$ switches OFF and $Q_4$ switches ON. *Again, the output goes to ground level.*

### 9.41 What are the advantages of CMOS logic?

*Solution:*
The main advantage of integrated circuit CMOS logic over all other logic systems is its *extremely low power dissipation*. At a maximum of 10 nW per gate, the low dissipation allows greater circuit density within a given size of IC package. The resultant low supply current demand also makes CMOS *ideal for battery-operated instruments*. Typical supply voltages employed for CMOS are 5–10 V; however, operation with a supply of 1–18 V is possible. The circuitry is immune to *noise levels* as high as 30% of the supply voltage. The extremely high input resistance of MOSFETs gives CMOS gates typical input resistances of $10^9$ Ω, and this makes it possible to have *fan-outs* greater than 50. Typical *propagation delay time* for CMOS is 25 ns. As in the case of NMOS and PMOS, the relatively low switching time is due to the high output resistance.

The logic 0 and logic 1 levels for CMOS are typically 30 and 70% of $V_{DD}$, respectively. With a 5 V supply, this gives $V_{IH(min)} = 3.5$ V and $V_{IL(max)} = 1.5$ V. CMOS gates draw virtually zero input current. Therefore, even with a large number of gate inputs connected to one output, the output voltages are $V_{OH(min)} \approx V_{DD}$, and $V_{OL(max)} \approx 0$.

### 9.42 What precautions are necessary for handling MOS devices?

*Solution:*

The silicon dioxide layer, which isolates the gate from the substrate, is so thin that is very susceptible to *burn-through* from electrostatic charges. You must be very careful and use the following *guidelines* when handling MOS devices:

1. Store the integrated circuits in a *conductive foam* or leave them in their original container.
2. Work on a *conductive surface* (for example, a metal table top) that is properly grounded.
3. *Ground* test equipment and soldering irons.
4. Wear a *wrist strap* to connect your wrist to ground with a length of wire and a 1 M$\Omega$ series resistor.
5. Do not connect *signals* to the inputs while the device power supply is OFF.
6. Connect all *unused inputs* to $V_{DD}$ or ground.
7. Do not wear *electrostatic-prone clothing* such as wool, silk, or synthetic fibers.
8. Do not *remove or insert* an IC with the power ON.

### 9.43 Give an example of CMOS series numbering.

*Solution:*

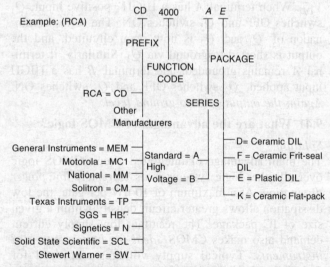

**Fig. 9.38**   *Example of CMOS Series Numbering.*

## INTEGRATED INJECTION LOGIC (I²L)

Integrated circuit logic systems are compared in terms of switching speed, power dissipation, fan-out and noise margin. Two other very important factors are *physical size and cost of manufacture*. Individual I²L gates require a fraction of the area of other logic types, i.e., the *circuit density* is much greater. Also *power dissipation per gate* can be comparable with CMOS logic, *very fast switching* is possible, and *fabrication techniques* are simple and inexpensive. These improvements are due to two factors: *elimination of resistors* and what is termed *merging* of transistors.

Integrated-injection logic is the most recent logic family to be introduced commercially. Its main advantage is the high *packing density* of gates that can be achieved in a given area of a semiconductor chip. This allows more circuits to be placed in the chip to form *complex* digital functions. As a consequence *this family is used mostly for LSI functions*. It is not available in SSI packages containing individual gates.

### 9.44 Briefly explain integrated injection logic.

*Solution:*

In this system $Q_1$ and $Q_3$ act as *current sources* to the bases of $Q_2$ and $Q_4$, respectively. If input A goes LOW, the current to the base of $Q_2$ will be shorted to ground, preventing the transistor from conducting. In a similar manner, input B controls $Q_4$. Thus, if either point A OR B is HIGH, the output will be LOW, a NOR function.

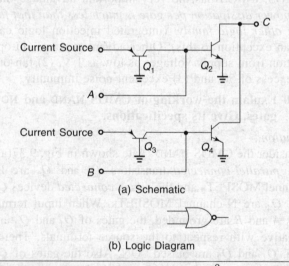

(a) Schematic

(b) Logic Diagram

**Fig. 9.39**   *Integrated Injection Logic* (I²L).

The collector of $Q_1$ is made of the same material as the base of $Q_2$, making it possible to be the same physical elements. This greatly improves the density that a given chip can contain. There are no resistors, further reducing the size of the gate. Therefore, I²L is used in large scale functions, where bipolar devices are required. It is slightly faster (10 ns) than TTL.

## 9.45 Give a comparison of logic families in tabular form.

*Solution:*

**Table 9.1** *Comparison of IC Logic Types*

| | DTL | RTL | HTL | TTL 74 | TTL 74H | TTL 74L | TTL 74S | TTL 74AS | TTL 74LS | TTL 74ALS | ECL | N-MOS and P-MOS | CMOS | $I^2L$ |
|---|---|---|---|---|---|---|---|---|---|---|---|---|---|---|
| Propagation delay time (ns) | 30 | 12 | 119 | 10 | 6 | 33 | 3 | 1.5 | 9 | 4 | 50 to 2 | 100 | 25 | *10 to 250 |
| Power dissipation per gate (mW) | 15 | 15 | 50 | 10 | 22.5 | 1 | 20 | 20 | 2 | 1 | 25 | 0.25 | 10 nW | *6 nW to 70 µW |
| Noise margin (V) | 1.4 | 0.7 | 7.5 | 0.4 | 0.4 | 0.4 | 0.4 | 0.4 | 0.4 | 0.4 | 0.25 | 2 | $0.3\ V_{DD}$ | 0.25 |
| Noise immunity rating | good | poor | excellent | good | good | good | good | good | good | good | fair | excellent | excellent | fair |
| Fan-out | 8 | 5 | 10 | 10 | 10 | 10 | 10 | 10 | 10 | 10 | 25 | >50 | >50 | *depends upon injection current |

# SUMMARY

- All logic devices are similar in nature but very much different regarding the details of their characteristics.
- Digital logic may be implemented in a number of ways.
- Each logic family has different characteristics which makes each of them especially suitable for a particular application.
- Important considerations are physical size, voltage requirements, current-carrying capabilities, switching speed, noise immunity, and power dissipation.
- Usually a single type of logic gate is used throughout a logic system, but sometimes different types of logic gates have to be interfaced.
- The shorter the propagation delay, the higher the speed of the circuit and the higher the frequency at which it can operate.
- With careful design, digital systems can be made nearly noise free.
- The speed power product is sometimes specified as a figure of merit.
- In any logic configuration, the number $N$ of inputs is called the fan-in and the number $M$ of outputs is called the fan-out.
- TTL is the most widely used digital logic family.
- The main use of the open-collector gates is when the outputs of two or more gates or other devices have to be tied together.
- Under some circumstances it is convenient to have a third state corresponding to a higher impedance condition when the output is allowed to float.
- With ECL, logic gates switch very fast.
- CMOS has low power consumption.
- Handling precautions are necessary for MOS devices.
- The main advantage of $I^2L$ is high packing density.

# REVIEW QUESTIONS

1. What is a logic family?
2. How will you categorise the integration level of digital devices?
3. Explain the term load factor.
4. Write the expression for fan-out.
5. How are digital ICs categorised?
6. What is the difference between RTL and DTL?
7. What are the advantages gained by the use of multi-emitter transistors in logic circuits?
8. Explain the significance of an expander circuit.
9. List the names and abbreviations of the four input and output currents of a digital IC.
10. What is meant by fan-out?
11. What is the difference between sink and source current?
12. Describe the function of a pull-up resistor when it is used with an open-collector TTL output.
13. In which TTL state does the largest amount of current flow?
14. Which TTL series is the best at high frequencies?
15. What are the two accepted ways to handle unused inputs to an AND gate?
16. What are the three possible output states of a tri-state IC?
17. Why ECL is faster than TTL?
18. Why are CMOS devices shipped in conductive foam?
19. What type of MOS technology is predominant in LSI devices such as microprocessors?
20. What determines the fan-out limitations of MOS logic?
21. What is the main advantage of $I^2L$?

# SUPPLEMENTARY PROBLEMS

22. Determine the maximum value of the pull-up resistance for an open-collector TTL gate to achieve a fan-out of 10 given that $I_{OH} = 40$ mA. The leakage current flowing through the collector of TTL output transistor is 50 mA and $V_{OH(min)} = 2.4$ V. (See Fig. 9.40)
23. For the circuit given in Fig. 9.41 identify the logic function performed by it. Also determine the high level fan-out, if $R_P$ (pull-up resistor) = 10 k$\Omega$. Compute the maximum value of $R_P$ for a fan-out of 5. Assume that the input diodes have a leakage current of 100 $\mu$A, $V_T$ (cut-in value of diode) = 0.7 V, $V_D$ (forward voltage drop) = 0.8 V, $V_{BE}$ (cut-in) = 0.5 V, $V_{CE(sat)}$ = 0.2 V, and transistor leakage current is negligible.

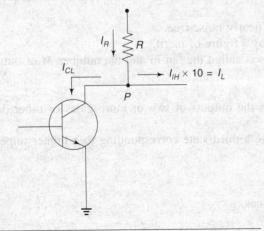

**Fig. 9.40**

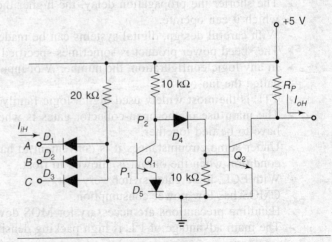

**Fig. 9.41**

24. Given below are the specifications of a low-power Schottky TTL NOR gate. Calculate its propagation delay, power dissipation, fan-out, fan-in, noise margin, and also find its figure of merit.

| Parameter | Value |
|---|---|
| $V_{CC}$ | 5 V |
| $I_{CH}$ (high level supply current) | 1.6 mA (feeding 4 gates) |
| $I_{CL}$ (low level supply current) | 2.8 mA (feeding 4 gates) |
| $V_{oH}$ (min) | 2.7 V |
| $V_{oL}$ (min) | 0.4 V |
| $V_{IH}$ (max) | 2.0 V |
| $V_{IL}$ (max) | 0.8 V |
| $I_{oH}$ (max) | 4.0 mA (out) |
| $I_{oL}$ (max) | 8.0 mA (in) |
| $I_{IH}$ (max) | 0.02 mA (in) |
| $I_{IL}$ (max) | 0.4 mA (in) |
| $t_{pLH}$ | 10 ns |
| $t_{pHL}$ | 10 ns |

25. In Fig. 9.23 for Problem 9.25, when the output is HIGH, how do you account for the input voltage being only about 3.4 V instead of 5 V?

26. Calculate the static fan-out for the circuit of Fig. 9.42. Assume that the NOR output voltage can drop from its nominal (HIGH) value of $-0.7$ V by $\Delta V = 50$ mV. Use $\beta = 100$.

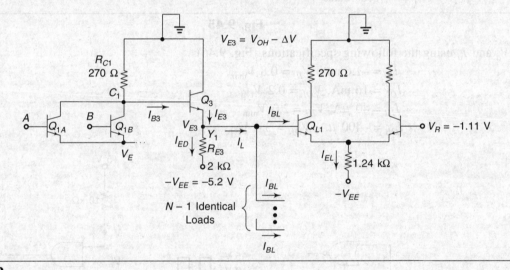

**Fig. 9.42**

27. Two identical RTL gates are wire-ANDed. Each gate has a fan-out of 5. Calculate the fan-out of the combined gate. What operation is performed by this gate?

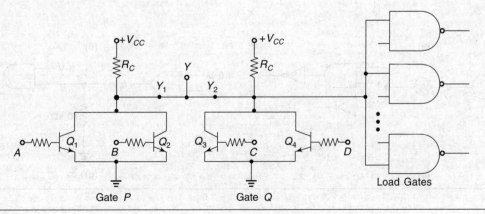

**Fig. 9.43**

28. Explain the operation of the DCTL gate shown in Fig. 9.44. What logic function does it perform?
29. Explain the operation of the DTL gate in Fig. 9.45. What logic function does it perform?

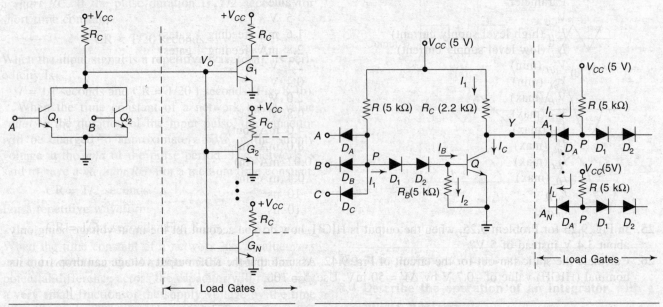

**Fig. 9.44**                    **Fig. 9.45**

30. Find $V_a$ and $I_a$ using the following specifications (Fig. 9.46):

$$I_{IL} = -1.6 \text{ mA}, \quad V_{IL} = 0.8 \ V_{max},$$
$$I_{OL} = 16 \text{ mA}, \quad V_{OL} = 0.2 \ V_{typ},$$
$$I_{IH} = 40 \ \mu\text{A}, \quad V_{IH} = 2.0 \ V_{min}$$
$$I_{OH} = -400 \ \mu\text{A}, \quad V_{OH} = 3.4 \ V_{typ}.$$

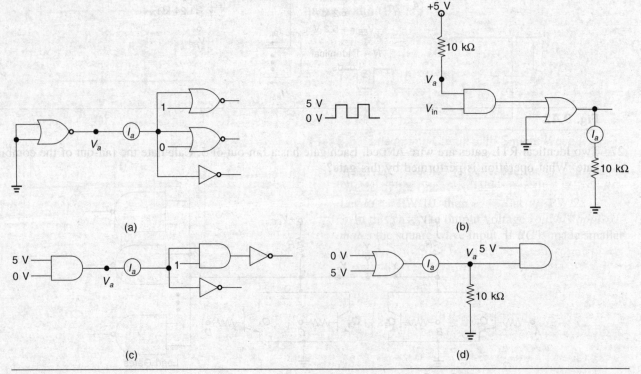

**Fig. 9.46**

31. The output of an inverter is modeled under static conditions by a voltage source of approximately 5 V in series with a resistance of 2 kΩ at logic HIGH, and a source of approximately 0.9 V in series with a resistance of 500 Ω at logic LOW. If the input currents drawn by the inverter are zero at logic LOW and 2.25 μA at logic HIGH, calculate the fan-out. Explain the difference between static and dynamic fan-out. (Fig. 9.47)

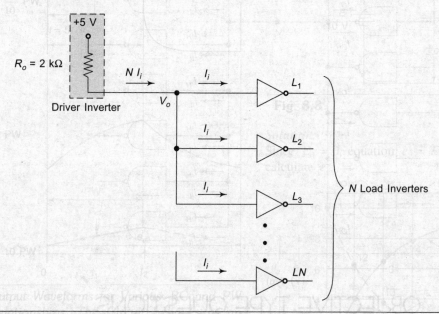

**Fig. 9.47**

32. Determine the range of $R_C$ in Fig. 9.48(a) if two open-collector gates are wire-ANDed and the output is used to drive three identical gates of open-collector family. It is required that the output must not drop below 4 V at logic HIGH. Use $\beta_R = 0.4$ and $\beta_F = 50$ for all the transistors in the gates. Each gate has the configuration as shown in Fig. 9.48(b).

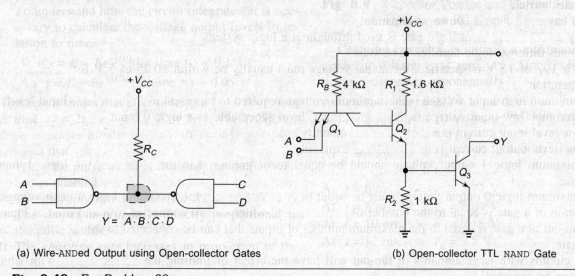

(a) Wire-ANDed Output using Open-collector Gates    (b) Open-collector TTL NAND Gate

**Fig. 9.48**  *For Problem 32.*

33. For an open-collector TTL gate the specifications are:

$$V_{OH} = 2.4 \text{ V}; \ V_{OL} = 0.4 \text{ V}; \ I_{OH} = 250 \text{ μA};$$
$$I_{OL} = 16 \text{ mA}; \ I_{IH} = 40 \text{ μA}; \ I_{IL} = -1.6 \text{ mA}$$

If five such gates are wire-ANDed, and are loaded by similar six gates, calculate the value of collector resistance $R_C$ required (Fig. 9.49). Assume $V_{CC} = 5$ V.

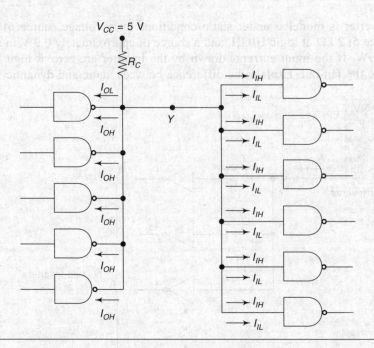

**Fig. 9.49**

# OBJECTIVE TYPE QUESTIONS

Test your
understanding

## Fill in the Blanks

34. There is no single, ideal set of _____ that fulfils all requirements.
35. Two major integrated circuit types are _____ and _____.
36. TTL gates switch _____.
37. CMOS has _____ power dissipation.
38. Usually a _____ of logic gate is used throughout a logic system.
39. Sometimes different logic families have to be _____.
40. Where a $V_{CC}$ of +5 V is specified, the actual voltage must usually be within ±0.25 of 5 V for _____ gate operation.
41. The minimum high-input voltage is the minimum voltage required to represent a _____ input level.
42. The maximum low-input voltage is the _____ level acceptable as a logic 0 input.
43. The low level input current is a _____ quantity.
44. The low-level output current is a _____ quantity.
45. The minimum logic 1 output voltage should be equal to or greater than the _____ logic 1 input voltage.
46. The maximum logic 0 output voltage must be equal to or _____ the maximum logic 0 input voltage.
47. The fan-in of a gate is equal to the number of _____ which can be connected to it and used as inputs.
48. The fan-out of a gate is equal to the maximum number of inputs that can be connected to the _____ of each gate.
49. Using circuits with large amounts of fan-out will have the effect of limiting the _____ with which gates can be operated.
50. The switching speed of a logic gate is defined in terms of its _____ time.
51. The propagation delay time specified on the logic gate data sheets is usually the _____ of $t_{PLH}$ and $t_{PHL}$.
52. The noise immunity of a logic gate does not depend solely on _____.
53. A gate that switches slowly is less sensitive to fast noise spikes than one that has a very short _____ time.
54. Noise immunity is usually described as _____.

55. DTL circuits are essentially diode gates followed by transistor _____ stages.
56. A transistor provides means of _____ a term.
57. A transistor provides a _____, enabling more inputs to be connected to an output.
58. By providing all gate outputs with a transistor stage, it gives a wider _____ between logic levels.
59. The diodes place a limit on the _____ due to the charge stored in their junctions.
60. HTL is much more immune to _____ than DTL.
61. The input signal to a TTL NAND gate travels through three stages of internal circuitry: input, control and _____.
62. A forward-biased NPN transistor will have approximately _____ volts across its base-emitter junction.
63. A forward-biased NPN transistor will have approximately _____ volts across its collector-emitter junction.
64. The letters $L$ and $H$ in the abbreviation $t_{PLH}$ refer to the transition in the _____ signal.
65. Open inputs degrade ac noise immunity as well as the _____ of a circuit.
66. Unused inputs on AND and NAND gates should be tied _____.
67. Unused inputs on OR and NOR gates should be tied to _____.
68. Decoupling capacitors tend to hold the $V_{CC}$ level at each IC _____.
69. Reducing all the internal resistance values of the standard TTL series increases _____ but it reduces propagation delay.
70. The 74HXX series has almost _____ the propagation delay but almost double the power consumption of the standard TTL series.
71. The 74LXX series has almost _____ the propagation delay but almost half the power consumption of the standard TTL series.
72. The lower the speed-power product the _____.
73. The oxide isolation process is used by _____ and _____ series.
74. Oxide isolation has reduced the propagation delay in the 74FXX series to almost _____.
75. Emitter-coupled logic provides the highest _____ ICs.
76. The drawback of ECL is its very high _____.
77. Two very important factors of integrated circuit logic are _____ and cost of manufacture.
78. The main advantage of I²L is high _____.
79. I²L is used mostly for _____ functions.
80. Eliminating the resistors reduces the capacitance and improves the _____ of integrated injection logic.
81. I²L is also known as _____.
82. Typical switching times for I²L range from _____ to _____.
83. I²L can operate from _____ or _____ supply voltages.
84. Power dissipation per gate for I²L can be anywhere from _____ to _____.
85. The speed-power product is a type of _____.
86. The operating frequency for CMOS is _____ for determining power dissipation.
87. Where speed is important, any of the _____ families except 74L may be suitable.
88. Where speed is important, _____ or _____ may be chosen.
89. ECL has a fan-out of _____.
90. TTL has a fan-out of _____.
91. CMOS is _____ than TTL.
92. CMOS has _____ noise immunity.
93. In situations where low power dissipation and/or large fan-out are required _____ is the only choice.
94. I²L is suitable for applications where low _____ is important.
95. I²L is suitable for applications where high _____ is important.
96. The HC/HCT series consumes _____ depending on frequency.
97. The HC/HCT is _____ with the TTL family.
98. The HC/HCT is also _____ voltage-level compatible with the TTL family.
99. The HC/HCT series offers greater _____.
100. The HC/HCT series offers greater voltage and temperature operating _____.
101. BiCMOS combines the _____ of bipolar transistors and CMOS transistors.
102. BiCMOS forms an extremely _____ power, _____ speed family of digital logic.
103. The BiCMOS series is mostly _____ to microprocess or bus interface logic.
104. The BiCMOS logic is mainly available in _____ configuration.

105. The actual power dissipation of BiCMOS depends on how often the IC is _____.
106. The actual power dissipation of BiCMOS depends on the HIGH/LOW _____ when it is active.
107. The 74LV series has been developed to meet the extremely _____ requirements of battery-powered, hand-held devices.
108. The power consumption of CMOS logic ICs decreases approximately with the _____ of the power supply voltage.
109. CMOS technology is _____ for low-power and low-voltage applications.

### True/False Questions

State whether the following statements are True or False.
110. The part number for a basic logic gate varies from manufacturer to manufacturer.
111. The rise time is the length of time required for a digital signal to travel from 0 V to its HIGH level.
112. A TTL output acts as a current sink in the LOW state.
113. If a logic circuit has fan-out of five, the circuit has five outputs.
114. A logic with $I_{PD(\text{avg})} = 12$ ns and $P_{D(\text{avg})} = 15$ mW has a greater speed-power product than one which 8 ns and 30 mW.
115. When NAND gate inputs are tied together, they are always treated as a single load on the signal source.
116. The HIGH-state noise margin is the difference between $V_{IH(\text{min})}$ and $V_{CC}$.
117. The high speed of ECL ICs is achieved by fully saturating the ON transistor.
118. CMOS power drain increases with operating frequency.
119. Unused CMOS inputs can be left unconnected.
120. TTL is better suited than CMOS in high-noise environments.
121. CMOS switching speed increases with frequency.
122. CMOS switching speed increases with the supply voltage.
123. $I^2L$ is not available in SSI packages containing individual gates.
124. Integrated circuit resistors can easily occupy 10 times the area of a transistor.
125. The 4000B CMOS has severe output current limitations.
126. The voltage and current levels of all gates involved in interfacing need not to be looked into.
127. In general, a pull-up resistor is not always required when interfacing TTL to CMOS.
128. A pull-up resistor takes up valuable room on a printed-circuit board.

### Multiple Choice Questions

129. If a logic circuit has a fan-out of 4, then the circuit
    (a) has 4 inputs              (b) can drive a maximum of 4 inputs
    (c) has 4 outputs            (d) gives output 4 times the input
130. RTL consists of
    (a) resistors, transistors and inductors
    (b) resistors and transistors
    (c) resistors, diodes and bipolar junction transistors
    (d) resistors, capacitors and diodes
131. Which of the following logic families has the least propagation delay?
    (a) RTL          (b) CMOS          (c) DTL           (d) $I^2L$
132. Which of the following logic families dissipates minimum power?
    (a) CMOS          (b) DTL           (c) ECL           (d) TTL
133. In general, the propagation delay time of MOS devices
    (a) is of the same order as that of bipolar transistors
    (b) is less than that of bipolar transistors
    (c) is more than that of bipolar transistors
    (d) may be more or less than that of bipolar devices
134. The propagation delay time of a non-saturated bipolar logic family
    (a) is less than that of a saturated bipolar logic family
    (b) is the same as that of a saturated bipolar logic family
    (c) is more than that of a saturated bipolar logic family
    (d) is more than that for NMOS logic family
135. Bipolar logic families employ
    (a) junction field-effect transistors          (b) p-n junctions
    (c) n-p-n transistors                 (d) MOSFETs

136. The logic family with highest noise margin is
    (a) $I^2L$           (b) TTL         (c) HTL         (d) CMOS
137. The figure of merit has minimum value for
    (a) $I^2L$           (b) TTL         (c) NMOS       (d) ECL
138. Recommended fan-out for TTL gate is
    (a) 10            (b) 20           (c) 4           (d) 50
139. Current hogging is a serious drawback in
    (a) DTL         (b) TTL         (c) DCTL       (d) ECL
140. The main advantages of TTL with totem-pole output as compared to other TTL types are
    (a) higher fan-in and fan-out          (b) fast switching and low power dissipation
    (c) higher noise margin and low cost      (d) none of these
141. The main disadvantage of TTL with totem-pole output is
    (a) high power dissipation                (b) low fan-out
    (c) that wire-ANDing operation is not allowed
    (d) low noise margin
142. Which of the following logic families has complementary output?
    (a) DTL         (b) TTL         (c) $I^2L$        (d) ECL
143. Which of the following logic families has maximum fan-out?
    (a) CMOS       (b) PMOS       (c) ECL        (d) $I^2L$
144. Which of the following series is a TTL-IC family, designed to operate satisfactorily in the temperature range from –55 to +125°C for military applications?
    (a) 5300 series     (b) 5400 series     (c) 7300 series     (d) 7400 series
145. MOSFET is also known as
    (a) UJT         (b) CMOS       (c) IGFET       (d) bipolar junction transistor
146. The logic family suitable for making LSI is
    (a) TTL         (b) DTL         (c) $I^2L$       (d) RTL
147. The speed at which Schottky TTL can operate is
    (a) lower than that of standard TTL      (b) equal to that of standard TTL
    (c) higher than that of standard TTL      (d) lower than or equal to that of standard TTL
148. $I^2L$ is a modified version of
    (a) RTL         (b) DTL         (c) TTL         (d) DCTL
149. The figure of merit of a logic family is given by
    (a) gain × bandwidth              (b) propagation delay time × power dissipation
    (c) fan-out × propagation delay time    (d) noise margin × power dissipation
150. The figures of merit of some logic families are given below. Select the logic family with the best figure of merit.
    (a) 1 pJ        (b) 100 pJ       (c) 135 pJ       (d) 300 pJ
151. The Schottky TTL consists of
    (a) bipolar junction transistors
    (b) bipolar junction transistors and resistors
    (c) bipolar junction transistors, diodes and resistors
    (d) Schottky transistors, diodes and resistors
152. Schottky low power TTL devices are preferred over standard TTL devices because of
    (a) their lowest value of figure of merit    (b) their lowest propagation delay time
    (c) their lowest power dissipation        (d) their lowest supply voltage requirement
153. ECL is
    (a) a non-saturated bipolar logic family    (b) a saturated bipolar logic family
    (c) a unipolar logic family            (d) none of the above
154. The switching speed of ECL is very high because
    (a) the transistors are switched between cut-off and saturation regions
    (b) the transistors are switched between active and saturation regions
    (c) the transistors are switched between active and cut-off regions
    (d) the transistors may operate in any of the three regions
155. The speed of operation of a TTL circuit is
    (a) same as that of a DTL circuit        (b) less than that of a DTL circuit
    (c) equal to or higher than that of a DTL circuit    (d) definitely higher than that of a DTL circuit

156. When a logic gate is driving another logic gate, the condition which must be satisfied for proper operation is
    (a) $V_{OH} > V_{IH}$ and $V_{OL} > V_{IL}$
    (b) $V_{OH} < V_{IH}$ and $V_{OL} > V_{IL}$
    (c) $V_{OH} < V_{IH}$ and $V_{OL} < V_{IL}$
    (d) $V_{OH} > V_{IH}$ and $V_{OL} < V_{IL}$

157. An open input terminal of a TTL gate
    (a) will assume a very high voltage
    (b) will behave as if it is connected to logic 0 level
    (c) will behave as if it is connected to logic 1 level
    (d) will assume some voltage between logic 0 and 1 levels

158. TTL circuits with active pull-up are preferred because of their suitability for
    (a) wired-AND operation
    (b) bus operated system
    (c) wired logic operation
    (d) reasonable dissipation and speed of operation

159. For $I^2L$, the logic levels corresponding to 0 and 1, respectively are
    (a) 0 and 5 V
    (b) 0.2 and 5 V
    (c) 0.2 and 0.8 V
    (d) 0.8 and 5 V

160. $I^2L$ consists basically of
    (a) normal bipolar junction transistors
    (b) multiple collector transistors
    (c) multiple emitter transistors
    (d) one multiple emitter and some normal transistors

161. Wired logic is not possible in
    (a) ECL
    (b) TTL with active pull-up
    (c) open-collector TTL
    (d) TTL with passive pull-up

162. The TTL logic family with minimum value of figure of merit is
    (a) Schottky TTL
    (b) low power TTL
    (c) high power TTL
    (d) low power Schottky TTL

163. ECL circuits have higher fan-out because of their
    (a) high input impedance
    (b) low output impedance
    (c) high input impedance and low output impedance
    (d) complementary outputs

164. Tristate logic has
    (a) only two output states; 0 and 1
    (b) three output states; 0, 1, and high impedance
    (c) logic 0 output when tristated
    (d) logic 1 output when tristated

165. Tristate logic is used for
    (a) improving the figure of merit
    (b) increasing the fan-out
    (c) bus oriented systems
    (d) improving the speed of operation

166. The most commonly used logic for LSI is
    (a) TTL
    (b) HTL
    (c) RTL
    (d) NMOS

167. MOS logic circuit consists of
    (a) only MOS devices
    (b) MOS devices and resistors
    (c) MOS devices and diodes
    (d) MOS and bipolar devices

168. CMOS logic consists of
    (a) only n-channel MOS devices
    (b) only p-channel MOS devices
    (c) MOS devices and capacitors
    (d) p-channel and n-channel MOS devices

169. The logic family best suited for high noise level industrial environment is
    (a) TTL
    (b) HTL
    (c) MOS
    (d) ECL

170. In ECL negative supply voltage is used because of
    (a) reduction in noise at the output
    (b) saving in power
    (c) ease of wired-OR operation
    (d) increase in speed of operation

171. The most popular logic family for SSI and MSI digital ICs is
    (a) $I^2L$
    (b) NMOS
    (c) TTL
    (d) DTL

172. An open input terminal of MOS logic
    (a) will assume a very high voltage which can damage the device
    (b) will behave as if it is connected to logic 0 level
    (c) will behave as if it is connected to logic 1 level
    (d) will assume some voltage between logic 0 and logic 1 level

173. An open input terminal of ECL gate
    (a) will behave as if it is connected to logic 0 level
    (b) will behave as if it is connected to logic 1 level

(c) will assume a very high voltage which can damage the device

(d) will assume some voltage between logic 0 and logic 1 levels

174. MOS devices are used for VLSI because of
    (a) their higher propagation delay
    (b) lower silicon chip area required
    (c) availability of p-channel and n-channel devices
    (d) availability of enhancement and depletion mode MOSFETs

175. A CMOS inverter consists of
    (a) an n-channel MOSFET and a resistor
    (b) a p-channel MOSFET and a resistor
    (c) n-channel and p-channel MOSFETs
    (d) n-channel and p-channel MOSFETs and resistors

176. The supply voltage permissible for CMOS devices is
    (a) +5 V
    (b) –5 V
    (c) 3–15 V
    (d) ±12 V

177. Standard TTL is a
    (a) current source logic
    (b) current sink logic
    (c) non-saturated bipolar logic
    (d) unipolar logic

178. Schottky TTL is a
    (a) non-saturated bipolar logic
    (b) saturated bipolar logic
    (c) current source logic
    (d) high threshold logic

179. The logic family with lowest propagation time (or highest speed) is
    (a) CMOS
    (b) NMOS
    (c) TTL
    (d) ECL

180. The logic swing of a gate is about 0.8 V. This gate belongs to the logic family
    (a) TTL
    (b) NMOS
    (c) CMOS
    (d) ECL

181. The logic swing is maximum for the logic family
    (a) $I^2L$
    (b) ECL
    (c) CMOS
    (d) TTL

182. The logic levels for ECL are taken as
    (a) '0' = –1.8 V and '1' = –0.8 V
    (b) '0' = 0 V and '1' = 1 V
    (c) '0' = 0.2 V and '1' = 5 V
    (d) none of these

# ANSWERS

1. The various approaches to digital design are called logic families.
2. The integration level of digital devices is categorised by the number of standard gates they contain.
3. The maximum number of similar gate inputs that any one gate output can drive is termed the loading factor of the gate.
4. Fan-out = $I_{OL(max)}/I_{IL(max)}$.
5. According to how their gates are interconnected.
6. The input resistors in RTL are replaced by diodes in DTL.
7. (a) Minimum number of chip interconnections,
   (b) Space saving,    (c) Simple manufacturing requirements.
8. It provides a buffer, enabling more inputs to be connected to an output.
9. Input current HIGH condition, $I_{IH}$; Input current LOW condition, $I_{IL}$
   Output current HIGH condition, $I_{OH}$; Output current LOW condition, $I_{OL}$.
10. It is the number of gates of the same subfamily that can be connected to a single output without exceeding the current rating of the gate.
11. Sink current flows into the gate and goes to ground. Source current flows out of the gate and supplies other gates.
12. It pulls the output of the gate upto 5 V when the output transistor is off.
13. LOW.          14. 74AS.
15. Connect to +$V_{CC}$ through a 1 kΩ resistor; connect to another used input.
16. HIGH, LOW, Hi-Z.
17. Because of the unsaturated state of the ON transistor.
18. To prevent static charge build up.          19. NMOS.

20. Gate input capacitances that cause an increase in load capacitance for each additional load.
21. High packing density of gates.
22. 5.8 kΩ                                    23. Three-input AND; fan-out = 2 (2.9); $R_p$ = 5.8 kΩ
24. $t_p$ = 10 ns; $P_D$ = 2.75 mW; fan-out = 20 fan-in = 20
25. There is a 0.2 V drop across the 1.6 kΩ, 0.7 V across $V_{BE4}$, 0.7 V across $D_2$, leaving 3.4 V at the output terminal.
26. N = 550                                   27. 10; Four-input NOR gate                              28. NOR
29. NAND
30. (a)    $V_a$ = 3.4 $V_{typ}$, $I_a$ = 120 μA                      (b)$V_a$ = 4.6 V, $V_{in}$ = LOW, $I_a$ = 20 μA$_{typ}$,
    (c) $V_a = V_{OL}$ = 0.2 $V_{typ}$, $I_a$ = 3.2 mA            (d) $V_d = V_{OH}$ = 3.4 $V_{typ}$, $I_a$ = 360 μA
31. N = 537; If the input signal is changing slowly, the fan-out is called the *static or dc fan-out*; if the input signal is switching at a fast rate, the fan-out is called the *dynamic fan-out*. Dynamic fan-out is significantly lower than static fan-out.
32. 27 Ω ≤ $R_C$ ≤ 1235 Ω

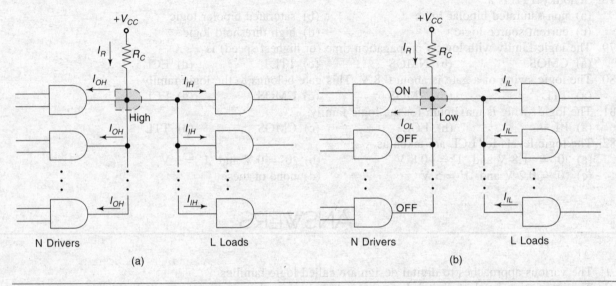

**Fig. 9.50**   *Solution for Problem 32. Wired-AND Gates Driving Loads. (a) Logic HIGH output (b) Logic LOW Output.*

33. For Y = 1 (HIGH), $R_C$ = 1.74 kΩ; For Y = 0 (LOW), $R_C$ = 0.72 kΩ

| | | | |
|---|---|---|---|
| 34. logic circuit | 35. TTL, CMOS | 36. very fast | 37. very low |
| 38. single type | 39. interfaced | 40. reliable | 41. logic 1 |
| 42. highest | 43. negative quantity | 44. positive quantity | 45. minimum |
| 46. less than | 47. gate outputs | 48. output | 49. speed |
| 50. propagation delay | 51. average | 52. noise margin | 53. propagation delay |
| 54. poor, fair, good, or excellent | 55. inverter | 56. complementing | 57. buffer |
| 58. voltage swing | 59. switching speed | 60. noise spikes | 61. totem-pole output |
| 62. 0.7 | 63. 0.3 | 64. output | 65. switching speed |
| 66. HIGH | 67. ground | 68. constant | 69. power consumption |
| 70. half | 71. double | 72. better | 73. 74ALSXX and 74FXX |
| 74. 2.7 ns | 75. speed | 76. power consumption | 77. physical size |
| 78. packing density | 79. very fast switching | 80. switching speed | 81. merged transistor logic |
| 82. 10 ns, 250 ns | 83. low, high. | 84. 6 μW, 70 μW | 85. Figure of merit |
| 86. critical | 87. TTL | 88. ECL or Schottky TTL (74 S or 74 AS) | |
| 89. 25 | 90. 10 | 91. faster | 92. excellent |
| 93. CMOS | 94. power | 95. gate density | 96. less power |
| 97. pin compatible | 98. input/output | 99. noise immunity | 100. ranges |
| 101. best features | 102. low, high | 103. limited | 104. octal (8-bit) |
| 105. inactive | 106. duty cycle | 107. low power design | 108. square |
| 109. tailored | 110. False | 111. False | 112. True |

| | | | |
|---|---|---|---|
| 113. False | 114. False | 115. False | 116. False |
| 117. False | 118. True | 119. False | 120. False |
| 121. False | 122. True | 123. True | 124. True |
| 125. True | 126. False | 127. False | 128. True |
| 129. (b) | 130. (b) | 131. (d) | 132. (a) |
| 133. (c) | 134. (a) | 135. (c) | 136. (c) |
| 137. (a) | 138. (a) | 139. (c) | 140. (b) |
| 141. (c) | 142. (d) | 143. (a) | 144. (b) |
| 145. (c) | 146. (c) | 147. (c) | 148. (d) |
| 149. (b) | 150. (a) | 151. (d) | 152. (a) |
| 153. (a) | 154. (c) | 155. (d) | 156. (d) |
| 157. (c) | 158. (d) | 159. (c) | 160. (b) |
| 161. (b) | 162. (d) | 163. (c) | 164. (b) |
| 165. (c) | 166. (d) | 167. (a) | 168. (d) |
| 169. (b) | 170. (a) | 171. (c) | 172. (a) |
| 173. (b) | 174. (b) | 175. (c) | 176. (c) |
| 177. (b) | 178. (a) | 179. (d) | 180. (d) |
| 181. (c) | 182. (a) | | |

# Arithmetic Circuits

## INTRODUCTION

A range of devices is available for performing binary arithmetic functions. Their *usefulness and cost-effectiveness* is thrown into some doubt these days due to the low cost and availability of the *microprocessor.* They will always have a place where the arithmetic requirement is very *simple or basic,* or where a simple arithmetic procedure is a small part of a much more complex function best performed by discrete hardware. Complicated arithmetic calls for complicated circuits, and it is in these circumstances that the designer should really consider whether a microprocessor might be a better solution.

## ADDITION AND SUBTRACTION

In binary arithmetic we must not only add the digit of equivalent significance of the two numbers to be summed but also the *carry* bit (in case it is present) of the next lower significant digit. This operation may be carried out in two steps: first add the two bits corresponding to the $2^k$ digit, and then add the resultant to the carry from the $2^{k-1}$ bit. When you subtract several columns of binary digits, you must take into account the borrowing and should also keep track of the differences and *borrows.*

**10.1 Explain the general form of binary addition in the least significant and more significant columns.**

*Solution:*

The *general form* of binary addition in the least significant column can be written as:

$$A_0 + B_0 = \Sigma_0 + C_{out} \qquad\qquad 10.1$$

The sum output is given by the *summation* symbol ($\Sigma$) called sigma, and the *carry-out* is given by $C_{out}$. The truth table in Table 10.1 shows the *four possible conditions when adding two binary digits.*

**Table 10.1** *Truth Table for Addition of two Binary Digits in the Least Significant Column*

| $A_0$ | $B_0$ | $\Sigma_0$ | $C_{out}$ |
|-------|-------|------------|-----------|
| 0 | 0 | 0 | 0 |
| 0 | 1 | 1 | 0 |
| 1 | 0 | 1 | 0 |
| 1 | 1 | 0 | 1 |

If a *carry out* is produced, it must be added to the next-more-significant column as a *carry-in* ($C_{in}$). Figure 10.1 shows this operation and truth table. In the truth table, the $C_{in}$ term comes from the value of $C_{out}$ from the *previous* addition. Now, with three possible inputs there are eight combinations of outputs ($2^3 = 8$).

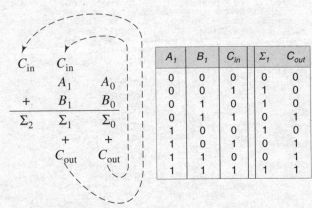

| $A_1$ | $B_1$ | $C_{in}$ | $\Sigma_1$ | $C_{out}$ |
|-------|-------|----------|------------|-----------|
| 0 | 0 | 0 | 0 | 0 |
| 0 | 0 | 1 | 1 | 0 |
| 0 | 1 | 0 | 1 | 0 |
| 0 | 1 | 1 | 0 | 1 |
| 1 | 0 | 0 | 1 | 0 |
| 1 | 0 | 1 | 0 | 1 |
| 1 | 1 | 0 | 0 | 1 |
| 1 | 1 | 1 | 1 | 1 |

**Fig. 10.1** *Addition in the More Significant Columns Requires Including $C_{in}$ with $A_1 + B_1$*

*In order to perform binary addition, we represent all binary numbers in groups of 8 or 16, because that is the standard used for arithmetic in most digital computers today.*

## 10.2 Explain the general form of binary subtraction in the least significant and more significant columns.

*Solution:*

The *general form* of binary subtraction in the least significant column can be written as:

$$A_0 - B_0 = R_0 + B_{out} \qquad 10.2$$

The difference, or *remainder,* from the subtraction is $R_0$, and if a *borrow* is required, $B_{out}$ is 1. The truth table in Table 10.2 shows the *four possible conditions when subtracting two binary digits.*

**Table 10.2** *Truth Table for Subtraction of Two Binary Digits in the Least Significant Column*

| $A_0$ | $B_0$ | $R_0$ | $B_{out}$ | |
|---|---|---|---|---|
| 0 | 0 | 0 | 0 | Borrow required |
| 0 | 1 | 1 | 1 | because $A_0 < B_0$ |
| 1 | 0 | 1 | 0 | |
| 1 | 1 | 0 | 0 | |

If a borrow is required, $A_0$ must borrow from $A_1$ in the next more-significant column. When $A_0$ borrows from its left, $A_0$ increases by 2 (just as in decimal subtraction where the number increases by 10).

## 10.3 Elaborate on binary subtraction in the second and more significant columns.

*Solution:*

The second column and all more significant columns first have to determine if $A$ was borrowed-from *before* subtracting $A - B$. Therefore, they have *three input conditions*, for a total of eight different possible combinations, as illustrated in Fig. 10.2.

| | | | | | $A_1$ | $B_1$ | $B_{in}$ | $R_1$ | $B_{out}$ | |
|---|---|---|---|---|---|---|---|---|---|---|
| $B_{in}$ | $B_{in}$ | | | | 0 | 0 | 0 | 0 | 0 | Borrow ($B_{out}$) |
| $A_1$ | $A_0$ | | | | 0 | 0 | 1 | 1 | 1 | required |
| $-$ | | | | | 0 | 1 | 0 | 1 | 1 | because $B_{in}$ |
| | $B_1$ | $B_0$ | | | 0 | 1 | 1 | 0 | 1 | needs to |
| | $R_1$ | $R_0$ | | | 1 | 0 | 0 | 1 | 0 | borrow from |
| | $+$ | $+$ | | | 1 | 0 | 1 | 0 | 0 | $A_1$, which is |
| | $B_{out}$ | $B_{out}$ | | | 1 | 1 | 0 | 0 | 0 | zero. |
| | | | | | 1 | 1 | 1 | 1 | 1 | |

**Fig. 10.2** *Subtraction in the More Significant Columns.*

## 10.4 Subtract 4 – 1 ($0100_2 - 0001_2$).

*Solution:*

| $4_{10}$ | | $A_3$ | $A_2$ | $A_1$ | $A_0$ | 0 | 1̸ | 0̸ | 0̸ |
|---|---|---|---|---|---|---|---|---|---|
| $-1_{10}$ | | $-B_3$ | $B_2$ | $B_1$ | $B_0$ | 0 | 0 | 0 | 1 |
| $3_{10}$ | | $R_3$ | $R_2$ | $R_1$ | $R_0$ | 0 | 0 | 1 | 1 | $= 3_{10}$ |

To subtract 0100 – 0001, $A_0$ must borrow from $A_1$; but $A_1$ is zero. Therefore, $A_1$ must first borrow from $A_2$, making $A_2$ a 0. Now $A_1$ is a 2. $A_0$ borrows from $A_1$, making $A_1$ a 1 and $A_0$ a 2. Now we can subtract to get 0011 ($3_{10}$).

## 10.5 What is the most widely used method of representing binary numbers and performing arithmetic in computer systems?

*Solution:*

The most widely used method of representing binary numbers and performing arithmetic in computer systems is by using the *two's-complement method*. With this method both positive and negative numbers can be represented using the same format, and *binary subtraction is greatly simplified.*

Most computer systems are based on 8-bit or 16-bit numbers. In an *8-bit system,* the total number of different combinations of bits is 256 ($2^8$); in a *16-bit system* the number is 65,536 ($2^{16}$).

To be able to represent *both* positive and negative numbers, the two's complement format uses the *most significant bit* (MSB) of the 8-or 16-bit number to signify whether the number is positive or negative. *The MSB is therefore called the sign bit and is defined as 0 for positive numbers and 1 for negative numbers.* Signed two's complement numbers are shown in Fig. 10.3.

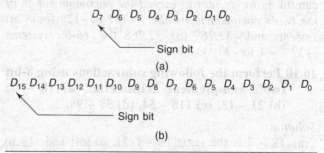

**Fig. 10.3** *Two's Complement Numbers: (a) 8-bit Number; (b) 16-bit Number.*

The *range of positive numbers* in an 8-bit system is 0000 0000 to 0111 1111 (0 to 127). The *range of negative numbers* in an 8-bit system is 1111 1111 to 1000 0000 (–1 to –128). In general, the maximum positive number is equal to ($2^{N-1} - 1$), and the maximum negative number is $-(2^{N-1})$ where $N$ is the number of bits in the number *including* the sign bit.

## 10.6 Convert $35_{10}$ to two's complement.

*Solution:*

If the decimal number is *positive*, the two's complement number is the *true binary equivalent* of the decimal number.

$$\text{True binary} = 0010\ 0011$$
$$\text{Two's complement} = 0010\ 0011$$

### 10.7 Convert $-35_{10}$ to two's complement.

*Solution:*

If the decimal number is *negative*, the two's complement number is found by: (a) *Complementing* each bit of the true binary equivalent of the decimal number (this is called the one's complement); (b) *Adding 1* to the one's complement number to get the magnitude bits (the sign bit will always end up being 1).

| | | |
|---|---|---|
| True binary | = | 0010 0011 |
| One's complement | = | 1101 1100 |
| Add 1 | = | +1 |
| Two's complement | = | 1101 1101 |

### 10.8 Convert 1011 0010 from two's complement form to decimal.

*Solution:*

The sign bit is 1, so the decimal result will be negative.

| | | |
|---|---|---|
| Two's complement | = | 1011 0010 |
| One's complement | = | 0100 1101 |
| Add 1 | = | +1 |
| True binary | = | 0100 1110 |
| Decimal equivalent | = | −78 |

### 10.9 Briefly explain the advantages of two's complement method.

*Solution:*

The *same* digital circuitry can be used for addition *and* subtraction, and there is no need to always subtract the smaller number from the larger number. We must be careful, however, *not to exceed the maximum range of the two's complement number:* +127 to −128 for *8-bit systems* and +32,767 to −32,768 for *16-bit systems* $(+2^{N-1} - 1$ to $-2^{N-1})$.

### 10.10 Perform the following subtractions using 8-bit two's complement arithmetic: (a) 18 − 7; (b) 21 − 13; (c) 118 − 54, (d) 59 − 96.

*Solution:*

(a) 18 − 7 is the same 18 + (−7), so just add 18 to negative 7.

| | | |
|---|---|---|
| +18 | = | 0001 0010 |
| −7 | = | 1111 1001 |
| Sum | = | 0000 1011 = $11_{10}$ |

The *carry-out* of the MSB is ignored. It will always occur for *positive* sums. The 8-bit answer is 0000 1011.

(b)
| | | |
|---|---|---|
| +21 | = | 0001 0101 |
| −13 | = | 1111 0011 |
| Sum | = | 0000 1000 = $8_{10}$ |

(c)
| | | |
|---|---|---|
| +118 | = | 0111 0110 |
| −54 | = | 1100 1010 |
| Sum | = | 0100 0000 = $64_{10}$ |

(d)
| | | |
|---|---|---|
| +59 | = | 0011 1011 |
| −96 | = | 1010 0000 |
| Sum | = | 1101 1011 = $-37_{10}$ |

### 10.11 Why is hexadecimal notation popularly used?

*Solution:*

Hexadecimal representation is a method of representing *groups of 4 bits* as a single digit. Hexadecimal notation has been widely adopted by manufacturers of computers and microprocessors because it *simplifies* the documentation and use of their equipment. Eight-and 16-bit computer system data, program instructions, and addresses use hexadecimal to make them *easier to interpret and work with*, than their binary equivalents.

Hexadecimal is a base 16 numbering system.

### 10.12 Add 4F + 2D in hexadecimal.

*Solution:*

$$
\begin{array}{rcl}
4F & \rightarrow & 0100\ \ 1111_2 \\
+2D & \rightarrow & +0010\ \ 1101_2 \\
\hline
& & 0111\ \ 1100 = 7C_{16}
\end{array}
$$

### 10.13 Subtract A05C − 24CA in hexadecimal.

*Solution:* $C - A = 12 - 10 = 2$. 5 borrows from 0, which borrows from 'A' $(5 + 16 = 21)$; $21 - \text{'}C\text{'} = 21 - 12 = 9$. 0 borrowed from the *A*, but it was also borrowed from, so it now becomes 15; $15 - 4 = 11$, which is '*B*'. '*A*' was borrowed from so it is now 9; $9 - 2 = 7$

Therefore,    $A05C - 24CA = 7B92$

### 10.14 Explain binary coded decimal; the 4-bit code.

*Solution:* If human beings had 16 fingers and toes, we probably would have adopted *hexadecimal* as our primary numbering system instead of decimal, and dealing with microprocessor-generated numbers would have been so much easier. But, unfortunately, we normally deal in base 10 *decimal* numbers. *Digital electronics naturally works in binary*, and we have to group four binary digits together to get enough combinations to represent the 10 different decimal digits. This 4-bit code is called *binary-coded decimal* (BCD).

So what we have is a *4-bit code* that is used to represent the decimal digits that we need while reading a display on calculators or computer output. The problem arises when we try to add or subtract these BCD numbers. The range of *valid* BCD numbers is from 0000 to 1001. Therefore, when adding BCD numbers we have to build extra circuitry to check the result to be certain that each group of 4-bits is a *valid* BCD number.

*Addition* is the most important operation because subtraction, multiplication and division can be done by a series of additions or two's complement additions.

### 10.15 Convert the following decimal numbers to BCD and add them. Convert the result back to decimal to *check* your answer.

(a) 8 + 7          (b) 9 + 9

*Solution:*

(a)
| | | |
|---|---|---|
| 8 | = | 1000 |
| +7 | = | 0111 |

Sum    =    1111    (invalid BCD number)
Add 6 =    0110
$\overline{\phantom{aaa}10101}$ =    0001    0101$_{BCD}$

=    15$_{10}$

(b)  9    =    1001
+9    =    1001
Sum    =    10010    (invalid because of carry)
↖
carry
Add 6 =    0110
$\overline{\phantom{aaa}11000}$ =    0001    1000$_{BCD}$

=    18$_{10}$

**10.16 Convert the following decimal numbers to BCD and add them. Convert the result back to decimal to *check* your answer.**
  **(a)  52 + 63**       **(b)  78 + 69**

*Solution:*

(a) 52    = 0101 0010
  +63    = 0110 0011
  Sum    = 1011 0101

  Add 6 = 0110        invalid BCD number
  $\overline{1\ 0001\ 0101}$ = 0001    0001    0101$_{BCD}$

=    1 1 5$_{10}$

(b) 78    = 0111    1000   | Both groups of 4 BCD
  +69    = 0110    1001   | bits are invalid
  Sum    = 1110    0001◄

carry
  Add 6 =                0110
  $\overline{\phantom{aaaa}1110\quad 0111}$
  Add 6 = 0110
  $\overline{10100\quad 0111}$ = 0001 0100    0111$_{BCD}$

=    1 4 7$_{10}$

## ADDERS/SUBTRACTORS

A *half-adder* is a basic adder circuit. By itself it cannot perform addition of numbers of more than 1 bit. It lacks provision for carries from preceding bits. *Full-adders* for binary numbers must receive carries as well as the addend and augend as inputs. A carry input, $C_I$, is the carry output, $C_o$, of the preceding addition. A full-adder may be constructed from two half-adders and an OR gate. During a subtraction, we first need to take the 2's complement of the subtrahend. Then we can add the complemented subtrahend to obtain the answer. With a *controlled inverter,* we can produce the 1's complement.

**10.17 Explain the addition of two 2-bit binary numbers with the help of truth tables.**

*Solution:*

All arithmetic operations and procedures can be implemented using *adders* formed from the basic logic gates. For a large number of digits we can use *medium-scale-integration* (MSI) circuits, which actually have several adders within a single integrated package.

By reviewing the truth table in Fig. 10.4, we can determine the input conditions that produce each *combination of sum and carry output bits.* Figure 10.4 shows the addition of two 2-bit numbers. This could easily be *expanded* to cover 4-8-or 16-bit addition. Notice that addition in the least significant bit column requires analysing *only two inputs* ($A_o$ plus $B_o$) to determine the sum ($\Sigma_o$) and carry ($C_{out}$). But any more significant columns ($2^1$ column and above) require the inclusion of a *third input*, which is the carry ($C_{in}$) from the column to its right. For example, the carry-out ($C_{out}$) of the $2^0$ column becomes the carry-in ($C_{in}$) to the $2^1$ column. Figure 10.4(c) shows the inclusion of a third input for the truth table of the more significant column additions.

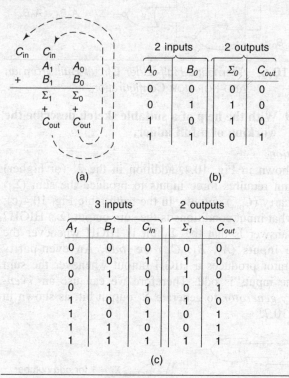

(a)

| 2 inputs | | 2 outputs | |
|---|---|---|---|
| $A_0$ | $B_0$ | $\Sigma_0$ | $C_{out}$ |
| 0 | 0 | 0 | 0 |
| 0 | 1 | 1 | 0 |
| 1 | 0 | 1 | 0 |
| 1 | 1 | 0 | 1 |

(b)

| 3 inputs | | | 2 outputs | |
|---|---|---|---|---|
| $A_1$ | $B_1$ | $C_{in}$ | $\Sigma_1$ | $C_{out}$ |
| 0 | 0 | 0 | 0 | 0 |
| 0 | 0 | 1 | 1 | 0 |
| 0 | 1 | 0 | 1 | 0 |
| 0 | 1 | 1 | 0 | 1 |
| 1 | 0 | 0 | 1 | 0 |
| 1 | 0 | 1 | 0 | 1 |
| 1 | 1 | 0 | 0 | 1 |
| 1 | 1 | 1 | 1 | 1 |

(c)

**Fig. 10.4**  *(a) Addition of Two 2-bit Binary numbers (b) Truth Table for the LSB Addition; (c) Truth Table for the More Significant Column.*

**10.18 With the help of a suitable sketch, describe the working of a half-adder.**

*Solution:*
Designing logic circuits to automatically implement the desired outputs for a truth table is simple. For the LSB truth table; for what input conditions is the $\Sigma_0$ bit HIGH? The answer is *A* OR *B HIGH but not both* (exclusive-OR function). For what inputs condition is the $C_{out}$ *bit* HIGH? The answer is *A* AND *B HIGH* (AND function). Therefore, the circuit design to perform addition in the LSB column can be implemented using an exclu ve-

OR and an AND gate. That circuit is called a *half-adder* and is shown in Fig. 10.5. If the exclusive-OR function in Fig. 10.5 is implemented using an AND-NOR-NOR configuration, we can tap off the AND gate for the *carry*, as shown in Fig. 10.6. The AND-NOR-NOR configuration is an Ex-OR. A combinational logic circuit used to add *two* binary digits is known as a *half adder*.

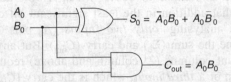

$$S_0 = \bar{A}_0 B_0 + A_0 \bar{B}_0$$
$$C_{out} = A_0 B_0$$

**Fig. 10.5**   *Half-adder Circuit, using Ex-OR and AND Gates for Addition in the LSB Column.*

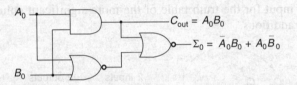

$$C_{out} = A_0 B_0$$
$$\Sigma_0 = \bar{A}_0 B_0 + A_0 \bar{B}_0$$

**Fig. 10.6**   *Alternative Half-adder Circuit Built from an AND-NOR-NOR Configuration.*

### 10.19  With the help of a suitable sketch describe the working of a full adder.

*Solution:*

As shown in Fig. 10.4, addition in the $2^1$ (or higher) column requires three inputs to produce the sum ($\Sigma_1$) and carry ($C_{out}$) outputs. In the truth table Fig. 10.4(c); for what input conditions is the sum output ($\Sigma_1$) HIGH? The answer is that the $\Sigma_1$ bit is HIGH whenever the three inputs ($A_1$, $B_1$, $C_{in}$) are *odd*. An even-parity generator produces a HIGH output whenever the sum of the inputs is odd. Therefore we can use an *even-parity generator* to generate $\Sigma_1$ output bit, as shown in Fig. 10.7.

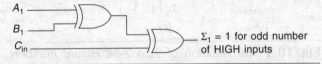

$\Sigma_1 = 1$ for odd number of HIGH inputs

**Fig. 10.7**   *The Sum ($\Sigma_1$) Function of the Full-adder is Generated from an Even-parity Generator.*

What inputs conditions produce a HIGH at $C_{out}$? The answer is that $C_{out}$ is HIGH whenever any two of the inputs are HIGH. Therefore, we can take care of $C_{out}$ with three ANDs and an OR, as shown in Fig. 10.8.

The two parts of the full-adder circuit shown in Figs 10.7 and 10.8 can be combined to form the complete *full-adder* circuit shown in Fig. 10.9. In the figure the $\Sigma_1$ *function* is produced using the same logic as that in Fig. 10.7 (an Ex-OR feeding an Ex-OR). The $C_{out}$ function comes from $A_1 B_1$ or $C_{in}$ ($\bar{A}_1 B_1 + A_1 \bar{B}_1$). A

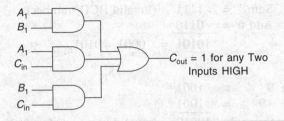

$C_{out} = 1$ for any Two Inputs HIGH

**Fig. 10.8**   *Carry-out ($C_{out}$) Function of the Full-adder.*

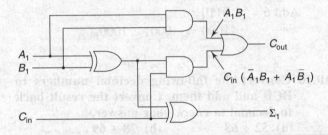

$A_1 B_1$
$C_{out}$
$C_{in}$ ($\bar{A}_1 B_1 + A_1 \bar{B}_1$)
$\Sigma_1$

**Fig. 10.9**   *Logic Diagram of a Full-adder.*

combinational logic circuit used to add *three* binary digits is known as a *full-adder*.

### 10.20  Apply the following input bits to the adder of Fig. 10.9 to verify its operation ($A_1 = 0$, $B_1 = 1$, $C_{in} = 1$).

*Solution:*
The full-adder operation is shown in Fig. 10.10.

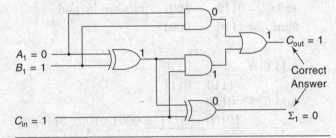

$A_1 = 0$
$B_1 = 1$
$C_{in} = 1$
$C_{out} = 1$
Correct Answer
$\Sigma_1 = 0$

**Fig. 10.10**   *Full-adder Operation for Problem 10.20.*

### 10.21  Draw and explain the block diagram of a 4 bit binary adder.

*Solution:*
We can simplify the representation of half-adder and full-adder circuits by drawing only *a box with the input and output lines,* as shown in Fig. 10.11. When drawing multibit adders, a *block diagram* is used to represent the addition in each column.

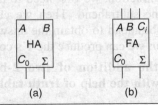

(a)                    (b)

**Fig. 10.11**   *Block Diagram of (a) Half-adder; (b) Full-adder.*

For example, in case of a 4-bit adder, the $2^0$ column needs only a half-adder, because there will be no carry-in. *Each of the more significant columns requires a full-adder* as shown in Fig. 10.12.

Note that the LSB half-adder has no carry-in. The carry-out ($C_{out}$) of the *LSB* becomes the carry-in ($C_{in}$) to the next full-adder to its left. The carry out ($C_{out}$) of the *MSB* full-adder is actually the highest-order sum output ($\Sigma_4$).

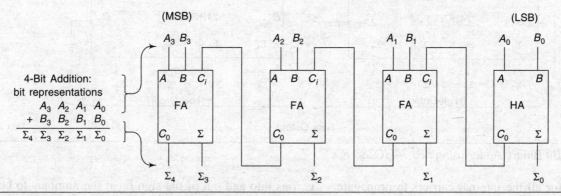

**Fig. 10.12** *Block Diagram of a 4-bit Binary Adder.*

### 10.22 Explain the 7483, 4-bit full adder. Give a brief description of available MSI adder ICs.

*Solution:*

Medium-Scale-Integration (MSI) ICs are available with four full-adders in a single package. Table 10.3 lists the most popular adder ICs. Each adder in the table contains four full-adders, and *all are functionally equivalent; however their pin layouts differ* (refer to data manual for pin layouts). *Each of them will add two 4-bit binary words plus one incoming carry.* The binary sum appears on the sum outputs ($\Sigma_1$ to $\Sigma_4$) and the outgoing carry.

**Table 10.3** *MSI Adder ICs*

| Device | Family | Description |
|--------|--------|-------------|
| 7483 | TTL | 4-Bit binary full-adder, fast carry |
| 74HC283 | CMOS | 4-Bit binary full-adder, fast carry |
| 4008 | CMOS | 4-Bit binary full-adder, fast carry |

Figure 10.13 shows the functional diagram and the logic diagram for the 7483. In the figure *the least significant* binary inputs ($2°$) come into the $A_1B_1$ terminals, and *the most significant* ($2^3$) come into the $A_4B_4$ terminals.

### 10.23 Show the external connections to two 4-bit adder ICs to form an 8-bit adder capable of performing the following addition:

$$A_7\ A_6\ A_5\ A_4\ A_3\ A_2\ A_1\ A_0$$
$$+\ B_7\ B_6\ B_5\ B_4\ B_3\ B_2\ B_1\ B_0$$
$$\overline{\Sigma_8\ \Sigma_7\ \Sigma_6\ \Sigma_5\ \Sigma_4\ \Sigma_3\ \Sigma_2\ \Sigma_1\ \Sigma_0}$$

*Solution:*

We can choose any of the IC adders listed in Table 10.3 for our design. Let's choose *74HC283*, which is the *high-speed CMOS version of the 4-bit adder* (it has the same logic symbol as the 7483). The two 8-bit

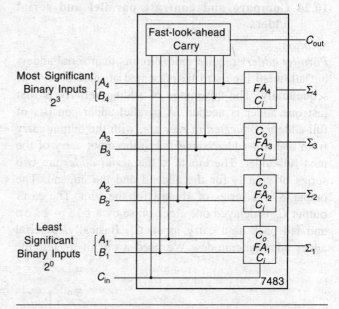

**Fig. 10.13** *The 7483, 4-Bit Full-adder.*

numbers are brought into the $A_1B_1$-to-$A_4B_4$ inputs of each chip, Fig. 10.14, and the sum output comes out of the $\Sigma_4$ to $\Sigma_1$ outputs of each chip.

The $C_{in}$ of the least significant addition ($A_0 + B_0$) is grounded (0) because there is no carry-in (*it acts like a half-adder*), and if it were left floating, the IC would not know whether to assume a 1 state or a 0 state.

The carry-out ($C_{out}$) from the addition of $A_3 + B_3$ must be connected to the carry-in ($C_{in}$) of the $A_4 + B_4$ addition, as shown. The fast-look-ahead carry circuit ensures that the carry-out ($C_{out}$) signal from the *low-order addition* is provided in the carry-in ($C_{in}$) of the *high-order addition* within a very short period of time so that the $A_4 + B_4$ addition can take place without

8 bit Inputs

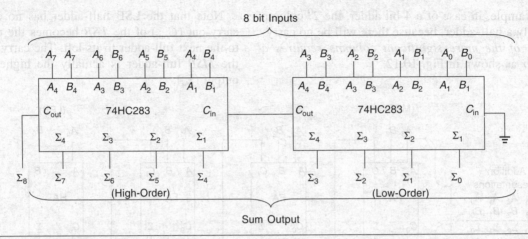

**Fig. 10.14**   *8-Bit Binary Adder using two 74HC283 ICs.*

having to wait for all the internal carriers to propagate through all four of the low-order additions first.

### 10.24 Compare and contrast parallel and serial adders.

*Solution:*

*Parallel adders* require more circuits than serial adders but allow all inputs to be presented at once instead of sequentially. The advantage of adding serially is that just one adder is needed. A parallel adder consists of full-adders *connected in cascade*, with the output carry from one full-adder connected to the input carry of the next full-adder. The inputs to the *serial adder* are two series of signals for the addend and the augend. The output $S$ is a series of signals for the sum. The carry output $C_0$ is delayed one clock pulse by a `flip-flop` and fed back as a carry input $C_1$. Basically, a serial adder adds magnitudes. We need a circuit to *test* the

carries into and out of the sign bit if the numbers to be added are in two's complement. Using one's complement we not only have to test sign bit carries but also have to provide an *end-around carry*.

### 10.25 With the help of a diagram describe a parallel-adder using NAND gates.

*Solution:*

Parallel addition of two numbers can be carried out by having a full-adder for each pair of bits that must be added, *except* for the least significant bits, which require only a half adder. To add two 8-bit numbers in parallel would require seven full adders *plus* a half adder.

In adder circuit using NAND gates, Fig. 10.15, it is apparent that the construction of a parallel 8-bit adder would be quite complicated. N-bit adders are available as integrated circuits, but *once constructed, a parallel adder is limited to the size of numbers it can handle.* An 8-bit adder cannot handle 9-bit numbers.

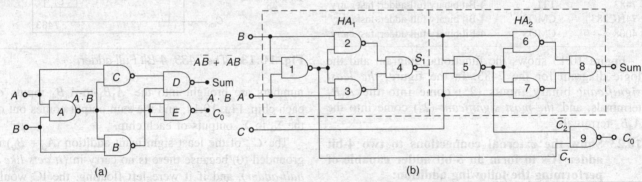

**Fig. 10.15**   *Adder Circuit using NAND Gates: (a) Half Adder (b) Full Adder.*

### 10.26 Describe serial addition.

*Solution:*

In serial addition the two numbers are added *one bit at a time,* just as they would be added manually. This can be done by using two shift registers, a full-adder and a `flip-flop` as shown in Fig. 10.16.

The two first bits are taken from the serial outputs of the shift registers and added. The *sum* is fed back to the serial input of one shift register (register $A$ in this example) while *the carry is stored in the* `flip-flop`. This procedure continues until all bits of the two numbers have been added, when the sum will be stored

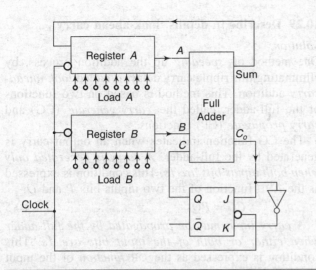

**Fig. 10.16** *Circuit Diagram for Serial Addition.*

in the first shift register. If required, a further number may be loaded into the second shift register and added to the sum.

**10.27 Implement a full-adder using Karnaugh maps.**

*Solution:*

Figure 10.17 shows an arrangement for adding two 4-bit binary numbers $A_3 A_2 A_1 A_0$ and $B_3 B_2 B_1 B_0$ to give a 5-bit result $X_4 X_3 X_2 X_1 X_0$, where $A_3$, $B_3$, and $X_4$ represent the *most significant bits,* and $A_0$, $B_0$, and $X_0$ represent the *least significant bits*. It is common practice to number the bits of binary numbers from the right and to start from 0. Thus an *n*-bit number has digits from 0 to *n*-1.

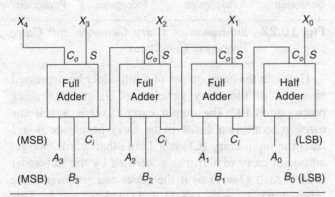

**Fig. 10.17** *An Arrangement to Add Two 4-bit Numbers.*

It can be seen that each full-adder has three inputs ($A$, $B$, and the carry input $C_i$) and two outputs (the sum $S$, and the carry output $C_o$). The function of the full-adder is described by the *truth table* of Fig. 10.18.

*Boolean expressions* can be obtained directly from this truth table and simplified using algebraic manipulation. Alternatively, the data can be represented using *Karnaugh maps*, as shown in Fig. 10.19.

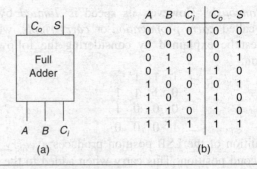

| A | B | $C_i$ | $C_o$ | S |
|---|---|---|---|---|
| 0 | 0 | 0 | 0 | 0 |
| 0 | 0 | 1 | 0 | 1 |
| 0 | 1 | 0 | 0 | 1 |
| 0 | 1 | 1 | 1 | 0 |
| 1 | 0 | 0 | 0 | 1 |
| 1 | 0 | 1 | 1 | 0 |
| 1 | 1 | 0 | 1 | 0 |
| 1 | 1 | 1 | 1 | 1 |

(a)        (b)

**Fig. 10.18** *A Full-adder.*

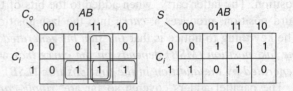

**Fig. 10.19** *Representation of a Full-adder using Karnaugh Maps.*

From either method of simplification we find that

$$C_o = AB + AC_i + BC_i \qquad 10.3$$

and

$$S = \bar{A}\bar{B}C_i + \bar{A}B\bar{C_i} + ABC_i + A\bar{B}\bar{C_i} \qquad 10.4$$

These functions can be implemented directly, as shown in Fig. 10.20.

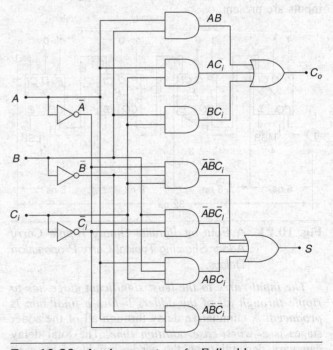

**Fig. 10.20** *Implementation of a Full-adder.*

**10.28 Describe a *n*-bit binary ripple-carry adder showing typical carry propagation delays.**

*Solution:*

The parallel adder performs additions at a relatively *high speed*, since it adds the bits from each position *simultaneously*. However, its speed is *limited* by an effect called *carry propagation* or *carry ripple,* which can best be explained by considering the following addition:

$$
\begin{array}{r}
1\ \ 1\ \ 1 \\
0\ \ 1\ \ 1\ \ 1 \\
+\ \ 0\ \ 0\ \ 0\ \ 1 \\
\hline
1\ \ 0\ \ 0\ \ 0 \\
\end{array}
$$

Addition of the LSB position produces a *carry* into the second position. This carry when added to the bits of the second position, produces a *carry* into the third position. The latter carry, when added to the bits of the third position, produces a *carry* into the last position. The key thing to notice is that *the sum bit generated in the last position (MSB) depends on the carry that was generated by the addition in the first position (LSB).*

The parallel adders covered so far are *ripple-carry types* in which the carry output of each full-adder stage is connected to the carry input of the next higher-order stage. *The sum and carry outputs of any stage cannot be produced until the input carry occurs; this leads to a time delay in the addition process,* as illustrated in Fig. 10.21. The *carry propagation delay* for each full-adder is the time from the application of the input carry until the output carry occurs, assuming that the *P* and *Q* inputs are present.

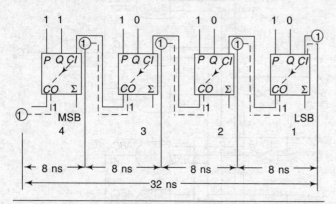

**Fig. 10.21** *A Four-bit Parallel Binary Ripple Carry Adder Showing Typical Carry Propagation Delays.*

*The input carry to the least significant stage has to ripple through all of the adders before a final sum is produced.* A cumulative delay through all of the adder stages is a *worst-case addition time.* The total delay can vary depending on the carries produced by each stage. If two numbers are added such that no carries occur between stages, the add time is simply the *propagation time* through a single full-adder from the application of the data bits on the inputs to the occurrence of a sum output.

**10.29 Describe in details 'look-ahead carry'.**

*Solution:*

One method of *speeding* up the addition process, by eliminating this ripple carry delay, is called *look-ahead-carry* addition. This method is based on two functions of the full-adder, called the *carry generate* (CG) and *carry propagate* (CP) functions.

The CG function indicates when an output carry is generated by the full-adder. *A carry is generated only when both inputs bits are 1s.* This condition is expressed as the AND function of the two inputs bits *P* and *Q*:

$$CG = PQ \qquad\qquad 10.5$$

*A carry input may be propagated by the full-adder when either or both of the input bits are 1s.* This condition is expressed as the OR *function* of the input bits *P* and *Q*:

$$CP = P + Q \qquad\qquad 10.6$$

The *carry generate* and *carry propagate* conditions are illustrated in Fig. 10.22.

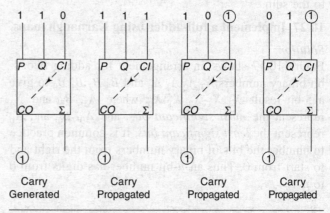

**Fig. 10.22** *Illustration of Carry Generate and Carry Propagate Conditions.*

How can the carry output of a full-adder be expressed in terms of the carry generate (CG) and the carry propagate (CP)? The output carry (CO) is a 1 if the carry generate is a 1 OR if the carry propagate is a 1 AND the input carry (CI) is a 1. In other words, we get an output carry of 1 if it is *generated* by the full-adder (*P* = 1 AND *Q* = 1) or if the adder can *propagate* the input carry (*P* = 1 OR *Q* = 1) and $C_{\text{in}}$ = 1. This relationship is expressed as

$$CO = CG + CP \cdot CI \qquad\qquad 10.7$$

**10.30 How will you form a BCD adder using the integrated circuit 4-bit binary adders?**

*Solution:*

BCD adders can also be formed using the integrated circuit 4-bit binary adders. The problem is that when the sum of any group-of-four BCD *exceeds* 9, or when there is a *carry-out*, the number is *invalid* and must be *corrected* by adding 6 to the invalid answer to get the correct BCD answer. (*The valid range of BCD numbers is 0000 to 1001*).

For example, adding $0111_{BCD} + 0110_{BCD}$ (7 + 6) gives us an *invalid result*:

$$
\begin{array}{r}
0111 \\
+\ 0110 \\
\hline
1101 \quad \text{invalid} \\
+\ 0110 \quad \text{add 6 to correct} \\
\hline
1\quad 0011
\end{array}
$$

carry to next BCD digit

The corrected answer is $0001\ 0011_{BCD}$, which equals 13.

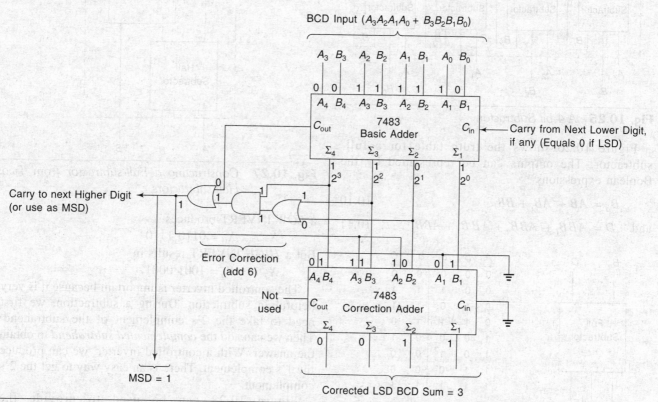

**Fig. 10.23** *BCD Adder Illustrating the Addition 7 + 6 = 13 (0111 + 0110 = 0001 0011$_{BCD}$).*

### 10.31 Explain binary subtraction.

*Solution:*
The process of binary subtraction can be tackled in a manner similar to that of addition. We can construct a *half-subtractor*, as shown in Fig. 10.24(a), with a truth table as given in Fig. 10.24(b).

Since we are now concerned with subtraction rather than addition, we have *difference* (D) and *borrow* (B) outputs rather than *sum* and *carry*. It is also necessary to *differentiate* between the two inputs $A$ and $B$ to *determine* which one is subtracted from which. In the example shown the output is equal to $(A-B)$.

From the truth table we can see that

$$B_o = \bar{A} \cdot B \qquad 10.8$$

and

$$D = \bar{A}B + A\bar{B} = A \oplus B \qquad 10.9$$

It can be seen that $D$ is identical to $S$ for a half-adder, but that *the borrow output is not the same as the carry.*

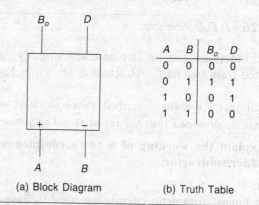

| A | B | $B_o$ | D |
|---|---|-----|---|
| 0 | 0 | 0 | 0 |
| 0 | 1 | 1 | 1 |
| 1 | 0 | 0 | 1 |
| 1 | 1 | 0 | 0 |

(a) Block Diagram      (b) Truth Table

**Fig. 10.24** *A Half-subtractor.*

### 10.32 Explain multiple-bit binary subtraction.

*Solution:*
In order to perform *multiple-bit subtraction* we again need to consider *the effect of one stage on the next.*

Figure 10.25 shows a 4-bit subtractor using four full-subtractors. *This circuit can be cascaded to allow larger numbers to be used.*

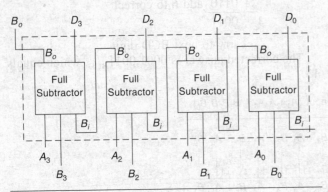

**Fig. 10.25**   *A 4-bit Subtractor.*

Figure 10.26 shows the truth table for a full-subtractor. The outputs can be represented by the Boolean expressions

$$B_o = \bar{A}B + \bar{A}B_i + BB_i \qquad\qquad 10.10$$

and $\quad D = \bar{A}\bar{B}B_i + \bar{A}B\bar{B_i} + A\bar{B}\bar{B_i} + ABB_i \qquad 10.11$

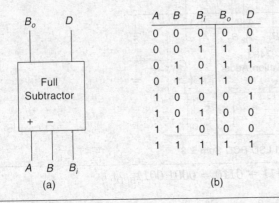

| A | B | $B_i$ | $B_o$ | D |
|---|---|---|---|---|
| 0 | 0 | 0 | 0 | 0 |
| 0 | 0 | 1 | 1 | 1 |
| 0 | 1 | 0 | 1 | 1 |
| 0 | 1 | 1 | 1 | 0 |
| 1 | 0 | 0 | 0 | 1 |
| 1 | 0 | 1 | 0 | 0 |
| 1 | 1 | 0 | 0 | 0 |
| 1 | 1 | 1 | 1 | 1 |

(a)                              (b)

**Fig. 10.26**   *A Full-subtractor.*

These functions can be implemented directly, or constructed from two half-subtractors as shown in Fig. 10.27.

The subtractor circuits described above work as we would expect, *provided that the result is not negative.*

### 10.33 Explain the working of a two's complement adder/subtractor.

*Solution:*
Often in binary arithmetic circuits we need to have a device that completes an entire binary string when told to do so by some *control signal.* Figure 10.28 shows a *controlled inverter.* When INVERT is LOW, it transmits the *8-bit input* to the output; when INVERT is HIGH, it transmits the *1's complement.* For instance, if the input number is

$$D_7 \ldots D_0 = 0110\ 1110$$

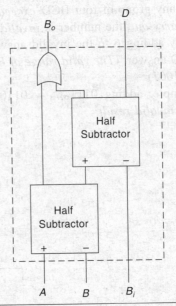

**Fig. 10.27**   *Constructing a Full-subtractor from Two Half-subtractors.*

a *LOW* INVERT produces
$$X_7 \ldots X_0 = 0110\ 1110$$
But a *HIGH* INVERT results in
$$X_7 \ldots X_0 = 1001\ 0001$$

The controlled inverter is important because it is very helpful in subtraction. During a subtraction, we first need to take the 2's complement of the subtrahend. Then we can add the *complemented subtrahend* to obtain the answer. With a controlled inverter, we can produce the 1's complement. There is an easy way to get the 2's complement.

Figure 10.28 can be used to provide the complementing function. If the INVERT (C) is HIGH, each of the data bits is *complemented* at the output. If the INVERT (C) is LOW, the data bits pass through to the output *uncomplemented.* Two 7486 quad Ex-OR ICs could be used to implement this design.

Positive two's-complement numbers are exactly the same as *regular true binary numbers* and can be added using regular binary addition. Also, subtraction in two's-complement arithmetic is performed by converting the number to be subtracted to a *negative* number in the two's-complement form and then using regular binary addition. Therefore, *once our numbers are in two's-complement form, we can use a binary adder to get the answer whether we are adding or subtracting.*

For example, to perform the subtraction 18 − 9, we would first convert 9 to a negative two's-complement number by *complementing each bit and then adding 1.* We would then add 18 + (−9).

Two's complement of 18 = 0001 0010
+ Two's complement of −9 = 1111 0111
Sum = 0000 1001   $= 9_{10}$

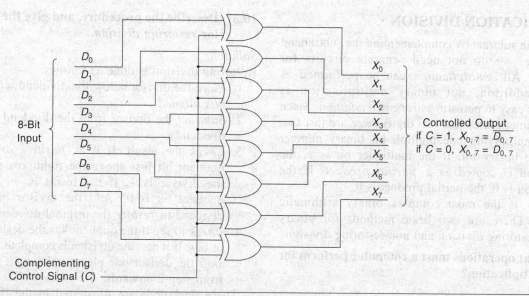

**Fig. 10.28** *Controlled Inverter (Complementing) Circuit.*

All we need for a combination adder/subtractor circuit is an *input switch* or signal to signify addition or subtraction so that we will know whether to form a positive or a negative two's-complement of the second number. Then we will just use a binary adder to get the final result.

To form negative two's complement, we can use the controlled inverter circuit of Fig. 10.28 and add 1 to its output.

**10.34 Illustrate the subtraction 42 − 23 = 19 using the CMOS 4008.**

*Solution:*

The 4008 are CMOS 4-bit binary adders. The 8-bit number on the $A$ inputs ($A_7$ to $A_0$) is brought directly into the adders. The other 8-bit binary number comes in on the $B_7$ to $B_0$ lines. If the $B$ number is to be subtracted, the complementing switch will be in the up (1) position, causing each bit in the number to be complemented (*one's complement*). At the same time, the low-order $C_{in}$ receives a 1, which has the effect of adding a 1 to the already complemented number $B$, making it a *negative two's complement number*.

Now the 4008s perform a regular binary addition. If the complementing switch is up, the number on the $B$ inputs is *subtracted* from the number on the $A$ inputs. If it is down, the *sum* is taken. *The $C_{out}$ of the MSB is ignored.* The result can range from 0111 1111 (+127) to 1000 0000 (−128).

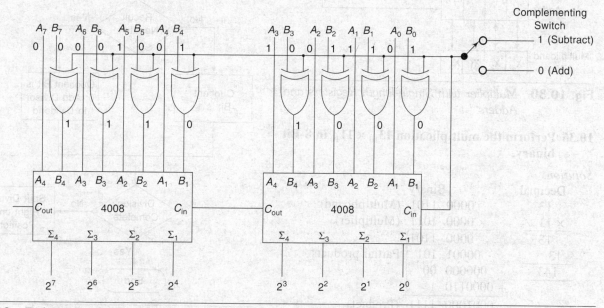

**Fig. 10.29** *Eight-bit Two's-Complement Adder/Subtractor, Illustrating the Subtraction 42 − 23 = 19.*

## MULTIPLICATION/DIVISION

Since we can subtract by complementing the subtrahend and *adding*, we do not need separate circuits for subtraction. All *multiplication* can be performed as repeated addition, but binary multiplication is particularly easy to perform as *repeated addition*. Since binary arithmetic uses just two digits there are just two rules for multiplying one multiple-bit binary number by a single binary bit. If the multiplier bit is 1, the multiplicand is copied as a *partial product*. If the multiplier bit is 0, the partial product is 0.

*Division* is the most complex binary arithmetic operation. There are two basic methods for binary division: restoring division and non-restoring division.

### 10.35 What operations must a computer perform for multiplication?

*Solution:*

A computer must perform three types of operations for multiplication.

1. It must *determine* whether a multiplier is 1 or 0 so that it can designate the partial product as multiplicand or 0.
2. It must *shift* partial products.
3. It must *add* partial products.

These operations are illustrated in Fig. 10.30. We need not wait until all partial products are formed before summing them. *We can sum them up as soon as they are formed, two at a time.*

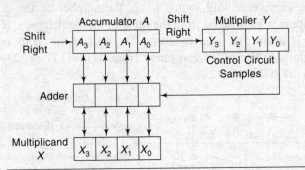

**Fig. 10.30** *Multiplier with Single-length Registers and Adders.*

### 10.36 Perform the multiplication $13_{10} \times 11_{10}$ in 8-Bit binary.

*Solution:*

| Decimal | Binary | |
|---|---|---|
| 13 | 0000 1101 | (Multiplicand) |
| × 11 | × 0000 1011 | (Multiplier) |
| 13 | 0000 1101 | |
| 13 | 00001 101 | Partial products |
| 143 | 000000 00 | |
| | + 0000110 1 | |
| | 0001000 1111 | (Product) |

8-bit answer = $10001111 = 143_{10}$

### 10.37 Describe the procedure, and give the flowchart for *restoring division*.

*Solution:*

Restoring division is done as follows:

1. Place the divisor below the dividend *with leftmost bits aligned.*
2. *Subtract* the divisor from the dividend (or partial dividend).
3. *Check* the result. If it is *positive or zero,* the quotient bit just above the rightmost position of the divisor is 1. If the result is *negative,* the quotient bit is 0. *Add* the divisor back to the dividend to *restore* the original dividend.
4. *Check* to see if the quotient has the desired number of bits. If it has, the division is complete. Otherwise, *shift* the divisor one place to the right and *repeat* from step 2 onwards.

These operations are illustrated in the flowchart in Fig. 10.31.

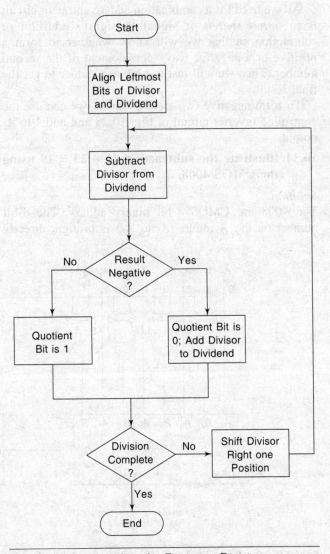

**Fig. 10.31** *Flowchart for Restoring Division.*

## 10.38 Illustrate the division of 1001 by 1101 by the method of restoring division.

*Solution:*

$$
\begin{array}{r}
Q_0 Q_{-1} Q_{-2} Q_{-3} Q_{-4} \\
0\ .\ 1\ 0\ 1\ 1
\end{array}
$$

$$
1101\ \big)\ 1\ 0\ 0\ 1\ .\ 0\ 0\ 0\ 0
$$

| | |
|---|---|
| $-1\ 1\ 0\ 1$ | Subtract |
| $-0\ 1\ 0\ 0$ | Negative, $Q_0 = 0$ |
| $+1\ 1\ 0\ 1$ | Restore |
| $+1\ 0\ 0\ 1\ 0$ | |
| $-\ 1\ 1\ 0\ 1$ | Shift and subtract |
| $+1\ 0\ 1\ 0$ | Positive, $Q_{-1} = 1$ |
| $-1\ 1\ 0\ 1$ | Shift and subtract |
| $-0\ 0\ 1\ 1$ | Negative, $Q_{-2} = 0$ |
| $+1\ 1\ 0\ 1$ | Restore |
| $+1\ 0\ 1\ 0\ 0$ | Shift and subtract |
| $-1\ 1\ 0\ 1$ | Positive, $Q_{-3} = 1$ |
| $+0\ 1\ 1\ 1\ 0$ | Shift and subtract |
| $-1\ 1\ 0\ 1$ | Positive, $Q_{-4} = 1$ |
| $+1$ | Remainder = 1 |

The *binary point* is at the right of the numbers. We extend the dividend with 0s as desired—for example, 1001.0000. We number the quotient digits with subscripts showing the exponent of 2 for each position. $Q_0 = 2^0$, $Q_{-1} = 2^{-1} = 1/2$, etc. We show addition and positive results with *plus signs* and subtraction and negative results with *minus signs*.

## 10.39 Describe the procedure, and give the flowchart for *non-restoring* division.

*Solution:*

Non-restoring division is done as follows:

1. Place the divisor below the dividend *with left most bits aligned.*
2. *Subtract* the divisor from the dividend.
3. *Check* to see if the result is negative. If it is *positive or zero*, the quotient bit just above the rightmost bit of the divisor is 1. Shift the divisor to the right and subtract the divisor from the dividend. Go to step 4. If the result is *negative*, the quotient bit just above the rightmost bit of the divisor is 0. Shift the divisor one place to the right and add to the dividend.
4. *Check* to see if the quotient has the desired number of bits. If it has, the division is complete. Otherwise, repeat step 3.

These operations are illustrated in the flowchart in Fig. 10.32.

## 10.40 Illustrate the division of 1001 by 1101 by the method of non-restoring division.

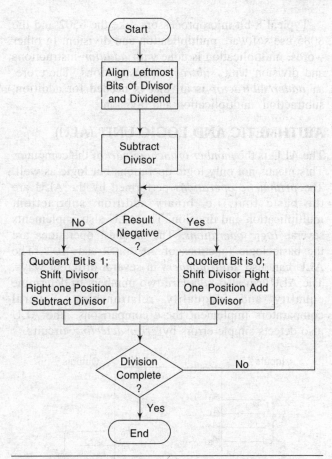

**Fig. 10.32** *Flowchart for Non-restoring Division.*

*Solution:*

$$
\begin{array}{r}
Q_0\ Q_{-1}\ Q_{-2}\ Q_{-3}\ Q_{-4} \\
0\ .\ 1\ 0\ 1\ 1
\end{array}
$$

$$
1101\ \big)\ 1\ 0\ 0\ 1\ 0\ 0\ 0\ 0
$$

| | |
|---|---|
| | Subtract |
| $-1\ 1\ 0\ 1$ | Negative, $Q_0 = 0$ |
| $-0\ 1\ 0\ 0\ 0$ | Shift and add |
| $+\ 1\ 1\ 0\ 1$ | Positive, $Q_{-1} = 1$ |
| $+\ 1\ 0\ 1\ 0$ | Shift and subtract |
| $-\ 1\ 1\ 0\ 1$ | Negative, $Q_{-2} = 0$ |
| $-\ 0\ 0\ 1\ 1\ 0$ | Shift and add |
| $+\ 1\ 1\ 0\ 1$ | Positive, $Q_{-3} = 1$ |
| $+\ 1\ 1\ 1\ 0$ | Shift and subtract |
| $-\ 1\ 1\ 0\ 1$ | Positive, $Q_{-4} = 1$ |
| $+\ 1$ | Remainder = 1 |

## 10.41 Explain how binary multiplication and division is done.

*Solution:*

Although it is possible to construct circuits to perform multiplication and division using simple logic gates, it is fairly unusual as the *complexity* of the circuits makes them impractical. It is more common to perform these functions using *dedicated logic circuits* containing a large number of gates, or to use a microprocessor.

Typical 8-bit microprocessors, like the 6502 and the 8085 use software multiplication and division. In other words, multiplication is done with *addition* instructions and division with *subtraction* instructions. Therefore, an *adder/subtractor* is all that is needed for addition, subtraction, multiplication and division.

## ARITHMETIC AND LOGIC UNIT (ALU)

The ALU is the *number crunching part* of the computer. This means not only logic operations but logic as well. The *arithmetic operations* performed by the ALU are the basic four, i.e. binary addition, subtraction, multiplication and division. The ALU also implements several *logic operations*. The simplest operations are the basic logic functions of AND, OR and NOT. The ALU can also *shift numbers* in several different ways. The ALU can also *compare* two numbers to determine equality and inequality relationships. Several comparators implement these comparisons. The ALU also detects simple errors by *error detecting* circuits.

### 10.42 What is the significance of ALUs? How do they work? Describe a typical ALU.

*Solution:*

Arithmetic and logic units (ALUs) are available in large-scale integrated circuit packages (LSI). Typically, *an ALU is a multipurpose device capable of providing several different arithmetic and logic operations.* The specific operation to be performed is chosen by the user by placing a specific *binary code* on the mode select inputs. Microprocessors may also have ALUs *built in* as one of their many operational units. In such cases, the specific operation to be performed is chosen by software instructions.

The 74181 (TTL) or 74HC181 (CMOS) is a *4-bit ALU* that provides 16 *arithmetic* plus 16 *logic* operations. Its logic symbol and function table are given in Fig. 10.33. The *mode control input* ($M$) is used to set the mode of operation as either *logic* ($M = H$) or *arithmetic* ($M = L$). When $M$ is *HIGH*, all internal carries are *disabled,* and the device performs *logic operations*

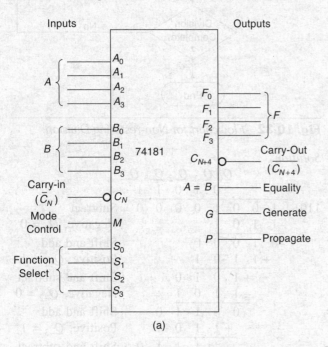

| | | | | $M = H$ | $M = 1$ Arithmetic Operations |
|---|---|---|---|---|---|
| Selection | | | | Logic | $\overline{C}_n = H$ |
| $S_3$ | $S_2$ | $S_1$ | $S_0$ | Functions | (no Carry) |
| L | L | L | L | $F = \overline{A}$ | $F = A$ |
| L | L | L | H | $F = \overline{A + B}$ | $F = A + B$ |
| L | L | H | L | $F = \overline{A}B$ | $F = A + \overline{B}$ |
| L | L | H | H | $F = 0$ | $F = $ minus 1 (2's comp.) |
| L | H | L | L | $F = \overline{AB}$ | $F = A$ plus $A\overline{B}$ |
| L | H | L | H | $F = \overline{B}$ | $F = (A + B)$ plus $A\overline{B}$ |
| L | H | H | L | $F = A \oplus B$ | $F = A$ minus $B$ minus 1 |
| L | H | H | H | $F = A\overline{B}$ | $F = A\overline{B}$ minus 1 |
| H | L | L | L | $F = \overline{A} + B$ | $F = A$ plus $AB$ |
| H | L | L | H | $F = \overline{A \oplus B}$ | $F = A$ plus $B$ |
| H | L | H | L | $F = B$ | $F = (A + \overline{B})$ plus $AB$ |
| H | L | H | H | $F = AB$ | $F = AB$ minus 1 |
| H | H | L | L | $F = 1$ | $F = A$ plus $A^*$ |
| H | H | L | H | $F = A + \overline{B}$ | $F = (A + B)$ plus $A$ |
| H | H | H | L | $F = A + B$ | $F = (A + \overline{B})$ plus $A$ |
| H | H | H | H | $F = A$ | $F = A$ minus 1 |

*Each bit is shifted to the next-more-significant position.

(b)

**Fig. 10.33** *The 74181 ALU (a) Logic Symbol, (b) Function Table.*

on the individual bits ($A_0$ to $A_3$, $B_0$ to $B_3$), as indicated in the 'function table.'

When $M$ is *LOW*, the internal carries are *enabled* and the device performs *arithmetic operations* on the two 4-bit binary inputs. Ripple carry output is provided at $C_{N+4}$, and fast-look-ahead carry is provided at $G$ and $P$ for high-speed arithmetic operations. The carry-in and carry-out terminals are each active-LOW (as signified by the bubble), which means that a 0 signifies a carry.

Once the mode control ($M$) is set you have 16 choices with either the logic or arithmetic categories. The specific function you want is selected by applying the appropriate binary code to the *function select* inputs ($S_3$ to $S_0$).

For example, with $M = H$ and $S_3 S_2 S_1 S_0 = LLLL$, the $F$ outputs will be equal to the complement of $A$ (see the function table). This means that $F_0 = \overline{A}_0$, $F_1 = \overline{A}_1$, $F_2 = \overline{A}_2$, and $F_3 = \overline{A}_3$. Yet another example is with $M = $

H and $S_3S_2S_1S_0 = HHHL$; the F outputs will be equal to $A + B$ (A OR B). This means that $F_0 = A_0 + B_0$, $F_1 = A_1 + B_1$, $F_2 = A_2 + B_2$, and $F_3 = A_3 + B_3$.

From the function table we can see that other logic operations (AND, NAND, NOR, Ex-OR, Ex-NOR, and several others) are available. The function table in Fig. 10.33(b) also shows the result of the 16 different *arithmetic operations* available when $M = L$. Note that the results listed are with carry-in ($\bar{C}_N$) equal to H (no carry). For $\bar{C}_N = L$, just add 1 to all results. All results produced by the device are in the two's-complement notation. Also, in the function table, note that the $+sign$ means *logical* OR and the word PLUS means arithmetic sum.

For example, to subtract B from A ($A_3A_2A_1A_0 - B_3B_2B_1B_0$), set $M = L$ and $S_3S_2S_1S_0 = LHHL$. The result at the F outputs will be the two's-complement of A minus B minus 1; therefore, to get just A minus B, we need to add for 1. (This can be done automatically by setting $\bar{C}_N = 0$). Also, as discussed earlier for two's complement subtraction, a carry-out (borrow) is generated ($\overline{(C_{N+4}} = 0$) when the result is positive or zero. Just ignore it.

Read through the function table to see the other 5 arithmetic operations that are available.

**10.43 Show the external connections to a 74181 to form a 4-bit subtracter. Label the input and output pins with the binary states that occur when subtracting 13 – 7 (A = 13, B = 7).**

*Solution:*
The 4-bit subtractor is shown in Fig. 10.34. The ALU is set in the subtract mode by setting $M = 0$ and $S_3S_2S_1S_0 = 0110$ (*LHHL*). 13 (1101) is input at A and 7 (0111) is input at B.

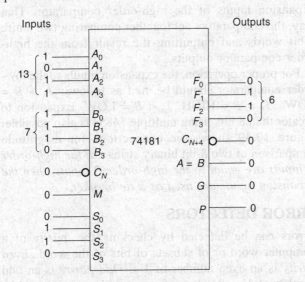

**Fig. 10.34** *Four-bit Binary Subtractor using the 74181 ALU to Subtract (13 – 7).*

By setting $C_N = 0$, the output at $F_0$, $F_1$, $F_2$, $F_3$ will be A minus B instead of A minus B minus 1 as shown in the function table, Fig. 10.33(b). The result of the subtraction is a positive 6(0110) with a carry-out ($C_{N+4}$ = 0). With 2's complement subtraction, there is a carry-out for any positive or zero answer, which is ignored.

## COMPARATORS

The output of a voltage comparator changes rapidly from one level to another when the input arrives at a *predetermined* voltage. The change in output level occurs at the instant that the two input voltages become equal. The input voltages are *compared* hence the name comparator.

The *equality comparison* is the easiest to implement and can be done with a two-level circuit. *Inequality comparisons* are more difficult and can be implemented either in series or in parallel.

**10.44 Discuss basic comparator operation. Draw the diagram and explain the working of a binary comparator for comparing two 4-bit binary strings.**

*Solution:*
Often in the evaluation of digital information it is important to *compare* two binary strings (or binary words) to determine if they are *exactly equal*. This comparison process is performed by a *digital comparator*.

The basic digital comparator evaluates two binary strings *bit by bit* and outputs a 1 if they are exactly equal. *An* Ex-NOR *gate is the easiest way to compare the equality of bits*. If both bits are equal (0-0 or 1-1), the Ex-NOR puts out a 1.

In order to compare binary numbers containing more than just 2 bits, we need additional Ex-NORs, and the output of all of them must be 1. For example, to design a comparator to evaluate two 4-bit numbers, we need four Ex-NORs. To determine *total equality* connect all four outputs into an AND gate. That way, if all four outputs are 1's, the AND gate puts out a 1. Figure 10.35 shows a comparator circuit built from Ex-NORs and an AND gate.

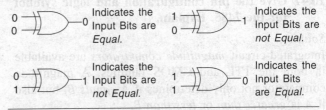

**Fig. 10.35** *Basic Comparator Operation (Ex-OR Gates).*

In Fig. 10.36, if $A_0$ & $B_0$ are equal, 1-1 or 0-0, the top Ex-NOR will output a 1. The same holds true for the second, third, and fourth Ex-NOR gates. If all of them output a 1, the AND gate outputs a 1, indicating *equality*.

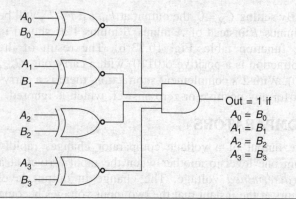

**Fig. 10.36**   *Binary Comparator for Comparing two 4-bit Binary Strings.*

**10.45 Referring to Fig. 10.36 determine if the following pairs of input binary numbers will output a 1.**

    (a) $A_3A_2A_1A_0 = 1\ 0\ 1\ 1$
        $B_3B_2B_1B_0 = 1\ 0\ 1\ 1$
    (b) $A_3A_2A_1A_0 = 0\ 1\ 1\ 0$
        $B_3B_2B_1B_0 = 0\ 1\ 1\ 1$

*Solution:*

(a) When the $A$ and $B$ numbers are applied to the inputs, each of the four Ex-NORs will output 1's, so the output of the AND gate willl be 1 (equality).

(b) For this case, the first three Ex-NORs will output 1's, but the last Ex-NOR will output a 0 because it inputs are not equal. The AND gate will output a 0 (*inequality*).

**10.46 Apply each of the following sets of binary numbers to comparator inputs, and determine the output by following the logic levels through the cirucuit.**

    (a) **10 and 10**    (b)    **11 and 10**

*Solution:*

(a) The output is 1 for inputs 10 and 10, as shown in Fig. 10.37(a).

(b) The output is 0 for inputs 11 and 10, as shown in Fig. 10.37(b).

**10.47 Give the pin configuration and logic symbol for the 7485. Explain.**

*Solution:*

Integrated-circuit *magnitude comparators* are available in both the TTL and CMOS families. A magnitude comparator not only determines if *A equals B*, but also if *A* is *greater than* or *less than B*.

    *The 7485 is a TTL 4-bit magnitude comparator.* The pin configuration and logic symbol for the 7485 are given in Fig. 10.38. The 7485 can be used just like the basic comparator of Fig. 10.36 by using the *A* inputs, *B* inputs, and the equality output ($A = B$). The 7485 has the *additional feature* of telling which number is larger

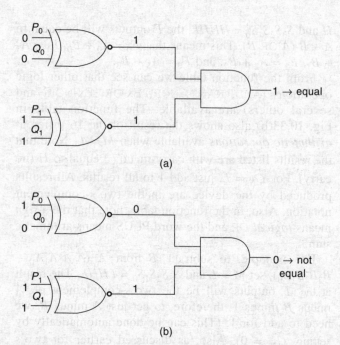

**Fig. 10.37**

if the equality is not met. The $A > B$ output is 1 if $A$ is larger than $B$, and the $A < B$ output is 1 if $B$ is larger than $A$.

    The basic comparator circuit can be expanded to any number of bits. The AND gate sets the condition that all corresponding bits of the two numbers must be equal if the two numbers themselves are equal.

    The *expansion inputs* $I_A < B$, and $I_A > B$ are used for expansion to a system capable of comparisons greater than 4 bits. For example, to set up a circuit capable of comparing two *8-bit words*, two 7485s are required. The $A > B$, $A = B$, and $A < B$ outputs of the low-order (least significant) comparator are connected to the expansion inputs of the high-order comparator. That way, the comparators act together comparing two entire 8-bit words and outputting the result from the high-order comparator outputs.

    For proper operation, the expansion inputs to the low-order comparator should be *tied* as follows: $I_A > B$ = LOW, $I_A = B$ = HIGH, $I_A < B$ = LOW. Expansion to greater than 8 bits using multiple 7485s is also possible. Figure 10.39 shows the connections for magnitude comparison of two 8-bit binary strings. *If the high-order A inputs are equal to the high-order B inputs, then the expansion inputs are used as a tie breaker.*

## ERROR DETECTORS

Errors can be detected by checking the *parity* of a computer word or of subsets of bits of the word. *Even parity* is an even number of 1's. *Odd parity* is an odd number of 1's. *Parity generators* add one or more bits to make the parity of the extended word either even or odd as desired.

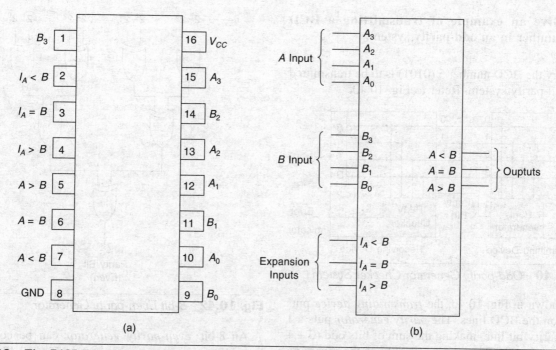

**Fig. 10.38**    *The 7485 Four-bit Magnitude Comparator: (a) Pin Configuration, (b) Logic Symbols.*

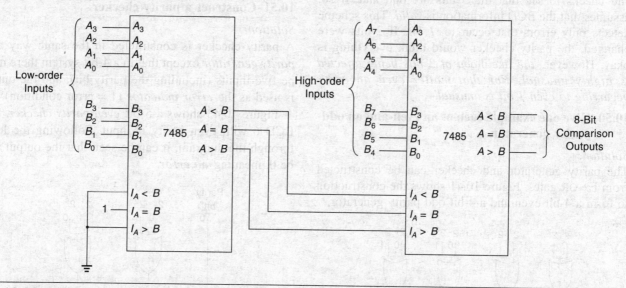

**Fig. 10.39**    *Magnitude Comparison of Two 8-bit Binary Strings (or Binary Words).*

### 10.48 Describe a simple parity generator/checker system.

*Solution:*

Parity systems are defined as either *odd parity* or *even parity*. The parity system adds an *extra bit* to the digital information being transmitted. A 4-bit system will require a fifth bit, an 8-bit system will require a ninth bit, and so on.

In a 4-bit system such as BCD or hexadecimal, the fifth bit is the *parity bit* and will be a 1 or 0, depending on what the other 4-bits are. In an *odd-parity system*, the parity bit that is added must make the sum of all 5-bits odd. In an *even-parity system*, the parity bit makes the sum of all 5 bits even.

The *parity generator* is the circuit that creates the parity bit. On the receiving end, a *parity checker* determines if the 5-bit result is of the right parity. The type of system (odd or even) must be decided before hand so that the parity checker knows what to look for (this is called *protocol*). Also, the parity bit can be placed next to the MSB or LSB as long as the device on the receiving end knows which bit is *parity* and which bit is *data*.

### 10.49 Give an example of transmitting a BCD number in an odd-parity system.

*Solution:*

Let us say the BCD number 5 (0101) is to be transmitted in an odd-parity system. Refer to Fig. 10.40.

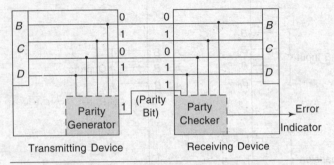

**Fig. 10.40** *Odd-parity Generator/Checker System.*

As shown in Fig. 10.40, the *transmitting device* puts a 0101 on the BCD lines. The *parity generator* puts a 1 on the parity-bit line, making the sum of bits odd (0 + 1 + 0 + 1 + 1 = 3). The *parity checker* at the receiving end checks to see that the 5 bits are odd and, if so, assumes that the BCD information is *valid*. This scheme detects only errors that occur to *1 bit*. If 2-bits were changed, the parity checker would think everything is okay. However, *the likelihood of 2 bits being affected is highly unusual. For that matter even an error occurring to even 1 bit is unusual.*

### 10.50 Give one example each of an even-and an odd-parity generator.

*Solution:*

The parity generator and checker can be constructed from Ex-OR gates. Figure 10.41 shows the construction to form a 4-bit even and a 4-bit odd parity generator.

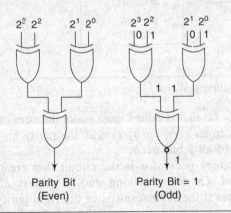

**Fig. 10.41** *Even-and Odd-parity Generators.*

The *odd-parity generator* has the BCD number 5 (0101) at its inputs. If you follow the logic through with these bits, you will see that the parity bit will be a 1, just what is required. Computer systems generally transmit 8 or 16 bits of parallel data at a time.

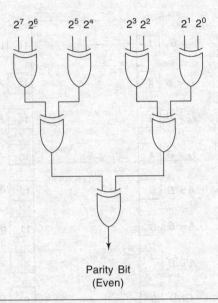

**Fig. 10.42** *8-bit Even-parity Generator.*

An 8-bit *even-parity generator* can be constructed by adding more gates, as shown in Fig. 10.42.

### 10.51 Construct a parity checker.

*Solution:*

A parity checker is constructed in the same way as a *parity generator* except that in a 4-bit system there must be five inputs (including the parity bit), and the output is used as the *error indicator* (1 = error condition).

Figure 10.43 shows a 5-bit *even-parity checker*. The BCD 6 with even parity is input. Following the logic through the diagram, it can be seen that the output will be 0, meaning *no error*.

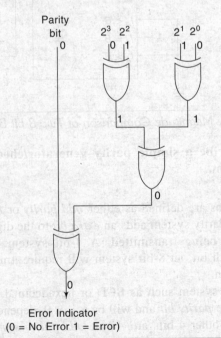

**Fig. 10.43** *Five-Bit Even-parity Checker.*

# SUMMARY

■■■■■■■

- ➤ When adding you must take care of the carries.
- ➤ When subtracting you must take care of the borrows.
- ➤ A half-adder is a basic adder circuit. By itself it cannot perform addition of numbers of more than 1 bit.
- ➤ Full-adders may be constructed from two half-adders and an OR gate.
- ➤ Multiplication can be performed as repeated addition.
- ➤ Division can be performed as repeated subtraction.
- ➤ The ALU is the number crunching part of the computer. It provides several different arithmetic and logic operations.
- ➤ The equality comparison is the easiest to implement.
- ➤ Inequality comparisons are more difficult and can be implemented either in series or in parallel.
- ➤ Errors can be detected by checking the parity of a computer word or of subsets of bits of the word.
- ➤ The parity generator is the circuit that creates the parity bit.

■■■■■■■

# REVIEW QUESTIONS

**Test your understanding**

1. Binary addition in the least significant column deals with how many inputs and how many outputs?
2. Which bit in an 8-bit two's complement number is used as the sign bit?
3. Are the following two's-complement numbers positive or negative?
   (a) 1010 0011      (b) 0010 1101
   (c) 1000 0000
4. Which of the following decimal numbers cannot be converted to 8-bit two's-complement notation?
   (a) 89            (b) 135            (c) –107            (d) –144
5. Why is hexadecimal commonly used when working with 8-, 16-, and 32-bit computer systems?
6. What procedure is used to correct the result of a BCD addition if the sum is greater than 9.
7. Name the inputs and outputs of a half-adder.
8. Why are the input requirements of a full-adder different from those of a half-adder?
9. What input conditions to a full-adder produce a 1 at the carry-out ($C_{out}$)?
10. All the adders in the 7483 4-bit adders are full-adders. What is done with the carry-in ($C_{in}$) to make the first adder act like a half-adder?
11. What is the purpose of the fast-look-ahead carry in the 7483 IC?
12. How many inputs does a full-adder have? How many outputs?
13. For what input conditions is the $\Sigma_0$ bit HIGH?
14. For what input conditions is the $C_{out}$ bit HIGH?
15. For what input conditions is the sum output ($\Sigma_1$) HIGH?
16. What input conditions produce a HIGH at $C_{out}$?
17. What is the purpose of the AND and OR gates in the BCD adder circuit of Fig. 10.23?
18. The complementing switch in Fig. 10.29 is placed in the 1 position to subtract $B$ from $A$. Explain how this position converts the binary number on the $B$ inputs into a signed two's-complement number.
19. What is the purpose of the mode control input to the 7481 arithmetic/logic unit?
20. If all the inputs to a 7485 comparator are LOW except for the $I_A < B$ input, what will the output be?
21. How can you tell when a correction is needed in BCD addition?
22. What are the three basic parts of a BCD adder circuit?
23. Describe how the BCD adder circuit detects the need for a correction and executes it.
24. Draw the block diagram of a half-subtractor. Label inputs and outputs.
25. Draw a truth table for a half subtractor.
26. Draw the block diagram of a full subtractor. Label inputs and outputs.
27. Draw the truth table for a full subtractor.
28. Calculate the sum of the 2's complement numbers 1110 and 1101. Give the answer in 2's complement and in decimal.

29. Calculate the sum of the 2's complement numbers 0110 and 1100. Give the answer in 2's complement and in decimal.
30. Using odd parity, what bit would be transmitted with the 7-bit ASCII code 1011000 as a parity bit.

# SUPPLEMENTARY PROBLEMS

**Test your understanding**

31. Explain a 4-bit parallel adder.
32. Explain the working of a carry anticipation circuit.
33. Illustrate and explain a 4-bit parallel binary subtractor.
34. Realise a full-subtractor using NAND gates only.
35. Draw a 6-bit binary adder using two 7483 4-bit adders.
36. Draw a 16-bit binary adder using four 4008 CMOS 4-bit adders.
37. Draw the block diagram of a 4-bit sequential multiplier and explain.
38. Design a BCD adder stage to provide decimal adjustment.
39. Draw the block diagram of a bit-parallel, digit-serial BCD adder and explain.
40. Design a 3-bit ripple comparator implementing $X_2 X_1 X_0 > Y_2 Y_1 Y_0$.
41. Design a parallel binary comparator that compares the 4-bit binary string $A$ to the 4-bit binary string $B$. If the strings are exactly equal, provide a HIGH-level output to drive a warning buzzer.
42. Draw the logic symbol and function table for the 74280 9-bit parity generator/checker.
43. Illustrate a two's-complement subtractor using parallel addition to perform subtraction.
44. Show a serial adder constructed from a full adder and an *RS* flip-flop with inputs 0011 and 0001.
45. Illustrate a parity generator/checker system used in an 8-bit, even-parity computer configuration.

# OBJECTIVE TYPE QUESTIONS

**Test your understanding**

## *Fill in the Blanks*

46. When adding two hex digits, if the sum is greater than _____ (9, 15, 16), the result will be a two-digit answer.
47. When subtracting hex digits, if the least significant digit borrows from its left, its value increases by _____ (10, 16).
48. When adding two BCD digits, the sum is invalid and needs correction, if it is _____ or if _____.
49. The half-adder is a _____ adder circuit.
50. The half-adder sums the inputs _____.
51. While a half-adder performs the basic binary addition, it cannot by itself perform the addition of numbers of more than _____.
52. The sum output ($\Sigma$) of a full-adder is 1 if the sum of its three inputs is _____ (odd, even).
53. Adders are formed from basic _____.
54. MSI adder circuits have _____ adders within a _____ integrated package.
55. We can use an _____ generator to generate $\Sigma_1$ output bit.
56. When drawing multibit adders, a _____ is used to represent the addition in each column.
57. The carry-out ($C_{out}$) from each full-adder is _____ connected to the carry-in ($C_{in}$) of the next full-adder.
58. The time taken for the output to change as a result of a change in an input signal is termed the _____.
59. Logical depth is the maximum number of _____ through which the signal will pass between the input and output.
60. An 8-bit adder cannot handle _____ numbers.
61. The parallel adder performs addition at a relatively high _____.
62. The serial adder adds _____ at a time.
63. The sum and carry outputs of any stage cannot be produced until the _____ occurs.
64. The input carry to the least significant stage has to _____ all of the adders before a final sum is produced.

65. One method of _____ the addition process is called look-ahead-carry addition.
66. In a binary subtractor we have a _____ and _____ outputs rather than the sum and carry.
67. When the INVERT is LOW, in a controlled inverter, it _____ the input to the output.
68. When the INVERT is HIGH, in a controlled inverter, it transmits the _____.
69. The basic comparator circuit can be _____ to any number of bits.
70. A magnitude comparator not only determines if *A* equals *B*, but also if *A* _____ *B* or if *A* is _____ *B*.
71. Parallel adders are _____ (combinational, sequential) logic circuits.
72. The 7483 IC contains a 4-bit binary _____.
73. Two 7483 ICs can be _____ to form an 8-bit parallel binary adder.
74. An adder such as the 7483 IC does not have a memory device, such as a latch, built into the IC and is classified as a _____ (combinational, sequential) logic device.
75. The _____ (74LS32, 74LS181) is a more complex IC that performs many of the same operations (such as add, subtract, shift, compare, AND, OR, etc.) as the ALU of a microprocessor or microcontroller.
76. A widely used technique for multiplying using digital circuits is the _____ method.
77. Most elementary 8-bit microprocessors _____ (do, do not) have a multiply instruction.
78. When microprocessors process both positive and negative numbers, _____ representations are used.
79. The 2's complement number 0111 represents _____ in binary and _____ in decimal.
80. The 2's complement number 1111 represents _____ in decimal.
81. In 2's complement representation, the MSB is the _____ bit. If the MSB is 0 the number is _____ (negative, positive) whereas if the MSB is 1, the number is _____ (negative, positive).
82. The decimal number –6 equals _____ in 2's complement 4-bit representation.
83. The decimal number +5 equals _____ in 2's complement 4-bit representation.
84. Decimal 90 equals _____ in binary and _____ in 2's complement.
85. Decimal –90 equals _____ in 2's complement.
86. Adding 0111 1111 (2's c) and 1111 0000 (2's c) yields _____ in 2's complement or _____ in decimal.
87. Adding 1000 0000 (2's c) and 0000 1111 (2's c) yields _____ in 2's complement or _____ in decimal.
88. Subtracting 0001 0000 (2's c) from 1110 0000 (2's c) yields _____ in 2's complement or _____ in decimal.
89. Subtracting 1111 1111 (2's c) from 0011 0000 (2's c) yields _____ in 2's complement or _____ in decimal.
90. The ALU carries out arithmetic and _____ operations (OR, AND, NOT, etc). It processes _____ numbers rather than decimal numbers.
91. A half adder adds _____ bits. A full adder adds _____ bits, producing a SUM and a _____.
92. A binary adder is a logic circuit that can add _____ binary numbers at a time. The 7483 is a TTL binary adder. It can add two _____ binary numbers.
93. With signed binary numbers, also known as sign-magnitude numbers, the leading bit stands for the _____ and the remaining bits for the _____.
94. Signed binary numbers require too much hardware. This has led to the use of _____ complements to represent negative numbers. To get the 2's complement of binary number, you first take the _____ complement, then add _____.
95. If you take the 2's complement twice, you get the original binary number back because of this property, taking the _____ complement of a binary number is equivalent to changing the _____ of a decimal number.
96. In a microcomputer positive numbers are represented in _____ form and negative numbers in 2's complement form. The leading bit still represents the _____.
97. The maximum positive number in an N-bit system is equal to _____, and the maximum negative number is _____ where N is the number of bits including the sign-bit (2's complement form).

## True/False Questions

State whether the following statements are True or False.

98. In binary subtraction, the borrow-out of the least significant column becomes the borrow-in of the next more significant column.

99. Binary multiplication and division are performed by a series of additions and subtractions.
100. The procedure for subtracting numbers in two's complement notation is exactly the same as for adding numbers.
101. When subtracting a smaller number from a larger number in two's complement, there will always be a carry-out of the MSB, which will be ignored.
102. If $M = H$ and $S_3, S_2, S_1, S_0 = L, L, H, H$ on the 74181 then $F_3, F_2, F_1, F_0$ will be set to $L, L, L, L$.
103. More than one output of the 7485 comparator can be simultaneously HIGH.
104. Whenever the sum of two signed binary numbers has a sign bit of 1, the magnitude of the sum is in 2's-complement form.
105. When the adder/subtractor circuit is used for subtraction, the 2's complement of the subtrahend appears at the input of the adder.
106. The 4-bit subtractor based on 1's complement end-around-carry is an impractical circuit because of inaccuracy.
107. Signed binary numbers require too less hardware.

## Multiple Choice Questions

108. Which of the following is known as a half adder:
    (a) XOR gate
    (b) XNOR gate
    (c) NAND gate
    (d) NOR gate
109. The logic network shown in Fig. 10.44 is a
    (a) half adder
    (b) half subtractor
    (c) full adder
    (d) full subtractor

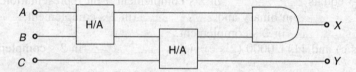

**Fig. 10.44**

110. For the logic network shown in Fig. 10.44, the outputs $X$ and $Y$ are given by
    (a) $X = (AB + AB)C$
        $Y = (B \oplus C)A + BC$
    (b) $X = (A \oplus B)C + AB$
        $Y = A \oplus B \oplus C$
    (c) $X = AB + BC + AC$
        $Y = (A \oplus B)C$
    (d) none of these
111. In digital systems subtraction is performed by using
    (a) half adders        (b) half subtractors
    (c) adders with 1's complement representation of negative numbers
    (d) none of the above
112. The difference bit output of a half subtractor is the same as
    (a) difference bit output of a full subtractor
    (b) sum bit output of a half adder
    (c) sum bit output of a full adder
    (d) carry bit output of a half adder
113. How many inputs and outputs does a full adder have?
    (a) two inputs; two outputs
    (b) two inputs; one output
    (c) three inputs; two outputs
    (d) two inputs; three outputs
114. How many inputs and outputs does a full subtractor have?
    (a) two inputs; one output
    (b) two inputs; two outputs
    (c) two inputs; three outputs
    (d) three inputs; two outputs
115. A full adder can be realised using
    (a) one half adder, two OR gates
    (b) two half adders, one OR gate
    (c) two half adders, two OR gates
    (d) none of these
116. For checking the parity of a digital word, it is preferable to use
    (a) AND gates
    (b) NAND gates
    (c) EX-OR gates
    (d) NOR gates

117. The most suitable gates to check whether the number of ones in a digital word is even or odd is
     (a) Ex-OR
     (b) NAND
     (c) NOR
     (d) AND, OR and NOT
118. In BCD addition, 0110 is required to be added to the sum for getting the correct result, if
     (a) the sum of two BCD numbers is not a valid BCD number
     (b) the sum of the two BCD numbers is not a valid BCD number or a carry is produced
     (c) a carry is produced
     (d) none of the above is true
119. BCD subtraction is performed by using
     (a) 1's complement representation
     (b) 2's complement representation
     (c) 5's complement representation
     (d) 9's complement representation
120. The ALU is used to perform
     (a) only logic operations
     (b) only arithmetic operations
     (c) arithmetic and logic operations
     (d) control operations

# ANSWERS

1. 2 inputs, 2 outputs
2. $D_7$
3. (a) negative,       (b) positive,       (c) negative
4. *b, d*
5. Because it simplifies the documentation and use of equipment
6. Add 6 (0110)
7. Inputs: $A_0$, $B_0$; Outputs: $\Sigma_0$, $C_{out}$
8. Because it needs a carry-in from the previous adder.
9. When any two of the inputs are HIGH
10. Connect it to zero
11. To speed up the arithmetic process
12. three; two
13. *A* OR *B* HIGH, but not both
14. *A* AND *B* HIGH
15. The $\Sigma_1$ bit is HIGH whenever the three inputs ($A_1$, $B_1$, $C_{in}$) are odd.
16. $C_{out}$ is HIGH whenever any two of the inputs are HIGH
17. They check for a sum greater than 9 to provide a $C_{out}$
18. It provides a $C_{in}$, and it puts a 1 on the inputs of the XOR gates which inverts *B*.
19. It sets the mode of operation for either arithmetic or logic.
20. $A < B = 1$
21. The sum of at least one decimal digit position is greater than 1001(9)
22. Two 4-bit adders and correction logic
23. The correction logic detects a sum greater than 9 and then causes a 0110 to be added to the sum.
24.                                           25.

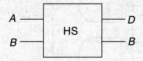

| A | B | D | B |
|---|---|---|---|
| 0 | 0 | 0 | 0 |
| 0 | 1 | 1 | 1 |
| 1 | 0 | 1 | 0 |
| 1 | 1 | 0 | 0 |

26.

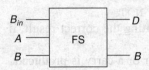

27.

| A | B | $B_{in}$ | D | B |
|---|---|---|---|---|
| 0 | 0 | 0 | 0 | 0 |
| 0 | 0 | 1 | 1 | 1 |
| 0 | 1 | 0 | 1 | 1 |
| 0 | 1 | 1 | 0 | 1 |
| 1 | 0 | 0 | 1 | 0 |
| 1 | 0 | 1 | 0 | 0 |
| 1 | 1 | 0 | 0 | 0 |
| 1 | 1 | 1 | 1 | 1 |

28.  1011, –5         29.  0010, +2         30.  0

31.

$$
\begin{array}{ll}
0101 & X_3 X_2 X_1 X_0 \\
0111 & Y_3 Y_2 Y_1 Y_0 \\
\hline
1100 & S_3 S_2 S_1 S_0
\end{array}
$$

33.

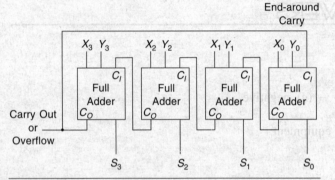

**Fig. 10.45**   *4-bit Parallel Adder.*

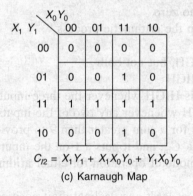

**Fig. 10.47**   *4-bit Parallel Binary Subtractor.*

32.

$$
\begin{array}{ll}
 & C_{I2} \\
\phantom{+}X_3\,X_2\,X_1\,X_0 & \text{Addend} \\
+\,Y_3\,Y_2\,Y_1\,Y_0 & \text{Augend} \\
\hline
\phantom{+}S_3\,S_2\,S_1\,S_0 & \text{Sum}
\end{array}
$$

(a) Addition with Look-ahead Carry

| Inputs | | | | Output |
|---|---|---|---|---|
| $X_1$ | $Y_1$ | $X_0$ | $Y_0$ | $C_{I2}$ |
| 0 | 0 | 0 | 0 | 0 |
| 0 | 0 | 0 | 1 | 0 |
| 0 | 0 | 1 | 0 | 0 |
| 0 | 0 | 1 | 1 | 0 |
| 0 | 1 | 0 | 0 | 0 |
| 0 | 1 | 0 | 1 | 0 |
| 0 | 1 | 1 | 0 | 0 |
| 0 | 1 | 1 | 1 | 1 |
| 1 | 0 | 0 | 0 | 0 |
| 1 | 0 | 0 | 1 | 0 |
| 1 | 0 | 1 | 0 | 0 |
| 1 | 0 | 1 | 1 | 1 |
| 1 | 1 | 0 | 0 | 1 |
| 1 | 1 | 0 | 1 | 1 |
| 1 | 1 | 1 | 0 | 1 |
| 1 | 1 | 1 | 1 | 1 |

(b) Truth Table for Anticipated Carry in $C_{I2}$

Karnaugh Map:

| $X_1 Y_1$ \ $X_0 Y_0$ | 00 | 01 | 11 | 10 |
|---|---|---|---|---|
| 00 | 0 | 0 | 0 | 0 |
| 01 | 0 | 0 | 1 | 0 |
| 11 | 1 | 1 | 1 | 1 |
| 10 | 0 | 0 | 1 | 0 |

$C_{I2} = X_1 Y_1 + X_1 X_0 Y_0 + Y_1 X_0 Y_0$

(c) Karnaugh Map

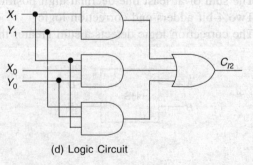

(d) Logic Circuit

**Fig. 10.46**   *Carry Anticipation Circuit.*

34.

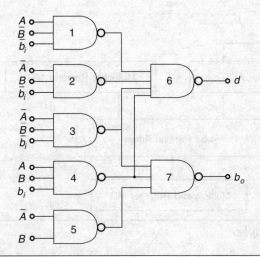

**Fig. 10.48** *Full-subtractor using NAND Gates Only.*

35.

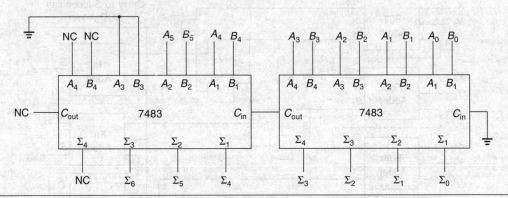

**Fig. 10.49** *Six-bit Binary Adder using Two 7483 4-bit Adders.*

36.

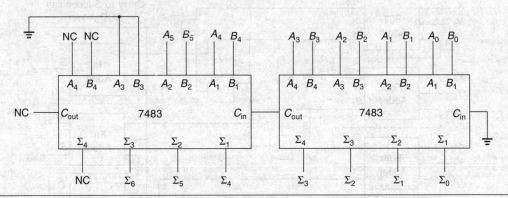

**Fig. 10.50** *Sixteen-bit Binary Adder using Four 4008 CMOS 4-bit Adders.*

37.

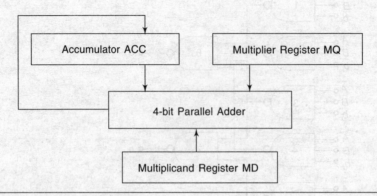

**Fig. 10.51** *4-bit Sequential Multiplier.*

38.

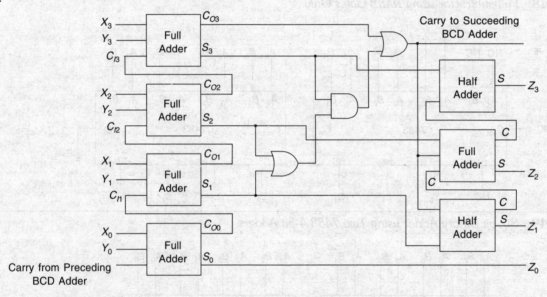

**Fig. 10.52** *BCD Adder Stage to Provide Decimal Adjustment.*

39.

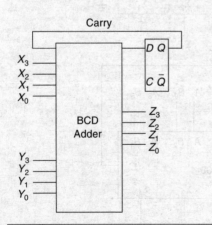

**Fig. 10.53** *Bit-parallel, Digit-serial BCD Adder.*

40.

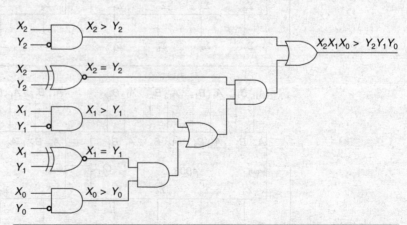

**Fig. 10.54** *Three-bit Ripple Comparator Implementing $X_2X_1X_0 > Y_2Y_1Y_0$.*

41.

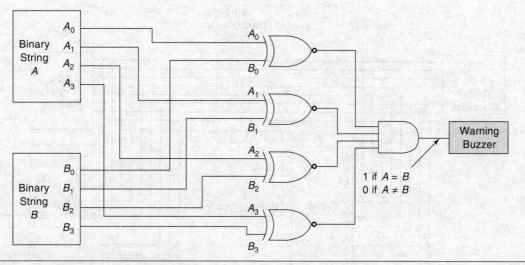

**Fig. 10.55** *Parallel Binary Comparator.*

42.

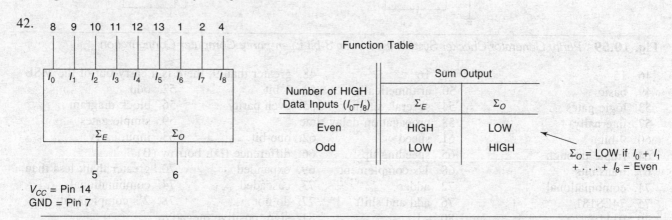

| Function Table | | |
|---|---|---|
| | Sum Output | |
| Number of HIGH Data Inputs ($I_0$–$I_8$) | $\Sigma_E$ | $\Sigma_O$ |
| Even | HIGH | LOW |
| Odd | LOW | HIGH |

$\Sigma_O$ = LOW if $I_0 + I_1$ + . . . + $I_8$ = Even

$V_{CC}$ = Pin 14
GND = Pin 7

**Fig. 10.56** *Logic Symbol and Function Table for the 74280 9-bit Odd/Even Parity Generator/Checker.*

43.

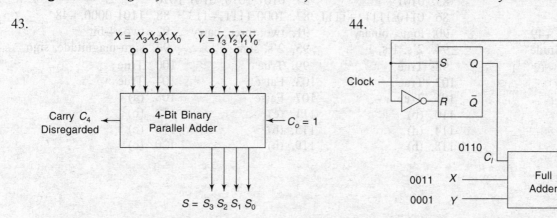

**Fig. 10.57** *Two's Complement Subtractor using Parallel Addition to Perform Subtraction.*

44.

**Fig. 10.58** *Serial Adder.*

45.

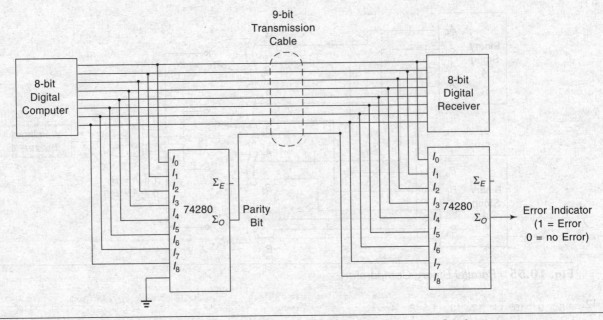

**Fig. 10.59**    *Parity Generator/Checker System used in an 8-bit Even-parity Computer Configuration.*

| | | | |
|---|---|---|---|
| 46. 15 | 47. 16 | 48. greater than 9; there is a carry-out of the MSB | |
| 49. basic | 50. arithmetically | 51. 1 bit | 52. odd |
| 53. logic gates | 54. several; single | 55. even parity | 56. block diagram |
| 57. internally | 58. propagation delay time | | 59. simple gates |
| 60. 9-bit | 61. speed | 62. one-bit | 63. input carry |
| 64. ripple through | 65. speeding up | 66. difference (D); borrow (B) | |
| 67. transmits | 68. 1's complement | 69. expanded | 70. greater than; less than |
| 71. combinational | 72. adder | 73. cascaded | 74. combinational |
| 75. 74LS181 | 76. add and shift | 77. do not | 78. 2's complement |
| 79. 0111; +7 | 80. −1 | 81. sign, positive, negative | |
| 82. 1010 | 83. 0101 | 84. 0101 1010, 0101 1010 | |
| 85. 1010 0110 | 86. 0110 1111, +1111 | 87. 1000 1111, −113 | 88. 1101 0000, −48 |
| 89. 0011 0001, +49 | 90. logic, binary | 91. two, three, carry | 92. two, 4-bit |
| 93. sign, magnitude | 94. 2's, 1's, 1 | 95. 2's, sign | 96. sign-magnitude, sign |
| 97. $(2^{N-1} - 1), - (2^{N-1})$ | 98. True | 99. True | 100. True |
| 101. True | 102. True | 103. False | 104. True |
| 105. False | 106. True | 107. False | 108. (a) |
| 109. (c) | 110. (b) | 111. (c) | 112. (b) |
| 113. (c) | 114. (d) | 115. (b) | 116. (c) |
| 117. (a) | 118. (b) | 119. (b) | 120. (c) |

Chapter

# 11

# Combinational Logic Circuits

## INTRODUCTION

The purpose of Boolean function *simplification* is to obtain an algebraic expression that, when implemented, results in a *low-cost circuit*. However, the criteria that determines a low-cost circuit or system must be defined if we are to evaluate the success of the achieved simplification. The design procedure of combinational circuits *minimises* the number of gates required to implement a given function. This *classical procedure* assumes that, given two circuits that perform the same function, the one that requires *fewer gates* is preferable because it will cost less. This is not necessarily true when integrated circuits are used.

Since several IC gates are used in a single IC package, it becomes economical *to use as many of the gates from an already used package, even if by doing so, we increase the total number of gates.* Moreover, some of the *interconnections* among gates in many ICs are *internal* to the chip and it is more economical to use as many internal interconnections as possible in order to *minimise* the number of wires between *external pins*. With integrated circuits it is not the count of gates that determines the cost but the number and type of ICs employed and the number of external interconnections needed to implement the given functions.

The first question that must be answered before going through a detailed design of a combinational circuit is whether the function is already available in an *IC package*. Numerous *MSI devices* are available commercially. These devices perform *specific* digital functions commonly employed in the design of digital computer system. If an MSI device cannot be found to produce *exactly* the function needed, a resourceful

designer may be able to formulate a method so as to incorporate an MSI device in his circuit. The selection of MSI components in preference to *SSI gates* is extremely important, since it would invariably result in a considerable reduction of IC packages and interconnecting wires.

## LOGIC NETWORKS

Logic functions can be performed with essentially two types of *logic circuits or networks*. These approaches are: *Combinational Logic*: A network of several gates that are connected to generate a specific output *with no storage involved*. This type of network *combines* the input variables in such a way that the output is always dependent on the combination of inputs. A combinational lock with several dials, (Fig. 11.1a), which is often used in bicycles, is an example of combinational logic.

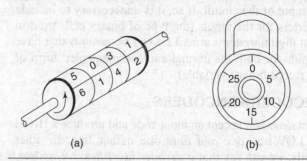

**Fig. 11.1** *Examples of Locks with Combinational Logic (a) and Sequential Logic (b).*

*Sequential Logic:* Logic operations with this type of network occur in a definite *sequence*, providing the ability to store or delay signals. A combination lock with just one dial that must be turned to several numbers in sequence (Fig. 11.1b) is an example of sequential logic.

### 11.1 Draw the block diagram of a combinational circuit and explain.

*Solution:*

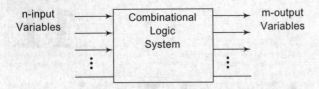

**Fig. 11.2**  *Block Diagram of a Combinational Circuit.*

A block diagram of a combinational circuit is shown in Fig. 11.2. Then *input variables* come from an external *source;* the *m-output variables* go to an external *destination.* In many applications the source and/or destination are *storage registers* located either in the vicinity of the combinational circuit or in a remote external device. By definition, an external register does not influence the behavior of the combinational circuit because, if it does, the total system becomes a sequential circuit.

For *n*-input variables, there are $2^n$-*possible combinations* of binary input values. For each possible input combination, there is *one and only one* possible output combination. A combinational circuit can be described by *m* Boolean functions, one for each output variable. Each output function is expressed in terms of the *n* input variables.

Each input variable to a combinational circuit may have one or two wires. When only one wire is available, it may represent the variable either in the uncomplemented (*normal*) form or complemented (*inverted*) form. It is necessary to provide an inverter for each literal not available in the input wire. On the other hand, an input variable may appear in two wires, supplying both the normal and complemented forms to the input of the circuit. If so, it is unnecessary to include inverters for the inputs (the type of binary cells used in most digital systems are `flip-flop` *circuits* that have outputs for both the normal and complemented form of the stored binary variable).

## DECODERS/ENCODERS

Most *decoders* accept an input code and produce a HIGH (or LOW) at *one and only* one output line. In other words, we can say that *a decoder identifies, recognises, or detects a particular code.* The opposite of this decoding process is called encoding and is performed by a logic circuit called an *encoder.* An encoder has a number of inputs lines, only one of which is activated at a given time and produces an output code, depending on which input is activated.

### 11.2 Describe the working of the basic binary decoder.

*Solution:*
The basic function of a decoder is to *detect* the presence of a specified combination of bits (code) on its inputs and to indicate that presence by a *specified output level.* In its general form, a decoder has *n* input lines to handle *n* bits from 1 to $2^n$ output lines to indicate the presence of one or more *n*-bit combinations.

Suppose we wish to determine when a binary 1001 occurs on the inputs of a digital circuit. *An* AND *gate can be used as the basic decoding element because it produces a HIGH output only when all of its inputs are HIGH.* Therefore, we must ensure that all of the inputs to the AND gate are HIGH when the binary number $1001_2$ occurs. This can be done by *inverting* the two middle bits (0's), as shown in Fig. 11.3.

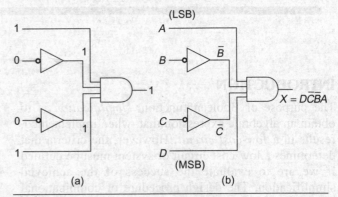

**Fig. 11.3**  *Decoding Logic for $1001_2$ with an Active-HIGH Output.*

The logic equation for the decoder of Fig. 11.3(a) is developed as illustrated in Fig. 11.3(b). The output function is zero except when $A = 1$, $B = 0$, $C = 0$, and $D = 1$ are applied to the inputs. *A* is the *LSB* and *D* is the *MSB.* In the representation of a binary number or other weighted code, the LSB is always the right most bit in a *horizontal arrangement,* and the top-most bit in a *vertical arrangement,* unless specified otherwise.

If a NAND *gate* is used in place of the AND gate, as shown in Fig. 11.4, a LOW output will indicate the presence of the proper binary code.

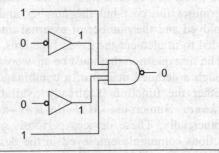

**Fig. 11.4**  *Decoding Logic for $1001_2$ with an Active-LOW Output.*

**11.3 Determine the logic required to decode the binary number $1011_2$ by producing a HIGH indication on the output.**

*Solution:*

The *decoding function can be formed by complementing only the variables that appear as 0 in the binary number* as follows:

$$X = D\,\bar{C}\,BA$$

This function can be implemented by connecting the true (uncomplemented) variables *directly* to the input of an AND gate, and *inverting* the variable $C$ before applying it to the AND gate input. The decoding logic is shown in Fig. 11.5.

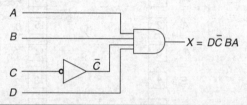

**Fig. 11.5** *Decoding Logic for Producing a HIGH Output when $1011_2$ is on the Inputs.*

**11.4 Design a system that reads a four-bit BCD code and converts it to its appropriate decimal number by turning 'on' a decimal indicating lamp.**

*Solution:*

Figure 11.6 illustrates such a system. This decoder is made up of a *combination* of logic gates that produces a HIGH at one of the 10 outputs, based on the levels at the four inputs.

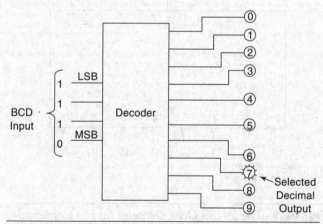

**Fig. 11.6** *A BCD Decoder Selects the Correct Decimal-Indicating Lamp Based on the BCD Input.*

**11.5 Design a three-bit binary-to-octal decoder.**

*Solution:*

To design a decoder, it is useful first to make a *truth table* of all possible input/output combinations. An octal decoder must provide eight outputs, one for each of the eight different combinations of inputs shown in Table 11.1.

**Table 11.1**   *Truth Tables for an Octal Decoder.*

| (a) Active-HIGH Outputs | | | | | | | | | | |
|---|---|---|---|---|---|---|---|---|---|---|
| Input | | | Output | | | | | | | |
| $2^2$ | $2^1$ | $2^0$ | 0 | 1 | 2 | 3 | 4 | 5 | 6 | 7 |
| 0 | 0 | 0 | 1 | 0 | 0 | 0 | 0 | 0 | 0 | 0 |
| 0 | 0 | 1 | 0 | 1 | 0 | 0 | 0 | 0 | 0 | 0 |
| 0 | 1 | 0 | 0 | 0 | 1 | 0 | 0 | 0 | 0 | 0 |
| 0 | 1 | 1 | 0 | 0 | 0 | 1 | 0 | 0 | 0 | 0 |
| 1 | 0 | 0 | 0 | 0 | 0 | 0 | 1 | 0 | 0 | 0 |
| 1 | 0 | 1 | 0 | 0 | 0 | 0 | 0 | 1 | 0 | 0 |
| 1 | 1 | 0 | 0 | 0 | 0 | 0 | 0 | 0 | 1 | 0 |
| 1 | 1 | 1 | 0 | 0 | 0 | 0 | 0 | 0 | 0 | 1 |

| (b) Active-LOW Outputs | | | | | | | | | | |
|---|---|---|---|---|---|---|---|---|---|---|
| Input | | | Output | | | | | | | |
| $2^2$ | $2^1$ | $2^0$ | 0 | 1 | 2 | 3 | 4 | 5 | 6 | 7 |
| 0 | 0 | 0 | 0 | 1 | 1 | 1 | 1 | 1 | 1 | 1 |
| 0 | 0 | 1 | 1 | 0 | 1 | 1 | 1 | 1 | 1 | 1 |
| 0 | 1 | 0 | 1 | 1 | 0 | 1 | 1 | 1 | 1 | 1 |
| 0 | 1 | 1 | 1 | 1 | 1 | 0 | 1 | 1 | 1 | 1 |
| 1 | 0 | 0 | 1 | 1 | 1 | 1 | 0 | 1 | 1 | 1 |
| 1 | 0 | 1 | 1 | 1 | 1 | 1 | 1 | 0 | 1 | 1 |
| 1 | 1 | 0 | 1 | 1 | 1 | 1 | 1 | 1 | 0 | 1 |
| 1 | 1 | 1 | 1 | 1 | 1 | 1 | 1 | 1 | 1 | 0 |

Before the design is made, we must decide if we want an *active-HIGH-level output* or an *active-LOW-level output* to indicate the value selected. For example, the *active-HIGH* truth table in Table 11.1(a) shows us that, for input 011(3), output 3 is HIGH, and all other outputs are LOW. The *active-LOW* output is just the opposite (output 3 is LOW, all other outputs are HIGH).

Therefore, we have to know whether the indicating lamp (or other receiving device) requires a HIGH level to activate or a LOW level. *Most of the devices used in digital electronics are designed to activate from a LOW-level signal, so most decoder designers use active-LOW outputs*, as shown in Table 11.1(b). The combinational logic requirements to produce a LOW at output 3 for an input of 011 are shown in Fig. 11.7.

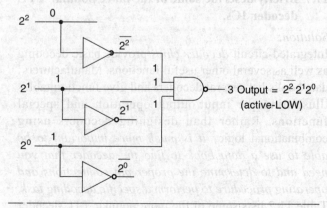

**Fig. 11.7** *Logic Requirements to Produce a LOW at Output 3 for a 011 Input.*

### 11.6 Design a complete *octal decoder*.

*Solution:*

To design the complete octal decoder, we need a separate NAND gate for each of the eight outputs. The input connections for each of the NAND gates can be determined by referring to Table 11.1(b).

For example, the NAND gate five inputs are connected to the $2^2$ _ $\bar{2}^1$ _ $2^0$ inputs lines. NAND gate 6 is connected to the $2^2$ _ $2^1$ _ $\bar{2}^0$ inputs lines and so on. The complete circuit is shown in Fig. 11.8. Each NAND gate in Fig. 11.8 is wired so that its output goes LOW when the *correct combination* of input levels is present at its input. BCD and hexadecimal decoders can be designed in a similar manner.

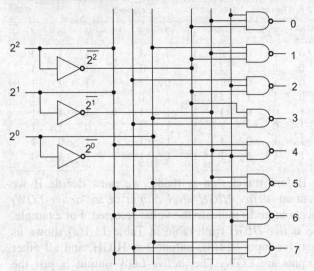

**Fig. 11.8** *Complete Circuit for an Active-LOW Output Octal (1-of-8) Decoder.*

The octal decoder is sometimes referred to as *1-of-8 decoder* because, based on the input code, one of the eight outputs will be active. It is also known as a *3-line-to-8-line-decoder,* because it has three input lines and eight output lines.

### 11.7 Briefly describe some of the more popular TTL decoder ICs.

*Solution:*

Integrated-circuit *decoder chips* provide basic decoding as well as several other useful functions. Manufacturers' data books list several decoders and give function tables illustrating the input/output operation and special functions. Rather than designing decoders using combinational logic, *it is much more important to be able to use a data book to find the decoder that you need and to determine the proper pin connections and operating procedure to perform a specific decoding task.* Table 11.2 lists some of the more popular TTL decoder ICs. Equivalent CMOS ICs are also available.

**Table 11.2** *Decoder ICs*

| Device Number | Function |
|---|---|
| 74138 | 1-of-8 octal decoder (3-line-to-8-line) |
| 7442 | 1-of-10 BCD decoder (4-line-to-10-line) |
| 74154 | 1-to-16 hex decoder (4-line-to-16-line) |
| 7447 | BCD-to-seven-segment decoder |

### 11.8 Give the (a) pin configuration and (b) logic symbol of octal decoder IC 74138. Explain briefly.

*Solution:*

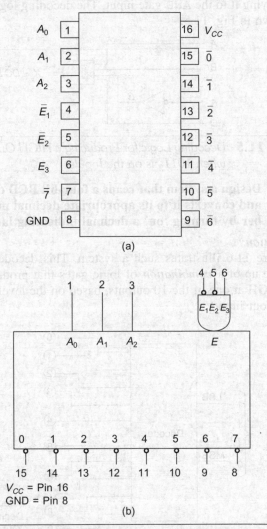

**Fig. 11.9** *The 74138 Octal Decoder (a) Pin Configuration and (b) Logic Symbol.*

The 74138 is an octal decoder capable of decoding the eight possible codes into eight separate active-LOW outputs. *It also has three enable inputs for additional flexibility.*

Just by looking at the logic symbol, Fig. 11.9(b), we can figure out the complete operation of the IC chip.

1. The inversion bubbles on the decoded outputs indicate *active-LOW operation.*

2. The three inputs $\bar{E}_1$, $\bar{E}_2$, and $E_3$ are used to *enable* the chip.

3. The chip is disabled (all outputs HIGH) *unless* $E_1$ = LOW, *and* $E_2$ = LOW *and* $E_3$ = HIGH.

4. The *enables* are useful for go/no-go operation of the chip based on some *external control signal*.

5. When the chip is *disabled*, the X's in the binary output columns $A_0$, $A_1$, and $A_2$ indicate *don't-care levels*, meaning the outputs will all be HIGH no matter at what level $A_0$, $A_1$, and $A_2$ are.

6. When the chip is *enabled*, the binary inputs $A_0$, $A_1$, and $A_2$ are used to *select* which output goes LOW. In this case, $A_0$ is the LSB input.

**11.9 Draw the (a) pin configuration and (b) logic symbol of the 7442 BCD-to-decimal decoder IC.**

*Solution:*

The 7442 is a BCD-to-decimal decoder. It has four pins for the BCD input bits (0000 to 1001) and 10 active-LOW outputs for the decoded decimal numbers. Figure 11.10 gives the pin configuration and logic symbol.

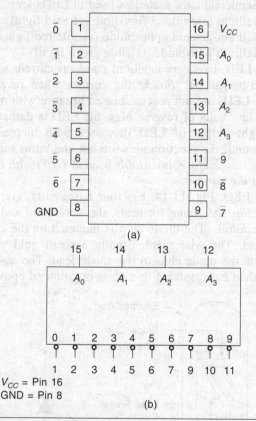

$V_{CC}$ = Pin 16
GND = Pin 8

**Fig. 11.10** *The 7442 BCD-to-Decimal Decoder: (a) Pin Configuration and (b) Logic Symbol.*

**11.10 Describe the *hexadecimal 1-of-16 decoder IC 74154*.**

*Solution:*

The *74154 is a 1-of-16 decoder*. It accepts a four-bit binary input (0000 to 1111), decodes it, and provides an active-LOW output to one of the 16 output pins. It also has a *two-input active-LOW enable gate* for disabling the outputs. If either enable input ($E_0$ or $E_1$) is made HIGH, the outputs are forced HIGH regardless of the $A_0$ to $A_3$ inputs. The *operational information* for the *74154* is given in Fig. 11.11.

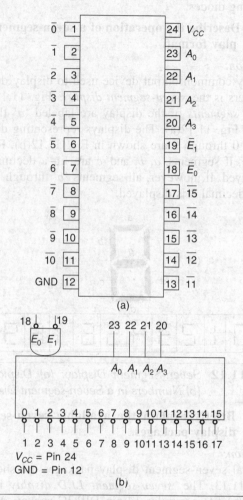

$V_{CC}$ = Pin 24
GND = Pin 12

**Fig. 11.11** *The 74154 Hexa Decimal 1-of-16 Decoder IC: (a) Pin Configuration and (b) Logic Symbol.*

The inverted-input AND gate is used in the circuit to disable all output NAND gates if either $\bar{E}_0$ or $\bar{E}_1$ is made HIGH.

## DIGITAL DISPLAYS

There are many occasions when digital data from various portions of a system are displayed. Sometimes the data is displayed in raw binary format, but more often it is converted to some type of *decimal display* so that operators can more readily interpret the results being *displayed*. It is not unusual for a digital display to represent the *end result* of an entire set of computations and logic operations. Some examples of equipments where this is the case are counters, digital voltmeters, and electronic calculators.

The red light associated with the power switch on a piece of test equipment is the simplest form of a digital display. There is no universal lamp type which is used everywhere. *The type of lamp used is a function of the particular application.* Some lamp types found in digital systems are incandescent, neon, fluorescent, and light-emitting diodes.

### 11.11 Describe the operation of a seven-segment display format.

*Solution:*

A very common output device used to display decimal numbers is the *seven-segment display,* Fig. 11.12. The seven *segments* of the display are labeled '*a*' through '*g*' in Fig. 11.12(a). The displays representing decimal digits 0 through 9 are shown in Fig. 11.12(b). For example, if segments *a*, *b*, and *c* are lit, a decimal 7 is displayed. If, however, all segments '*a*' through '*g*' are lit, a decimal 8 is displayed.

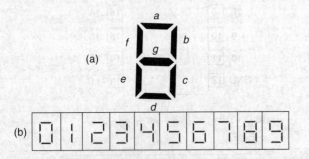

**Fig. 11.12** *Seven-Segment Display: (a) Display and (b) Numbers in a Seven-segment Display.*

### 11.12 Briefly explain the available seven-segment display packages.

*Solution:*

Several seven-segment display packages are shown in Fig. 11.13. The *seven-segment LED display* in Fig. 11.13(a) fits a regular 14-pin DIP IC socket. Another *single-digit* seven-segment LED display is shown in Fig. 11.13(b). This display fits crosswise into a wider DIP IC socket. The unit in Fig. 11.13(c) is a *multidigit* LED display widely used in digital clocks.

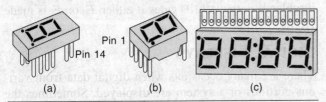

**Fig. 11.13** *(a) DIP Seven-Segment LED Display (b) A Common 10-pin Single-digit Package (c) A Multidigit Package.*

### 11.13 How seven-segment displays operate?

*Solution:*

The seven-segment display may be constructed with each of the segments being a thin filament that glows. This type of unit is called an *incandescent display* and is similar to a regular lamp. Another type of display is *gas-discharge tube,* which operates at high voltages. It gives off an orange glow. The modern *vacuum fluorescent* (VF) display gives off a blue-green glow when lit and operates at low voltages. The newer *liquid-crystal display* (LCD) creates numbers in a black or silvery colour. The common *LED display* gives off a characteristic reddish glow when lit.

### 11.14 Explain the construction and working of a light emitting diode.

*Solution:*

Light emitting diodes are specially doped *pn* junctions which emit light on proper biasing. When a *pn* junction is forward biased, the electrons from the *n*-type material move across the junction and enter the *p*-type material. These electrons combine with the holes. This *recombination* results in a net decrease in the energy of the electrons. This energy is given off in the form of heat or light or both. *The colour of the light emitted depends upon the semiconductor material used in the LED.* Semiconductor materials used in LEDs are:

1. Gallium arsenide    (invisible infrared light)
2. Gallium-arsenide-phosphide (visible red light)
3. Gallium phosphide  (visible green light)

The LED, like a *pn* junction, *conducts* current when forward-biased and *blocks* the current when reverse-biased. LEDs are not reverse-biased because with more than a few volts of reverse bias, the LED is damaged. The light output of LED increases with increasing current until the junction gets too hot and burns out. *A resistor is, therefore, invariably used in series with LED to limit the current.*

The LED, Fig. 11.14, has four basic parts, viz; the diode *chip*, the *frame* for leads, the *wire band* and the *encapsulation*. The diode chip is mounted on the cathode lead. The wire band, usually a small gold wire, connects the diode chip to the anode lead. The assembly is then encapsulated in a clear or coloured epoxy.

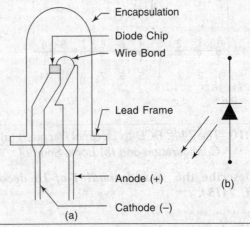

**Fig. 11.14** *Light Emitting Diode (LED) (a) Configuration and (b) Symbol.*

## 11.15 With the help of a diagram, explain the working of a liquid crystal display (LCD).

*Solution:*

Liquid crystal materials find wide application in *digital display consumer products*, such as electronic watches and calculators. Figure 11.15 depicts a typical *liquid crystal display* (LCD). It consists of a two-piece transparent case with the liquid crystal material filling the space in between. Very thin electrodes are deposited on a transparent material (such as tin oxide) on the inner surface of both the base and the cover. The electrodes are shaped to give the desired shape for display. The exterior of either the cover or the base may be coated with a mirror-like material.

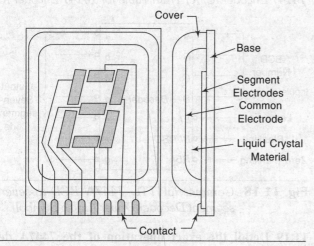

**Fig. 11.15** *Liquid Crystal Display.*

Liquid crystals are liquids in which the intermolecular bonds have definite relationships, like in crystals. *When a liquid crystal material is subjected to an electric field, its optical characteristics change.* The electric field, in the case of some materials is ac, whereas in other materials it is dc. Four main phenomena can take place in liquid crystal when subjected to an electric field.

(i) The *first mode* is based on the phenomenon of a change in colour or the optical density of the material. When the optical density increases, less light can pass through the LCD.

(ii) The *second mode* involves the controlled rotation of polarised light. As bias is applied to the liquid crystal, the molecules rotate the light.

(iii) The *third mode* is the change of the index of refraction of the liquid crystal material with an applied electric field.

(iv) The *fourth mode* is dynamic scattering, in which the light entering the liquid crystal is scattered in all directions instead of being transmitted straight through. When a bias is applied to the electrodes, the scattering effect is eliminated and the light is transmitted directly through the crystal material.

## 11.16 Differentiate between an encoder and a decoder.

*Solution:*

If you were to communicate between a Russian speaking person who did not know the English language, you would need someone to *translate* the Russian into English and then from the English into Russian. A similar problem exists in digital electronics. Almost all digital circuits (calculators, computers) understand only binary numbers. But most people understand only *decimal numbers*. Thus, we must have electronic devices that can translate from decimal to binary numbers and from binary to decimal numbers.

Figure 11.16 depicts a typical system that might be used to translate from decimal to binary numbers and back to decimals. The device that translates from the keyboard decimal numbers to binary is called an *encoder;* the device labeled *decoder* translates from binary to decimal numbers.

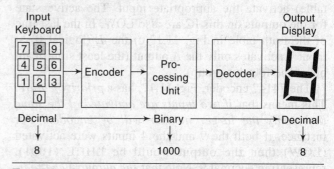

**Fig. 11.16** *A System using Encoders and Decoders.*

As an example of a *conversion*, if you press the decimal number 8 on the keyboard, the encoder will convert the 8 into the binary number 1000. The decoder will convert the binary 1000 into the decimal number 8 on the output display.

Encoders and decoders are very common electronic circuits in all digital devices. Encoders and decoders, that translate from any of the *commonly used codes* in digital electronics are available. Most of the encoders and decoders are *packaged as single ICs*.

## 11.17 Describe the 10-line-to-4-line priority encoder IC 74147.

*Solution:*

The 74147 is a decimal-to-BCD (10-line-to-4-line) encoder, called a *priority encoder* by the manufacturer. Figure 11.17(a) is a block diagram of this encoder. If the decimal input 3 on the encoder is activated, then the logic circuit inside the unit outputs the BCD number 0011 as shown.

A more accurate description of a *10-line-to-4-line priority encoder* is shown in Fig. 11.17(b). This is a *connection diagram* furnished by National Semiconductors. The bubbles at both the inputs (1 to 9) and outputs (*A* to *D*) mean that the priority encoder has both *active low inputs* and *active low outputs*.

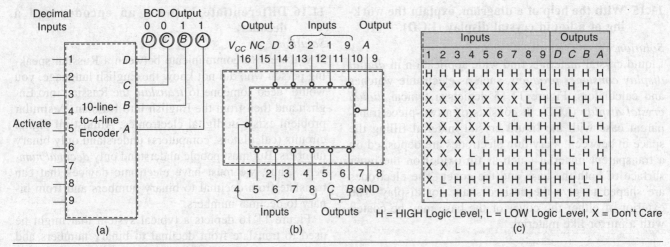

**Fig. 11.17**  *(a) 10-line-to-4-line Encoder. (b) Pin Diagram for 74147 Encoder IC. (c) Truth Table for 74147 Encoder IC.*

A truth table for the 74147 priority encoder is given in Fig. 11.17(c). Only *LOW logic levels* (L on the truth table) activate the appropriate input. The active state for the outputs on this IC are also LOW. In the last line of the truth table in Fig. 11.17(c) the *L* (logical 0) at input 1 activates only the *A* output (the least significant bit of the four-bit group).

The 74147 encoder, Fig. 11.17, has a *priority feature.* This means that *if two inputs are activated at the same time, only the larger number will be encoded.* For instance, if both the 9 and the 4 inputs were activated (LOW) then the output would be LHHL (1001), representing decimal 9. Note that *the outputs need to be complemented (inverted) to form the true binary number.*

The 74147 TTL IC is packaged in a 16-pin DIP. Internally, the IC consists of circuitry equivalent to about 30 logic gates.

## 11.18 Describe the commercial TTL 7447A BCD-to-seven-segment decoder/driver.

*Solution:*

The logic symbol for a commercial *TTL 7447A* BCD-to-seven-segment decoder/driver is shown in Fig. 11.18. The BCD number to be decoded is applied to the *inputs* labelled *D, C, B,* and *A.* When activated with a LOW, the *lamp-test* (LT) input activates all outputs (*a* to *g*). When activated with a LOW, the *blanking input* (BI) makes all outputs HIGH, turning all attached displays OFF. When activated, with a LOW, the *ripple-blanking input* (RBI) blanks the display *only if it contains a 0.* When the RBI input becomes active, the BI/RBO pin temporarily becomes the *ripple-blanking output* (RBO) and drops to LOW. *Blanking means to cause no LEDs on the display to light.*

The seven outputs on the 7447A IC are all *active LOW outputs.* The outputs are normally HIGH and drop to a LOW when activated.

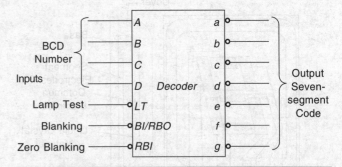

**Fig. 11.18**  *Commercial TTL 7447A BCD-to-seven-segment Decoder/Driver (Logic Symbol).*

## 11.19 Detail the exact operation of the 7447A decoder/driver IC.

*Solution:*

The exact operation of the *7447A decoder/driver IC* is detailed in Fig. 11.19(a). The decimal displays generated by the *7447A decoder* are shown in Fig. 11.19(b). *Invalid BCD inputs* (decimals 10, 11, 12, 13, 14, and 15) do generate a unique output on the 7447A decoder.

The 7447A decoder/driver IC is typically connected to a *common-anode* seven-segment LED display, Fig. 11.19(c). It is especially important that the seven 150 Ω *limiting resistors* be wired between the 7447A IC and the seven-segment display.

Assume that the BCD input to the 7447A decoder/driver in Fig. 11.19(c) is 0001 (LLLH) corresponding to line 2 of the truth table in Fig. 11.19(a). This *input combination* causes segments *b* and *c* on the seven-segment display to light (*outputs b and c drop to LOW*). Decimal 1 is displayed. The LT and two BIs are not shown in Fig. 11.19(c). *When not connected, they are assumed to be floating HIGH and therefore disabled in this circuit.* These floating inputs should be connected to +5 V to make sure they stay HIGH.

| Decimal or Function | INPUTS | | | | | | BI/BRO | OUTPUTS | | | | | | | Note |
|---|---|---|---|---|---|---|---|---|---|---|---|---|---|---|---|
| | LT | RBI | D | C | B | A | | a | b | c | d | e | f | g | |
| 0 | H | H | L | L | L | L | H | ON | ON | ON | ON | ON | ON | OFF | |
| 1 | H | X | L | L | L | H | H | OFF | ON | ON | OFF | OFF | OFF | OFF | |
| 2 | H | X | L | L | H | L | H | ON | ON | OFF | ON | ON | OFF | ON | |
| 3 | H | X | L | L | H | H | H | ON | ON | ON | ON | OFF | OFF | ON | |
| 4 | H | X | L | H | L | L | H | OFF | ON | ON | OFF | OFF | ON | ON | |
| 5 | H | X | L | H | L | H | H | ON | OFF | ON | ON | OFF | ON | ON | |
| 6 | H | X | L | H | H | L | H | OFF | OFF | ON | ON | ON | ON | ON | |
| 7 | H | X | L | H | H | H | H | ON | ON | ON | OFF | OFF | OFF | OFF | |
| 8 | H | X | H | L | L | L | H | ON | ON | ON | ON | ON | ON | ON | 1 |
| 9 | H | X | H | L | L | H | H | ON | ON | ON | OFF | OFF | ON | ON | |
| 10 | H | X | H | L | H | L | H | OFF | OFF | OFF | ON | ON | OFF | ON | |
| 11 | H | X | H | L | H | H | H | OFF | OFF | ON | ON | OFF | OFF | ON | |
| 12 | H | X | H | H | L | L | H | OFF | ON | OFF | OFF | OFF | ON | ON | |
| 13 | H | X | H | H | L | H | H | ON | OFF | OFF | ON | OFF | ON | ON | |
| 14 | H | X | H | H | H | L | H | OFF | OFF | OFF | ON | ON | ON | ON | |
| 15 | H | X | H | H | H | H | H | OFF | OFF | OFF | OFF | OFF | OFF | OFF | |
| BI | X | X | X | X | X | X | L | OFF | OFF | OFF | OFF | OFF | OFF | OFF | 2 |
| RBI | H | L | L | L | L | L | L | OFF | OFF | OFF | OFF | OFF | OFF | OFF | 3 |
| LT | L | X | X | X | X | X | H | ON | ON | ON | ON | ON | ON | ON | 4 |

H = High level, L = LOW level, X = Irrelevant

Notes:

1. The blanking input (*BI*) must be open or held at a HIGH logic level when output functions 0 through 15 are desired. The ripple-blanking input (*RBI*) must be open or HIGH if blanking of a decimal zero is not desired.

2. When a LOW logic level is applied directly to the blanking input (*BI*), all segment outputs are OFF regardless of the level of any other input.

3. When ripple-blanking input (*RBI*) and inputs *A, B, C*, and *D* are at a LOW level with the lamp test (*LT*) input HIGH, all segment outputs go OFF and the ripple-blanking output (*RBO*) goes to a LOW level (response condition).

4. When the blanking input/ripple-blanking output (*BI/RBO*) is open or held HIGH and a LOW is applied to the lamp test (*LT*) input, all segment outputs are ON.

(a)

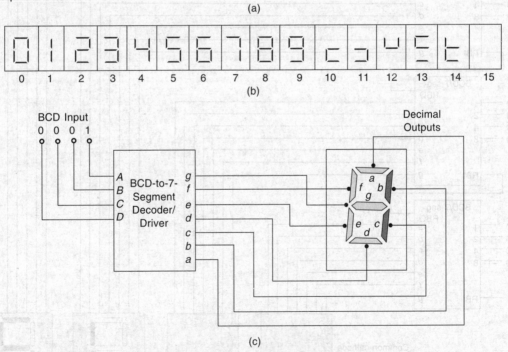

(b)

(c)

**Fig. 11.19** *(a) Truth Table for 7447A Decoder. (b) Format of Readouts on Seven-segment Display using the 7447A Decoder IC. (c) A Decoder Driving a Seven-segment Display.*

### 11.20 Illustrate and explain zero suppression logic.

*Solution:*

An additional feature found on many seven-segment decoders is the *zero suppression logic*. This extra function is useful in multidigit displays because *it is used to blank out unnecessary zeros in the display*. For instance, the number 0005.300 would be displayed as 5.3, which is read more easily. Blanking of the zeros on the front of the number is called *leading zero suppression*, and blanking of the zeros after the number is called *trailing zero suppression*.

*Leading zero suppression:* Two additional functions have been added to each BCD-to-seven-segment decoder, a ripple blanking input (*RBI*) and a ripple blanking output (*RBO*). The highest-order digit position is always blanked if a 0 code appears on its BCD inputs

*and* the blanking input is HIGH. Each lower-order digit position is blanked if a 0 code appears on its BCD inputs, *and* the next higher-order digit is a 0 as indicated by a HIGH on its blanking output. *The ripple blanking output of any decoder indicates that it has a BCD 0 on its inputs, and all higher-order digits are also 0. The blanking output of each stage is connected to the blanking input of the next lower-order stage.* This is shown in Fig. 11.20(a).

*Trailing zero suppression:* For the decimal (fractional) portion of the display, trailing zero suppression is used. The lowest-order digit is blanked if it is 0, and each digit that is 0 *and* is followed by 0's in all the lower-order positions is also blanked. This is shown in Fig. 11.20(b).

As an example, in Fig. 11.20(a), the highest-order digit is 0, which is, therefore, *blanked*. Also, the next

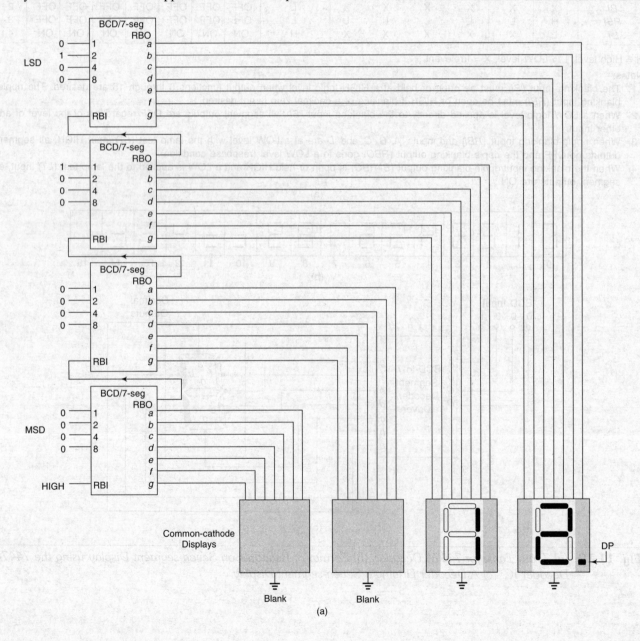

(a)

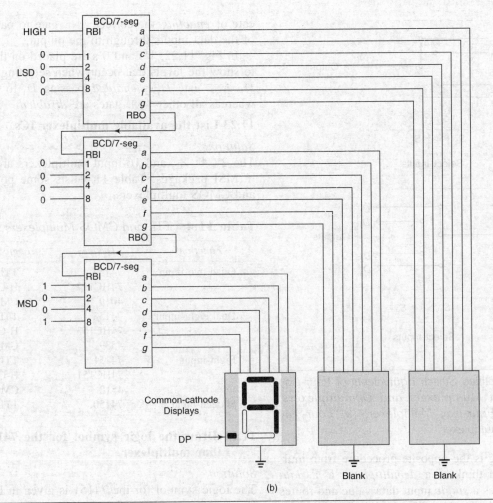

**Fig. 11.20** *Zero Suppression Logic; (a) Leading Zero and (b) Trailing Zero.*

digit is a 0, and because the highest-order digit is 0, it is also blanked. The remaining two digits are displayed. In Fig. 11.20(b), the lowest-order digit is blanked because it is a 0. The next digit is also 0 and its blanking input is HIGH, so it is blanked. The highest-order digit (9) is displayed. *The blanking output of each decoder stage is connected to the blanking input of the next higher-order stage.*

## DATA SELECTORS

A *digital multiplexer* or *data selector* is a logic circuit that accepts *several* digital data inputs and selects *one* of them at any given time to pass on to the output. The routing of the desired data input to the output is controlled by SELECT inputs, often referred to as ADDRESS inputs.

A *demultiplexer* performs the *reverse* operation; it takes a *single* input and distributes it over *several* outputs. The select input code determines to which output the DATA input will be transmitted.

## 11.21 Differentiate between a multiplexer and a demultiplexer.

*Solution:*

A digital *multiplexer* or *data selector* is a logic circuit that accepts *several* digital data inputs and selects *one* of them at any given time to pass on to the output. *Control signals* are also input to tell which data-input line to select for transmission (data selection). Figure 11.21(a) shows that the *data select control inputs* ($S_1$, $S_0$) are responsible for determining which data-input ($D_0$ to $D_3$) is selected to be transmitted to the data-output line $Y$. The $S_1$, $S_0$ inputs will be a *binary code* that corresponds to the data-input line you want to select. Table 11.3 lists the codes for input data selection.

**Table 11.3** *Data Select Inputs Codes for Fig. 11.21(a)*

| Data Select Control Inputs | | Data Input Selected |
|---|---|---|
| $S_1$ | $S_0$ | |
| 0 | 0 | $D_0$ |
| 0 | 1 | $D_1$ |
| 1 | 0 | $D_2$ |
| 1 | 1 | $D_3$ |

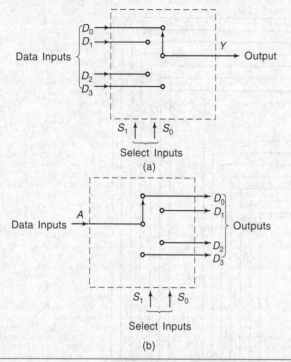

**Fig. 11.21**  *Simplified Switch Equivalents of Four-way Data Multiplexers and Demultiplexers; (a) Four-way Multiplexer; (b) Four-way Demultiplexer.*

Demultiplexing is the opposite procedure from multiplexing. We can think of a *demultiplexer* as a *data distributor*. It takes a *single* input data value and routes it to *one of several* outputs, as illustrated in Fig. 11.21(b).

**11.22 Describe a simple four-line multiplexer.**

*Solution:*
A simple four-line multiplexer built from SSI logic gates is shown in Fig. 11.22. The control inputs ($S_1$, $S_0$) take

care of *enabling* the correct AND gate to pass just one of the data inputs through to the output.

In Fig. 11.22, 1's and 0's are placed on the diagram to show the levels that occur when selecting data input $D_1$. AND gate $D_1$ is *enabled*, passing $D_1$ to the output, whereas all other AND gates are *disabled*.

**11.23 List the available multiplexer ICs.**

*Solution:*
The 2-, 4-, 8-, and 16-input multiplexers are available in MSI packages. Table 11.4 lists some popular TTL and CMOS multiplexers.

**Table 11.4**  *TTL and CMOS Multiplexers*

| Function | Device | Logic Family |
|---|---|---|
| Quad two-input | 74157 | TTL |
|  | 74HC157 | H-CMOS |
|  | 4019 | CMOS |
| Dual eight-input | 74153 | TTL |
|  | 74HC153 | H-CMOS |
|  | 4539 | CMOS |
| Eight-input | 74151 | TTL |
|  | 74HC151 | H-CMOS |
|  | 4512 | CMOS |
| Sixteen-input | 74150 | TTL |

**11.24 Draw the logic symbol for the 74151 eight-line multiplexer.**

*Solution:*
The logic symbol for the 74151 is given in Fig. 11.23. Because the 74151 has eight lines to select from ($I_0$ to $I_7$) it requires three data select inputs ($S_2$, $S_1$, $S_0$) to determine which input to choose ($2^3 = 8$). *True Y* and *complemented* ($\bar{Y}$) outputs are provided. The active-LOW enable input ($\bar{E}$) disables all inputs when it is HIGH and forces *Y* LOW regardless of all other inputs.

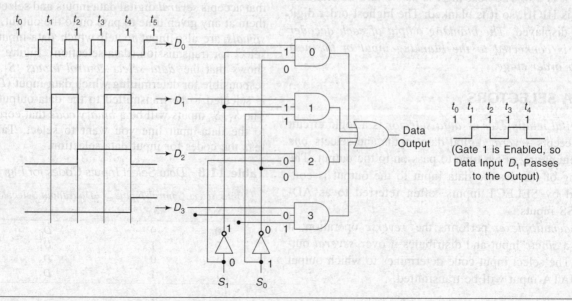

**Fig. 11.22**  *Logic Diagram for a Four-line Multiplexer.*

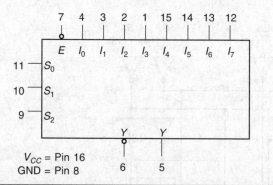

**Fig. 11.23** *The 74151 Eight-line Multiplexer-logic Symbol.*

**11.25 Using two 74151s, design a 16-line multiplexer controlled by four data select control inputs.**

*Solution:*
The multiplexer is shown in Fig. 11.24. Because there are 16 *data input lines*, we must use four *data select inputs* ($2^4 = 16$). $A$ is the *LSB* data select line and $D$ is the *MSB*.

When the data select is in the range from 0000 to 0111, the $D$ line is 0, which *enables* the low-order (left) multiplexer selecting the $D_0$ to $D_7$ inputs and *disables* the high-order (right) multiplexer.

When the data select inputs are in the range from 1000 to 1111, the $D$ line is 1, which *disables* the low-order multiplexer and *enables* the high-order multiplexer, allowing $D_8$ to $D_{15}$ to be selected. Since the $Y$ output of a disabled multiplexer is 0, an OR gate is used to *combine* the two outputs, allowing the output from the enabled multiplexer to get through. (See Fig. 11.24)

**11.26 Draw the pin connections and internal logic of the data demultiplexer IC 74LS139 and explain.**

*Solution:*
The 74LS139 is a common example of a *data demultiplexer* which contains two independent four-way demultiplexers within a 16-pin DIL-package. Each *four-way* demultiplexer has a single active-low enable input, $\overline{EN}$, two select inputs, $S_0$ and $S_1$, and four outputs, 0 to 3. The pin connections for the 74LS139 are shown in Fig. 11.25.

As for its *data multiplexer* counterpart, the 74LS153, the two halves of the device, referred to as $A$ and $B$ are conveniently brought out to pins on *opposite sides* of the package; the $A$-side using pins 1 to 7 whilst the $B$-side uses pins 9 to 15. The supply, which follows the normal convention of pin-8 (0 V) and pin-14 (+5 V) is *common* to both halves of the device. (See Fig. 11.25 )

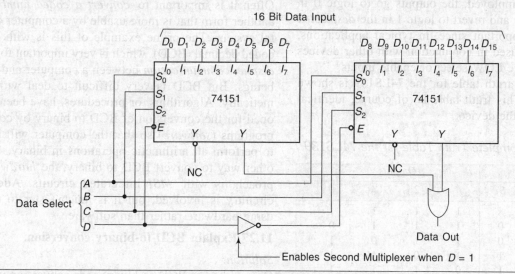

**Fig. 11.24** *Using Two 74151's to Design a 16-line Multiplexer.*

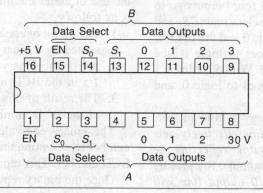

**Fig. 11.25** *Pin Connections for the 74LS139.*

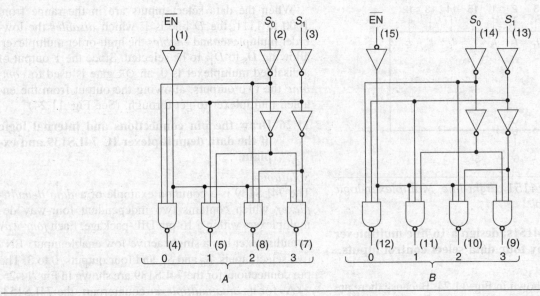

**Fig. 11.26**  *Internal Logic of the 74LS139.*

The internal logic of the 74LS139 is shown in Fig. 11.26. This shows how the two *select signals*, $S_0$ and $S_1$, are gated with the enable signals, $\overline{EN}$, in each of the 4-three-input NAND gates. Since NAND rather than AND gates are employed, the outputs go to logic 0 in the *selected state* and revert to logic 1 in the *deselected state*. This is important since, in typical applications, the 74LS139 is used in conjunction with other devices which have active LOW select or enable inputs.

The complete truth table for the 74LS139 is shown in Table 11.5. This truth table is, of course, identical for each half of the device.

**Table 11.5**  *Complete Truth Table for the 74LS139.*

| Inputs | | | Outputs | | | |
|---|---|---|---|---|---|---|
| EN | $S_0$ | $S_1$ | 3 | 2 | 1 | 0 |
| 1 | × | × | 1 | 1 | 1 | 1 |
| 0 | 0 | 0 | 1 | 1 | 1 | 0 |
| 0 | 1 | 0 | 1 | 1 | 0 | 1 |
| 0 | 0 | 1 | 1 | 0 | 1 | 1 |
| 0 | 1 | 1 | 0 | 1 | 1 | 1 |

When the EN line is at logic 1 all four outputs go to logic 1 regardless of the state of the select inputs $S_0$ and $S_1$. When both select inputs are at logic 0 and the EN line is taken LOW, the 0 output line goes to logic 0 (the other three outputs remain at logic 1). With $S_0$ at logic 1 and $S_1$ at logic 0 the 1 output line goes to logic 0, and so on.

Taking the four-way switch analogy a little further, it should be noted that, *the enable line effectively acts as a data signal input, the selected output reflecting the state of this line.* If we have selected output 0 (by placing a logic 0 on both $S_0$ and $S_1$), *the 0 output line will follow the logical state of the EN input*; i.e. when $\overline{EN}$ goes LOW the 0 output will go LOW and when $\overline{EN}$ goes HIGH the 0 output will go HIGH.

## CODE CONVERTERS

Often it is important to *convert a coded number* into another form that is more usable by a computer or digital system. The prime example of this is with binary-coded decimal (BCD), which is very important for *visual display communication* between a computer and human beings. But BCD is very difficult to deal with arithmetically. Algorithms, or procedures, have been developed for the conversion of BCD to binary by computer programs (*software*) so that the computer will be able to perform all arithmetic operations in binary. Yet another way to convert BCD to binary, the *hardware* approach, is with *MSI* integrated circuits. Additional circuitry is involved, but it is much faster to convert using hardware rather than software.

**11.27 Explain BCD-to-binary conversion.**

*Solution:*
One method of BCD-to-binary code conversion involves the use of adder circuits. The basic *conversion process* is as follows:

1. The *value of each bit* in the BCD number is represented by a binary number.
2. All of the binary representations of *bits that are 1's* in the BCD number are added.
3. The result of this addition is the *binary equivalent* of the BCD number.

The binary equivalent of each BCD bit is a binary number representing the *weight* of that bit within the total BCD number. This representation is given in Table 11.6.

Once the binary representation for each 1 in the BCD number is determined, adder circuits can be used to add the 1's in each column of the binary representation. The 1's occur in a given column only when the corresponding BCD bit is a 1. *The occurrence of a BCD 1 can therefore be used to generate the proper binary 1 in the appropriate column of the adder structure.* To handle a two-decimal digit (two-decade) BCD code, eight BCD input lines and seven binary outputs are required. (It takes 7 binary bits to represent numbers up through 99.)

**Table 11.6**  *Binary Representations of BCD Bit Weights*

| BCD Bit | BCD Weight | 64 | 32 | 16 | 8 | 4 | 2 | 1 |
|---|---|---|---|---|---|---|---|---|
| | | *Binary Representation* | | | | | | |
| $A_0$ | 1 | 0 | 0 | 0 | 0 | 0 | 0 | 1 |
| $B_0$ | 2 | 0 | 0 | 0 | 0 | 0 | 1 | 0 |
| $C_0$ | 4 | 0 | 0 | 0 | 0 | 1 | 0 | 0 |
| $D_0$ | 8 | 0 | 0 | 0 | 1 | 0 | 0 | 0 |
| $A_1$ | 10 | 0 | 0 | 0 | 1 | 0 | 1 | 0 |
| $B_1$ | 20 | 0 | 0 | 1 | 0 | 1 | 0 | 0 |
| $C_1$ | 40 | 0 | 1 | 0 | 1 | 0 | 0 | 0 |
| $D_1$ | 80 | 1 | 0 | 1 | 0 | 0 | 0 | 0 |

Referring to Table 11.6, notice that the *'1' (LSB) column* of the binary representation has only a single 1 and no possibility of an input carry, so that a straight connection from the $A_0$ bit of the BCD input to the least significant binary output is sufficient. In the *'2' column* of binary representation, the possible occurrence of two 1's can be accommodated by adding the $B_0$ bit and the $A_1$ bit of the BCD number. In the *'4' column* of binary representation, the possible occurrence of two 1's is handled by adding the $C_0$ bit and the $B_1$ bit of the BCD number. In the *'8' column* of the binary representation, the possibility of occurrence of three 1's is handled by adding $D_0$, $A_1$, and $C_1$ bits of the BCD numbers. In the *'16' column*, the $B_1$ and the $D_1$ bits are added. In the *'32' column,* only a single 1 is possible, so the $C_1$ bit is added to the carry from the '16' column. In the *'64' column*, only a single 1 can occur, so the $D_1$ bit is added only to the carry from the '32' column. A method of implementing these requirements with full-adders is shown in Fig. 11.27.

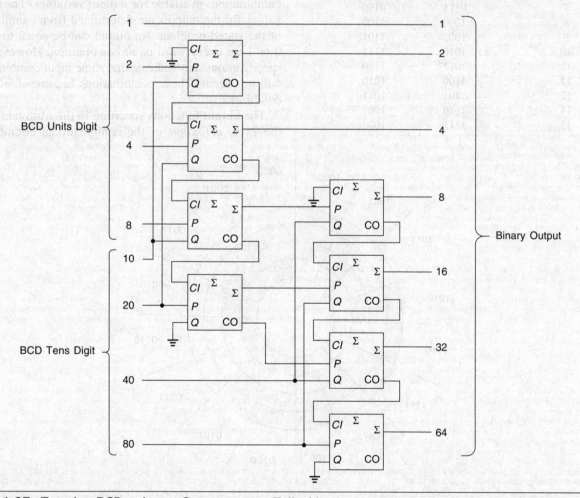

**Fig. 11.27**  *Two-digit BCD-to-binary Converter using Full-adders.*

**11.28 Explain the difference between the Gray code and the regular binary code.**

*Solution:*

The difference between the Gray code and the regular binary code is illustrated in Table 11.7. *The Gray code varies by only 1 bit from one entry to the next and from the last entry (15) back to the beginning (0).* Now, if each Gray code represents a different position on a rotating wheel, as the wheel turns, the code read from one position to the next will vary by only 1 bit (see Fig. 11.28).

**Table 11.7** *Four-bit Gray Code*

| Decimal | Binary | Gray |
|---------|--------|------|
| 0  | 0000 | 0000 |
| 1  | 0001 | 0001 |
| 2  | 0010 | 0011 |
| 3  | 0011 | 0010 |
| 4  | 0100 | 0110 |
| 5  | 0101 | 0111 |
| 6  | 0110 | 0101 |
| 7  | 0111 | 0100 |
| 8  | 1000 | 1100 |
| 9  | 1001 | 1101 |
| 10 | 1010 | 1111 |
| 11 | 1011 | 1110 |
| 12 | 1100 | 1010 |
| 13 | 1101 | 1011 |
| 14 | 1110 | 1001 |
| 15 | 1111 | 1000 |

**11.29 Discuss the detailed procedure for the design of combinational circuits.**

*Solution:*

The design of combinational circuits starts from the *verbal outline* of the problem and ends in a *logic circuit diagram*, or a set of Boolean functions from which the logic diagram can be easily obtained. The procedure involves the following steps:

1. The problem is *stated*.
2. The number of available input variables and required output variables is *determined*.
3. The input and output variables are *assigned* letter symbols.
4. The truth table that defines the required relationships between inputs and outputs is *derived*.
5. The simplified Boolean function for each output is *obtained*.
6. The logic diagram is *drawn*.

A *truth table* for a combinational circuit consists of input columns and output columns. The 1's and 0's in the input columns are obtained from the $2^n$ binary combinations available for *n* input variables. The binary values for the outputs are determined from examination of the stated problem. An output can be equal to either 0 or 1 for every *valid input combination*. However, the specifications may indicate that some input combinations will not occur. These combinations become *don't-care conditions*.

The output functions specified in the truth table give the *exact definition* of the combinational circuit. It is

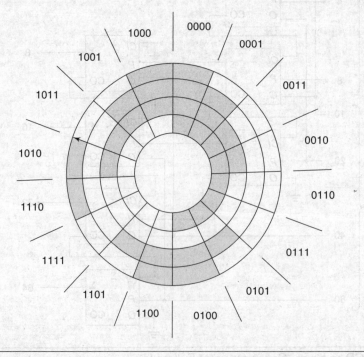

**Fig. 11.28**   *Gray Code Wheel.*

important that the verbal specifications be interpreted correctly into a truth table. Sometimes the designer must use his intuition and experience to arrive at the *correct interpretation*. Word specifications are very seldom complete and exact. Any wrong interpretation which results in an incorrect truth table produces a combinational circuit that *will not fulfill* the stated requirements.

The output Boolean functions from the truth table are *simplified* by any available method, such as algebraic manipulation, the map method, or the tabulation procedure. Usually there will be a variety of simplified expressions from which to choose. However, in any particular application, certain restrictions, limitations, and criteria will serve as a *guide* in the process of *choosing* a particular algebraic expression. A practical design method would have to consider such constraints as (1) minimum *number of gates*, (2) minimum *number of inputs* to a gate, (3) minimum *propagation time* of the signal through the circuit, (4) minimum *number of interconnections*, and (5) limitations of the *driving capabilities* of each gate. Since all these criteria cannot be satisfied simultaneously, and since the importance of each constraint is dictated by the particular application, *it is difficult to make a general statement as to what constitutes an acceptable simplification*. In most cases the simplification begins by satisfying an elementary objective, such as producing a simplified Boolean function in a standard form, and from that proceeds to meet any other *performance criteria*.

In practice, designers tend to go from the Boolean functions to a wiring list that shows the interconnections among various standard logic gates. In that case the design need not go any further than the required simplified output Boolean functions. However, a logic diagram is helpful for visualizing the *gate implementation* of the expressions.

**11.30 Discuss the detailed procedure for the analysis of combinational circuits.**

*Solution:*
The *design* of a combinational circuit starts from the verbal specifications of a required function and culminates with a set of output Boolean functions or a logic diagram. The *analysis* of a combinational circuit is somewhat the *reverse process*. It starts with a given logic diagram and culminates with a set of Boolean functions, a truth table, or a verbal explanation of the circuit operation. If the logic diagram to be analyzed is accompanied by a function name or an explanation of what it is assumed to accomplish, then the analysis problem reduces to a verification of the stated function.

The first step in the analysis is *to make sure that the given circuit is combinational and not sequential*. The diagram of a combinational circuit has logic gates with no feedback paths or memory elements.

Once the logic diagram is verified as a combinational circuit, one can proceed to obtain the output Boolean functions set or the truth table. If the circuit is accompanied by a verbal explanation of its function, then the Boolean functions or the truth table is sufficient for verification. If the function of the circuit is under investigation, then it is necessary to interpret the operation of the circuit from the derived truth table. The success of such investigation is enhanced if one has previous experience and familiarity with a wide variety of digital circuits. *The ability to correlate a truth table with an information-processing task is an art one acquires with experience.*

To obtain the *output Boolean functions* from a logic diagram, proceed as follows:

1. Label with arbitrary symbols all gate outputs that are a function of the input variables. *Obtain the Boolean functions for each gate.*
2. Label with other arbitrary symbols *those gates which are a function of input variables and/or previously labeled gates*. Find the Boolean functions for these gates.
3. *Repeat the process* outlined in step 2 until the outputs of the circuit are obtained.
4. By *repeated substitution* of previously defined functions, *obtain the output Boolean functions in terms of input variables only*.

# SUMMARY

- ➢ Logic functions can be performed by two types of networks.
- ➢ No storage is involved in combinational networks.
- ➢ Logic operations with sequential networks occur in a definite sequence providing the ability to store or delay signals.
- ➢ A decoder identifies, recognises, or detects a particular code.
- ➢ Encoding is the opposite of decoding.
- ➢ A very common output device used to display numbers is the seven-segment display.
- ➢ Encoders and decoders translate from decimal to binary and from binary to decimal.

> ➤ A digital multiplexer accepts several digital data inputs and selects one of them at any given time to pass on to the output.
> ➤ A digital demultiplexer takes a single input and distributes it over several outputs.
> ➤ Code converters convert a coded number into another form that is more usable by a computer or digital system.
> ➤ The design of combinational circuits follows a systematic procedure.
> ➤ A logic diagram is helpful in visualizing the gate implementation of the expressions.

# REVIEW QUESTIONS

1.  Where are decoders used?
2.  A BCD-to-decimal decoder has how many inputs and how many outputs?
3.  Define an active-LOW enable.
4.  Where are encoders used?
5.  What is meant by a priority encoder?
6.  What is the function of LT pin in a 7447IC?
7.  How many 74154 4-line-to-16-line decoders are necessary to decode a 6-bit binary number?
8.  In how many ways can a decoder with three inputs and $2^3 = 8$ outputs, be referred to?
9.  Can more than one decoder output be activated at one time?
10. How does the 7445 differ from the 7442?
11. Which LED segments will be on for a decoder/driver input of 1001?
12. How does a decoder differ from an encoder?
13. How does a priority encoder differ from an ordinary encoder?
14. What does the label HPRI mean?
15. What does the symbol $\triangleright$ mean inside a symbol block?
16. What is the function of a multiplexer's select inputs?
17. What are some of the major applications of multiplexers?
18. Explain the difference between a multiplexer and a demultiplexer.
19. What is a code converter?
20. How many binary outputs would a three-digit BCD-to-binary converter have?
21. How many 74184ICs are required to convert a three-digit BCD number to binary?

# SUPPLEMENTARY PROBLEMS

22. Draw the logic symbol for 4-line-to-16 line decoder.
23. Illustrate a method of driving a 7-segment liquid crystal display (LCD).
24. Describe a method driving a LCD segment 'on and off'.
25. Design a 1-of-4 decoder.
26. Draw a 1-of-16 decoder with enable inputs 1G and 2G.
27. How will you wire a 7447A decoder and seven segment display?
28. How will you wire a CMOS decoder/driver system to a LCD?
29. Draw the block diagram of a system used to decode and drive an LCD.
30. Use 74150s and any other logic necessary to multiplex 32 data lines on to a single data-output line.

# OBJECTIVE TYPE QUESTIONS

## Fill in the Blanks

31. The 7442 BCD decoder has active _____ (LOW, HIGH) inputs and active _____ (LOW, HIGH) outputs.
32. The decoder is made up of a _____ of logic gates.
33. 1-of-$2^n$ decoder is so named because one _____ address can activate one of _____ outputs.
34. The enable input enables or _____ the circuit.
35. Decoders are used to _____ information from one code to another.
36. Encoding is the _____ process from decoding.
37. Decoders are versatile circuits that convert information from $n$ inputs to a maximum of _____ output lines.
38. In a 1-of-$2^n$ decoder, one $n$-bit address can _____ one of $2^n$ outputs.
39. The input line for an _____ signal has a circle to show inversion.
40. Decoders can be used as _____ to send data to a desired output.
41. An additional feature found on many seven-segment decoders is the _____.
42. Blanking of zeros on the _____ of the number is called leading zero suppression.
43. Blanking of zeros after the number is called _____ zero suppression.
44. The inventor of the Gray code was _____ of Bell Labs.
45. On a single LED, the flat area on the rim of the plastic identifies the _____ lead.
46. The RBI and RBO inputs of the 7447A are commonly used for blanking _____ on calculator and cash register multidigit displays.
47. The LCD uses a liquid crystal, or _____ fluid, which transmits light differently when affected by a magnetic field from an ac voltage.
48. A(n) _____ voltage applied to an LCD will destroy the unit.
49. The LCD unit consumes a _____ amount of power.

## True/False Questions

State whether the following statements are True or False.
50. An octal decoder with active-LOW outputs will output seven LOWs and one HIGH for each combination of inputs.
51. A hexadecimal decoder is sometimes called a 4-line-to-10-line decoder.
52. Only one of the three enable inputs must be satisfied to enable the 74183 decoder IC.
53. Regardless of the values of inputs, no output is activated unless the enable signal is 1.
54. A decoder with a data input is called a demultiplexer.
55. Blanking inputs cannot control display brightness.
56. More than one output of a BCD-to-7-segment decoder/driver cannot be active at one time.
57. When a multiplexer is used to implement a logic function, the logic functions are applied to the multiplexer's data inputs.
58. The circuit of a demultiplexer is basically the same as for a decoder.
59. The Gray code is not a BCD-type code.

## Multiple Choice Questions

60. A multiplexer has
    (a) one data input and a number of data outputs
    (b) one data output and a number of data inputs
    (c) one data output, a number of data inputs, and a number of select inputs
    (d) one data output and a number of select inputs.
61. A multiplexer with 4-bit data select input is a
    (a) 4 : 1 multiplexer  (b) 8 : 1 multiplexer  (c) 16 : 1 multiplexer  (d) 32 : 1 multiplexer
62. A multiplexer can be used as a
    (a) logic element  (b) Flip-Flop  (c) counter  (d) 7-segment LED driver
63. A 4-variable logic expression can be realised by using only one
    (a) NAND gate  (b) NOR gate  (c) demultiplexer  (d) 16 : 1 multiplexer

64. A demultiplexer can be used to realise a
    (a) counter
    (b) shift-register
    (c) combinational circuit
    (d) display system
65. In a hexadecimal-to-binary priority encoder
    (a) $O$(hex) has the highest priority
    (b) 7(hex) has the lowest priority
    (c) $F$(hex) has the lowest priority
    (d) $F$(hex) has the highest priority
66. The number of 4-line-to-16-line decoders required to make an 8-line-to-256-line decoder is
    (a) 8              (b) 17              (c) 32              (d) 64
67. When 7-segment LED displays are employed to display numbers, zero blanking arrangement is used to blank out
    (a) all the zeros
    (b) all the leading zeros
    (c) all the trailing zeros
    (d) the zero in the MSD
68. Time multiplexing is employed in digital display systems to
    (a) improve the speed of operation
    (b) reduce cost and space requirements
    (c) reduce power requirements
    (d) achieve all of the above
69. A 7-segment common-anode LED display requires
    (a) BCD-to-7 segment decoder with active-LOW outputs
    (b) BCD-to-7 segment decoder with active-HIGH outputs
    (c) negative supply voltage for the anode
    (d) positive supply voltage for the anode and BCD-to-7 segment decoder with active-LOW outputs

# ANSWERS

1. Decoders are used to route data to desired output lines, to address memories, and to convert information from one code to another code.
2. 4 inputs, 10 outputs.
3. An enable signal that enables when it is LOW is called an active-LOW enable signal.
4. Encoders are used to generate a coded output (such as BCD or binary) from a single numeric input line.
5. An encoder in which priorities are assigned to various inputs.
6. It is used to test all the segments of a 7-segment LED.
7. Two.
8. (1) 3-line-to-8-line decoder, (2) Binary-to-octal decoder, (3) Converter, (4) 1-of-8 decoder.
9. No
10. The 7445 has open-collector outputs that can handle up to 30 V and 80 mA.
11. $a$, $b$, $c$, $f$, $g$.
12. An encoder produces an output code corresponding to the activated input-A decoder activates one output.
13. In a priority encoder, the output code corresponds to the highest-numbered output that is activated.
14. HIGH Priority.
15. Buffer or driver.
16. The binary number of the select inputs determines which data input will pass through to the output.
17. Parallel-to-serial conversion, data routing, logic function generation, operations sequencing.
18. A multiplexer selects one of many input signals to be passed to its output; a demultiplexer selects one of many outputs to receive the input signal
19. A code converter takes input data represented in one type of binary code and converts it to another type of binary code
20. Three digits can represent decimal values up to 999. To represent 999 in straight binary requires 10 bits
21. 6.
22. (See Fig. 11.29)
23. (See Fig. 11.30)
24. (See Fig. 11.31)
25. (See Fig. 11.32)

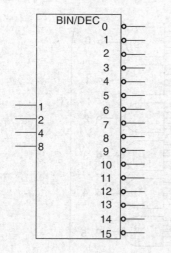

**Fig. 11.29**

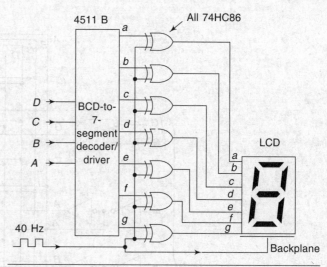

**Fig. 11.30**

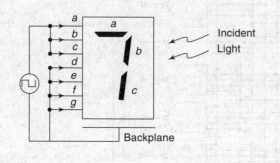

**Fig. 11.31**

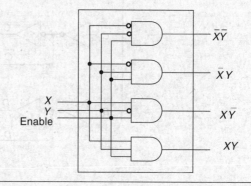

**Fig. 11.32**

26. (See Fig. 11.33)
27. (See Fig. 11.34)
28. (See Fig. 11.35)
29. (See Fig. 11.36)
30. (See Fig. 11.37)

| | | | |
|---|---|---|---|
| 31. HIGH, LOW | 32. combination | 33. $n$-bits, $2^n$ | 34. puts on |
| 35. convert | 36. opposite | 37. $2^n$ | 38. activate |
| 39. active-LOW | 40. demultiplexers | 41. zero suppression | 42. front |
| 43. trailing | 44. Frank Gray | 45. cathode | 46. leading zeros |
| 47. nematic | 48. dc | 49. very small | 50. False |
| 51. False | 52. False | 53. True | 54. True |
| 55. False | 56. False | 57. False | 58. True |
| 59. True | 60. (c) | 61. (c) | 62. (a) |
| 63. (d) | 64. (c) | 65. (d) | 66. (b) |
| 67. (b) | 68. (c) | 69. (d) | |

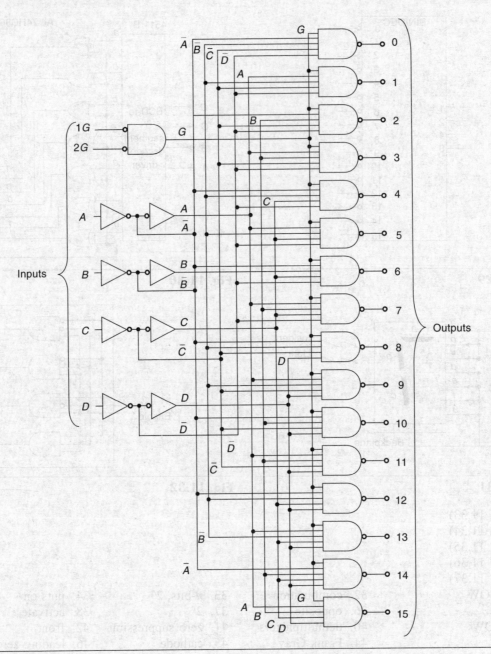

**Fig. 11.33**

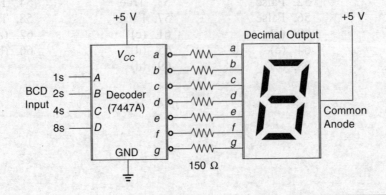

**Fig. 11.34**

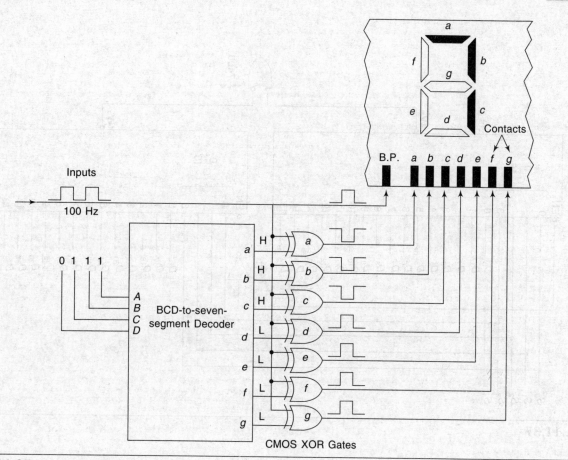

**Fig. 11.35**

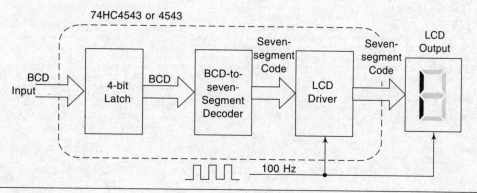

**Fig. 11.36**

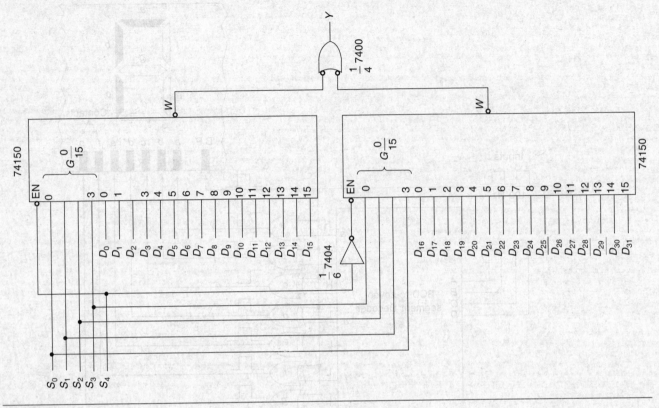

**Fig. 11.37**

# Flip-Flops

## INTRODUCTION

Sequential logic describes logic circuitry that follows a *specific order*. The devices (combinations of logic gates) can store or delay certain bits, which provides a *memory* function. Each stage in a sequential logic circuit depends on the results of the *previous* stage for its own inputs. Such types of circuits include the flip-flop (*bistable* multivibrator), the *one-shot* (*monostable* multivibrator), the *free-running* (*astable* multivibrator) and the *Schmitt trigger* (a *bistable device* that is activated by a certain analog voltage level).

To have a sequential system, we must know what has happened in the *past*. Therefore we must have storage devices to retain this information until we are ready to use it. *The basic unit for this storage is the* flip-flop (abbreviated FF). It can be flipped to one of its two binary states, and will remain in that state until caused to flop back again to its other state by some external stimulus.

## 12.1 Compare combinational and sequential circuits.

*Solution:* (See Table 12.1)

## 12.2 Describe the working of a regenerative switching circuit.

*Solution:*
Figure 12.1 shows two inverters connected in a ring. If the output of the first inverter $Q$ is equal to 1, this

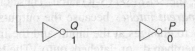

**Fig. 12.1** *A Regenerative Switching Circuit*

signal is fed to the input of the second inverter making its output $P$ equal to 0. This in turn forms the input to the first inverter which makes its output 1. Thus the circuit is *stable* with $Q = 1$ and $P = 0$. Alternatively, if $Q = 0$, this corresponds to a *second* stable state with

**Table 12.1**

| Combinational Circuit | Sequential Circuit |
|---|---|
| 1. It is a digital logic circuit whose output at any time depends solely on the combined set of inputs applied to it simultaneously at that instant of time. | 1. It is a digital logic circuit whose output depends on the present inputs as well as on the previous history of inputs. |
| 2. It contains no memory elements. | 2. It contains at least one memory element. |
| 3. It can be totally described by the set of output values only. | 3. Its performance is totally described by the set of subsequent state values as well as set of output values. |
| 4. It is easy to design, due to absence of memory. | 4. It is difficult to design due to presence of memory. |
| 5. Faster in speed because all inputs are primary inputs applied simultaneously. | 5. It is comparatively slower in speed because it has secondary inputs also, which are applied after a delay. |
| 6. It needs more hardware for its realization. | 6. It needs less hardware for its realization. |
| 7. It is expensive in cost. | 7. It is cheaper in cost. |

$Q = 0$ and $P = 1$. The circuit, therefore, has two stable states. It also has *two outputs Q and P*, where $P = \bar{Q}$. We can, therefore, consider the circuit to be a form of *bistable multivibrator*. This arrangement is an example of regenerative switching in which the output of one stage is amplified and fed back to *reinforce* the output signal, *forcing* the circuit into one state or the other.

The circuit of Fig. 12.1 is of little practical use. Its *state* is determined when power is applied and it then remains in that state until power is removed. There is no provision for *entering* the information required to be stored in it.

## S/R LATCH

A group of flip-flops sensitive to *pulse duration* is usually called a latch, whereas a group of flip-flops sensitive to *pulse transition* is called a register. For example, IC type 7475 is a 4-bit latch, whereas IC type 74175 is a 4-bit register.

The *latch* is a type of temporary storage device. The main difference between latches and flip-flops is the method used for changing their state.

### 12.3 Describe the operation of a transparent latch.

*Solution:*
In Fig. 12.2 we have a circuit with two input signals $R$ and $S$ and two output signals labeled $Q$ and $\bar{Q}$. If one input of a two-input NOR gate is held at 0, the relationship between the other input and output is that of an *inverter*. Figure 12.2 illustrates the simplest form of *data storage*, the *Set-Reset* (S-R) latch. These circuits are called *transparent latches* because the outputs respond immediately to changes at the input, and the input state will be remembered, or latched onto. The latch will sometimes have an *enable input* which is used to control the latch to *accept or ignore* the S-R input states.

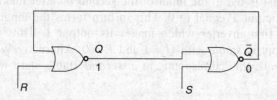

**Fig. 12.2** *A Latch formed from Two* NOR *Gates.*

### 12.4 Describe in detail the working of a Set-Reset (S-R) latch implemented with NAND gates.

*Solution:*
The S-R latch is the easiest to understand. Figure 12.3 shows an S-R latch implemented with NAND gates, called a NAND gate latch or simply a latch. The two NAND gates are *cross-coupled* so that the output of NAND-A is connected to one of the inputs of NAND-B and vice versa. Under normal conditions, the outputs will always be the inverse of each other. There are two latch inputs—

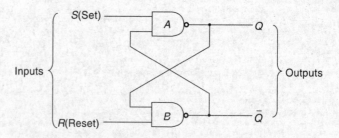

**Fig. 12.3** *S-R Latch Implemented with* NAND *Gates.*

the SET input sets $Q$ to the 1 state; the CLEAR input clears or resets $Q$ to the 0 state. The 'set' and 'reset' inputs are sometimes called the *Preset* and *Clear* inputs.

1. Assume that $S = 1$, $R = 1$ and $Q = 0$. Now $Q = 0$ and $R = 1$ are the states of the inputs of gate $B$. Therefore, the output of gate $B$ is at 1. The output of gate $B$ is connected to an input of gate $A$ so if $S = 1$, both inputs of gate $A$ are at the logic 1 state. This means that the output of gate $A$ must be 0 (as was originally specified). *The 0 state of $Q$ is continuously disabling gate $B$* so that any change in $R$ has no effect. Also, *the 1 state of $\bar{Q}$ is continuously enabling gate $A$* so that any change in $S$ will be transmitted through to $Q$. The above conditions constitute one of the stable states of the device, referred to as the *Reset state*, since $Q = 0$.

2. Now assume that with the S-R latch in the Reset state, the $S$ input goes to 0. The output of gate $A$, i.e., $Q$, will go to 1 and with $Q = 1$ and $R = 1$, the output of gate $B$, i.e. $\bar{Q}$, will go to 0. With $\bar{Q}$ now at 0, gate $A$ is *disabled*, keeping $Q$ at 1. Consequently, when $S$ returns to the 1 state, it has no effect on the latch, whereas a change in $R$ will cause a change in the output of gate $B$. The above conditions constitute the other stable state of the device, called the *Set state*, since $Q = 1$. *The change of state of $S$ from 1 to 0 has caused the latch to change from the Reset state to the Set state.*

3. Now assume that with the S-R latch in the Set state, $R$ changes from 1 to 0, $\bar{Q}$ goes to 1 *enabling* gate $A$. This causes $Q$ to go to 0, since $S = 1$, *disabling* gate $B$. In other words, *the change in $R$ causes the latch to go to the Reset state.* It will remain in the Reset state regardless of further changes in $R$.

4. Now assume that $S = 0$ and $R = 0$. When this happens, both $Q$ and $\bar{Q}$ will be forced to 1 and remain so for as long as both $S$ and $R$ at kept at 0. However, when both inputs return to 1, there is no way of knowing whether the latch will be in the Reset state or the Set state. This condition is said to be *indeterminate*. Because of this indeterminate state, *great care must be taken when using S-R latches to ensure that both inputs are not instructed simultaneously.*

**12.5 Describe the working of NAND gate version of S-R latch with the help of a transition table.**

*Solution:*

We can represent the action of S-R latch using a truth table which is often called a *transition table* since it indicates the transitions between states. When using any latch, it is tedious to draw it out fully in terms of gates and so special symbols are used. The symbol for the NAND S-R latch is given in Fig. 12.4. *The circles on the S and R inputs indicate that the latch is activated by a 0 level.*

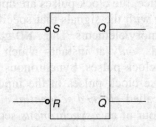

**Fig. 12.4** *S-R Latch Activated by* Negative-going Inputs (NAND *Version*).

**Table 12.2**

(a) Transition Table

| Initial Conditions | | Inputs (Pulsed) | | Final Output | |
|---|---|---|---|---|---|
| Q | $\bar{Q}$ | S | R | Q | $\bar{Q}$ |
| 1 | 0 | 0 | 0 | Indeterminate | |
| 1 | 0 | 0 | 1 | 1 | 0 |
| 1 | 0 | 1 | 0 | 0 | 1 |
| 1 | 0 | 1 | 1 | 1 | 0 |
| 0 | 1 | 0 | 0 | Indeterminate | |
| 0 | 1 | 0 | 1 | 1 | 0 |
| 0 | 1 | 1 | 0 | 0 | 1 |
| 0 | 1 | 1 | 1 | 0 | 1 |

(b) Simplified Version

| S | R | Q |
|---|---|---|
| 0 | 0 | Indeterminate |
| 0 | 1 | Set (1) |
| 1 | 0 | Reset (0) |
| 1 | 1 | Hold |

**12.6 Describe the working of a NOR gate S-R latch.**

*Solution:*

When NOR gates are used the *S* and *R* inputs are *transposed* compared with the NAND version. Also, *the stable state is when S and R are both 0.* A change of state is affected by pulsing the appropriate input to the 1 state. The *indeterminate state* is when both *S* and *R* are simultaneously at logic 1.

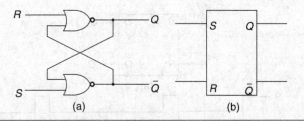

**Fig. 12.5** *(a) S-R Latch Implemented with* NOR *gates (b) Symbol for S-R Latch*

**Table 12.3**

| S | R | Q |
|---|---|---|
| 0 | 0 | Hold |
| 0 | 1 | Reset (0) |
| 1 | 0 | Set (1) |
| 1 | 1 | Indeterminate |

**12.7 Show the pin configuration of a quad-NOR gate 7402.**

*Solution:*

The pin configuration of a quad-NOR gate 7402 is given in Fig. 12.6 Looking at its pin layout in conjunction with Fig. 12.5(a), we can draw the circuit of Fig. 12.6. By performing a *timing analysis* on the S-R latch we can see why it is called *transparent* and also observe the latching phenomenon.

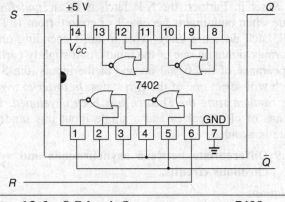

**Fig. 12.6** *S-R Latch Connections using a 7402.*

**12.8 Connect the waveforms given in Fig. 12.7(b) to the S-R latch in Fig. 12.7(a) and sketch the output waveform that will result. Give your observations.**

*Solution:*

*Observations*

1. The S-R latch is *latched* in the Set condition even after the HIGH is removed from the *S* input.
2. The latch is considered *transparent* because the *Q* output (Fig 12.7(c)) responds immediately to input changes.

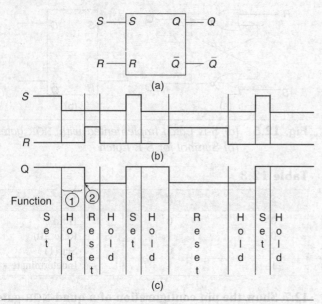

**Fig. 12.7**  *For P12.8 (a) S-R Latch (b) Given Waveforms (c) Output Waveform.*

## D-LATCH

In applications such as memories and so-called data latches, it is necessary to *remember* what the logic state of a single input has been even after the input has subsequently changed. The simple S-R latch cannot do this, since it requires two inputs, one to *Set* the latch and one to *Reset* it. Further, the S-R latch is in an *undefined state* when both inputs become 1 or go to 0 from 1. The S-R latch does not know what to do. Depending on a spurious signal on one of the inputs, or a slightly earlier appearance of the signal on one of the inputs, the S-R latch will select one of the two states. *In order to avoid the random state the D latch has been developed.* By means of clock pulses and a single input this random state is avoided.

### 12.9 Differentiate between asynchronous and synchronous circuits.

*Solution:*
The *external outputs* in a sequential circuit are not only a function of *internal inputs* but also of the present state of the *memory* elements. The next state of memory elements is also a function of external inputs and the present state. Thus, *a sequential circuit is specified by a time sequence of inputs, outputs and internal states.*

There are two main types of sequential circuits. Their classification depends on the *timing* of their signals. A *synchronous* sequential circuit is a system whose behaviour can be defined from the knowledge of its signals at discrete instants of time. Synchronous circuits operate sequentially, in step, with a control input. One way of achieving this goal is to use pulses of limited duration throughout the system so that one pulse amplitude represents logic-1 and another pulse amplitude (or the absence of a pulse) represents logic-0. The

difficulty with a system of pulses is that *any* two pulses arriving from *separate* independent sources to the inputs of the *same* gate will exhibit unpredictable delays, will separate the pulses slightly, and will result in *unreliable operation*. Practical synchronous sequential logic systems use *fixed amplitudes* such as voltage levels for the binary signals. Synchronization is achieved by a timing device called a *master-clock generator* which generates a periodic train of clock pulses distributed throughout the system in such a way that memory elements are affected only with the arrival of the synchronization pulse. In practice, the clock pulses are applied into AND gates together with the signals that specify the required change in memory elements. The AND gate outputs can transmit signals *only* at instants which coincide with the arrival of clock pulses. Synchronous sequential circuits which use clock pulses in the inputs of memory elements are called *clocked sequential circuits.*

The behaviour of an *asynchronous* sequential circuit depends on the *order* in which its inputs signals change and can be affected at *any* instant of time. The memory elements commonly used in asynchronous sequential circuits are *time-delay devices.* The memory capability of a time-delay device is due to the fact that it takes a finite time for the signal to propagate through the device. In practice, the *internal propagation delay* of logic gates is of sufficient duration to produce the needed delay, so that physical time delay units may be unnecessary. In gate-type asynchronous systems, the memory elements of Fig. 12.8 consist of logic gates whose propagation delays constitute the required memory. Thus, an asynchronomous sequential circuit may be regarded as *a combinational circuit with feedback.* Because of the feedback among logic gates, an asynchronous sequential circuit may, at times, become *unstable.* Instability imposes many problems. Hence they are not as commonly used as synchronous systems.

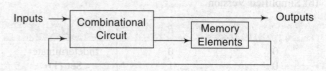

**Fig. 12.8**  *Block Diagram of a Sequential Circuit.*

### 12.10 Explain the working of a gated S-R latch.

*Solution:*
To make an S-R latch synchronous, we add a *gated input* to enable and disable the S and R inputs. Figure 12.9 shows the connections that convert the cross-coupled NOR S-R latch into a gated latch.

The $S_x$ and $R_x$ lines are the *original* Set and Reset inputs. With the addition of the AND gates, however, the $S_x$ and $R_x$ lines will be kept LOW-LOW (Hold condition) as long as the Gate Enable is LOW. The latch will operate normally while the Gate enable is HIGH.

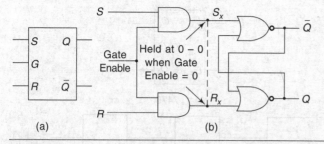

**Fig. 12.9** *Gated Cross-coupled* NOR *S-R Latch (a) Symbol (b) Circuit.*

The function table in Fig. 12.10 illustrates the operation of the gated S-R latch. *Function table is a table that illustrates all the possible input and output states for a given digital IC or device.*

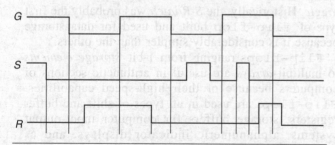

| G | S | R | Q | $\bar{Q}$ | Comments | |
|---|---|---|---|---|---|---|
| 0 | 0 | 0 | Q | $\bar{Q}$ | Hold | |
| 0 | 0 | 1 | Q | $\bar{Q}$ | Hold | Gate Inputs |
| 0 | 1 | 0 | Q | $\bar{Q}$ | Hold | Disabled |
| 0 | 1 | 1 | Q | $\bar{Q}$ | Hold | |
| 1 | 0 | 0 | Q | $\bar{Q}$ | Hold | |
| 1 | 0 | 1 | 0 | 1 | Reset | Gate Inputs |
| 1 | 1 | 0 | 1 | 0 | Set | Enabled |
| 1 | 1 | 1 | 0 | 0 | Unused | |

**Fig. 12.10** *Gated S-R Latch Function Table.*

**12.11** For the *G, S,* and *R* inputs in Fig. 12.11 into the gated S-R latch, sketch the output wave at *Q*, and list the latch functions.

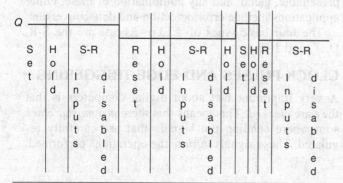

**Fig. 12.11** *G, S, and R Inputs into a Gated S-R Latch.*

*Solution:*

**Fig. 12.12** *Output Wave at Q for Inputs in Fig. 12.11 and Latch Functions.*

**12.12 Describe the working of a gated D-latch.**

*Solution:*

It is possible to set and reset an S-R latch from *one* input by feeding the Set input *direct* from the data input and the Reset input from the *inverted* data. When the data input is HIGH the latch will be Set, and when it is LOW, the latch will be Reset. However, this would be rather pointless, since the latch outputs would then *follow every change* in the data input. *To avoid this a gate is required that will isolate the data input from the latch after the desired data has been stored.*

There is a single input (*D*) to Set and Reset the latch. *S* and *R* will be *complementary* to each other and *S* is connected to a single line labeled *D* (*Data*). The operation is such that *Q will be the same as D while G is HIGH, and Q will remain latched when G goes LOW.*

S-R and clocked S-R latches have limited use, and possibly one of the simplest ways in which the circuit can be made more versatile is to add a single NOT gate to produce the D-type latch shown in Fig. 12.13.

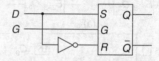

**Fig. 12.13** *The S-R Latch with a Data Input (D) and a Single* NOT *Gate to Produce the D-type Latch.*

**12.13 Determine the *Q* output waveform if the inputs shown in Fig. 12.14 are applied to the gated D-latch which is initially Reset.**

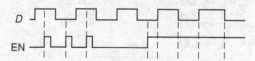

**Fig. 12.14** *Input Waveforms Applied to the Gated-D-Latch which is Initially Reset.*

*Solution:*

**Fig. 12.15** *Solution for Problem 12.13.*

**12.14 Sketch the output waveforms at *Q* for the inputs at *D* and *G* of the gated D-latch in Fig. 12.13.**

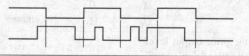

**Fig. 12.16** *Inputs at D and G of the Gated D-Latch in Fig. 12.13.*

*Solution:*

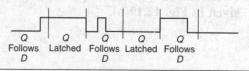

**Fig. 12.17** *Solution for Problem 12.14.*

## 12.15 Illustrate and explain integrated circuit D latch 7475.

*Solution:*

The 7475, (Fig. 12.18) an integrated circuit D latch, contains four transparent D latches. Latches 0 and 1 share a common enable ($E_{0-1}$) and latches 2 and 3 share a common enable ($E_{2-3}$). From the function table we can see that $Q$ output will follow $D$ (*transparent*) as long as the enable line ($E$) is HIGH (called *active-HIGH enable*). When $E$ goes LOW, the $Q$ output will become latched to the value that $D$ was just before the HIGH-to-LOW transition of $E$.

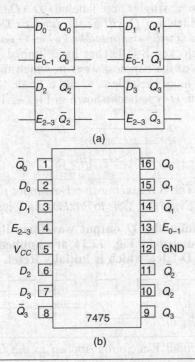

(a)

Fig. 12.18 *Integrated Circuit 7475 Quad Bistable D Latch (a) Logic Symbol and (b) Pin Configuration.*

**Table 12.4** *Function Table for the 7475 D Latch.*

| Inputs | | Outputs | | |
|---|---|---|---|---|
| D | EN | Q | $\bar{Q}$ | Comment |
| 0 | 1 | 0 | 1 | Reset |
| 1 | 1 | 1 | 0 | Set |
| X | 0 | $Q_0$ | $\bar{Q}_0$ | No change |

$Q_0$ is the prior output level.
X represents a "don't care".

## 12.16 For the inputs at $D_0$ and $E_{0-1}$ for the 7475 D latch shown in Fig. 12.19(a) sketch the output waveform at $Q_0$. The input waveforms are given in Fig. 12.19(b).

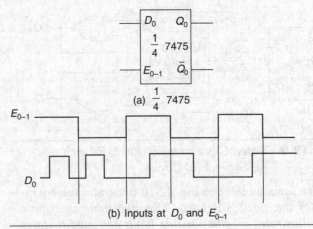

(a) $\frac{1}{4}$ 7475

(b) Inputs at $D_0$ and $E_{0-1}$

**Fig. 12.19**

*Solution:*

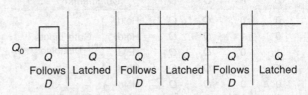

**Fig. 12.20** *The Output Waveforms at $Q_0$ of Fig 12.19(a).*

### FLIP-FLOPS

A device that exhibits *two different stable states* is extremely useful as a memory element in a binary system. Any electrical circuit that has this characteristic falls into the category of devices commonly known as flip-flops. They are also called *multivibrators* and *toggle*. Historically, the *S-R latch* was probably the first type of flip-flop built and used for data storage because it is considerably simpler than the others.

Flip-flops ranging from 1-bit *storage elements* to multibit-*arrays* are useful in arithmetic sections of computers because of their high-speed capabilities. Flip-flops are used in all types of shift and buffer registers, storage buffers for computer input-output systems, alphanumeric indicator displays, and as accumulators in conjunction with adders *to store and update data when clocked*. Flip-flops are also used in all types of counter applications including up/down, presettable, gated, and any combination of these. Other applications include error detection and data conversion.

The four basic types of flip-flops are the S-R, D, T, and J-K.

### CLOCK PULSES AND EDGE TRIGGERING

A very important fact about digital computers is that they are *clocked*. This means that there is a *master clock* somewhere sending out signals that are carefully regulated. These signals *initiate* the operations performed.

We can examine the operation of the flip-flops *before* and *after* the clock initiates an action. Initiating signals are often called *clock pulses* (Fig. 12.21).

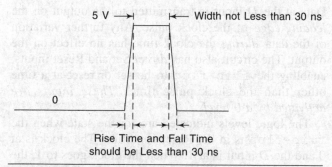

**Fig. 12.21** *Clockpulse.*

The clock pulse which is used in TTL and other systems should have a duration not less than 30 ns. The rise time and fall time of the pulse should be of the same order. Greater rise and fall times may cause oscillations in logic circuits.

A majority of circuits now respond to the *edges of square waves,* as in Fig. 12.22. Clocked circuits change only when the clock pulse arrives, some on the *positive-going* part of the clock pulse (Fig. 12.22a) when it changes from 0 to 1, others on the *negative-going* part of the clock pulse (Fig. 12.22b) when it changes from 1 to 0.

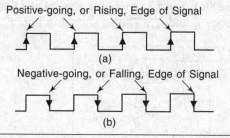

**Fig. 12.22** *Clock Waveforms.*

This distinction is parcticulary important since *most* flip-flops *respond to either a falling edge or a rising edge but not both.* The system rests between such edges. The reason for the *rest periods* is to give the circuit time to assume their new states and to give all transients time to die down.

## EDGE TRIGGERED S-R FLIP-FLOP

A clock input is included in edge-triggered flip-flops. This input is marked with a *small triangle,* as shown in Fig. 12.23(a). If the flip-flop responds to a negative-going edge, a *bubble* is placed at the clock input, as shown in Fig. 12.23(b). Sometimes the clock input is simply *marked CK or CP* instead of the triangle. Manufacturers who adopt this practice will specify whether the flip-flop is edge-triggered or not.

**12.17** **Illustrate the operation of a positive edge-triggered S-R flip-flop. Explain.**

*Solution:* (See Fig. 12.24)

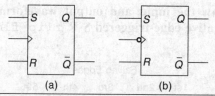

**Fig. 12.23** *(a) This Symbol is used for a Positive-going Edge-clocked* Flip-Flop. *(b) This symbol is used for a Negative-going Edge-clocked* Flip-Flop.

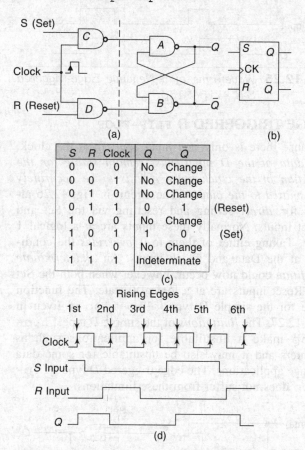

| S | R | Clock | Q | $\bar{Q}$ | |
|---|---|-------|---|-----------|---|
| 0 | 0 | 0 | No | Change | |
| 0 | 0 | 1 | No | Change | |
| 0 | 1 | 0 | No | Change | |
| 0 | 1 | 1 | 0 | 1 | (Reset) |
| 1 | 0 | 0 | No | Change | |
| 1 | 0 | 1 | 1 | 0 | (Set) |
| 1 | 1 | 0 | No | Change | |
| 1 | 1 | 1 | Indeterminate | | |

(c)

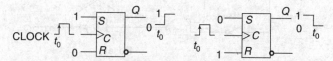

(i) $S = 1$, $R = 0$ Flip-Flop SETS on Rising Clock Edge. (If already SET, it remains SET.)

(ii) $S = 0$, $R = 1$ Flip-Flop RESETS on Rising Clock Edge. (If already RESET, it remains RESET)

(iii) $S = 0$, $R = 0$ Flip-Flop does not change. (If SET, it remains SET; If RESET, it remains RESET.)

(e)

**Fig. 12.24** *(a) Positive Edge-triggered S-R* flip-flop, *(b) Symbol, (c) Function Table, (d) Waveforms and (e) Operation.*

**12.18 Draw the input and output waveforms of a negative edge-triggered S-R `flip-flop`.**

*Solution:*

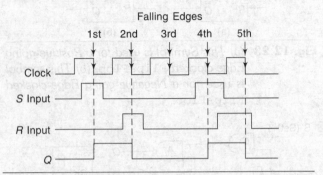

**Fig. 12.25** *Waveforms of a Negative Edge-triggered S-R* `Flip-Flop`.

## EDGE TRIGGERED *D* `FLIP-FLOP`

Because there is only one input apart from the clock, *the data at the D input must remain stable for the duration of the clock pulse if it is to be accurately transmitted to the output.* The circuit in Fig. 12.26 allows for *direct* setting and resetting via the Set and Reset inputs. Normally these inputs are at a logical 1 state. Taking either of them to 0 *overrides* the condition at the Data and Clock inputs. An *indeterminate condition* could now occur, however when both the Set and Reset inputs are at a logical 0 state. The function table for the simple D type `flip-flop` is given in Fig. 12.27. The *limitations* of the simple D type `flip-flop` make it unsuitable for applications such as counters and it may also be unsuitable for some data storage applications. The edge triggered *D* type `flip-flop` does not suffer from these limitations.

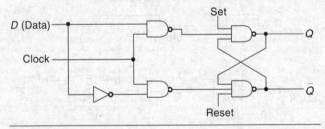

**Fig. 12.26** *D-Type* `Flip-Flop` *with Direct Setting and Resetting.*

| Set | Reset | Data | Q | Q̄ | |
|-----|-------|------|---|---|---|
| 1 | 1 | 0 | 0 | 1 | } After Clock |
| 1 | 1 | 1 | 1 | 0 | } Pulse |
| 1 | 0 | 0 | 0 | 1 | } Forced |
| 1 | 0 | 1 | 0 | 1 | } Reset |
| 0 | 1 | 0 | 1 | 0 | } Forced |
| 0 | 1 | 1 | 1 | 0 | } Set |
| 0 | 0 | 0 | 1 | 1 | } Indeterminate when |
| 0 | 0 | 1 | 1 | 1 | } Inputs are Removed. |

**Fig. 12.27** *Function Table for the Simple D Type* `Flip-Flop`.

**12.19 Explain in detail the working of a positive edge-triggered D-type `flip-flop`.**

*Solution:*
Data at the *D* input is transmitted to the output on the *leading edge* of the clock pulse. Any further variation of the data *during* the clock time has no effect on the output. The circuit also has *direct* Set and Reset inputs, enabling the `flip-flop` to be set or reset at a time other than the clock pulse time. *These inputs are activated by a 0 level.*

The logic levels indicated are for the state when the `flip-flop` is in the Reset condition. The clock is at 0 and the *D* input is at 1. When the clock goes to 1, the output of gate *B* will go to 0, causing the S-R `flip-flop` formed by *E* and *F* to be set. If, while the clock is still 1, the *D* input goes to 0, the output of gate *D* will go to 1. This has no effect on the output since *gate C is inhibited by the output of gate B*. When the clock goes to 0, the output of *B* goes back to 1 but *C* is now inhibited by the lack of a clock pulse, thus leaving the output `flip-flop` in its set state.

The circuit for the `flip-flop` is given in Fig. 12.28(a). The symbol for the `flip-flop` is given in Fig. 12.28(b). The arrow on the clock connection shows that the `flip-flop` clocks on the leading edge of the clock pulse. The truth table for the `flip-flop` is given in Fig. 12.28(c). The `flip-flop` gets set at a time midway between $t_n$ and $t_{n+}$. This is shown in Fig. 12.28(d).

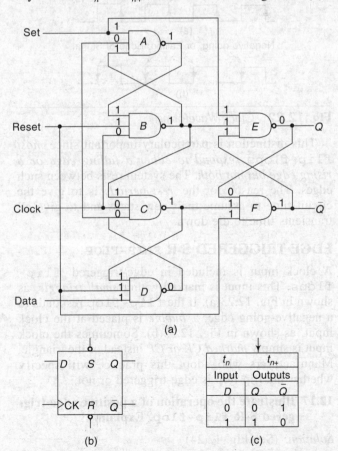

(a)

(b)

| $t_n$ | $t_{n+}$ | |
|-------|----------|--|
| Input | Outputs | |
| D | Q | Q̄ |
| 0 | 0 | 1 |
| 1 | 1 | 0 |

(c)

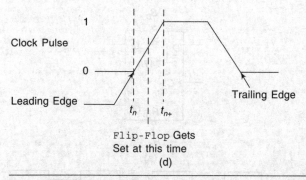

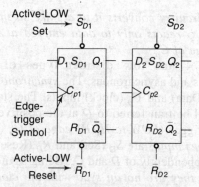

(d)

**Fig. 12.28** *Positive Edge-triggered* D Flip-Flop *with Direct Set and Reset. (a) Circuit, (b) Symbol and (c) Truth Table (*$t_n$ *is the Time Immediately before the Clock Pulse,* $t_{n+}$ *is the time Immediately after the Leading Edge of the Clock Pulse), (d) The* Flip-Flop *gets set at a Time Midway between* $t_n$ *and* $t_{n+}$.

**12.20 By referring to the description and truth table for the edge-triggered** $D$ **type** flip-flop, **sketch the voltage pattern at the** $Q$ **output for the following input conditions:**

| Clock:    | 0 | 0 | 1 | 1 | 0 | 0 | 1 | 1 | 0 | 0 | 1 | 1 | 0 | 0 |
|-----------|---|---|---|---|---|---|---|---|---|---|---|---|---|---|
| Data (D): | 0 | 1 | 1 | 1 | 1 | 0 | 0 | 1 | 1 | 1 | 1 | 0 | 0 | 0 |
| Reset:    | 0 | 1 | 1 | 1 | 1 | 1 | 1 | 1 | 1 | 1 | 1 | 1 | 1 | 1 |
| Set:      | 1 | 1 | 1 | 1 | 1 | 1 | 1 | 1 | 1 | 1 | 1 | 1 | 1 | 1 |

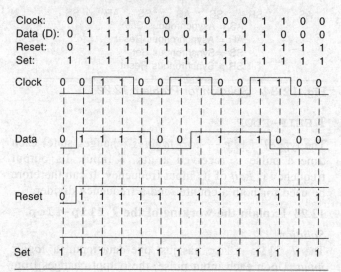

**Fig. 12.29** *Description and Truth Table for Edge-triggered* D Flip-Flop *Input Waveforms.*

*Solution:*

| $Q$ Output | 0 | 0 | 1 | 1 | 1 | 1 | 0 | 0 | 0 | 0 | 1 | 1 | 1 | 1 |
|------------|---|---|---|---|---|---|---|---|---|---|---|---|---|---|

**Fig. 12.30** *Solution for Problem 12.20.*

**12.21 Give the pin configuration and logic symbol of integrated circuit D** flip-flop **7474 and explain.**

*Solution:*

The 7474 is an *edge-triggered* device; the trigger point is at the *positive edge* of $C_p$ (LOW-to-HIGH transition). Edge-triggered devices are made to respond to only the

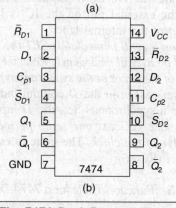

$D, C_p$ = Synchronous Inputs (Data, Clock)
$\bar{S}_D, \bar{R}_D$ = Synchronous Inputs (Set, Reset)
$Q, \bar{Q}$ = Outputs

(a)

(b)

**Fig. 12.31** *The 7474 Dual* D Flip-Flop: *(a) Logic Symbol (b) Pin Configuration.*

*edge* of the clock signal by converting the positive clock input pulse into a *single, narrow spike.* Figure 12.31 shows a circuit similar to that inside the 7474 to convert the single edge of $C_p$ into a *positive* spike. This is called a *positive-edge detection circuit.*

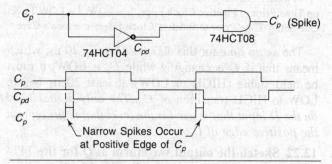

**Fig. 12.32** *Positive Edge-detection Circuit and Waveforms.*

The original clock pulse, $C_p$, is input to an inverter. The *inverted, delayed signal,* $\overline{C_{pd}}$ is fed into an AND gate, along with $C_p$. The output waveform, $C_p'$, is a very narrow pulse, called a *spike,* that lines up with the positive edge of $C_p$. This is now used as a trigger signal inside the $D$ flip-flop. Therefore, *even though a very wide pulse is entered at* $C_p$ *of the 7474, the edge-*

*detection circuitry converts it to a spike so that the D* flip-flop *reacts only to data entered at D at the positive edge of* $C_p$.

The 7474 has tow distinct types of inputs: synchronous and asynchronous. The *synchronous inputs* are the $D$ (Data) and $C_p$ (clock) inputs. The state at the $D$ input will be transferred to $Q$ at the positive edge of the input trigger (*LOW-to-HIGH edge of* $C_p$ ($\uparrow$)). The *asynchronous inputs* are $S_D$ (Set) and $R_D$ (Reset), which operate independently of $D$ and $C_p$. Being asynchronous means that *they are not in sync with the clock pulse*, and the $Q$ outputs will *respond immediately* to input changes at $\overline{S_D}$ and $\overline{R_D}$. The bubble at $S_D$ and $R_D$ means that they are *active-LOW inputs*, and because of inversion the external pin on the IC is labeled as the *complement* of the internal label.

*A LOW on* $S_D$ *will immediately SET the* flip-flop, *and a LOW on* $R_D$ *will immediately Reset the* flip-flop, *regardless of the states at the synchronous (D, $C_p$) inputs.*

The lower case *h* in the $D$ column indicates that, in order to do a synchronous Set, the $D$ input must be in the HIGH state *at least one setup period prior to the positive edge of the clock*. The same rules apply for the lower case *l* (Reset).

**Table 12.5** *Function Table for a 7474* D flip-flops

| Operating Mode | Inputs | | | | Outputs | |
|---|---|---|---|---|---|---|
| | $\overline{S_D}$ | $\overline{R_D}$ | $C_p$ | $D$ | $Q$ | $\bar{Q}$ |
| Asynchronous Set | L | H | x | x | H | L |
| Asynchronous Reset | H | L | x | x | L | H |
| Not Used | L | L | x | x | H | H |
| Synchronous Set | H | H | $\uparrow$ | h | H | L |
| Synchronous Reset | H | H | $\uparrow$ | l | L | H |

a$\uparrow$ = Positive Edge of Clock; H = HIGH; h = HIGH Level One Set-up Time Prior to Positive Clock Edge; L = LOW; l = LOW Level One Setup Time Prior to Positive Clock Edge; x = Don't Care.

The *setup time* for this flip-flop is 20 ns, which means that if $D$ is changing while $C_p$ is LOW, it must be held stable (HIGH or LOW) at least 20 ns before LOW-to-HIGH transition of $C_p$. The only digital level on the $D$ input that is used is the level that is present on the positive edge of $C_p$.

**12.22 Sketch the output waveform at $Q$ for the 7474 D flip-flop shown in Fig. 12.33(a) whose input waveforms are as given in Fig. 12.33(b).**

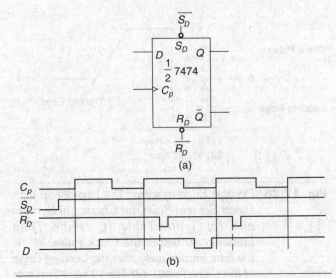

(a)

(b)

**Fig. 12.33** *(a) Logic Symbol and (b) Input Waveforms.*

*Solution:*

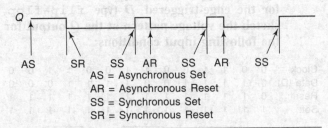

AS = Asynchronous Set
AR = Asynchronous Reset
SS = Synchronous Set
SR = Synchronous Reset

**Fig. 12.34** *Solution for Problem 12.22.*

### *T* FLIP-FLOP

The type $T$ flip-flop *toggles* (changes state) each time a pulse is received at its $T$ input. Its output frequency is *half* of its input frequency. It can therefore be used for both a counter and a frequency divider.

### 12.23 Explain the working of the *T* flip-flop.

*Solution:*

The $T$ flip-flop has just one data input, a *toggle input*. Upon each input pulse, the output changes from 1 to 0, then from 0 to 1. *If $T = 1$, the* flip-flop *changes state, if $T = 0$, the* flip-flop *stays in its current state.* $T$ flip-flops are not available as integrated circuits, but can be easily constructed from J-K flip-flops.

The logic symbol for a positive edge-triggered $T$ flip-flop is given in Fig. 12.35(a). In confirmity

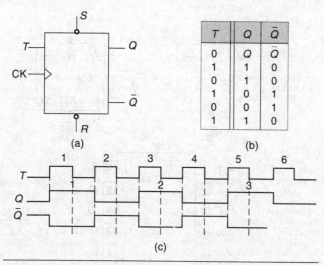

| T | Q | $\bar{Q}$ |
|---|---|---|
| 0 | Q | $\bar{Q}$ |
| 1 | 1 | 0 |
| 0 | 1 | 0 |
| 1 | 0 | 1 |
| 0 | 0 | 1 |
| 1 | 1 | 0 |

(a)  (b)

(c)

**Fig. 12.35** *(a) Positive Edge-triggered* T flip-flop *(b) Truth Table and (c) Input and Output Waveforms.*

with the truth table, Fig. 12.35(b), the positive-going edge determines the *change-over instant*.

When the input and output signals are examined, it is found that the output signal has half the input signal frequency, or in other words *the number of output pulses is half the number of inputs pulses*. Thus, the *T* flip-flop also functions as a frequency divider, or *divide-by-two* circuit.

## J-K FLIP-FLOP

The J-K flip-flop is available either as edge-triggered or master-slave. It is similar to the *D* type, except that there are now two controlling inputs, J and K, rather than one, that is *D*. This means that *there are more permutations possible for the output with respect to the inputs*; this occurs under the control of a clock pulse. The two alternatives, edge-triggered and master-slave, give sufficient scope for circuit design requirements. The J and K designations for the inputs have no known significance except that they are adjacent letters in the alphabet series.

### 12.24 Explain in detail the working of an edge-triggered J-K flip-flop.

*Solution:*
The behaviour of the J-K flip-flop can be determined completely by the voltages applied to the J and K terminals, and by the clock pulse, since it is a *clocked* flip-flop. The voltages on the J and K inputs may be used to *stop* the flip-flop from operating, to *force an output* of 1 or 0 on the *Q* terminals, or to make the flip-flop *change state* (from 0 to 1 or from 1 to 0) on each clock pulse. The unique features of J-K flip-flop are:

1. if the J and K inputs are *both at 1* when the clock pulse occurs, then the output will *change state* at

each clock pulse, from 1 to 0 to 1 to 0 to 1 and so on as long as there are clock pulses and as long as the J and K inputs are both held at 1. This last type of operation is sometimes described as *toggling* or *division-by-two*. For each two clock pulses into the clock input, there is one complete pulse at *Q* and of course its inverse at $\bar{Q}$. The pulse width of the output pulse will be equal to the time of two input clock pulses.

2. if the J and K inputs are *both at 0* when the clock pulse occurs, there will be *no change* in the output with a clock pulse, the flip-flop is *locked out* and the output *stores* the last digit which was at the terminal *Q*. If there is a 1 present at the J input and a 0 at the K input, then, *after* the clock pulse *Q* becomes 1 and $\bar{Q}$ becomes 0; this is irrespective of whatever was at these terminals *before* the clock pulse. If $J = 0$ and $K = 1$, then *after* the clock pulse, $Q = 0$ and $\bar{Q} = 1$. In either of these two cases, it does not matter what conditions were present *before* the clock pulse arrived.

3. There is no *indeterminate condition* in the operation of a J-K flip-flop as can be seen from the truth table.

Figure 12.36 shows a positive edge-triggered J-K flip-flop. It differs from the S-R edge-triggered flip-flop in that *the Q output is connected back to the input of gate $G_2$, and the $\bar{Q}$ output is connected back to the input of gate $G_1$*. The two control inputs are labeled J and K.

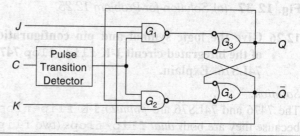

**Fig. 12.36** *Positive Edge-triggered J-K Flip-Flop.*

**Table 12.6** *Truth Table for a Positive Edge-triggered J-K flip-flop.*

| Inputs | | | Outputs | | |
|---|---|---|---|---|---|
| J | K | C | Q | $\bar{Q}$ | Comments |
| 0 | 0 | ↑ | $Q_0$ | $\bar{Q}_0$ | No change |
| 0 | 1 | ↑ | 0 | 1 | Reset |
| 1 | 0 | ↑ | 1 | 0 | Set |
| 1 | 1 | ↑ | $\bar{Q}_0$ | $Q_0$ | Toggle |

↑ = Clock Transition LOW to HIGH.
$Q_0$ = Output Level Prior to Clock Transition.

A J-K flip-flop can also be of the *negative edge-triggered* type in which case the clock input is *inverted*. The truth table in this case is identical except that it is triggered on the *falling edge* (↓) of the clock pulse.

**12.25 Draw the $Q$ output for the negative edge-triggered J-K flip-flop shown in Fig. 12.37. Assume that $Q$ is initially 0.**

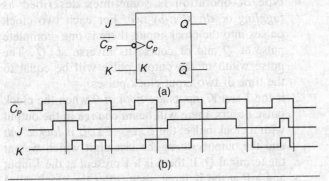

(a)

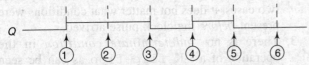

(b)

**Fig. 12.37** *Negative Edge-triggered J-K flip-flop (a) Logic Symbol and (b) Input Waveforms.*

*Solution:*

Q

① ② ③ ④ ⑤ ⑥

1. $J = 1$, $K = 0$ at the negative clock edge; $Q$ is Set
2. $J = 0$, $K = 0$ at the negative clock edge; $Q$ is held (transitions in $K$ before the edge are ignored)
3. $J = 0$, $K = 1$ at the negative clock edge; $Q$ is Reset
4. $J = 1$, $K = 1$ at the negative clock edge; $Q$ toggles
5. $J = 0$, $K = 1$ at the negative clock edge; $Q$ is Reset
6. $J = 0$, $K = 0$ at the negative clock edge; $Q$ is held

**Fig. 12.37** *(a) Solution for Problem 12.25.*

**12.26 Give the logic symbol and pin configuration of the integrated circuit J-K flip-flop 7476, 74LS76. Explain.**

*Solution:*

The 7476 and 74LS76 are *popular* J-K flip-flops, because they are both *dual* flip-flops (two flip-flops in each IC package) and they have *asynchronous inputs* ($\overline{R}_D$ and $\overline{S}_D$) as well as *synchronous inputs* ($\overline{C}_p$, J, K). The 7476 is a *positive pulse-triggered* (master-slave) flip-flop, and the 74LS76 is a *negative edge-triggered* flip-flop.

The *asynchronous* inputs $\overline{S}_D$ and $\overline{R}_D$ are active-low. That is LOW on $\overline{S}_D$ (Set) will set the flip-flop ($Q = 1$) and a LOW on $\overline{R}_D$ will Reset the flip-flop ($Q = 0$). The asynchronous inputs will cause the flip-flop to respond immediately without regard to the clock trigger input.

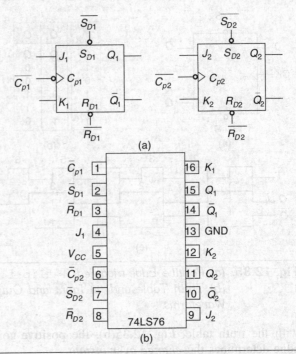

(a)

(b)

**Fig. 12.38** *The 74LS76 Negative Edge-triggered Flip-Flop: (a) Logic Symbol (b) Pin Configuration.*

**Table 12.7** *Function Table for the 74LS76[a]*

| Operating Mode | Inputs | | | | | Outputs | |
| --- | --- | --- | --- | --- | --- | --- | --- |
| | $\overline{S}_D$ | $\overline{R}_D$ | $\overline{C}_p$ | $J$ | $K$ | $Q$ | $\overline{Q}$ |
| Asynchronous Set | L | H | x | x | x | H | L |
| Asynchronous Reset | H | L | x | x | x | L | H |
| Synchronous Hold | H | H | ↓ | l | l | q | $\overline{q}$ |
| Synchronous Set | H | H | ↓ | h | l | H | L |
| Synchronous Reset | H | H | ↓ | l | h | L | H |
| Synchronous Toggle | H | H | ↓ | h | h | $\overline{q}$ | q |

[a]H = HIGH-voltage Steady State; L = LOW-voltage Steady State: h = HIGH Voltage one setup time Prior to Negative Clock Edge; l = LOW Voltage one setup time Prior to Negative Clock Edge; x = Don't Care; q = State of $Q$ Prior to Negative Clock Edge; ↓ = HIGh-to-LOW (negative) Clock Edge.

For *synchronous operations* using J, K, and $\overline{C}_p$, the asynchronous inputs must be *disabled* by putting a HIGH on both $\overline{S}_D$ and $\overline{R}_D$. The J and K inputs are read *one set up time prior* to the HIGH-to-LOW edge of the clock ($\overline{C}_p$). One set up time for the 74LS76 is 20 ns. This means that the state of J and K 20 ns before the negative edge of the clock is used to determine the synchronous operations to be performed. Of course, the 7476 master-slave will read the state of J and K during the *entire* clock pulse.

In the *toggle mode* (J = K = 1), after a negative clock edge, $Q$ becomes whatever $\bar{Q}$ was before the clock edge, and vice versa (that is, if $Q = 1$ *before* the negative edge, then $Q = 0$ *after* the negative clock edge).

## EXCITATION TABLE

Excitation table is generated by an *intuitive analysis of the truth table*. If the state of the output $Q_n$ *prior* to clocking is known and it is desired to have an output $Q_{n+1}$ *after* clocking, the table shows which data input is necessary. The term shown in the tables '$x$' represents a 'don't care' state. These 'don't care' states are valuable in logic design. They allow the designer to use fewer gates at the data inputs to control the gate operation while maintaining defined outputs for all input conditions.

### 12.27 Give the excitation tables for S-R, J-K, *D*, and *T* flip-flops.

*Solution:*

**Table 12.8** Flip-Flop *Excitation Tables*

| $Q(t)$ | $Q(t + 1)$ | $S$ | $R$ |
|---|---|---|---|
| 0 | 0 | 0 | X |
| 0 | 1 | 1 | 0 |
| 1 | 0 | 0 | 1 |
| 1 | 1 | X | 0 |

(a) *SR*

| $Q(t)$ | $Q(t + 1)$ | $J$ | $K$ |
|---|---|---|---|
| 0 | 0 | 0 | X |
| 0 | 1 | 1 | X |
| 1 | 0 | X | 1 |
| 1 | 1 | X | 0 |

(b) *JK*

| $Q(t)$ | $Q(t + 1)$ | $D$ |
|---|---|---|
| 0 | 0 | 0 |
| 0 | 1 | 1 |
| 1 | 0 | 0 |
| 1 | 1 | 1 |

(c) *D*

| $Q(t)$ | $Q(t + 1)$ | $T$ |
|---|---|---|
| 0 | 0 | 0 |
| 0 | 1 | 1 |
| 1 | 0 | 1 |
| 1 | 1 | 0 |

(d) *T*

## CONVERSIONS IN FLIP-FLOPS

Sometimes it is required to *convert* one type of flip-flop into another type. For this conversion we have to *combine* the excitation tables of the two flip-flops. The present and the next states of the output are shown. K-maps are drawn and simplified expression for the combinational logic is obtained. Then the required circuit is drawn.

### 12.28 How will you convert an S-R flip-flop into a J-K flip-flop?

*Solution:*
The truth table which combines the two excitation tables is shown in Fig. 12.39(a). The entries in the truth table are self explanatory. In the next step we draw K-maps and then *combine* the cells as shown in Fig. 12.39(b) and (c).

| R | S | Present State of Output | Desired State of Output | J | K |
|---|---|---|---|---|---|
| 0 | 0 | 0 | 0 | 0 | 0 |
| 0 | 0 | 1 | 1 | 0 | 0 |
| 0 | 0 | 0 | 0 | 0 | 1 |
| 1 | 0 | 1 | 0 | 0 | 1 |
| 0 | 1 | 0 | 1 | 1 | 0 |
| 0 | 0 | 1 | 1 | 1 | 0 |
| 0 | 1 | 0 | 1 | 1 | 1 |
| 1 | 0 | 1 | 0 | 1 | 1 |

(a) Truth Table for Conversion of S-R Flip-Flop into J-K Flip-Flop.

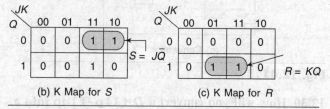

(b) K Map for $S$  $S = J\bar{Q}$

(c) K Map for $R$  $R = KQ$

**Fig. 12.39** *(a) Truth Table for Conversion (b) K map for S (c) K map for R.*

It is seen in Fig. 12.39 that we have to produce the relations $S = J\bar{Q}$ and $R = KQ$. For this purpose we need two AND gates as shown in Fig. 12.40. The AND gates can be omitted by obtaining the AND functions by the first two NAND gates of S-R flip-flop. Now we need NAND gates with three inputs as shown in Fig. 12.40(b).

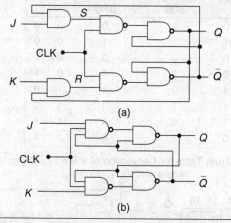

(a)

(b)

**Fig. 12.40** *(a) Conversion using AND Gates. (b) Conversion using NAND Gates.*

### 12.29 How will you convert a *T* flip-flop into a *D* flip-flop?

*Solution:*
We prepare a truth table indicating the *T* inputs, present state of output, next state of output and the desired *D*

input. This is shown in Fig. 12.41(a). Then we draw K-map as shown in Fig. 12.41(b). The K-map gives the Boolean expression $T = D\bar{Q} + \bar{D}Q$. From this expression we draw the logic circuit shown in Fig. 12.41(c).

| T | Present State of Q | Next State of Q | D |
|---|---|---|---|
| 0 | 0 | 0 | 0 |
| 1 | 1 | 0 | 0 |
| 1 | 0 | 1 | 1 |
| 0 | 1 | 1 | 1 |

(a) Truth Table for Conversion of *T* Flip-Flop into *D* Flip-Flop.

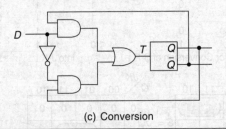

$T = \bar{D}Q + D\bar{Q}$

(b) K-Map

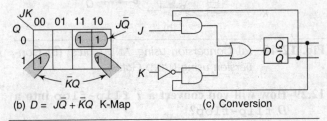

(c) Conversion

**Fig. 12.41**

**12.30  How will you convert a *D* flip-flop into a J-K flip-flop?**

*Solution:*

The truth table for this conversion is shown in Fig. 12.42(a). Using this truth table we draw the K-map, Fig. 12.42(b). The K-map gives the Boolean expression $D = J\bar{Q} + \bar{K}Q$. The logic circuit for this expression is shown in Fig. 12.42(c).

| D | Present State of Q | Next State of Q | J | K |
|---|---|---|---|---|
| 0 | 0 | 0 | 0 | 0 |
| 1 | 1 | 1 | 0 | 0 |
| 0 | 0 | 0 | 0 | 1 |
| 0 | 1 | 0 | 0 | 1 |
| 1 | 0 | 1 | 1 | 0 |
| 1 | 1 | 1 | 1 | 0 |
| 1 | 0 | 1 | 1 | 1 |
| 0 | 1 | 0 | 1 | 1 |

(a) Truth Table for Conversion of a *D* flip-flop into a J-K Flip-Flop.

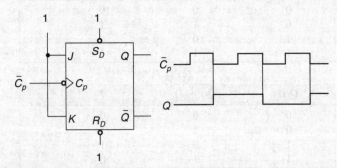

(b) $D = J\bar{Q} + \bar{K}Q$ K-Map          (c) Conversion

**Fig. 12.42**

**12.31  Illustrate the conversion of (a) a J-K flip-flop into a *D* flip-flop and (b) a J-K flip-flop into a *T* flip-flop. Explain.**

*Solution:*

(a) The flip-flop in Fig. 12.43 will operate as a *D* flip-flop because the data are brought in on the *J* terminal and its complement is at the *K*; so if Data = 1, the flip-flop will be *Set* after the clock edge; if Data = 0 the flip-flop will be *Reset* after the clock edge. *However, the toggle mode and hold mode are lost using this configuration.*

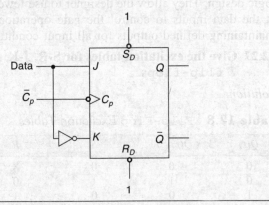

**Fig. 12.43** *D* Flip-Flop *Made from a* J-K Flip-Flop.

(b) It is often important for a flip-flop to operate in the *toggle mode*. This can be done simply by connecting both *J* and *K* to 1. This will cause the flip-flop to change states at each *active clock edge*, as shown in Fig. 12.44.

The frequency of the output waveform at *Q* will be *half* the frequency of the input waveform at $\bar{C}_p$.

**Fig. 12.44** J-K Flip-Flop *Connected as a Toggle* Flip-Flop.

## MASTER-SLAVE FLIP-FLOP

Flip-flop circuits frequently have flip-flop outputs fed back to the flip-flop inputs, or to combinational logic circuitry leading to the flip-flop inputs. Changes in `flip-flop` outputs are fed back to the `flip-flop` inputs, thus resulting in further changes in `flip-flop` outputs and, consequently, additional changes in inputs, and so on. If these changes produce *unpredictable, and hence undesirable output sequences,* the condition is called a *race*. One way to avoid races is to use *master-slave* `flip-flops`. A master-slave `flip-flop` is constructed from two separate `flip-flops`. One circuit serves as a *master* and the other as a *slave*, and the overall circuit is referred to as a master-slave `flip-flop`.

## 12.32 Explain the operation of a J-K master-slave `flip-flop`.

*Solution:*
A master-slave `flip-flop` is a combination of two clocked latches; the first is called the master and the second is the slave. *The master is positively clocked but the slave is negatively clocked.* This implies the following:
1. While the clock is *HIGH*, the master is active and the slave is inactive.
2. While the clock is *LOW*, the master is inactive and the slave is active.

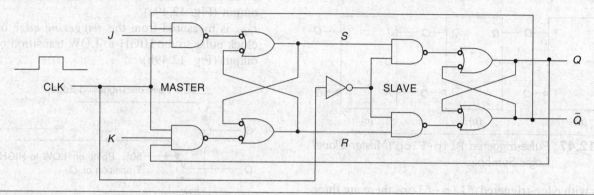

**Fig. 12.45** *Master-slave J-K* `Flip-Flop`.

*Set:* Let's assume LOW $Q$ and HIGH $\bar{Q}$. For an input condition of HIGH $J$, LOW $K$, and HIGH *CLK*, the master goes into the Set state, producing HIGH $S$ and LOW $R$. Nothing happens to the $Q$ and $\bar{Q}$ outputs because the slave is inactive while the clock is HIGH. When the clock goes LOW the HIGH $S$ and LOW $R$ force the slave into the set state, producing a HIGH $Q$ and a LOW $\bar{Q}$.

There are two distinct steps in setting the final $Q$ outputs. First, the *master* is set while the clock is HIGH. Second the *slave* is set while the clock is LOW. This action is sometimes called *cocking* and *triggering*. You cock the master during the positive half cycle of the clock, and you trigger the slave during the negative half cycle of the clock.

*Reset:* When the slave is set, $Q$ is HIGH and $\bar{Q}$ is LOW. For the input condition of LOW $J$, HIGH $K$, and HIGH *CLK*, the master will reset, forcing $S$ to go LOW and $R$ to go HIGH. Again, no changes can occur in $Q$ and $\bar{Q}$ because the slave is inactive while the clock is HIGH. When the clock returns to the LOW state, the LOW $S$ and HIGH $R$ force the slave to reset: this forces $Q$ to go LOW and $\bar{Q}$ to go HIGH.

*Cocking and triggering is the key idea behind the master-slave* `flip-flop`. *Every action of the master with a HIGH CLK is copied by the slave when the CLK goes LOW.*

*Toggle:* If the $J$ and $K$ inputs are both HIGH, the master toggles once while the clock is HIGH, the slave then toggles once when the clock goes LOW. *No matter what the master does, the slave copies it.* If the master toggles into the set state, the slave toggles into the set state. If the master toggles into the reset state, the slave toggles into the reset state.

*Level Clocking:* The master-slave `flip-flop` is level clocked in Fig. 12.45. While the clock is HIGH any changes in $J$ and $K$ can affect the $S$ and $R$ outputs. For this reason, you normally keep $J$ and $K$ constant during the positive half cycle of the clock. After the clock goes LOW, the master becomes inactive and you can allow $J$ and $K$ to change. *Level clocking* is a type of triggering in which the output of a `flip-flop` responds to the level (HIGH or LOW) of the clock signal. With positive level clocking, for example, the output can change *at any time* during the positive half cycle.

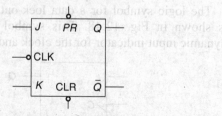

**Fig. 12.46** *Symbol for Master-slave* `Flip-Flop`. *The Bubble on the CLK Indicates that the Output Changes when the Clock goes Low.*

## PULSE-TRIGGERED `FLIP-FLOPs`

The term *pulse-triggered* means that data are entered into the `flip-flop` on the *leading edge* of the clock pulse, but the output does not reflect the input until the *trailing edge* of the clock pulse. The inputs must be *set* prior to the clock pulse's leading edge but the output is *postponed* until the trailing edge of the clock. A major *restriction* of the pulse-triggered `flip-flop` is that *the data inputs must not change while the clock pulse is HIGH* because the `flip-flop` is sensitive to any change of input levels during this time.

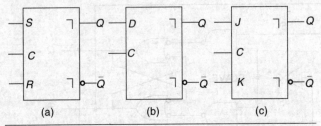

**Fig. 12.47** *Pulse-triggered* `Flip-Flop` *(Master-Slave) Logic Symbols.*

As with edge-triggered `flip-flops` there are three basic types of pulse-triggered `flip-flops`: S-R, D, and J-K. The J-K is by far the most commonly available in integrated circuit form. The logic symbols of all the three types are shown in Fig. 12.47. The key to identifying a pulse-triggered (master-slave) `flip-flop` by its logic symbol is the *postponed output symbol* (⌐) at the outputs. Notice that *there is no dynamic input indicator* (▷) at the clock input.

### 12.33  Explain a data lock-out `flip-flop`.

*Solution:*
The *data lock-out* `flip-flop` is similar to the pulse-triggered (master-slave) `flip-flop` except that it has a *dynamic clock input* so that it is sensitive to the data inputs only during a clock transition. After the leading-edge clock transition, the data inputs are disabled and do not have to be held constant while the clock pulse is HIGH. In essence, *the master portion of this* `flip-flop` *is like an edge-triggered device, and the slave portion performs as in a pulse-triggered device to produce a postponed output.*

The logic symbol for a data lock-out `flip-flop` is shown in Fig. 12.48. This symbol has *both* the dynamic input indicator for the clock and the postponed

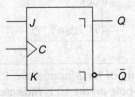

**Fig. 12.48** *Logic Symbol for a Data Lock-out J-K* `Flip-Flop`.

output indicators. This type of `flip-flop` is actually classified by most manufacturers as *a master-slave with a special lock-out feature.*

### 12.34  Discuss the operating characteristics of `flip-flops`.

*Solution:*
1. *Propagation Delay Time* is the interval of time required after the input signal has been applied for the resulting output change to occur.
   $t_{PLH}$ is measured from the *triggering edge* of the clock pulse to the *LOW-to-HIGH* transition of the output (Fig. 12.49a).
   $t_{PHL}$ is measured from the *triggering edge* of the clock pulse to the HIGH-to-LOW transition of the output (Fig. 12.49b).

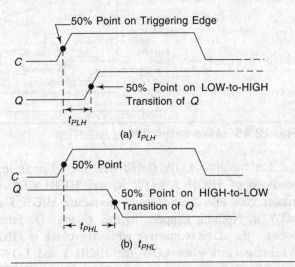

**Fig. 12.49** *Propagation Delays, Clock to Output.*

$t_{PLH}$ is measured from the *preset input* to the *LOW-to-HIGH* transition of the output. (Fig. 12.50a)
$t_{PHL}$ is measured from the *clear input* to the *HIGH-to-LOW* transition of the output (Fig. 12.50b).

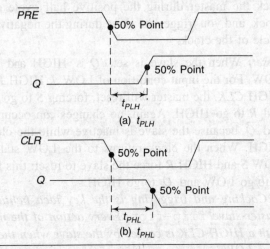

**Fig. 12.50** *Propagation Delays, Preset and Clear to Output.*

2. *Set-Up Time* ($t_s$) is the minimum interval required for the control levels to be *maintained constantly* on the inputs (*J* and *K*, or *S* and *R*, or *D*) *prior* to the triggering edge of the clock pulse for the levels to be *reliably clocked* into the flip-flop (Fig. 12.51).

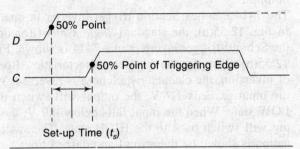

**Fig. 12.51**  *Set-up Time (*$t_s$*) for a* D Flip-Flop.

3. *Hold Time* ($t_h$) is the minimum interval required for the control levels to remain on the inputs *after* the triggering edge of the clock pulse for the levels to be *reliably clocked* into the flip-flop (Fig. 12.52).

4. *Maximum Clock Frequency* ($f_{max}$) is the highest rate at which a flip-flop can be *reliably triggered*. At clock frequencies above the maximum, the flip-flop would be unable to respond quickly enough and its operation would be impaired.

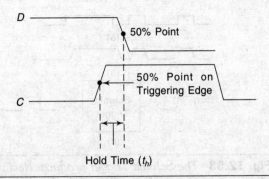

**Fig. 12.52**  *Hold Time (*$t_h$*) for a* D Flip-Flop.

5. *Pulse Widths* ($t_w$) for *reliable operation* are usually specified by the manufacturer for the clock, preset, and clear inputs. Typically, the clock is specified by its *minimum HIGH time* and its *minimum LOW time*.

6. *Power Dissipation* ($P_{TOT}$) The power dissipation of a flip-flop is the *total power consumption* of the device. The power dissipation is very important in most applications in which the *capacity of the d.c. supply* is a concern.

### 12.35 Compare the operating characteristics of flip-flops.

*Solution:*
Table 12.9 provides a *comparison* of several TTL devices and a CMOS device in terms of the *operating parameters*.

**Table 12.9**  *Comparison of Operating Characteristics of* Flip-flops

| Parameter | TTL | | | | | CMOS |
|---|---|---|---|---|---|---|
| (Time in ns) | 7474 | 74LS76A | 74L71 | 74107 | 74111 | 74HC112 |
| $t_{PHL}$ (CLK to $Q$) | 40 | 20 | 150 | 40 | 30 | 31 |
| $t_{PLH}$ (CLK to $Q$) | 25 | 20 | 75 | 25 | 17 | 31 |
| $t_{PHL}$ ($\overline{\text{CLR}}$ to $Q$) | 40 | 20 | 200 | 40 | 30 | 41 |
| $t_{PLH}$ ($\overline{\text{PRE}}$ to $Q$) | 25 | 20 | 75 | 25 | 18 | 41 |
| $t_s$ (set-up) | 20 | 20 | 0 | 0 | 0 | 25 |
| $t_h$ (hold) | 5 | 0 | 0 | 0 | 30 | 0 |
| $t_w$ (CLK HI) | 30 | 20 | 200 | 20 | 25 | 25 |
| $t_w$ (CLK LO) | 37 | — | 200 | 47 | 25 | 25 |
| $t_w$ ($\overline{\text{CLR}}$/$\overline{\text{PRE}}$) | 30 | 25 | 100 | 25 | 25 | 25 |
| $f_{max}$ (MHz) | 15 | 45 | 3 | 20 | 25 | 20 |
| Power (mW/F-F) | 43 | 10 | 3.8 | 50 | 70 | 0.12 |

## SCHMITT TRIGGERS

When a computer is running the gate outputs are rapidly switching from one state to another. If you look at these signals on an oscilloscope, you see signals that ideally represent *rectangular waves* like Fig. 12.53(a). When digital signals are transmitted and later received, they are often *corrupted* by noise, attenuation, or other factors, and they may end up looking like the ragged waveform shown in Fig. 12.53(b). If you try to use these *non-rectangular* signals to drive a gate or any other digital device, you may get *unreliable operation*.

This is where the Schmitt trigger comes in. It is designed to *clean up* ragged-looking pulses, producing almost vertical transitions between the HIGH and LOW state, and vice versa (Fig. 12.53(c)). In other words, *the Schmitt trigger produces a rectangular output, regardless of the input waveform*.

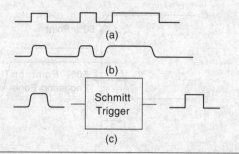

**Fig. 12.53** *The Schmitt Trigger produces Rectangular Output, Regardless of the Input Waveform.*

## 12.36 Explain in detail the operation of a Schmitt trigger.

*Solution:*
A Schmitt trigger is an electronic circuit that is used to detect whether a voltage has crossed over a given reference level. It has two stable states and is especially useful as a *signal-conditioning device*. Given a sinusoidal waveform, a triangular wave or any other periodic waveform, *the Schmitt trigger will produce a rectangular output that has sharp leading and trailing edges*. Fast rise and fall times like this are desirable for all digital circuits.

Figure 12.54 shows the *transfer function* ($V_{out}$ vs $V_{in}$) for any Schmitt trigger. The value of $V_{in}$ that causes the output to jump from '*LOW to HIGH*' is called the *positive-going threshold voltage* $V_{T+}$. The value of $V_{in}$ that causes the output to switch from '*HIGH to LOW*' is called the *negative-going threshold voltage*, $V_{T-}$.

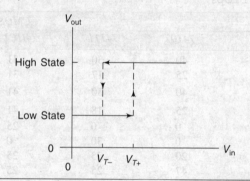

**Fig. 12.54** *Schmitt Trigger Transfer Characteristic.*

The output voltage is either HIGH or LOW. When the output is LOW, it is necessary to *raise* the input to slightly more than $V_{T+}$ to produce switching action. The output will then switch to the HIGH state and remain there until the input is *reduced* to slightly below $V_{T-}$. The output will then switch back to the low state. The arrows and the dashed lines show the *switching action*.

The difference between the two threshold voltages is known as *hysteresis*. It is possible to eliminate hysteresis by circuit design, but *a small amount of hysteresis is desirable because it ensures a rapid switching action over a wide temperature range*. Hysteresis can also be

a very beneficial feature. For instance, it can be used to provide noise immunity in certain applications, digital modems, for example.

## 12.37 Illustrate and explain the hex Schmitt-trigger inverter, the TTL 7414.

*Solution:*
The 7414 is a hex Schmitt trigger-inverter in one DIP. In Fig. 12.55(a), the standard *logic symbol* for one of the Schmitt-trigger inverters in a 7414 is shown. Figure 12.55(b) illustrates the transfer characteristics. Because of inversion, the characteristic curve is reversed. When the input exceeds 1.7 V, the output will switch to the LOW state. When the input falls below 0.9 V, the output will switch back to the HIGH state. The switching action is shown by the arrows and dashed lines.

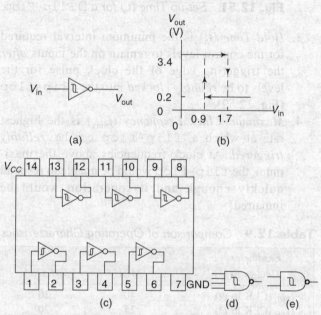

**Fig. 12.55** *(a) 7414 Schmitt-trigger Inverter (b) Because of Inversion the Transfer Characteristic Curve is Reversed from that Shown in Fig. 12.54 (c) Hex-Schmitt-trigger inverters (d) 4-Input* NAND *Schmitt Trigger (e) 2-Input* NAND *Schmitt Trigger.*

## 12.38 Use the Schmitt trigger to convert a small-sine wave, $E_s$, into a square wave $V_{out}$.

*Solution:*
The diode in Fig. 12.56 is used to short the negative 4 V from $E_s$ to ground to *protect* the Schmitt trigger in Fig. 12.56(a). The 1 k$\Omega$ resistor will *limit* the current through the diode when it is conducting.

$$I_D = (4 \text{ V} - 0.7 \text{ V})/1 \text{ k}\Omega = 3.3 \text{ mA}$$

$$I_{IH} = 40 \ \mu A$$

$$V_{1k} = 40 \ \mu A \times 1 \text{ k}\Omega = 0.04 \text{ V when } V_{in} \text{ is HIGH}$$

$$V_{1k} = 4 \text{ V}$$

The input to the Schmitt trigger will, therefore, be a half-wave signal with a 4.0 V peak. The output will be a square wave, as shown in Fig. 12.56(b).

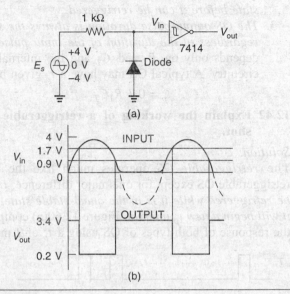

**Fig. 12.56**

## 555 TIMER

The 555 timer is a *TTL-compatible* integrated circuit that can be used as an oscillator to provide a clock waveform. It is basically a *switching circuit* that has two distinct output levels. With proper external components connected, neither of the output levels is stable. As a result the circuit continuously switches back and forth between these *two unstable states*. In other words, the circuit oscillates and the output is a periodic, rectangular waveform. Since neither output state is stable, the circuit is said to be astable, and is *often referred to as a free-running or astable multivibrator.*

### 12.39 Describe the working of 555 timer IC.

*Solution:*

The function block diagram of the 555 timer IC, Fig. 12.57, consists of a *potential dividing network* $R_1$, $R_2$, and $R_3$; two *voltage comparators;* a *set-reset* `flip-flop;` an *inverting buffer output stage,* and *two transistors.* The circuit functions satisfactorily with supply voltages ranging from 4.5 V to 18 V. The output of the set-reset `flip-flop` switches to LOW when a positive input is applied to the *set* terminal and switches to HIGH when a positive input appears at the *reset* terminals.

The potential divider provides a bias voltage to the inverting input terminal of comparator 1, and a different bias voltage to the non-inverting terminal of comparator 2. Access to the other inputs of the comparators is available via terminals 2 and 6, identified as *trigger* and *threshold,* respectively.

The comparator output levels *control* the `flip-flop,` and the `flip-flop` output is fed to the output

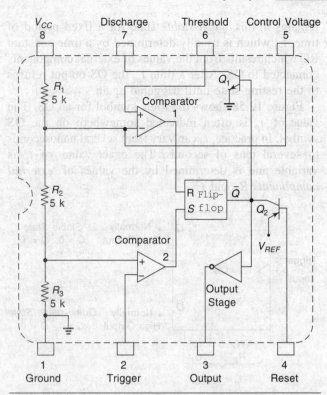

**Fig. 12.57** *Functional Block Diagram of 555 Timer IC.*

stage and to the base of *npn* transistor $Q_1$. When the `flip-flop` output is HIGH, $Q_1$ is biased on. In this condition the transistor is typically used to *discharge* a capacitor connected to terminal 7. $Q_1$ is off when the `flip-flop` output is LOW. The output stage provides a low output resistance and also inverts the output level of the `flip-flop.` The voltage at terminal 3 is LOW when the `flip-flop` output is HIGH, and HIGH when the `flip-flop` output is LOW. The output stage (at output terminal 3) can *sink* or *source* a maximum current of 200 mA.

Transistor $Q_2$ is a *pnp* device with its emitter connected to an internal reference voltage $V_{REF}$ which is always less than $V_{CC}$. If reset terminal 4 is connected to $V_{CC}$, the base-emitter junction of $Q_2$ is reverse biased, causing the transistor to remain *off*. When terminal 4 is pulled below $V_{REF}$ (i.e., towards ground level), $Q_2$ switches *on*. This turns $Q_1$ *on*, causes the output at terminal 3 to go to ground level, and *resets* the `flip-flop` to its HIGH output state.

### 12.40 Briefly describe a one-shot (OS) multivibrator.

*Solution:*

A digital circuit that is somewhat related to the `flip-flop` is the *one-shot* (monostable). *Like* the FF, the OS has two outputs, $Q$ and $\bar{Q}$, which are the inverse of each other. *Unlike* the FF, the OS has only one *stable* output state (normally $Q = 0$, $\bar{Q} = 1$), where it remains until it is triggered by an input signal. Once triggered, the OS outputs switch to the opposite state ($Q = 1$, $\bar{Q} = 0$). It remains in this *quasi-stable* state for a fixed period of time, $t_p$, which is usually determined by a time constant RC which results from the values of external components connected to OS. After a time $t_p$, the OS output returns to the resting state until triggered again.

Figure 12.58 shows the logic symbol for an OS. The value of $t_p$ is often indicated somewhere on the OS symbol. In practice, $t_p$ can vary from several nanoseconds to several tens of seconds. The exact value of $t_p$ is variable and is determined by the values of *external components* $R_T$ and $C_T$.

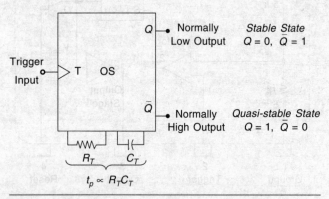

**Fig. 12.58**   *The Logic Symbol for a One-shot.*

### 12.41 Explain the working of non-retriggerable one-shot.

*Solution:*

The waveforms in Fig. 12.59 illustrate the operation of a *non-retriggerable OS* that triggers on positive-going transitions (PGTs) at its trigger ($T$) input. Note that

1. The PGTs at points *a*, *b*, *c*, and *e* will trigger the OS to its *quasi-stable state* for a time $t_p$ after which it automatically returns to the stable state.

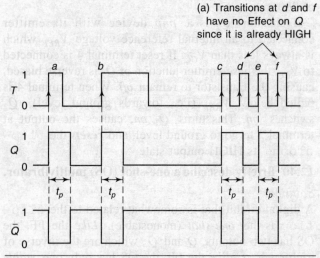

(a) Transitions at *d* and *f* have no Effect on *Q* since it is already HIGH

**Fig. 12.59**   *Typical Waveforms for Non-retriggerable Operation.*

2. The PGTs at points *d* and *f* have no effect on the OS because it has already been triggered to the quasi-stable state. *The OS must return to the stable state before it can be retriggered.*
3. *The OS output-pulse duration is always the same regardless of the duration of the input pulses.* $t_p$ depends only on $R_T$ and $C_T$ and the internal OS circuitry. A typical OS may have a $t_p$ given by:

$$t_p = 0.7\, R_T C_T$$

### 12.42 Explain the working of a retriggerable one shot.

*Solution:*

The *retriggerable OS* operates much like the non-retriggerable OS except for one major difference. *It can be retriggered while it is in the quasi-stable state, and it will begin a new* $t_p$ *interval.* Figure 12.60(a) compares the response of both types of OS using a $t_p$ of 2 ms.

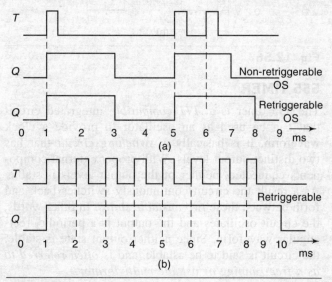

**Fig. 12.60**   *(a) Comparison of Non-retriggerable and Retriggerable OS Responses for* $t_p$ = 2 ms. *(b) Retriggerable OS begins a New* $t_p$ *each Time it Receives a Trigger Pulse.*

Both types of OS respond to the *first* trigger pulse at $t = 1$ ms by going HIGH for 2 ms and then returning LOW. The *second* trigger pulse at $t = 5$ ms triggers both one-shots to the HIGH state. The *third* trigger pulse at $t = 6$ ms has no effect on the *non-retriggerable OS*, since it is already in its quasi-stable state. However, this trigger pulse will *retrigger* the *retriggerable OS* to begin a new $t_p = 2$ ms interval. Thus it will stay HIGH for 2 ms *after* this third trigger pulse.

In effect, then, *a retriggerable OS begins a new* $t_p$ *interval each time a trigger pulse is applied regardless of the current state of its output Q.* In fact, trigger pulses can be applied at a rate fast enough that the OS will always be retriggered before the end of the $t_p$ interval and $Q$ will remain HIGH. This is shown in Fig. 12.60(b), where eight pulses are applied every 1 ms. $Q$ does not return LOW until 2 ms after the last trigger pulse.

### 12.43 What are the different types of multivibrators?

*Solution:*

Flip-flops have two stable states; therefore, we can say that they are *bistable multivibrators*. One shots have one stable state, and so they are called *monostable multivibrators*. Yet, a third type of multivibrator has no stable states; it is called an *astable* or *free-running multivibrator*. This type of logic circuit switches back and forth (*oscillates*) between two unstable output states. It is useful for providing clock signals for synchronous digital circuits.

### 12.44 How can a Schmitt trigger inverter be connected as an oscillator?

*Solution:*

Figure 12.61 shows how a Schmitt-trigger inverter can be connected as an oscillator. The signal at $V_{out}$ is an approximate square wave with a frequency that depends on the $R$ and $C$ values. The relationship between the frequency and RC values is shown in Fig. 12.61(b) for three different Schmitt-trigger inverters. *The circuit will fail to oscillate if R is not kept below these limits.*

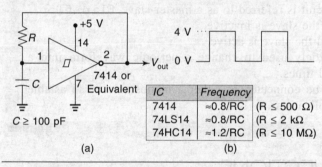

| IC | Frequency | |
|---|---|---|
| 7414 | ≈0.8/RC | (R ≤ 500 Ω) |
| 74LS14 | ≈0.8/RC | (R ≤ 2 kΩ |
| 74HC14 | ≈1.2/RC | (R ≤ 10 MΩ) |

(a)                     (b)

**Fig. 12.61** *Schmitt-trigger Oscillator, A 7413 Schmitt-trigger* NAND *may also be used.*

### 12.45 Show how a 555 timer can be used as an astable multivibrator.

*Solution:*

The 555 timer IC is a *TTL-compatible device* that can operate in several different modes. Figure 12.62 shows how external components can be connected to a 555 so that it operates as a free-running oscillator. Its output is a repetitive rectangular waveform that switches between

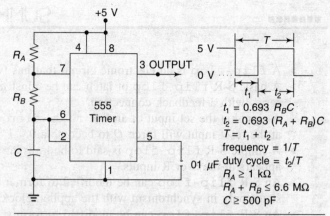

$t_1 = 0.693\ R_B C$
$t_2 = 0.693\ (R_A + R_B)C$
$T = t_1 + t_2$
frequency = $1/T$
duty cycle = $t_2/T$
$R_A \geq 1\ k\Omega$
$R_A + R_B \leq 6.6\ M\Omega$
$C \geq 500\ pF$

**Fig. 12.62** *555 Timer IC used as an Astable Multivibrator.*

two logic levels with the time interval at each logic level determined by $R$ and $C$ values. The formulas for these time intervals, $t_1$ and $t_2$, and the overall period of the oscillations, $T$, are given in the figure. The frequency of oscillations is the reciprocal of $T$ ($f = 1/T$), $t_1$ and $t_2$ *intervals cannot be equal unless $R_A$ is made zero.* This cannot be done without producing excess current through the device. This means that *it is impossible to produce a perfect 50 percent duty-cycle square wave output.* It is possible, however, to get very close to a 50 percent duty cycle by making $R_B \gg R_A$ (while keeping $R_A$ greater than 1 kΩ), so that $t_1 \approx t_2$.

### 12.46 Calculate the frequency and duty cycle of the 555 astable multivibrator output for $C = 0.001\ \mu F$, $R_A = 2.2\ k\Omega$, and $R_B = 100\ k\Omega$.

*Solution:*

$t_1 = 0.693\ (100\ k\Omega)(0.001\ \mu F) = 69.3\ \mu s$
$t_2 = 0.693\ (102.2\ k\Omega)(0.001\ \mu F) = 70.7\ \mu s$
$T = (69.3 + 70.7)\mu s = 140\ \mu s$
$f = 1/140\ \mu s = 7.29\ KHz$

Duty cycle = $70.7/140 = 50.5\%$

*Note:*

1. The duty cycle is *close to 50 percent* (square wave) because $R_B \gg R_A$.
2. It can be made *even closer* to 50 percent by making $R_B$ even larger compared with $R_A$.
3. If we change $R_A$ to 1 kΩ (its minimum allowed value), the results are $f = 7.18\ KHz$ and duty cycle = 50.3%.

# SUMMARY

■■■■■■

> A flip-flop is an electronic circuit that has two stable states. It is said to be bistable.
> A basic S-R flip-flop or latch can be constructed by connecting two NAND gates or NOR gates in series with a feedback connection.
> A signal at the set input of an S-R flip-flop will force the $Q$ output to become a 1, while a signal at the reset input will force $Q$ to become a 0.
> A simple S-R flip-flop is said to be transparent, that is, its output changes state whenever a signal appears at the S or R inputs.
> An S-R flip-flop can be modified to form a clocked S-R flip-flop whose output can change states only in synchronism with the applied clock.
> An S-R flip-flop can be modified to form a D flip-flop.
> In a $D$ latch, the stored data may be changed while the clock is HIGH. The last value of $D$ before the clock returns LOW is the data that is stored.
> With edge-triggered $D$ flip-flops, the data is sampled and stored on either the positive or negative clock edge.
> The value of $J$ and $K$ determine what a J-K flip-flop does on the next clock edge. When both are LOW, the flip-flop retains its last state. When $J$ is LOW and $K$ is HIGH, the flip-flop resets. When $J$ is HIGH and $K$ is LOW, the flip-flop sets. When both are HIGH, the flip-flop toggles.
> In the toggle mode, the J-K flip-flop can be used as a frequency divider.
> A major restriction of the pulse-triggered flip-flop is that the data inputs must not change while the clock pulse is HIGH because the flip-flop is sensitive to any change of input levels during this time.
> A master-slave flip-flop is constructed from two separate flip-flops. One circuit serves as a master, and the other as a slave and the overall circuit is referred to as a master-slave flip-flop.
> While the clock is HIGH, the master is active and the slave is inactive.
> While the clock is LOW, the master is inactive and the slave is active.
> A Schmitt trigger is a bistable circuit that is widely used to change a periodic waveform into a rectangular waveform having very fast rise and fall times.
> The 555 timer is a digital timing circuit that can be connected as either a monostable or an astable circuit. It is widely used as a timer in different applications.

■■■■■■■

# REVIEW QUESTIONS

Test your
understanding

1. What is the $Q$ output of a D latch when $EN = 1$ and $D = 1$?
2. What levels must be placed on $S$ and $R$ to Set an S-R flip-flop?
3. What procedures would you use to Reset the $Q$ output of a gated $D$ flip-flop?
4. What is the normal resting state of the Set and Clear inputs? What is the active state of each input?
5. When power is first applied to any flip-flop circuit, it is impossible to predict the initial states of $Q$ and $\bar{Q}$. What could be done to ensure that a NAND latch always starts off in the $Q = 1$ state?
6. What is the advantage of a JK flip-flop over an SR flip-flop?
7. What two types of inputs does a clocked FF have?
8. Explain how a data lock-out flip-flop differs from a pulse-triggered flip-flop?
9. What is meant by the term edge-triggered?
10. Which specific flip-flop can be operated at the highest frequency?
11. How must a JK flip-flop be connected to function as a divide-by-2 element?
12. How many flip-flops are required to produce a divide-by-32 device?
13. Why is the $S = 1$, $R = 1$ input state invalid in an active-HIGH SR latch?
14. List the three basic types of edge-triggered flip-flops classified by inputs.
15. Name two types of edge-triggered flips-flops classified by the method of triggering and explain the difference.

16. Describe basically how data are clocked into a pulse-triggered, master-slave `flip-flop`?
17. What is the major restriction when operating a pulse-triggered `flip-flop`?
18. Symbolically, how can a data lock-out `flip-flop` be distinguished from a pulse-triggered `flip-flop`?
19. Give four basic `flip-flop` applications.
20. What J-K input condition will always set $Q$ upon the occurrence of the active CLK transition?
21. How does the operation of an asynchronous input differ from that of a synchronous input?
22. List the conditions necessary for a positive edge-triggered J-K `flip-flop` with active-LOW asynchronous inputs to toggle to its opposite state.
23. How does a Schmitt-trigger logic device operate differently from a standard logic device?
24. What determines the $t_p$ value for an OS?
25. In the absence of a trigger pulse, what will be the state of an OS output?
26. Explain how a retriggerable-OS operates differently from a non-retriggerable OS?
27. Explain the difference in operation of an astable multivibrator and a monostable multivibrator.

# SUPPLEMENTARY PROBLEMS

**Test your understanding**

28. Draw the truth table of the S-R `flip-flop`.
29. Draw the truth table of the clocked S-R `flip-flop`.
30. Sketch the $Q$ waveform for the 7476 positive pulse-triggered `flip-flop` shown in Fig 12.63(a) with the input waveforms given in Fig. 12.63(b).

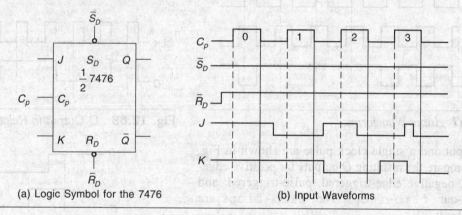

(a) Logic Symbol for the 7476    (b) Input Waveforms

**Fig. 12.63**

31. The 74109 is a positive edge-triggered J-K `flip-flop`. The logic symbol (Fig. 12.64a) and input waveforms (Fig. 12.64b) are given. Sketch $Q$.

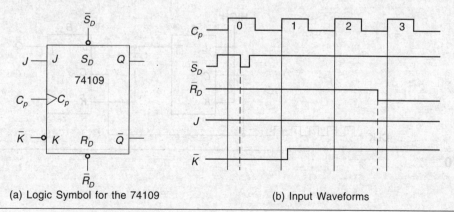

(a) Logic Symbol for the 74109    (b) Input Waveforms

**Fig. 12.64**

32. Given the waveforms in Fig. 12.65 for the *D* input and the clock, determine the *Q* output waveform if the flip-flop starts out at Reset.

33. Determine the *Q* output waveform if the inputs shown in Fig. 12.66 are applied to a gated S-R latch that is initially Reset.

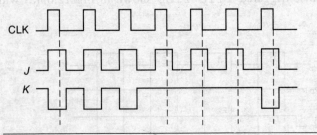

(a) Logic Symbol     (b) Input Waveforms

**Fig. 12.65**

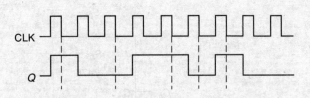

**Fig. 12.66**    *Input Waveforms.*

34. For a pulse-triggered, master-slave, J-K flip-flop with the inputs in Fig. 12.67, sketch the *Q* output waveform. Assume that *Q* is initially LOW.

35. The *Q* output of the edge-triggered flip-flop in Fig. 12.68 is shown in relation to the clock signal. Determine the input waveforms on the *S* and *R* inputs that are required to produce this output if the flip-flop is positive-edge triggered.

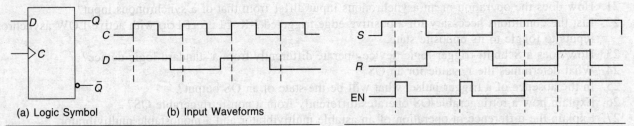

**Fig. 12.67**    *Input Waveforms.*

**Fig. 12.68**    *Q Output in Relation to CLK.*

36. The *D* input and a single clock pulse are shown in Fig. 12.69. Compare the resulting *Q* outputs for positive edge-triggered, negative edge-triggered, pulse-triggered, and data lock-out flip-flops. The flip-flops are initially Reset.

37. Sketch the output of the flip-flop in Fig. 12.70 in proper relation to the clock. The flip-flops are initially Reset.

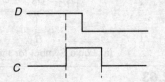

**Fig. 12.69**    *For S 12.9 D Input and a Single Clock Pulse.*

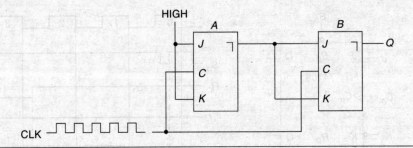

**Fig. 12.70**

38. The $V_{in}$ waveform to the 74132 Schmitt trigger NAND gate in Fig. 12.71(a) is given in Fig. 12.71(b). Sketch the output ($V_{out}$) waveform. Determine the duty cycle of $V_{out}$.
39. A 555 timer is configured to run as astable multivibrator as shown in Fig. 12.72. Determine its frequency.

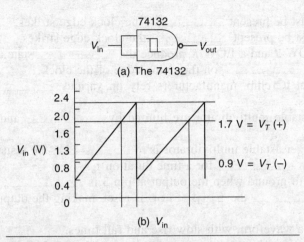

**Fig. 12.71**

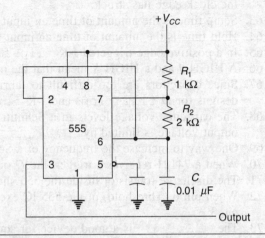

**Fig. 12.72**

# OBJECTIVE TYPE QUESTIONS

**Test your understanding**

## Fill in the Blanks

40. The $Q$ output of the 7475 $D$ latch follows the level on the $D$ input as long as $E$ is _____.
41. A group of flip-flops used for data storage is called a _____.
42. When the 7475 latch IC is in its data-enabled mode of operation, the _____ outputs follow their respective $D$ inputs.
43. A _____ at the enable input places the 7475 latch IC in the data-latched mode of operation.
44. In the data-latched mode, a change at any of the $D$ inputs to the 7475 latch IC has _____ effect on the outputs.
45. When a flip-flop is used to temporarily hold data, it is sometimes called a _____.
46. A positive-edge-triggered flip-flop changes state on the _____ transition of the clock pulse.
47. A negative-edge-triggered flip-flop changes state on the _____ transition of the clock pulse.
48. The > near the clock input inside a flip-flop logic symbol means data is _____ to the output on the _____ of the pulse.
49. A _____ J-K flip-flop uses the entire pulse to trigger the flip-flop.
50. A flip-flop is a _____ element that stores a binary digit as a LOW or HIGH voltage.
51. With an $RS$ latch a HIGH $S$ and a LOW $R$ sets the output to _____; a LOW $S$ and a HIGH $R$ _____ the output to LOW.
52. With a NAND latch a LOW $R$ and a LOW $S$ produce a _____ condition. This is why $R$ and $S$ are kept HIGH when inactive.
53. One use for latches is switch debouncers; they eliminate the effects of _____ bounce.
54. Computers use thousands of flip-flops. To coordinate the overall action, a common signal called the _____ is sent to each flip-flop.
55. With positive clocking the clock signal must be _____ for the flip-flop to respond.
56. Positive and negative clocking are also called level clocking because the flip-flop responds to the _____ of the clock, either HIGH or LOW.
57. In a $D$ latch, the data bit $D$ drives the $S$ input of the latch, and the complement $D$ drives the $R$ input; therefore, a HIGH $D$ _____ the latch, and a LOW $D$ resets it.
58. Since $R$ and $S$ are always in opposite states in a $D$ latch, the _____ condition is impossible
59. With a positive-edge-triggered $D$ flip-flop, the data bit is sampled and stored on the _____ edge of the clock pulse.
60. Preset and clear inputs are often called _____ set and _____ reset.

61. When preset goes LOW, the $Q$ output goes _____ and stays there no matter what the $D$ and CLK inputs are doing.
62. In a flip-flop, propagation delay time is the amount of time it takes for the _____ to change after the clock edge has struck.
63. Setup time is the amount of time an input signal must be present _____ the clock edge strikes.
64. Hold time is the amount of time an input signal must be present _____ the clock edge strikes.
65. In a positive-edge-triggered J-K flip-flop, a LOW $J$ and a LOW $K$ produce the _____ state.
66. A HIGH $J$ and a HIGH $K$ mean that the output will _____ on the rising edge of the clock.
67. Since capacitors are too difficult to fabricate on an IC chip, manufacturers rely on various _____ designs for $D$ flip-flops and J-K flip-flops.
68. The capacitor voltage levels in a Schmitt trigger astable multivibrator are limited by _____ and the output voltage is limited by _____.
69. One way to increase the frequency of a Schmitt trigger astable multivibrator is to _____ the resistor.
70. When a 74121 receives a trigger, the $Q$ outputs goes _____ for a time duration $t_p$.
71. The discharge transistor inside the 555 shorts pin 7 to ground when the output at pin 3 is _____.
72. When pin 6 (Threshold) of the 555 IC exceeds _____ the flip-flop is reset, making the output at pin 3 _____.
73. The _____ is a good device for squaring up a waveform with slow rise and fall times.
74. A Schmitt trigger is said to have _____ because its switching thresholds are different for positive-going and negative-going inputs.
75. Schmitt triggers are commonly used for _____.

### True/False Questions

State whether the following statements are True or False.

76. A flip-flop is different from a basic logic gate because it remembers the state of the inputs after they are removed.
77. Changes in $S$ and $R$ while a gate is enabled have no effect on the $Q$ output of a gated S-R flip-flop.
78. Changes to $D$ are ignored by the 7475 while $E$ is low.
79. The Set input can never be used to make $Q = 0$.
80. The clock input will affect the FF output only when the active transition of the control input occurs.
81. J-K flip-flop can be used as an S-C flip-flop but an SC flip-flop cannot be used as a J-K flip-flop.
82. The $Q$ output will equal the level at the $D$ input at all times.
83. A $D$ latch is in its transparent mode when EN = 0.
84. In a $D$ latch, the $D$ input can affect $Q$ only when EN = 1.
85. The J-K master-slave flip-flop is usually edge-triggered instead of level-clocked.
86. With a J-K master-slave flip-flop the slave is cocked when the clock is HIGH, and the master is triggered when the clock is LOW.
87. A master-slave J-K flip-flop is usually level-clocked instead of edge-triggered.
88. $J$ and $K$ are normally not kept constant while the clock is high.
89. When a non-retriggerable OS is pulsed while it is in its quasi-stable state, the output is not affected.
90. Toggle flip-flops cannot be cascaded end to end to form ripple counters.
91. The output of a monostable multivibrator has a predictable pulse width based on the width of the input trigger pulse.
92. The comparators inside the 555 IC timer will output a LOW if their (–) input is more positive than their (+) input.

### Multiple Choice Questions

93. Which of the following is used as latch
    (a) $J$-$K$ flip-flop
    (b) Master-slave J-K flip-flop
    (c) $T$ flip-flop
    (d) $D$ flip-flop
94. $D$ flip-flop can be used as a
    (a) differentiator
    (b) divider circuit
    (c) delay switch
    (d) none of the above
95. $T$ flip-flop is used as a
    (a) transfer data circuit
    (b) toggle switch
    (c) time delay switch
    (d) none of the above

96. Which of the following `flip-flops` is used to eliminate race around problem
    (a) R-S `flip-flop`
    (b) Master-slave J-K `flip-flop`
    (c) J-K `flip-flop`
    (d) none of the above

97. In a T `flip-flop` the output frequency is
    (a) same as the input frequency
    (b) one-half its inputs frequency
    (c) double the input frequency
    (d) none of the above

98. Race condition occurs in
    (a) synchronous circuit
    (b) asynchronous circuit
    (c) combinational circuit
    (d) all the digital circuits

99. A `flip-flop` has two outputs which are
    (a) always zero
    (b) always one
    (c) always complementary
    (d) none of the above

100. A `flip-flop` is used to store
    (a) one bit of information
    (b) two bits of information
    (c) one byte of information
    (d) one nibble of information

101. A `flip-flop` can be made using
    (a) basic gates
    (b) NAND gates
    (c) NOR gates
    (d) any of the above

102. In an S-R `flip-flop`, the S-R inputs must not be
    (a) S = R = 1
    (b) S = R = 0
    (c) S = 0, R = 1
    (d) S = 1, R = 0

103. When a `flip-flop` is set, its outputs will be
    (a) $Q = 0$, $\bar{Q} = 1$
    (b) $Q = 1$, $\bar{Q} = 0$
    (c) $Q = 0$, $\bar{Q} = 0$
    (d) $Q = 1$, $\bar{Q} = 1$

104. When a `flip-flop` is reset, its outputs will be
    (a) $Q = 0$, $\bar{Q} = 1$
    (b) $Q = 1$, $\bar{Q} = 0$
    (c) $Q = 0$, $\bar{Q} = 0$
    (d) $Q = 1$, $\bar{Q} = 1$

105. For a `flip-flop` with provisions for preset and clear
    (a) preset and clear operations are performed simultaneously
    (b) while presetting clear is disabled
    (c) while clearing preset is disabled
    (d) both (b) and (c) are true

106. In a J-K `flip-flop`, when J = K = 1 and clock is applied, the output $Q$ will
    (a) not change
    (b) become 0
    (c) become 1
    (d) be complement of the output before the clock was applied

107. Race around condition occurs in a J-K `flip-flop` when
    (a) both the inputs are 0
    (b) both the inputs are 1
    (c) the inputs are complementary
    (d) any one of the above input combinations are present

108. Master-slave configuration is used in `flip-flops` to
    (a) increase its clocking rate
    (b) reduce power dissipation
    (c) eliminate race around condition
    (d) improve its reliability

109. A transparent latch consists of a
    (a) T-type of `flip-flop`
    (b) D-type of `flip-flop`
    (c) T-or-D type of `flip-flop`
    (d) none of the above

110. `Flip-flops` can be used to make
    (a) latches
    (b) bounce-elimination switches
    (c) registers
    (d) all of the above

111. Schmitt trigger can be used as a
    (a) square wave generator
    (b) comparator
    (c) square wave generator and comparator
    (d) none of the above

112. For a sinusoidal input, the output from a Schmitt trigger is
    (a) sinusoidal
    (b) saw tooth wave
    (c) square wave
    (d) none of the above

113. Schmitt trigger is used as
    (a) voltage-to-frequency converter
    (b) frequency-to-voltage converter
    (c) square wave generator
    (d) none of the above

114. An astable multivibrator has
    (a) one stable state
    (b) one quasi-stable state
    (c) two quasi-stable states
    (d) none of the above

115. A monostable multivibrator has
    (a) no stable state     (b) one stable state     (c) two stable states     (d) none of the above

116. The gate width of a monostable multivibrator is given by
    (a) T = 1.1 RC        (b) T = 0.693 RC      (c) T = 0.963 RC      (d) T = 0.369 RC

117. Astable multivibrator is also known as
    (a) one shot multivibrator              (b) Schmitt trigger
    (c) free running multivibrator         (d) gating circuit

118. Bistable multivibrator is also known as
    (a) binary                         (b) `flip-flop`
    (c) Ecless Jordan circuit           (d) all of these

119. A pulse-stretcher is the same as a
    (a) free-running multivibrator       (b) bistable multivibrator
    (c) monostable multivibrator        (d) latch

120. A 1 $\mu$s pulse can be converted into a 1 ms pulse by using a
    (a) monostable multivibrator        (b) bistable multivibrator
    (c) astable multivibrator            (d) J-K `flip-flop`

121. A multivibrator circuit is in its stable state. When it is triggered by a pulse it goes to another state for some time and comes back to its original state. It is
    (a) an astable multivibrator         (b) a bistable multivibrator
    (c) a monostable multivibrator     (d) a latch

122. A monostable multivibrator circuit can be made using
    (a) logic gates      (b) OP AMPs      (c) 555 timer      (d) any of the above

123. The pulse-width of a monostable multivibrator can be controlled by
    (a) the amplitude of the trigger pulse      (b) the width of the trigger pulse
    (c) the timing resistor and capacitor       (d) any of the above

124. A 555 timer can be used as
    (a) an astable multivibrator only       (b) a monostable multivibrator only
    (c) a frequency divider only         (d) any of the above

# ANSWERS

1. 1               2. $S = 1, R = 0$        3. $D = 0, G = 1$      4. HIGH, LOW

5. Apply a momentary LOW to Set input

6. The J-K `flip-flop` does not have an invalid state    7. Synchronous control input and clock input

8. A data lock-out is sensitive to the input data only during a clock transition and not while the clock is in its active state

9. The FF output can change only when the appropriate clock transition occurs

10. 74LS76A                     11. Toggle ($J = 1, K = 1$)                12. 5

13. It forces both $Q$ and $\bar{Q}$ to the HIGH state, and when inputs are released, the resulting state of the latch is unpredictable

14. S-R, D, J-K

15. Positive edge-triggered is sensitive to data inputs only on positive-going edge of a clock. Negative edge-triggered is sensitive to data inputs only on negative-going edge of clock

16. Data go into master only on leading edge of clock, then into slave and to output on trailing edge of clock.

17. Data cannot be changed while the clock pulse is in its active state

18. The data lock-out `flip-flop` has a dynamic indicator on the clock input as well as the postponed output symbol

19. Counting, frequency division, data storage and data transfer

20. $J = 1, K = 0$

21. Asynchronous inputs work independently of the CLK input

22. $J = K = 1$, $\overline{PRE} = \overline{CLR} = 1$, and a PGT (positive-going transition) at CLK

23. It will produce clean, fast output signals even for slow-changing input signals

24. External $R$ and $C$ values

25. $Q = 0, \bar{Q} = 1$

26. For a retriggerable OS, each new trigger pulse begins a new $t_p$ interval regardless of state of $Q$ output.
27. Astable has no stable state. Monostable has one stable state.
28.

| Inputs | | Output | | Comments |
|---|---|---|---|---|
| R | S | $Q_{n+1}$ | $\bar{Q}_{n+1}$ | |
| 0 | 0 | 1 | 1 | Invalid, not allowed |
| 0 | 1 | 1 | 0 | Set |
| 1 | 0 | 0 | 1 | Reset |
| 1 | 1 | $Q_n$ | $Q_n$ | NC (No change) |

29.

| Inputs | | | Output | | Comments |
|---|---|---|---|---|---|
| CLK | R | S | $Q_{n+1}$ | $\bar{Q}_{n+1}$ | |
| 0 | 0 | 0 | $Q_n$ | $\bar{Q}_n$ | NC (No Change) |
| 0 | 0 | 1 | $Q_n$ | $\bar{Q}_n$ | NC (No Change) |
| 0 | 1 | 0 | $Q_n$ | $\bar{Q}_n$ | NC (No Change) |
| 0 | 1 | 1 | $Q_n$ | $\bar{Q}_n$ | NC (No Change) |
| 1 | 0 | 0 | $Q_n$ | $\bar{Q}_n$ | NC (No Change) |
| 1 | 0 | 1 | 1 | 0 | Set |
| 1 | 1 | 0 | 0 | 1 | Reset |
| 1 | 1 | 1 | 1 | 1 | Invalid (Race) |

30.

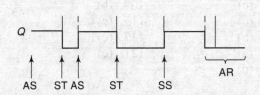

*Note:* AS Asynchronous Set
ST Synchronous Toggle
SS Synchronous Set
AR Asynchronous Reset

**Fig. 12.73**  *Solution for Problem 30.*

31.

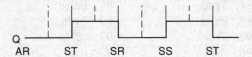

**Fig. 12.74**  *Solution for Problem 31.*

32.

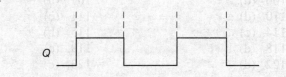

**Fig. 12.75**  *Solution for Problem 32.*

33.

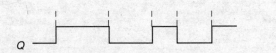

**Fig. 12.76**  *Solution for Problem 33.*

34.

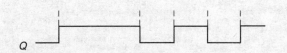

**Fig. 12.77**  *Solution for Problem 34.*

35.

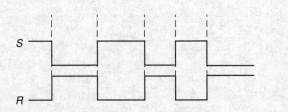

**Fig. 12.78**  *Solution for Problem 35.*

36.

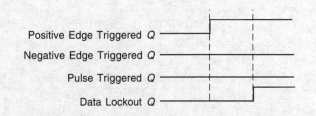

**Fig. 12.79**  *Solution for Problem 36.*

37.

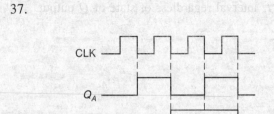

**Fig. 12.80** *Solution for Problem 37.*

38.

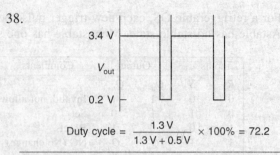

Duty cycle $= \dfrac{1.3 \text{ V}}{1.3 \text{ V} + 0.5 \text{ V}} \times 100\% = 72.2$

**Fig. 12.81**    *Solution for Problem 38.*

| | | | |
|---|---|---|---|
| 39. 28.8 kHz | 40. HIGH | 41. Register | 42. $Q$ |
| 43. LOW | 44. no | 45. latch | 46. positive going |
| 47. negative going | 48. transferred; edge | 49. master/slave | 50. memory |
| 51. HIGH, reset | 52. indeterminate | 53. contact | 54. clock |
| 55. HIGH | 56. level | 57. sets | 58. race |
| 59. rising | 60. direct, direct | 61. HIGH | 62. output |
| 63. before | 64. after | 65. inactive | 66. toggle |
| 67. direct-coupled | 68. $V_{T+}$ and $V_{T-0}$, $V_{OH}$ and $V_{OL}$ | | 69. decrease |
| 70. HIGH | 71. LOW | 72. 2/3 $V_{CC}$, LOW | 73. Schmitt trigger |
| 74. hysteresis | 75. signal conditioning | 76. True | 77. False |
| 78. True | 79. True | 80. True | 81. True |
| 82. False | 83. False | 84. True | 85. False |
| 86. False | 87. True | 88. False | 89. True |
| 90. False | 91. False | 92. True | 93. (d) |
| 94. (c) | 95. (b) | 96. (b) | 97. (b) |
| 98. (b) | 99. (c) | 100. (a) | 101. (d) |
| 102. (a) | 103. (b) | 104. (a) | 105. (d) |
| 106. (d) | 107. (b) | 108. (c) | 109. (b) |
| 110. (d) | 111. (c) | 112. (c) | 113. (c) |
| 114. (c) | 115. (b) | 116. (b) | 117. (c) |
| 118. (d) | 119. (c) | 120. (a) | 121. (c) |
| 122. (d) | 123. (c) | 124. (d) | |

# Registers and Counters

## INTRODUCTION

In a generic computer, *registers* are used extensively for temporary storage of data in areas other than memory. Registers of this kind are often large, having at least 32 bits. Special registers called *shift registers* are used less frequently, appearing primarily in the input-output part of the system. *Counters* are used in the various parts of the computer to control or keep track of the sequencing of activities. A counter is in fact a register that goes through a prescribed sequence on the application of input pulses.

## REGISTERS

Digital data may be *temporarily* stored. Storage in a computer may be divided into two main categories: *large scale* storage, consisting of hundreds or many thousands of bits; or *small scale*, temporary storage, usually of a few tens of bits or less. In large scale storage, due to the amount involved, *the circuitry has to be minimised.* Small scale storage may be satisfied using a number of flip-flops. Suppose an 8-bit binary number has to be stored until a device such as calculator or computer is ready to process it. This can be achieved by using eight *D*-type latches, *D*-type flip-flops, J-K flip-flops, or whatever. *A circuit which will store one or more bits of data is called a register.* Frequently a register is required to do more than just store data.

### 13.1 How information is transferred into and out of a register?

*Solution:*
A major use of flip-flops in digital computers is to construct registers that store information. A register is a

row of *associated* flip-flops. Information can be transferred *into and out of* registers with *n* flip-flops either in series (*1 bit per clock period*) or in parallel (*all n bits in one clock period*). There are four possible ways to transfer information into and out of a register. This is shown in Fig. 13.1 through 13.4.

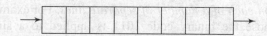

**Fig. 13.1** *Serial-input, Serial-output.*

The *serial-input, serial-output* arrangement of Fig. 13.1 is the *slowest*, since *n* clock periods (one for each of *n* bits) are required to input or output the information. We can accept such slow information transfer only when we are transferring information from and to *slow input/output devices*, such as teletypes. The main advantage of this connection is that the logic circuitry for the inputs and outputs is simple in that *only one set of input logic circuits and one set of output logic circuits is needed.*

The *parallel-input, serial-output* arrangement of Fig. 13.2 can receive *n* bits of information in one clock period but takes *n* clock periods to output them. *It is most useful when transferring data from a high-speed device to a slow speed device.*

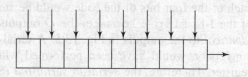

**Fig. 13.2** *Parallel-input, Serial-output.*

Conversely, the *serial-input, parallel-output* arrangement of Fig. 13.3 *can transfer data from a slow-speed device to a high-speed device.*

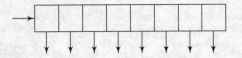

**Fig. 13.3**   *Serial-input, Parallel-output.*

The *fully parallel* information transfer possible with the arrangement of Fig. 13.4 is *the fastest method of transfer.* Just one clock period is required for either information input or information output. However, the logic circuitry required for this arrangement is complicated. *For both input and output, n copies of any needed logic circuits are required.*

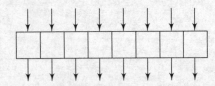

**Fig. 13.4**   *Parallel-input, Parallel-output.*

## 13.2 Explain serial-to-parallel conversion.

*Solution:*

Serial-to-parallel conversion is *the conversion of a serial data stream on a single line to a code presented as one bit on each of a number of separate lines.* For example, suppose the binary code 1011 is applied to a single input of a device. The code would be applied one bit after the other, starting with the least significant bit. This is called a *bit-serial signal.* The same code in parallel form would be four separate lines each containing one bit of the *code.* This is shown in Fig. 13.5.

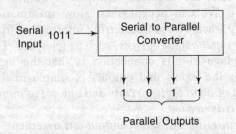

**Fig. 13.5**   *Serial-to-parallel Conversion.*

Suppose the above 4-bit serial signal was applied as the input to a 4-bit shift register. After four clock pulses each of the four bits of the code would be *stored* in one of the J-K `flip-flops`, i.e. the $Q$ outputs would be *identical* to the outputs in Fig. 13.5. A serial-to-parallel conversion would have been performed with the shift register. Therefore, the *serial-in serial-out* (SISO) shift register is also a *serial-in parallel-out* (SIPO) device.

The ability to convert a binary code from a serial to a parallel form is very important. Data is frequently transmitted from one device to another in *bit-serial form* as only one line is required. Computers, however, usually work on parallel data as it is *quicker* to do so. Therefore, transmitted data frequently needs to undergo serial-to-parallel conversion if it is to be input to a computer from a transmission line.

## 13.3 Explain parallel-to-serial conversion.

*Solution:*

Parallel-to-serial conversion is the *complementary operation* to serial-to-parallel conversion. As the name suggests, it involves taking a binary code presented on parallel data lines and *converting it to a bit-serial pattern on a single line.* Typical applications of parallel-to-serial conversion include transforming parallel data codes from computers and computer terminals into serial form for transmission to other computers or terminals. Various computer peripheral devices require data to be presented in serial form.

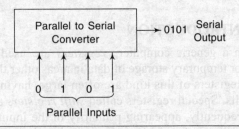

**Fig. 13.6**   *Parallel-to-serial Conversion.*

To convert successive parallel input groups to serial outputs, the *output clocking rate* must be $N$ times faster than the rate at which successive parallel inputs are applied, in order that no data is lost, where $N$ is the number of bits in the parallel data words. *This minimum speed difference allows all data to be shifted out before new data is applied.*

For a shift register to be used as a parallel-to-serial converter, it must be provided with parallel data inputs. There are two ways in which these inputs may be provided—synchronously or asynchronously.

*Synchronous inputs* are those which are transferred to `flip-flop` outputs by the occurrence of the normal shift clock pulse. *Asynchronous inputs* are independent of the clock—they use the direct set and clear inputs to transfer data to the `flip-flop` stages.

## SHIFT REGISTERS

Common *requirements* of registers are: to *store data* until required, to *move data* within the register, and to *present the data* to the receiving device in a manner different to that in which it was initially presented to the register. A device capable of performing these functions is called a *shift register,* because data is *shifted* to the right or left within the register. Suitable devices for use as registers are *edge-triggered* `flip-flops` such as the *D*-type or master-slave J-K.

### 13.4 Discuss the operation of a 4-bit J-K shift register.

*Solution:*

A 4-bit J-K shift register transmits data from its input to its output *every four* clock pulses. The Reset input provides a *direct reset facility* so that a pulse on this input will initiate the *whole* register, resetting all

`flip-flop` Q outputs to 0. Assume that the register has been reset and the serial input line is in the 1 state *prior to and during* the first clock pulse. The *J* input of `flip-flop` *A* will be at 1 and the *K* input will be at 0, resulting in a *0 to 1 transition* at $Q_a$ at the trailing edge of the clock pulse. Data goes into the *master* section of a J-K `flip-flop` on the *leading edge* of the clock and is transmitted to the *slave* on the *trailing edge*. This means that the $Q_a = 0$ condition will be transmitted to `flip-flop` *B*, not the new state of $Q_a = 1$.

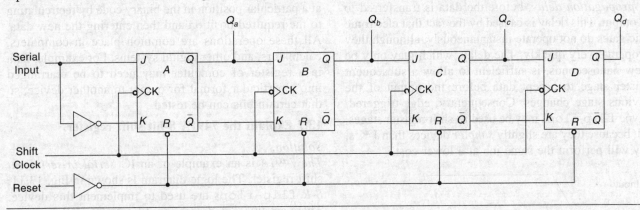

**Fig. 13.7** *4-bit J-K Shift Register.*

Consequently, $Q_b$ will remain at 0 since, at the leading edge of the first clock pulse, $J_b = 0$, $K_b = 1$. This also applies to `flip-flops` *C* and *D*, i.e., $Q_c$ and $Q_d$ also remain at 0 after the first clock pulse. Now, before the second clock pulse arrives, assume that the serial input line returns to 0. `Flip-flop` *A* will now go to the $Q_a = 0$ condition on the second clock pulse. `Flip-flop` *B* will go to the 1 condition because its *J* input would have been enabled by the 1 condition on the `flip-flop` *A* and its *K* input would consequently be 0. `Flip-flops` *C* and *D* remain in the 0 condition because their *J* and *K* inputs would still have been 0 and 1, respectively, prior to the clock pulse. Successive clock pulses will *shift* the 1 which was initially fed to `flip-flop` *A* on the first clock pulse to `flip-flop` *B* and then to *C* and on to *D*. After five clock pulses, all `flip-flops` will be back to the reset condition. The truth table illustrating the above operation is given in Table 13.1.

**Table 13.1**

| Before Clock Pulse | After Clock Pulse | | | |
|---|---|---|---|---|
| $J_a$ | $Q_a$ | $Q_b$ | $Q_c$ | $Q_d$ |
| 0 | 0 | 0 | 0 | 0 |
| 1 | 1 | 0 | 0 | 0 |
| 0 | 0 | 1 | 0 | 0 |
| 0 | 0 | 0 | 1 | 0 |
| 0 | 0 | 0 | 0 | 1 |
| 0 | 0 | 0 | 0 | 0 |

The following timing diagram shows when the output transitions occur for the J-K shift register in the above application:

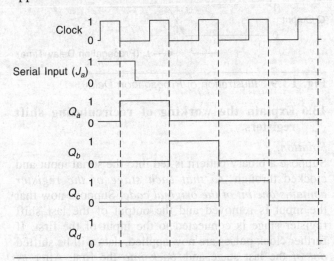

**Fig. 13.8** *Timing Diagram of 4-bit J-K Shift Register.*

This type of shift register is commonly called a *serial-in serial-out* shift register (SISO) because of the *bit-serial nature* of the input and output signals i.e. one bit follows another.

### 13.5 Why should the shift register stages be edge triggered? Illustrate propagation delay.

*Solution:*

Shift register stages must be *edge triggered*. This is because, if they are not, data will *ripple through* all the stages of the register while the clock is at 1. The J-K flip-flop *is ideal* because it *accepts* data on the clock leading edge and *transfers* it to its output on the trailing edge. Consider an edge-triggered *D*-type flip-flop. It both *accepts and transfers* it to its output on the clock leading edge. Is it, then, suitable as a shift register stage? At first it seems that it is not, since data may ripple through from one stage to the next as the clock goes to the 1 state. This, however, is not the case. After the input data is accepted, there is a finite time delay, called the *propagation delay*, before the data is transferred to the output. This delay is caused by the fact that electronic logic gates do not operate instantaneously, although they do operate very quickly. The delay, which may only be a few nanoseconds, is sufficient to allow a subsequent register stage to accept data before the output of the previous stage changes. Consequently, edge-triggered, *D*-type flip-flops may be used as shift register stages, and, because they are slightly *simpler* devices than J-K's, they will perform the same job at a lower cost.

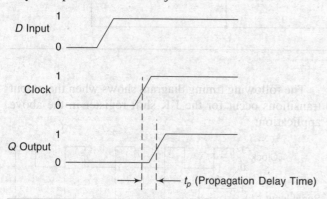

**Fig. 13.9**   *Illustration of Propagation Delay.*

### 13.6 Explain the working of recirculating shift registers.

*Solution:*
Suppose a binary pattern is fed into the serial input and clocked through *so that each stage of the register contains one bit of the original code.* Suppose now that the input is removed and the output of the last shift register stage is connected to the input of the first. If further clock pulses are now applied, data will be shifted *out of* the last stage and *back into* the first. After *N* clock pulses, where *N* is the number of shift stages, the data will be back in its original position.

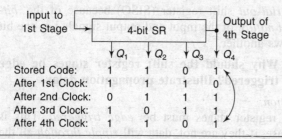

**Fig. 13.10**   *Recirculating Shift Register.*

When this is made to happen the data is said to be *recirculating.* A recirculating shift register is a convenient way of *storing* a data code for a large number of clock pulses *without* requiring a large number of register stages, since the data can be recirculated for as long as is required.

Alternatively it may be desired to move only a *few specific bits* from the top end of the register to the lower end. This can be done by applying the required number of clock pulses. Also, *new data* may be entered at a particular position in the binary code by recirculating to the required position and then entering the new data. All these operations are common place in computers, calculators, and other digital systems. For example, data in a register of computer may need to be rearranged into a particular format for output to another device, so that certain bits can be tested.

### 13.7 Explain the 7491A 8-bit shift register.

*Solution:*
The *7491A* is an example of an IC *serial in-serial out* shift register. The logic diagram is shown in Fig. 13.11. *S-R* flip-flops are used to implement this device. There are two *gated data input lines*, *A* and *B* for serial data entry. When data are entered on *A*, the *B* input must be HIGH and vice versa. The *serial data output* is $Q_H$, and its *complement* is $\bar{Q}_H$. A traditional logic block symbol is shown in Fig. 13.11. The *SRG8* designation means a shift register with an 8-bit capacity.

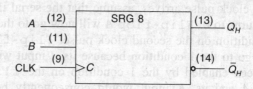

**Fig. 13.11**   *The 7491A Logic Symbol.*

### 13.8 Explain the 74164 8-bit serial in-parallel out shift register.

*Solution:*
The *74164* is an example of an IC shift register having *serial in-parallel out* operation. The logic block symbol is shown in Fig. 13.12. This device has two *gated serial inputs A* and *B*, and a CLR *input* that is active-LOW. The *parallel outputs* are $Q_A$ through $Q_H$.

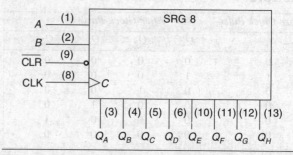

**Fig. 13.12**   *The 74164 Logic Symbol.*

### 13.9 Explain the 74165 8-bit parallel load shift register.

*Solution:*

The *74165* is an example of an IC shift register that has *parallel in-serial out* operation (it can also be operated in serial in serial out). Figure 13.13 shows a typical logic block-symbol.

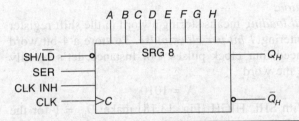

**Fig. 13.13** *The 74165 Logic Symbol.*

A LOW on the SHIFT/LOAD (SH/LD) input enables all the NAND gates for parallel loading. When the input data bit is a 1, the flip-flop is asynchronously SET by a LOW out of the *upper gate*. When an input data bit is a 0, the flip-flop is asynchronously RESET by a LOW out of the *lower gate*. The clock is *inhibited* during parallel loading. A HIGH on the SH/LD input *enables* the clock, causing the data in the register to shift right.

Data can be entered serially on the SER input. Also, the clock can be inhibited any time with a HIGH on the CLK INH input. The serial data outputs of the register are $Q_H$ and its complement $\bar{Q}_H$.

### 13.10 Explain the 74195 4-bit parallel access shift register.

*Solution:*

This device can be used for *parallel in-parallel out* operation. Since it also has a serial input, it can also be used for *serial in-serial out* and *serial in-parallel out* operation. It can be used for *parallel in-serial out* operation by using $Q_D$ as the output. A typical logic block symbol is shown in Fig. 13.14.

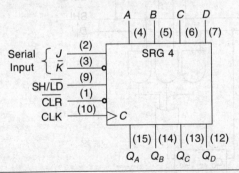

**Fig. 13.14** *The 74195 4-bit Parallel Shift Register.*

When the SHIFT/LOAD (SH/LD) input is LOW, the data on the parallel inputs are entered synchronously on the positive transition of the clock. When the SH/LD input is HIGH, stored data will *shift right* ($Q_A$ to $Q_D$)

synchronously with the clock. $J$ and $\bar{K}$ are the serial data inputs to the first stage of the register ($Q_A$); $Q_D$ can be used for serial output data. The active-LOW clear is asynchronous.

### 13.11 Explain the working of a shift-left register.

*Solution:*

Figure 13.15 illustrates a *shift-left register*. $D_{in}$ sets up the *right* flip-flop, $Q_0$ sets up the *second* flip-flop, $Q_1$ the *third* and so on. When the next positive clock edge strikes, therefore, *the stored bits move one position to the left*.

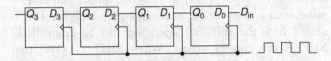

**Fig. 13.15** *Shift-left Register.*

As an example, here's what happens with $D = 1$ and

$$Q = 0000$$

All data inputs except the one on the right are 0's. The arrival of the *first rising clock edge* sets the right flip-flip, and the second word becomes

$$Q = 0001$$

The new word means $D_1$ now equals 1, as well as $D_0$. When the *next positive clock edge* hits, the $Q_1$ flip-flop sets and the register contents become

$$Q = 0011$$

The *third positive clock edge* results in

$$Q = 0111$$

The *fourth rising clock edge* gives

$$Q = 1111$$

### 13.12 Describe the working of a shift-right register.

*Solution:*

Figure 13.16 illustrates a *shift-right register*. Each $Q$ output sets up the $D$ input of the preceding flip-flop. *When the rising clock edge arrives, the stored bits move one position to the right.*

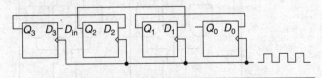

**Fig. 13.16** *Shift-right Register.*

As an example, here's what happens with $D_{in} = 1$ and

$$Q = 0000$$

All data inputs except the one on the left are 0's. The first positive clock edge sets the left flip-flip and the stored word becomes

$$Q = 1000$$

With the appearance of this word, $D_3$ and $D_2$ are 1's. The second rising clock edge gives

$$Q = 1100$$

The third clock pulse gives

$$Q = 1110$$

and the fourth clock pulse gives

$$Q = 1111$$

### 13.13 How can the shift-left operation be controlled?

*Solution:*
*A controlled shift register has control inputs that determine what it does on the next clock pulse.* Figure 13.17 shows how the shift-left operation can be controlled. SHL is the control signal. When SHL is LOW, the inverted signal $\overline{\text{SHL}}$ is HIGH. This forces each flip-flop output to *feed back* to its data input. Therefore, the data is *retained* in each flip-flop as the clock pulses arrive. In this way, a digital word can be stored indefinitely.

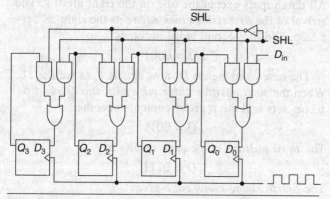

**Fig. 13.17**   *Controlled Shift Register (Shift Left).*

When SHL goes HIGH, $D_{\text{in}}$ sets up the right flip-flop, $Q_0$ sets up the second flip-flop, $Q_1$ the third flip-flop and so on. In this mode, the circuit acts as a *shift-left* register. Each positive clock edge shifts the stored bits one position to the left.

### 13.14 Differentiate between serial loading and parallel loading.

*Solution:*
*Serial loading* means storing a word in the shift register by entering *1 bit per clock pulse.* To store a 4-bit word we need four clock pulses. For instance, let's serially store the word

$$X = 1010$$

With SHL HIGH (Fig. 13.18) make $D_{\text{in}} = 1$ for the *first* clock pulse, $D_{\text{in}} = 0$ for the *second* clock pulse, $D_{\text{in}} = 1$ for the *third* clock pulse, and $D_{\text{in}} = 0$ for the *fourth* clock pulse.

| | |
|---|---|
| $Q = 0001$ | ($D_{\text{in}} = 1$: first clock pulse) |
| $Q = 0010$ | ($D_{\text{in}} = 0$: second clock pulse) |
| $Q = 0101$ | ($D_{\text{in}} = 1$: third clock pulse) |
| $Q = 1010$ | ($D_{\text{in}} = 0$: fourth clock pulse) |

In this way data is *entered* serially into the right end of the register and *shifted* left until all 4-bits have been *stored*. After the last bit is entered, SHL is taken LOW to *freeze* the register contents.

Serial load shift register has two *disadvantages*: it permits only one bit of information to be entered at a time, and loses all its data out the right side when it shifts right.

Parallel load shift register has two *advantages*: the circuit can load $X$ bits directly into the flip-flops and it takes only one clock pulse to store a digital word. Another step in the evolution of shift registers, this kind of entry is called *parallel or broadside loading.*

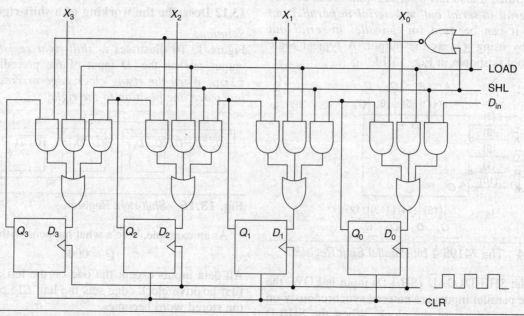

**Fig. 13.18**   *Shift Register with Parallel Loading.*

If LOAD and SHL are LOW, the output of the NOR gate is HIGH and `flip-flop` outputs return to their data inputs. This forces the data to be *retained* in each `flip-flop` as the positive clock edges arrive. In other words, *the register is inactive when LOAD and SHL are LOW, and the contents are stored indefinitely.*

When LOAD is LOW and SHL is HIGH, the circuit acts like a *shift-left register*. On the other hand when LOAD is HIGH and SHL is LOW the circuit acts like a *buffer register* because the $X$ bits set up the `flip-flops` for broadside loading. Having LOAD and SHL simultaneously HIGH is *forbidden* because it is impossible to do *both* operations on a single clock edge. A *buffer register* is the simplest kind of register. All it does is store a digital word.

By adding more `flip-flops` we can build a controlled shift-register of any length. And with more gates, the shift right operation can be included.

### 13.15 Briefly explain the working of the 74194 4-bit bidirectional universal shift register.

*Solution:*

The 74194 is an example of a *bidirectional shift register* in integrated circuit form. The pin configuration and logic block symbol of the IC are given in Fig. 13.19. The bidirectional shift register is designed to incorporate virtually all of the features a system designer may want in a shift register. The register has distinct modes of operation, namely:

(i) Parallel (broadside) load
(ii) Shift right (in the direction $Q_A$ toward $Q_D$)

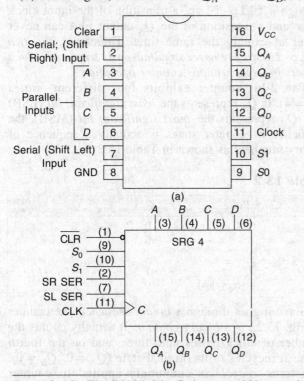

**Fig. 13.19** *The 74194 4-bit Bidirectional Universal Shift Register. (a) Pin Configuration; (b) Logic Block Diagram.*

(iii) Shift left (in the direction $Q_D$ toward $Q_A$)
(iv) Inhibit clock (do nothing)

*Synchronous parallel loading* is accomplished by applying the 4 bits of data and taking both mode control inputs, $S_0$ and $S_1$, HIGH. The data are loaded into the associated `flip-flops` and appear at the outputs after the positive transition of the clock input. *During loading, serial data flow is inhibited.*

Shift right is accomplished synchronously with the rising edge of the clock pulse when $S_0$ is HIGH and $S_1$ is LOW. Serial data for this mode is entered at the *shift right* data input. When $S_0$ is LOW and $S_1$ is HIGH, data shifts left synchronously and new data is entered at the *shift-left* serial input.

Clocking of the `flip-flop` is *inhibited* when both mode control inputs are LOW. The *mode* of the S54194/N74194 should be changed only while the clock input is HIGH.

### 13.16 Describe a three-state buffer register.

*Solution:*

The main application of three-state switches is to *convert* the two-state output of a register to a three-state output. Figure 13.20 shows a three-state buffer register, so called because of the *three-state switches* on the output lines.

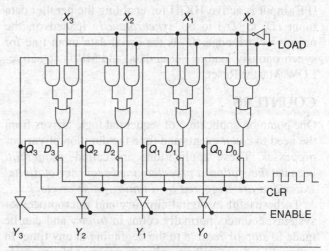

**Fig. 13.20** *Three-state Buffer Register.*

When ENABLE is LOW, the $Y$ outputs float. But when ENABLE is HIGH, the $Y$ outputs equal the $Q$ outputs; therefore

$$Y = Q$$

The rest of the circuit is a controlled buffer register. When LOAD is LOW, the contents of the register are unchanged. When LOAD is HIGH, the next positive clock edge loads $X_3 X_2 X_1 X_0$ into the register.

### 13.17 Explain the three-state buffer IC 74395A.

*Solution:*

The 74395A is a 4-bit shift (right) register with three-state outputs as shown in Fig. 13.21.

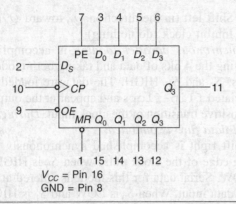

**Fig. 13.21** *Four-bit Shift Right Register with Three-state Outputs (the 74395A IC).*

$Q_0$ and $Q_3$ outputs are *three-stated* and will not be allowed to pass data unless a LOW is present at the Output Enable pin (OE). Also a *non-three-stated* output, $Q_3'$, is made available to enable the user to *cascade* with another register and shift data bits to the cascaded register whether the regular outputs ($Q_0$ to $Q_3$) are enabled or not (i.e. to cascade two 4-bit registers, $Q_3'$ would be connected to $D_S$ of the second stage).

Otherwise, the chip's operation is similar to previously discussed shift registers. The Parallel Enable (PE) input is active-HIGH for enabling the parallel data input ($D_0$ to $D_3$) to be *synchronously* loaded on the negative clock edge. $D_S$ is the serial data input line for synchronously loading serial data, and MR is an active-LOW Master Reset.

## COUNTERS

One common application of sequential logic arrives from the need to *count* events and time the duration of various processes. These applications are called *sequential* because *they follow a predetermined sequence of digital states and are triggered by a timing pulse or clock.*

To be useful in digital circuitry and microprocessor systems, counters normally count in *binary* and can be made to *stop or recycle* to the beginning at any time. In a *recycling counter,* the number of different binary states defines *modulus* (MOD) of the counter. For example, a counter that counts from 0 to 7 is called a *MOD-8* counter. For a counter to count from 0 to 7, it must have three binary outputs and one clock trigger input.

Normally, each *binary output* will come from the *Q* output of a flip-flop. Flip-flops are used because they can *hold*, or *remember*, a binary state until the next clock or trigger pulse comes along.

## ASYNCHRONOUS COUNTERS

The term *asynchronous* refers to events that do not have a fixed time relationship with each other and, generally, do not occur at the same time. An *asynchronous counter* is one in which the flip-flops (FFs) within the counter do not change states at exactly the same time because they do not have a common clock pulse.

**13.18 Explain the term asynchronous. Illustrate and explain a 2-bit asynchronous binary counter.**

*Solution:*
The term *asynchronous refers to events that do not occur at the same time.* With respect to counter operation, asynchronous means that the flip-flops within the counter are not made to change states at exactly the same time; they do not because the clock pulses are *not connected directly* to the C input of each flip-flop in the counter.

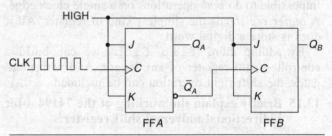

**Fig. 13.22** *A 2-bit Asynchronous Binary Counter.*

Figure 13.22 illustrates a 2-bit counter connected for *asynchronous operation*. The clock time CLK is connected to the clock input ($C$) of *only* the first stage, FFA. The second stage, FFB, is *triggered* by the $Q_A$ output of FFA. FFA changes state at the *positive-going edge* of each clock pulse, but FFB changes only when triggered by a *positive-going transition* of the $Q_A$ output of FFA. Because of the inherent propagation delay time through a flip-flop, a transition of the input clock pulse and a transition of the $Q_A$ output FFA can never occur at exactly the same time. Therefore, *the two flip-flops are never simultaneously triggered, which results in asynchronous counter operation.*

The 2-bit counter exhibits four different *states* ($2^2 = 4$). If $Q_A$ represents the *least significant bit* (LSB) and $Q_B$ represents the *most significant bit* (MSB), the sequence of counter states is actually a sequence of binary numbers as shown in Table 13.2.

**Table 13.2**

| Clock Pulse | $Q_B$ | $Q_A$ |
|---|---|---|
| 0 | 0 | 0 |
| 1 | 0 | 1 |
| 2 | 1 | 0 |
| 3 | 1 | 1 |
| 4 (recycles) | 0 | 0 |

Since it goes through a *binary sequence,* the counter in Fig. 13.22 is a *binary counter.* It actually counts the number of clock pulses upto three, and on the fourth pulse it recycles to its original state ($Q_A = 0$, $Q_B = 0$). The term *recycle* is commonly applied to counter operation; it refers to *the transition of the counter from its final state back to its original state.*

### 13.19 Describe the working of asynchronous decade counters.

*Solution:*

The maximum possible number of states (*maximum modulus*) of a counter is $2^n$, where *n* is the number of `flip-flops` in the counter. Regular binary counters have a maximum modulus; *they progress through all of their possible states.* Counters can also be designed to have a number of states in their sequence that is *less than* $2^n$. The resulting sequence is called *truncated* (abridged) sequence.

A very common modulus for counters with truncated sequences is 10. Counters with 10 states in their sequence are called *decade counters*. A decade counter with a counter sequence of 0 (0000) through 9 (1001) is a *BCD decade counter,* because its 10-state sequence is the BCD code. This type of counter is very useful in *display applications* in which BCD is required for conversion to a decimal read out.

*To obtain a truncated sequence, it is necessary to force the counter to recycle before going through all of its normal states.* The BCD decade counter, for example, must recycle back to the 0000 state after the 1001 state.

A *decade counter* requires four `flip-flops`. Three `flip-flops` are insufficient because $2^3 = 8$. One method of *truncating* after the count of 9 (1001) is to *decode* count $10_{10}$ (1010) with a NAND gate and connect the output of the NAND gate to the clear (CLR) inputs of the `flip-flops` as shown in Fig. 13.23.

Only $Q_B$ and $Q_D$ are connected to the NAND gate inputs. This is an example of *partial decoding*, in which the two unique states ($Q_B = 1$ and $Q_D = 1$) are sufficient to decode the count of $10_{10}$ because none of the other states (0 through 9) have both $Q_B$ and $Q_D$ HIGH at the same time. When the counter goes into count $10_{10}$ ($1010_2$), the decoding gate output goes LOW and asynchronous RESETS all of the `flip-flops`.

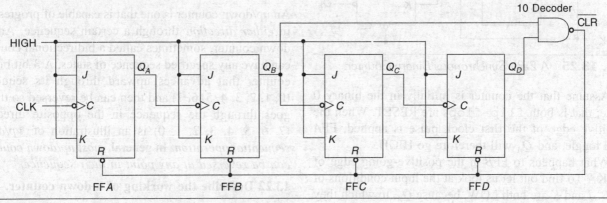

**Fig. 13.23** *An Asynchronously Clocked Decade Counter.*

### 13.20 Give two configurations of the 7493A 4-bit binary counter. Explain.

*Solution:*

The 7493A is an example of a specific *integrated circuit asynchronous counter*. This device consists of a single `flop-flop` and a 3-bit asynchronous counter. This arrangement is for flexibility. It can be used as a *divide-by-2 device* using only the single `flip-flop`, or it can be used as a *modulus-8 counter* using only the 3-bit counter portion. This device also provides *gated reset inputs*, $R_0(1)$ and $R_0(2)$. When both of these inputs are HIGH, the counter is RESET to the 0000 state by CLR.

Additionally, the 7493A can be used as a *4-bit modulus-16 counter* (counts 0 through 15) by connecting the $Q_A$ output to the CLK *B* input as shown in Fig. 13.24(a). It can also be configured as a *decade counter* (counts 0 through 9) with asynchronous recycling by using the gated reset inputs for partial decoding of $10_{10}$, as shown in Fig. 13.24(b).

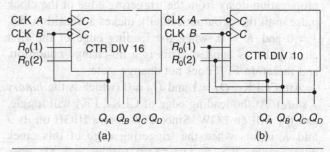

**Fig. 13.24** *Two Configurations of the 7493A Asynchronous Counter. The Qualifying Lable, CTR DIV n, Indicates a Counter with n States.*

## SYNCHRONOUS COUNTERS

The term *synchronous* refers to events that have a fixed time relationship with each other. With respect to counter operation, synchronous means that all the `flip-flops` in the counter are clocked at the same time by a common clock pulse.

**13.21 Describe the operation of a 2-bit synchronous binary counter.**

*Solution:*

The term synchronous as applied to counter operation means that *the counter is clocked such that each* `flip-flop` *in the counter is triggered at the same time.* This is accomplished by connecting the clock line to each stage of the counter, as shown in Fig. 13.25 for a two-stage counter. An arrangement different from that for the asynchronous counter, Fig. 13.22 must be used for the *J* and *K* inputs of FF*B* in order to achieve a binary sequence.

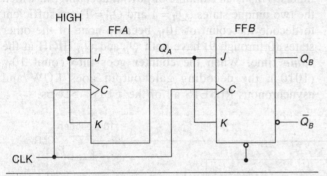

**Fig. 13.25** *A 2-Bit Synchronous Binary Counter.*

Assume that the counter is initially in the binary 0 state; that is both `flip-flops` are RESET. When the positive edge of the first clock pulse is applied, FF*A* will toggle, and $Q_A$ will therefore go HIGH.

What happens to FF*B* at the positive-going edge of $CLK_1$? To find out let us look at the input conditions of FF*B*. *J* and *K* are both LOW, because $Q_A$, to which they are connected, has not yet gone HIGH. There is a propagation delay from the triggering edge of the clock pulse until the *Q* output actually makes a transition. So, *J* = 0 and *K* = 0, when the leading edge of the first clock pulse is applied. This is a no-change condition, and therefore FF*B* does not change state.

After $CLK_1$, $Q_A = 1$ and $Q_B = 0$ (which is the *binary 1 state*). At the leading edge of $CLK_2$, FF*A* will toggle, and $Q_A$ will go LOW. Since FF*B* sees a HIGH on its *J* and *K* inputs when the triggering edge of this clock pulse occurs, the `flip-flop` toggles and $Q_B$ goes

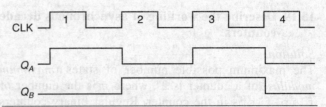

**Fig. 13.26** *Timing Diagram for the Counter of Fig. 13.25.*

HIGH. Thus, after $CLK_2$, $Q_A = 0$ and $Q_B = 1$ (which is a *binary 2 state*).

At the leading edge of $CLK_3$, FF*A* again toggles to set state ($Q_A = 1$), and FF*B* remains SET ($Q_B = 1$) because its *J* and *K* inputs are both LOW. After this triggering edge, $Q_A = 1$ and $Q_B = 1$ (which is *binary 3 state*).

Finally, at the leading edge of $CLK_4$, $Q_A$ and $Q_B$ go LOW because they both have a toggle condition on their *J* and *K* inputs. The counter has now *recycled* back to its original state, *binary 0*.

## UP/DOWN COUNTERS

An up/down counter is one that is capable of progressing in *either direction* through a certain sequence. An up/down counter, sometimes called a bidirectional counter, can have any specified sequence of states. A 3-bit binary counter that advances upward through its sequence (0, 1, 2, 3, 4, 5, 6, 7) and then can be reversed so that it goes through the sequence in the opposite direction (7, 6, 5, 4, 3, 2, 1, 0) is an illustration of *up/down sequential operation*. In general, *most up/down counters can be reversed at any point in their sequence.*

**13.22 Describe the working of a down counter.**

*Solution:*

In certain applications it is necessary to have a counter that counts *down* rather than up. This can be achieved using a circuit similar to that of a ripple counter by taking the clock signal for the following stages from $\bar{Q}$ rather than $Q$, as shown in Fig. 13.27.

In Fig. 13.27 it can be seen that the outputs are taken from $\bar{Q}_0 - \bar{Q}_3$ and not from $Q_0 - Q_3$. Table 13.3 shows the *output sequence* for the four-stage down-counter. This technique can be applied to counters of any modulus.

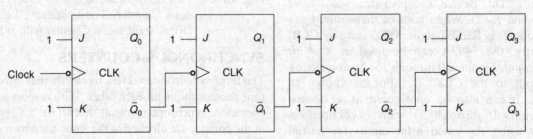

**Fig. 13.27** *A Ripple Down Counter.*

**Table 13.3** *The Output Sequence of the Down-counter*

| Number of Clock Pulses | $Q_3$ | $Q_2$ | $Q_1$ | $Q_0$ | Count |
|---|---|---|---|---|---|
| 0 | 0 | 0 | 0 | 0 | 0 |
| 1 | 1 | 1 | 1 | 1 | 15 |
| 2 | 1 | 1 | 1 | 0 | 14 |
| 3 | 1 | 1 | 0 | 1 | 13 |
| 4 | 1 | 1 | 0 | 0 | 12 |
| 5 | 1 | 0 | 1 | 1 | 11 |
| 6 | 1 | 0 | 1 | 0 | 10 |
| 7 | 1 | 0 | 0 | 1 | 9 |
| 8 | 1 | 0 | 0 | 0 | 8 |
| 9 | 0 | 1 | 1 | 1 | 7 |
| 10 | 0 | 1 | 1 | 0 | 6 |
| 11 | 0 | 1 | 0 | 1 | 5 |
| 12 | 0 | 1 | 0 | 0 | 4 |
| 13 | 0 | 0 | 1 | 1 | 3 |
| 14 | 0 | 0 | 1 | 0 | 2 |
| 15 | 0 | 0 | 0 | 1 | 1 |
| 16 | 0 | 0 | 0 | 0 | 0 |
| 17 | 1 | 1 | 1 | 1 | 15 |
| 18 | 1 | 1 | 1 | 0 | 14 |
| 19 | 1 | 1 | 0 | 1 | 13 |
| 20 | 1 | 1 | 0 | 0 | 12 |

The waveform diagram of a down counter is given in Fig. 13.28.

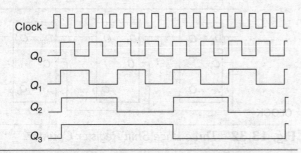

**Fig. 13.28** *Waveforms Diagram of a Ripple Down Counter.*

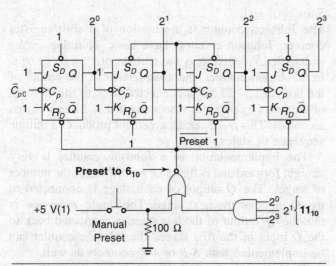

**Fig. 13.29** *A Mod 5 Up-counter that Counts in the Sequence 6-7-8-9-10.*

**13.23 Design a MOD-5 up-counter that counts in the sequence 6-7-8-9-10-6-7-8-9-10-, and so on.**

*Solution:*

The up-counter is shown in Fig. 13.29. By pressing the *manual Preset* push button, the $2^1$ and $2^2$ flip-flops get Set while the $2^0$ and $2^3$ flip-flops get Reset. This will give the number 6 ($0110_2$) at the output. In the *count mode,* when the count reaches the number 11 ($1011_2$), the output of the AND gate goes HIGH, causing the Preset line to go LOW and *recycling* the count to 6 again.

**13.24 Design a down-counter that counts in the sequence 6-5-4-3-2-6-5-4-3-2-6-5-, and so on.**

*Solution:*

The down-counter is shown in Fig. 13.30. When the Preset line goes LOW, the $2^0$ flip-flop is Set and the other two flip-flops are Reset (this gives a 6 at the $\bar{Q}$ outputs). As the counter counts down toward zero, the $2^1$ and $2^2$ will both go LOW at the count of 1 ($001_2$) and the Preset line will then go LOW again, starting the cycle over again.

**13.25 Draw the logic symbol for, and explain the synchronous Up/Down-Counter ICs 74192 and 74193.**

*Solution:*

Four-bit synchronous binary counters are available in a single IC package—two *popular synchronous IC counters* are the 74192 and 74193. They both have some features that are not available on the ripple counter ICs. They can *count up or down* and can be *preset to any desired count.* The 74192 is a *BCD decade up-down counter,* and the 74193 is a *4-bit binary up-down counter.* The logic symbol used for both counters is shown in Fig. 13.31.

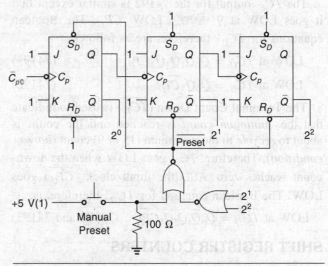

**Fig. 13.30** *A Down-counter that Counts in the Sequence 6-5-4-3-2-6-5-4-3-2-.*

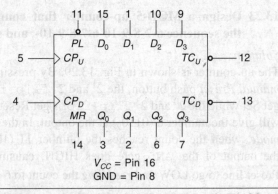

**Fig. 13.31** *Logic Symbol for the 74192 and 74193 Synchronous Counter ICs.*

There are two separate clock inputs: $C_{pU}$ for *counting up* and $C_{pD}$ for *counting down*. One clock must be held HIGH while counting with the other. The *binary output count* is taken from $Q_0$ to $Q_3$, which are the outputs from four internal J-K flip-flops. The *Master Reset* (MR) is an active-HIGH Reset for resetting the $Q$ outputs to zero.

The counter can be *preset* by placing any binary value on the parallel data inputs ($D_0$ to $D_3$) and then driving the *Parallel Load* ($\overline{PL}$) line LOW. The parallel load operation will change the counter outputs regardless of the conditions of the clock inputs.

The *Terminal Count Up* ($\overline{TC_U}$) and *Terminal Count Down* ($\overline{TC_D}$) are normally HIGH. The $\overline{TC_U}$ is used to indicate that the *maximum count* is reached and the count is about to *recycle* to zero (*carry condition*). The $\overline{TC_U}$ line goes LOW for the 74193 when the count reaches 15 AND the *input clock* ($CP_U$) goes HIGH to LOW. $\overline{TC_U}$ remains LOW until $C_{pU}$ returns HIGH. This LOW pulse at $\overline{TC_U}$ can be used as a clock input to the *next-higher-order* of a multistage counter.

The $\overline{TC_U}$ output for the 74192 is similar except that it goes LOW at 9 AND a LOW $CP_U$. The Boolean equations for $\overline{TC_U}$, therefore, are as follows:

$$\text{LOW at } \overline{TC_U} = Q_0 Q_1 Q_2 Q_3 \overline{CP_U} \qquad (74193)$$

$$\text{LOW at } \overline{TC_U} = Q_0 Q_3 \overline{CP_U} \qquad (74192)$$

The Terminal Count Down ($\overline{TC_D}$) is used to indicate that the *minimum count* is reached and the count is about to *recycle* to the maximum (15 or 9) count (*borrow condition*). Therefore, $\overline{TC_D}$ goes LOW when the down-count reaches zero AND the input clock ($\overline{CP_D}$) goes LOW. The Boolean equation for $\overline{TC_D}$, therefore, is:

$$\text{LOW at } \overline{TC_D} = \bar{Q_0} \bar{Q_1} \bar{Q_2} \bar{Q_3} \overline{CP_D} \qquad (74192 \text{ and } 74193)$$

## SHIFT REGISTER COUNTERS

A shift register counter is basically a shift register with the *serial output* connected back to the *serial input* to produce special sequences. These devices are classified as counters because *they exhibit a special sequence of states.* Two of the most common types of shift register counters are the ring counter and the Johnson counter.

### 13.26 Explain the working of a shift register counter.

*Solution:*

Shift register counters can be simply constructed from shift registers of any length. They have basic *counting cycles* of length *n*, where *n* is the number of flip-flops. D flip-flops *result in the simplest circuits.* The output of the last flip-flop (or the least significant stage) is *fed back* to the D input of the first flip-flop. The flip-flops are connected so that information shifts from left to right and back around from $Q_0$ to $Q_2$. In most instances only a single 1 is in the register and it is made to circulate around the register as long as clock pulses are applied. For this reason, it is called a *ring counter.*

Figure 13.32 illustrates a three-stage shift register counter. *The counter is sensitive to the initial state of its* flip-flops. If the register initially contains all 0's or all 1's, the counter will *stay* in that state. If the counter initially *holds* any other number it will count with a *cycle* of 3 or counts modulo 3.

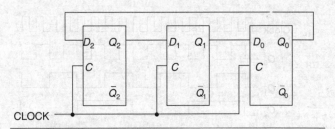

**Fig. 13.32** *Three-stage Shift Register Counter.*

### 13.27 Explain in detail the operation of a Johnson counter.

*Solution:*

The Johnson counter is a variation of a shift register counter. Johnson counters have basic *counting cycles* of length 2N, where N is the number of flip-flops. In a Johnson counter, the *complement* of the output of the last flip-flop is connected back to the D input of the first flip-flop (assuming that D flip-flops are used). This *feedback* arrangement produces a unique sequence of states.

The implementation of a Johnson counter is very straight forward and is the same *regardless* of the number of stages. The $Q$ output of each stage is connected to the D input of the next stage. The single *exception* is that the $\bar{Q}$ output of the last stage is connected back to the D input of the first stage. The Johnson counter can be implemented with *S-R* or *J-K* counters as well.

The circuit diagram of a three-stage Johnson counter is given in Fig. 13.33(a). The state transition diagram

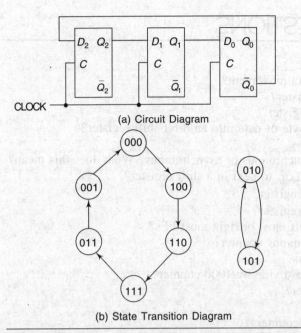

(a) Circuit Diagram

(b) State Transition Diagram

**Fig. 13.33** *Three-stage Count-by-6 Johnson Counter.*

of the same counter is given in Fig. 13.33(b). This counter has one basic *cycle of length 2 times 3,* or 6-000, 100, 110, 111, 011, 001, 000. It has another *cycle of length 2*-010, 101, 010. This Johnson counter, like the shift register counters, needs *logic circuits to start it in a desired state and to decode the outputs.*

### 13.28 How can a Johnson counter be used as a repetitive waveform generator?

*Solution:*
Using the basic gates, a clock oscillator, and a *repetitive waveform* generator circuit, we can create specialized waveforms to be used in digital control and sequencing circuits. *A popular general-purpose repetitive waveform generator is the Johnson shift counter.*

The Johnson shift counter of Fig. 13.34 outputs eight separate repetitive waveforms: *A, B, C, D* and their *complements* $\bar{A}$, $\bar{B}$, $\bar{C}$, $\bar{D}$. The input to the Johnson shift counter is a *clock oscillator* ($C_p$). The clock oscillator produces the $C_p$ waveform, which is input to the Johnson shift counter. The shift counter uses $C_p$ and internal circuitry to generate the eight repetitive waveforms shown. The Johnson shift counter is also known as *twisted ring counter.*

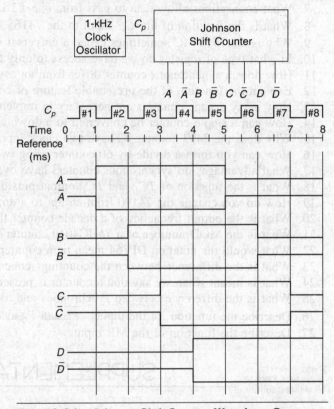

**Fig. 13.34** *Johnson Shift Counter Waveform Generator.*

## SUMMARY

> ➤ A circuit which will store one or more bits of data is called a register.
> ➤ Shift registers store data, move data, and present the data to the receiving device in a manner different to that in which it was initially presented to the register.
> ➤ Counters are sequential circuits which follow a predetermined sequence of digital states and are triggered by a timing pulse or clock.
> ➤ An asynchronous counter is one in which the flip-flops within the counter do not change states at exactly the same time because they do not have a common clock pulse.
> ➤ In synchronous counters, all the flip-flops in the counter are clocked at the same time by a common clock pulse.
> ➤ Up/down counters are capable of progressing in either direction through a certain sequence.
> ➤ A shift register counter is basically a shift register with the serial output connected back to the serial input to produce special sequences.

# REVIEW QUESTIONS

1. What are the basic types of shift registers in terms of data movement?
2. What is the difference between a counter and a shift register?
3. What two principal functions are performed by a shift register?
4. How many clock pulses are required to serially enter a byte of data into an 8-bit shift register?
5. Explain the function of SHIFT/LOAD input.
6. Is the parallel load operation in a 74165 shift register synchronous or asynchronous? What does this mean?
7. What connections allow data to pass from one `flip-flop` to next in a shift register?
8. What is the function of the $\overline{CE}$ input to the 74165 shift register?
9. Why is the 74194 IC sometimes called a universal shift register?
10. In what type of register do we have access to only the left most or right most FFs?
11. How does a synchronous counter differ from an asynchronous counter?
12. Explain the function of the presettable feature of counters.
13. How many decade counters are necessary to implement a divide-by-1000 counter?
14. How can a ripple-counter be converted to a down-counter?
15. Why does the 7493 counter IC have two clock inputs?
16. How can you form a divide-by-60 counter using two IC counters?
17. What advantages do synchronous counters have over ripple counters?
18. What is the function of $TC_U$ and $TC_D$ output pins on the 74193 synchronous counter IC?
19. How do you change the 74190 from an up- to a down-counter?
20. What is the output frequency of a decade counter that is clocked from a 50 kHz signal?
21. What is the MOD number of a 74HC4040 counter?
22. What would the notation DIV64 mean on a counter symbol?
23. What is the difference between the counting sequence of an up-and a down-counter?
24. What is meant when we say that a counter is presettable?
25. What is the difference between synchronous and asynchronous presetting?
26. Describe the function of the inputs $\overline{PL}$ and $P_0$ to $P_3$.
27. Describe the function of the MR input.

# SUPPLEMENTARY PROBLEMS

28. Illustrate and discuss the use of shift registers in serial communications.
29. Illustrate a 4-bit parallel-in parallel-out register.
30. Illustrate a 4-bit serial-in parallel-out register. Also draw its logic symbol.
31. Draw shift-left timing diagram.
32. Draw the logic symbol of 7493A connected as MOD-12 counter.
33. Illustrate propagation delay in a 3-bit asynchronous binary counter.
34. Make the necessary external connections to a 7490 to form a MOD-10 counter.
35. Make the necessary external connections to a 7492 to form a divide-by-6 frequency divider ($f_{out} = 1/6\ f_{in}$).
36. Design a Mod-6 synchronous binary up-counter.

# OBJECTIVE TYPE QUESTIONS

### Fill in the Blanks

37. Shift registers are basically _____ devices in which data can be _____ in or out in several ways.
38. A _____ shift register is one in which data can be moved internally in either direction.
39. A _____ shift register is one that has both serial and parallel inputs and outputs.

40. To input serial data into the 74164 shift register, one $D_S$ input must be held _____, while the other receives the serial data.
41. To make the 74194 act as a shift-left recirculating register, a connection must be made from _____ to _____ and $S_0$ and $S_1$ must be _____.
42. The outputs of the 74395A shift register are disabled by making OE _____, which makes $Q_0 - Q_3$ _____.
43. If both mode control inputs ($S_0$, $S_1$) to the 74194 are HIGH, the unit is in the _____ mode.
44. If both mode control inputs ($S_0$, $S_1$) to the 74194 are LOW, the unit is in the _____ mode.
45. Shift right on the 74194 is accomplished when $S_0$ is _____ and $S_1$ is _____ and when the clock pulse goes from _____ to _____.
46. The 74194 IC is in the parallel load mode when both mode control inputs ($S_0$, $S_1$) are _____. The four bits of data at the parallel inputs are loaded into the register by applying _____ clock pulses to the CLK input.
47. Sequential logic circuits have the characteristics of _____ in that their outputs are affected by the sequence of inputs that led up to the _____ set of inputs.
48. Registers form the _____ of computer memories and are also used for _____ conversion.
49. Standard _____ building blocks are available to simplify the construction of counters and registers.
50. Asynchronous counters are also called _____ counters.
51. The modulus of a counter is the number of states in its _____.
52. A mod-16 counter can function as a divide-by-16 frequency divider by taking the output from the _____ output.
53. To convert a 4-bit mod-16 counter to a mod-12 counter, the flip-flop must be Reset when the counter reaches the number _____.
54. Temporal code is the same as _____ form of data.
55. Spacial code is the same as _____ form of data.
56. State reduction, in the design of sequential circuits _____ the number of flip-flops.

### True/False Questions

State whether the following statements are True or False.
57. All flip-flops within a shift register are driven by the same clock input.
58. A serial in-parallel out register can have all of its bits displayed at one time.
59. The divide-by factor is not the same as the modulus.
60. Counters with truncated sequences have modulus numbers greater than $2^n$.
61. The $\overline{CE}$ input to the 74190 synchronous counter is the Chip Enable used to enable/disable the $Q$-outputs.
62. Liquid crystal displays (LCDs) use more power but are capable of emitting a brighter light than LEDs.
63. In an asynchronous counter, all FFs change state at the same time.
64. All BCD counters are decade counters.
65. The 74193 cannot be preset while MR is active.
66. The outputs of a ring counter are always square waves.
67. The decoding circuitry for a Johnson counter is simpler than that for a binary counter.
68. Ring and Johnson counters are asynchronous counters.
69. Flip-flops are wired together to form circuits that count.
70. A 4-bit binary counter has four binary place values and counts from 0000 to 1111 (decimal 0 to 15).
71. Manufacturers produce a wide variety of self-contained IC counters.
72. A delay line is used to avoid time delay in digital signals.

### Multiple-Choice Questions

73. The type of a register, in which data is entered into it only one bit at a time, but has all data bits available as output is
    (a) serial-in parallel-out register
    (b) serial-in serial out register
    (c) parallel-in serial out register
    (d) parallel-in parallel-out register
74. The type of register, in which we have access only to left most and right most flip-flops is
    (a) serial-in serial-out register
    (b) shift left register
    (c) shift left and shift right register
    (d) serial-in parallel out register
75. Shifting binary data to the left by one bit position using shift registers amounts to
    (a) division by 2  (b) subtraction of 2  (c) addition of 2  (d) multiplication by 2

76. Data can be changed from temporal code to spacial code by using
    (a) timer circuits    (b) shift registers    (c) synchronous counters (d) combinational circuits
77. Data can be changed from spacial code to temporal code by using
    (a) shift registers    (b) counters    (c) A/D converters    (d) D/A converters
78. A universal register
    (a) accepts serial input    (b) accepts parallel input
    (c) gives serial and parallel outputs    (d) is capable of all of the above
79. The maximum number of states that a counter with six flip-flops can count are
    (a) 6    (b) 8    (c) 64    (d) 256
80. The minimum number of flip-flops required for a mod-10 ripple counter are
    (a) 2    (b) 4    (c) 6    (d) 10
81. In a counter circuit consisting of *J-K* flip-flops, all the flip-flops get triggered simultaneously. This counter circuit is
    (a) a sequential circuit    (b) a combinational circuit
    (c) a synchronous circuit    (d) an asynchronous circuit
82. A ring counter consisting of five flip-flops will have
    (a) 10 states    (b) 5 states    (c) $2^5$ states    (d) none of the above
83. A twisted ring counter consisting of four flip-flops will have
    (a) 4 states    (b) 8 states    (c) $2^4$ states    (d) none of the above
84. The number of states in a decade counter is
    (a) 5    (b) 10    (c) 15    (d) 20
85. A 3-bit synchronous counter uses flip-flops with propagation delay time of 20 ns each. The maximum possible time required for change of state will be
    (a) 60 ns    (b) 40 ns    (c) 20 ns    (d) none of the above
86. The maximum possible number of states in a ripple counter consisting of 5 flip-flops is
    (a) 32    (b) 15    (c) 10    (d) 5
87. The maximum modulo number that can be obtained by a ripple counter using five flip-flops is
    (a) 32    (b) 16    (c) 15    (d) 5
88. The number of flip-flops required for a mod-16 ring counter are
    (a) 4    (b) 8    (c) 12    (d) 16
89. A BCD counter has
    (a) 12 distinct states    (b) 10 distinct states    (c) 6 distinct states    (d) 3 distinct states
90. The output frequency of a decade counter, clocked from a 50 kHz signal is
    (a) 500 kHz    (b) 50 kHz    (c) 5 kHz    (d) none of the above
91. The counter which requires maximum number of flip-flops for a given Mod number is
    (a) ripple counter    (b) BCD counter    (c) ring counter    (d) programmable counter
92. In a 4-bit binary ripple counter, for every input clock pulse
    (a) all the flip-flops get clocked simultaneously
    (b) only one flip-flop gets clocked at a time
    (c) only two flip-flops get clocked at a time
    (d) all the above statements are false
93. A sequential logic circuit consists of
    (a) only flip-flops    (b) only gates
    (c) only combinational logic circuits    (d) flip-flops and combinational logic circuits
94. The number of flip-flops required for a divide-by-12 circuit is
    (a) 16    (b) 12    (c) 8    (d) 4
95. A mod-2 counter followed by a mod-5 is the same as
    (a) a mod-7 counter    (b) a decade counter    (c) a mod-3 counter    (d) none of the above
96. The table which shows the necessary levels at *J* and *K* inputs to produce every possible flip-flop state transition is called
    (a) truth table (*J-K*)    (b) state transition table (*J-K*)
    (c) excitation table (*J-K*)    (d) none of the above

# ANSWERS

1.  (1) Serial in–serial out    (2) Serial in–parallel out (3) Parallel in–serial out (4) Parallel in–parallel out
2.  A counter has a special sequence of states. This is not so in the case of a register.
3.  (i) Data storage    (ii) Data movement (shifting)
4.  Eight    5. When SHIFT/LOAD is HIGH, the data are shifted one bit per clock pulse
6.  Asynchronous, the parallel load operation is not dependent on the clock.
7.  The output of a `flip-flop` connected to the input of the next `flip-flop` ($Q$ to $J$, $\bar{Q}$ to $K$).
8.  It's an active-LOW clock enable for starting/stopping the clock.
9.  Because the data can be input or output, serial or parallel, shift left or right, held, and reset
10. Serial in–serial out
11. All `flip-flops` in a synchronous counter are clocked simultaneously
12. The counter has been preset (initialized) to any given state
13. Three decade counters produce ÷ 1000.
14. By taking the binary output from $\bar{Q}$ outputs
15. One is for divide-by-2 section, and the other is for divide-by-8 section
16. By cascading a divide-by-10 with a divide-by-6
17. They don't have the problem of accumulated propagation delay.
18. They are the terminal count pins, which are used to indicate when terminal count is reached and the count is about to recycle
19. $\bar{U}/D = 1$    20. 5 kHz    21. 4096
22. The counter is MOD 64 and divides the frequency by 64
23. In an up-counter the count is increased by 1 with each clock pulse; in a down-counter the count is decreased by 1 with each clock pulse
24. The counter can be preset to any desired starting count
25. Asynchronous presetting is independent of the clock input while synchronous presetting occurs on the active edge of the clock signal
26. When $\overline{PL}$ is pulsed LOW, the counter is preset to the binary number present at inputs $P_0$ to $P_3$.
27. A HIGH at MR overrides all other inputs to reset counter to 0000.

28.

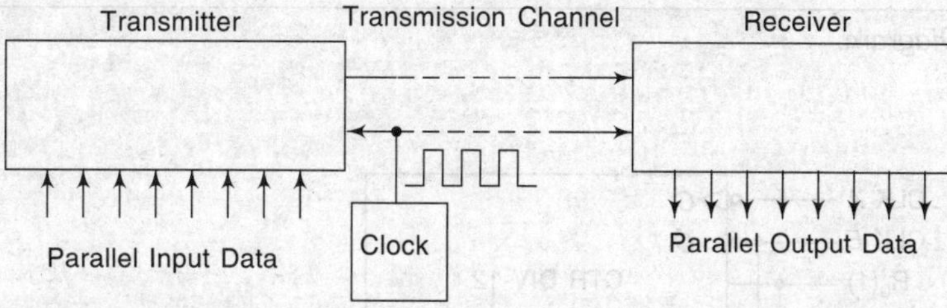

**Fig. 13.35**

*Note:* It requires *only two lines* (one for data and one for the clock) for the information to be communicated (rather than one line for each bit of the parallel data). Serial techniques are used extensively for *long distance communication.* In some systems the requirement to transmit the clock signal along with the data is removed by generating the clock signal at the receiver. This *reduces* the number of signal lines to *one.*

29.

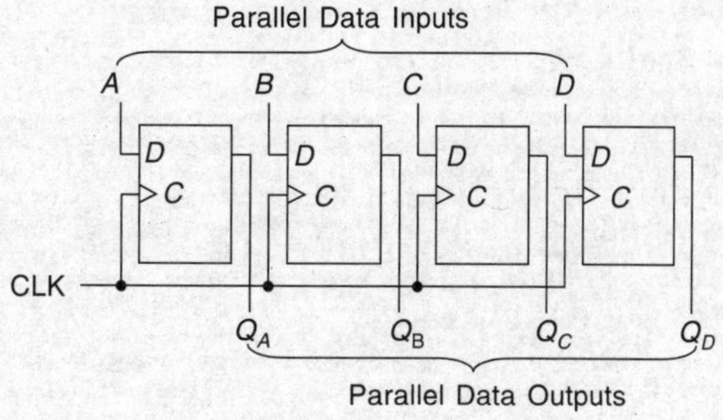

**Fig. 13.36**  *Four-bit Parallel-in Parallel-out Register.*

30. (See Fig 13.37)

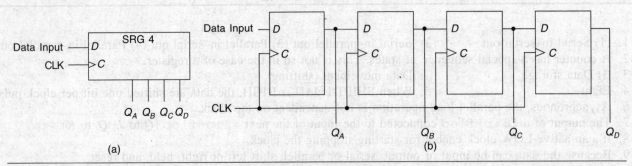

(a)

(b)

**Fig. 13.37**    *(a) Logic Symbol, (b) 4-bit Serial-in Parallel-out Register.*

31. (See Fig 13.38)

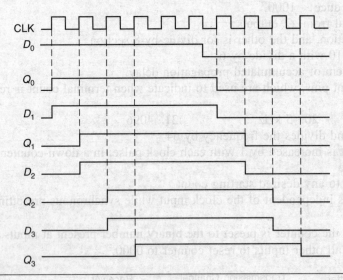

**Fig. 13.38** *Shift-left Timing Diagram.*

32. (See Fig 13.39)

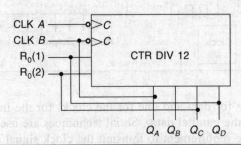

**Fig. 13.39**    *The 7493A Connected as a MOD-12 Counter.*

33. (See Fig 13.40)
34. (See Fig 13.41)
35. (See Fig 13.42)
36. (See Fig 13.43)

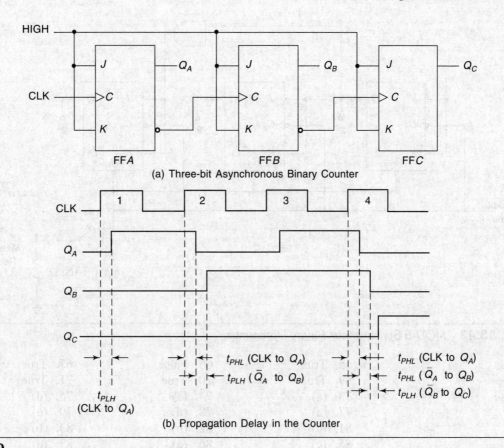

(a) Three-bit Asynchronous Binary Counter

(b) Propagation Delay in the Counter

**Fig. 13.40**

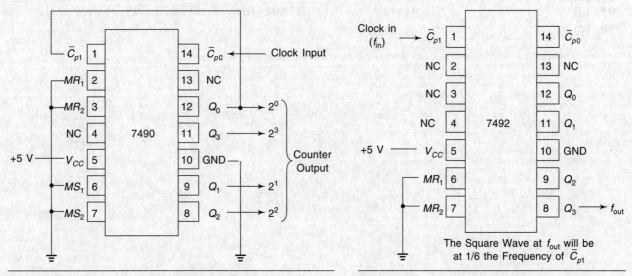

**Fig. 13.41** *Solution for 13.7 The MOD-10 Counter.*

**Fig. 13.42** *Divide-by-6 Frequency Divider.*

37. storage, shifted
38. bidirectional
39. universal
40. HIGH
41. $D_{SL}$, $Q_0$, 01
42. HIGH, float
43. parallel load
44. inhibit
45. HIGH, LOW, LOW, HIGH
46. HIGH, positive-going
47. memory, current
48. basis, serial to parallel
49. integrated circuit
50. ripple
51. sequence
52. $2^3$
53. 12
54. serial
55. parallel
56. reduces
57. True
58. True
59. False
60. False
61. False
62. False
63. False

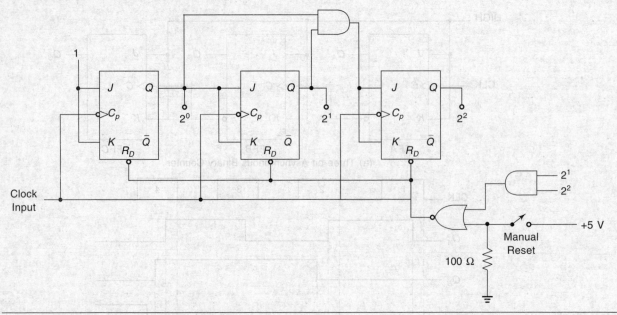

**Fig. 13.43** *MOD-6 Synchronous Binary Up-counter.*

| | | | |
|---|---|---|---|
| 64. True | 65. True | 66. False | 67. True |
| 68. True | 69. True | 70. True | 71. True |
| 72. False | 73. (a) | 74. (a) | 75. (d) |
| 76. (b) | 77. (a) | 78. (d) | 79. (c) |
| 80. (b) | 81. (c) | 82. (b) | 83. (b) |
| 84. (b) | 85. (c) | 86. (a) | 87. (a) |
| 88. (d) | 89. (b) | 90. (c) | 91. (c) |
| 92. (d) | 93. (d) | 94. (d) | 95. (b) |
| 96. (c) | | | |

# Sequential Machines

## INTRODUCTION

A large digital system cannot be understood through a detailed electrical analysis of all its circuits. There are just too many components and the electrical circuit laws are too difficult to solve. *The system as a whole can be understood only by a model that simplifies the system.* One such model is the sequential (finite state) machine. In this model, a digital system is viewed as one that moves in *discrete steps* from one state to another. Each transition is determined by the state in which it currently is, along with a set of inputs. In the transition, the machine may also output some discrete set of values.

A state in a digital *hardware system* is defined by some finite set of signal voltages, interpreted in a discrete manner (usually HIGH or LOW). A state in a *software system* might be defined by the set of values of the storage registers, including the current position in the stored program.

### 14.1 What are the applications of the finite-state machine model?

*Solution:*
The finite-state machine model has many applications. Every digital computer system is conceptually a finite-state machine, albeit one with a vast number of states. Many seemingly difficult language recognition problems yield to a finite-state machine synthesis. Many computer subsystems, such as peripheral device controllers or tape formatters are first designed as finite-state machines and are then transformed into their logic-circuit equivalents.

## TYPES OF STATE MACHINES

Sequential logic circuits can be classified into a category of circuits known as state machines of which there are two basic types. In the *Moore* state machine, shown in

Fig. 14.1, *the outputs depend only on the internal states and any inputs that are synchronized with the circuit.* Counters are examples of the Moore type of state machine, where the flip-flops are the memory portion.

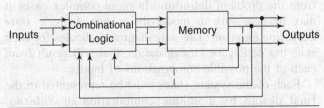

**Fig. 14.1** *Generalized Block Diagram of the Moore State Machine*

In the *Mealy* state machine, the outputs are determined by both the internal state and by inputs that are not synchronized with the circuit, as shown in Fig. 14.2.

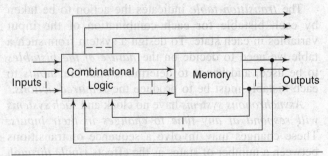

**Fig. 14.2** *Generalized Block Diagram of the Mealy State Machine*

### 14.2 Explain the steps involved in the design of sequential logic circuits.

*Solution:*
A *sequential system* consists of combinational logic with some *memory* within the feedback path. *Bistables* are a

unique example of simple sequential elements. These can be used to form larger systems such as *counters*. Sequential circuits can be designed to fulfil *particular tasks*.

Sequential systems may be either synchronous or asynchronous in nature. *Synchronous systems* are based on circuits that are controlled by a master clock; the values of the inputs and internal states are only of importance at times determined by *transitions* of this clock. Such arrangements often use *clocked bistables* as their building blocks. In *asynchronous* systems there is no clock. Internal states, and the outputs, may be affected at any time by changes in the inputs. Such systems are often based on *unclocked bistable latches* or use *time delays* within logic elements to represent *storage* within the feedback path.

In general, synchronous design is more *straight forward* than its asynchronous equivalent, the latter being susceptible to *timing problems* and *instability*.

The approach taken to the design of a sequential system will be greatly affected by the nature of the problem and the way it is defined. One of the first tasks is to determine all of the discrete *system states* that exist within the system. *The word state refers to a combination of internal and output variables of the system.* In simple systems the system states can be derived directly from the problem definition. In more complex cases it may be necessary to model the system using a *state transition diagram*. The state diagram indicates for each state the *action,* or *lack of action*, that will result from each of the possible combinations of inputs.

Each of the system states must be represented in the final design by a unique combination of *internal variables*. The number of variables required will be determined by the number of *independent states*. In many cases the internal variables will be represented by the outputs of bistables and in such cases the minimum number of bistables $N$ is related to the number of states $S$ by the relationship $2^N \geq S$.

The *transition table* indicates the action to be taken by each bistable for each combination of the input variables in each state. To design a system from such a table we need to decide on the *nature of the bistables* to be used, and hence to determine what the *inputs* to each bistable must be to produce the *required actions*.

*Asynchronous systems* have no clock and *such systems will respond at any time to changes in their inputs.* These changes may involve a sequence of transitions between a number of states as the effects *ripple through* the system. The memory elements in asynchronous systems are usually either unclocked bistables or logic gates providing a time. The latter act as memory elements since logic signals are effectively *stored* as they propagate through the circuit.

The design of asynchronous sequential systems is *more complicated* than that of their synchronous counterparts since the timing of signals plays an important role. In synchronous systems changes between states

can only occur at *active transitions* of the clock. However, in asynchronous systems changes between states may occur *any time* and the states may therefore be designed so that they are *stable*. The design of such systems involves many of the same components as synchronous design, although their execution is more complicated because of timing and instability considerations.

**14.3 Draw the state transition diagram and the state transition table of a *J-K* `flip-flop`. Explain.**

*Solution:*

The *J-K* `flip-flop` has two *inputs* ($J$ and $K$), one *output* ($Q$), and two states corresponding to $Q = 0$ and $Q = 1$. The states have been named $S_0$ and $S_1$ and are represented by two *circles* in Fig. 14.3. The *lines* joining the two circles represent possible transitions between these states. The *labels* on these lines indicate the input conditions for which these transitions will occur and the resultant output. The notation used for the labels is $JK/Q$. The diagram also shows *lines that leave each state and circle back to terminate on the same state.* The labels on these lines indicate the input conditions for the system to *stay in that state* and the output produced while in that state.

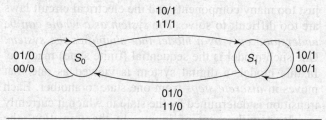

**Fig. 14.3** *State Transition Diagram of J-K* `flip-flop`.

When the circuit is in $S_0$ the output $Q_0$ is 0 and it will remain in that state while the inputs $JK$ are 01 or 00. A *transition* from $S_0$ to $S_1$ will occur for inputs 10 or 11, and if this occurs the output will go to 1. The names given to them are arbitrary and it would not affect the diagram if the labels are reversed.

From the state transition diagram it is possible to construct a *state transition table* (also called simply a *state table* or a *next state table*) which tabulates this information. *The table lists all the possible input combinations for each system state and indicates the resultant state (the next state).*

**Table 14.1** *State Transition Table for a* J-K `flip-flop`.

| Present State | Input Conditions JK | Next State | Output Q |
|---|---|---|---|
| $S_0$ | 00 | $S_0$ | 0 |
| | 01 | $S_0$ | 0 |
| | 10 | $S_1$ | 1 |
| | 11 | $S_1$ | 1 |
| $S_1$ | 00 | $S_1$ | 1 |
| | 01 | $S_0$ | 0 |
| | 10 | $S_1$ | 1 |
| | 11 | $S_0$ | 0 |

**14.4 Draw the state transition diagram and state transition table of a modulo-5 counter. Explain.**

*Solution:*

Most sequential systems have more than two states. Figure 14.4 illustrates the state transition diagram of a *modulo-5 counter* (a system with five states-$S_0$ to $S_4$).

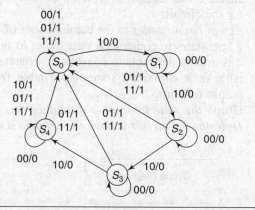

**Fig. 14.4** *State Transition Diagram of a Modulo-5 Counter.*

The operation of this circuit is not of paramount importance but is, in fact, that of a circuit with *two inputs N* (next) and *R* (reset) and *one output Q*. While the reset input is LOW (inactive) the circuit moves from state to state around the loop, moving on one state each time that *N* is HIGH during a clock pulse. The output *Q* is HIGH in state $S_0$, thus *the output is HIGH for one in every five counts*. Taking the *R* input HIGH causes the system to *jump* to $S_0$, where the output is 1, and to *remain* there *as long as R* is held HIGH. This arrangement is thus a form of *modulo-5, resettable counter*.

**Table 14.2** *State Transition Table for Modulo-5 Counter*

| Present State | Input Conditions NR | Next State | Output Q |
|---|---|---|---|
| $S_0$ | 0X | $S_0$ | 1 |
| | 10 | $S_1$ | 0 |
| | 11 | $S_0$ | 1 |
| $S_1$ | 00 | $S_1$ | 0 |
| | X1 | $S_0$ | 1 |
| | 10 | $S_2$ | 0 |
| $S_2$ | 00 | $S_2$ | 0 |
| | X1 | $S_0$ | 1 |
| | 10 | $S_3$ | 0 |
| $S_3$ | 00 | $S_3$ | 0 |
| | X1 | $S_0$ | 1 |
| | 10 | $S_4$ | 0 |
| $S_4$ | 00 | $S_4$ | 0 |
| | X1 | $S_0$ | 1 |
| | 10 | $S_0$ | 1 |

**14.5 With the help of a state transition diagram, explain the working of a self-starting shift-register counter.**

*Solution:*

A self-starting counter has *only one* counting cycle, which is reached from any of its possible initial states. It will, however, reach this cycle after, at worst, a few *wasted steps*.

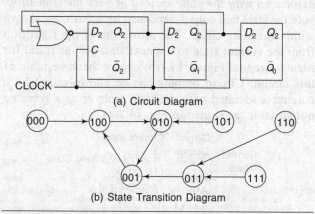

**Fig. 14.5** *A Three-State Self-Starting Shift Register Counter.*

**14.6 What is the major difference between the two classes of finite-state machines?**

*Solution:*

The *state diagram* of Fig. 14.6(a) shows the behaviour of an unspecified sequential circuit having one binary output. The four states—*A, B, C,* and *D*—are shown in *circles*. Transitions between states are shown by *arrows*. The *tail* of the arrow identifies the current state; its *head* identifies the next state. Two numbers separated by a *slash* (/) are associated with each arrow. The *left number* shows the current input; the *right number* shows the output associated with the transition. This state diagram has only 'two 1 outputs'. When the circuit is in state *B* or *C* and receives a '0 input', it returns to the same state and outputs a 1 pulse.

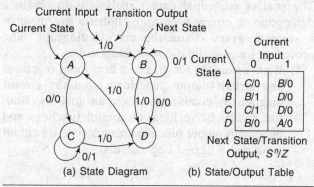

**Fig. 14.6** *A Mealy Circuit.*

The *state table* can be written from the state diagram. Figure 14.6(b) shows the state/output table of this circuit, so-called because it shows both the next state and the output transition. The *state/output table* also shows that the only 1 outputs occur on the transitions from *B* or *C* *back to the same state.*

A Moore circuit with four states is shown in Fig. 14.7(a). Because *the output of a Moore circuit is associated with the state instead of with the transition,* both the state and output, separated by a slash, are shown within the state circle. The arrow shows the transition from the current state to the next state just as it did for Mealy circuits. Figure 14.7(b) shows the state table of this circuit. Circuit outputs can be shown either by a column associated with the state table or as a separate output table, as shown in Fig. 14.7(c).

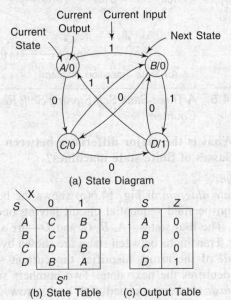

(a) State Diagram

(b) State Table     (c) Output Table

**Fig. 14.7**   *A Moore Circuit.*

## 14.7 Discuss synchronous sequential circuit analysis.

*Solution:*

The goal of sequential circuit analysis is to obtain a description of *circuit behaviour*—either a statement or a state diagram—from the circuit diagram. The procedure for *sequential circuit analysis* is:

1. *Write equations* for `flip-flop` input functions and circuit output functions from the circuit diagram by combinational circuit analysis. Both the `flip-flop` input or control functions and the circuit output functions may depend on circuit input and `flip-flop` outputs.

2. *Develop control tables* that display the `flip-flop` input equations somewhat like a Karnaugh map. Control tables show `flip-flop` control inputs as a function of circuit inputs and `flip-flop` outputs.

3. From the control tables and the `flip-flop` characteristic equations *develop a transition table* for the circuit.

4. *Assign circuit states* to the combinations of `flip-flop` states to construct a state table. At this point it is usually desirable to construct a separate output table or a combined state/output table from the output functions.

5. *Graph the state table* as a state diagram.

6. *Describe the circuit behaviour* in words if desired.

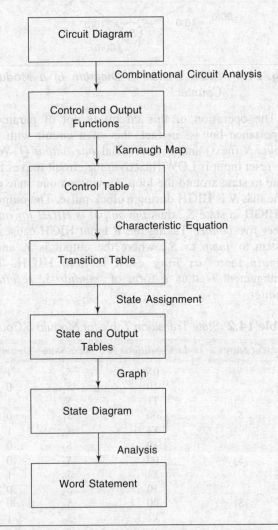

**Fig. 14.8**   *Procedure for Sequential Circuit Analysis.*

# SUMMARY

> ➤ Synchronous sequential circuits can be described by either a Moore model or a Mealy model.
> ➤ State diagrams show all circuit states, the transitions between them, and the associated inputs and outputs.
> ➤ Moore circuits have outputs that are associated with the states.
> ➤ Mealy circuits have outputs that are associated with transitions between states.
> ➤ The term state refers to a combination of internal and output variables of the system.

# REVIEW QUESTIONS

**Test your understanding**

1. Name the two categories of state machines.
2. In what category of state machines are counters classified?
3. Which sequential circuits are difficult to design and why?

# SUPPLEMENTARY PROBLEMS

**Test your understanding**

4. Draw the state diagram of an up/down counter.
5. Draw the state diagram of a three-stage, count-by-6 Johnson counter.
6. Draw the state diagram of the circuit shown below.

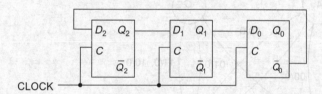

CLOCK

**Fig. 14.9**

# OBJECTIVE TYPE QUESTIONS

**Test your understanding**

### Fill in the Blanks

7. A sequential circuit has _____ and _____.
8. A diagram showing various desired states and the transitions of a sequential circuit is called _____ diagram.
9. A table showing present states, next states and conditions at flip-flops is called _____.

### True/False Questions

State whether the following statements are True or False.

10. A synchronous sequential machine is characterized by a quintuple.
11. Synchronous sequential machines are called non-deterministic machines.
12. As the number of states increases further, the encoding process expands correspondingly.
13. Mealy circuits have outputs that are associated with the states.
14. Moore circuits have outputs that are associated with transitions between states.

### Multiple Choice Questions

15. What indicates the next state in a state diagram?
    (a) circle          (b) arrow head         (c) arrow tail

# ANSWERS

1.  Moore and Mealy
2.  Moore machines
3.  Asynchronous sequential circuits; because of timing and instability problems
4.  (See Fig. 14.10)
5.  (See Fig. 14.11)

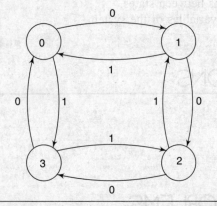

**Fig. 14.10**   *State Diagram of an Up/down Counter.*

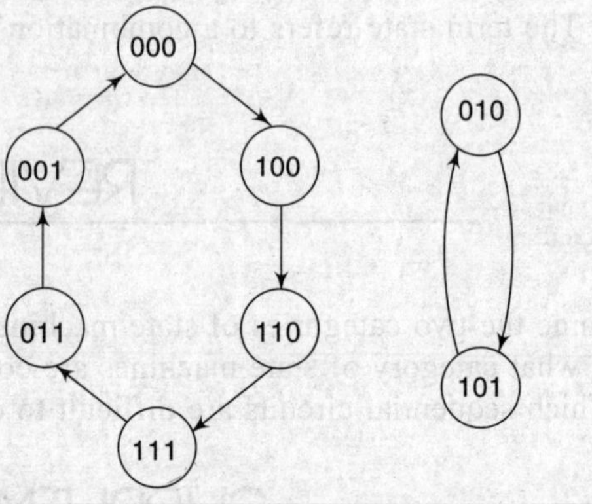

**Fig. 14.11**   *State Diagram of a Three-stage, Count-by-6 Johnson Counter*

6.

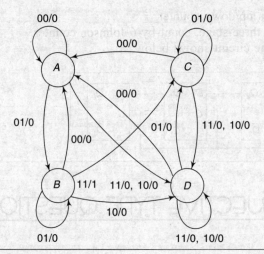

**Fig. 14.12**   *State Diagram*

7.  combinational logic, memory
8.  state transition
9.  excitation table
10. True
11. False
12. True
13. False
14. False
15. (b)

# Memory

## INTRODUCTION

A major advantage of digital systems over analog systems is the ability to easily *store* large quantities of digital information or data for *short* or *long* periods. This *memory* capability is what makes digital systems so versatile and adaptable to many situations.

In digital systems, memory circuits provide the means of storing information (data) on a *temporary* or *permanent* basis for *future recall.* The storage medium can be either a magnetic device such as magnetic tape or disk, or a semiconductor integrated circuit.

## SEMICONDUCTOR MEMORY

With *semiconductor memory ICs*, electrical signals are used to identify a particular *memory location* within the integrated circuit, and data can be *stored* in or *read from* that location in a matter of nanoseconds.

The technology used in the fabrication of memory ICs can be based on either the bipolar or MOS transistors. In general, *bipolar memories are faster* than MOS memories, but MOS *can be integrated more densely,* providing much more memory locations in the same amount of area.

The `flip-flop` is an electronic memory device. Groups of `flip-flops` called *registers* can be used to store information. This information can be *shifted* (transferred) to other locations. *FF registers* are high-speed memory elements which are used extensively in the internal operations of a digital computer, where digital information is continually moved from one location to another.

Advances in *LSI* and *VLSI* technology have made it possible to obtain large numbers of FFs on a single chip arranged in various *memory array formats.* These bipolar and MOS semiconductor memories are the *fastest* memory devices available, and their cost has been continuously decreasing as LSI technology improves.

**15.1 Explain the following terms giving *examples*:**

    **(a) Memory cell**        **(b) Memory word**
    **(c) Byte**             **(d) Capacity**
    **(e) Density**         **(f) Address**

*Solution:*

(a) *Memory cell:* A device or electrical circuit used to store a *single bit* (0 or 1) is called a memory cell. *Examples* of memory cells include a `flip-flop`, a charged capacitor, and a single spot on magnetic tape or disk.

(b) *Memory word:* A *group of bits* (cells) in a memory that represents instructions or data of some type is called a memory word. For *example,* a register consisting of eight `flip-flops` can be considered to be a memory that is storing an 8-bit word. Word sizes in modern computers typically range from 4 to 64 bits, depending on the size of the computer.

(c) *Byte:* A byte is a special term used for a *group of 8 bits.* Word sizes can be expressed in bits as well as in bytes. For *example*, a word size of 8 bits is also a word size of one byte; a word size of 16 bits is two bytes, and so on.

(d) *Capacity:* Capacity is a way of specifying *how many bits* can be stored in a particular memory device or complete memory system. For *example,* suppose that we have a memory which can store 4096 twenty-bit words. This represents a total capacity of 81,920 bits. We can also express this memory's capacity as $4096 \times 20$. When expressed this way, the *first number* (4096) is the number of words and the *second number* (20) is the number of bits per word (word size). The number of words in a memory is often a multiple of 1024. It is common to use the designation '*1K*' to represent $1024$ ($2^{10}$) when referring to memory capacity. For still large memories the designation '*1M*' represents $1,048,576$ ($2^{20}$).

(e) *Density:* Yet another term for capacity is density. When we say that one memory device has a greater density than another, we mean that *it can store more bits* in the same amount of space. It is more dense.

(f) *Address:* Address is a number that identifies the *location of a word* in the memory. Each word stored in a memory device or system has a unique address. Addresses are always expressed as a *binary number,* although octal, hexadecimal and decimal numbers are also used for convenience. For *example,* Fig. 15.1 illustrates a small memory consisting of eight words. Each of these eight words has a unique address represented as a 3-bit number ranging from 000 to 111. Whenever we refer to a specific word location in memory, we use its *address code* to identify it.

| Addresses | |
|---|---|
| 000 | Word 0 |
| 001 | Word 1 |
| 010 | Word 2 |
| 011 | Word 3 |
| 100 | Word 4 |
| 101 | Word 5 |
| 110 | Word 6 |
| 111 | Word 7 |

**Fig. 15.1**   *Each Word Location has a Unique Binary Address.*

**15.2** *Define* **the following terms:**
   **(a) Read operation   (b) Write operation**
   **(c) Access time**

*Solution:*
(a) *Read Operation:* The operation whereby the binary word stored in a specific memory location (address) is *sensed and then transferred* to another device is called read operation. For *example* if we want to use word 4 of the memory of Fig. 15.1 for some purpose, we have to perform a read operation on address 100. The read operation is often called a *fetch operation*, since a word is being fetched from the memory.

(b) *Write Operation:* The operation whereby a new word is placed into a particular memory location is called write operation. It is also referred to as *store operation.* Whenever a new word is written

into a memory location, it *replaces* the word that was previously stored there.

(c) *Access Time:* Access time is a measure of a memory devices *operating speed.* It is the amount of time required to perform a read operation. More specifically, it is the time between the memory receiving a new address input, and the data becoming available at the memory output. The symbol $t_{ACC}$ is used for access time.

## RAM AND ROM

Semiconductor memories are used as the *internal memory* of a computer where *fast operation* is important. A computer's internal memory—also called its *main memory* or *working memory*—is in constant communication with the central processing unit (CPU) as a *program* of instructions is being executed. A program and any data used by the program reside in the internal memory while the computer is working on that program RAM and ROM make up internal memory.

**15.3** *Define* **the following terms:**
   **(a) Volatile Memory**
   **(b) Random Access Memory (RAM)**
   **(c) Sequential Access Memory (SAM)**
   **(d) Read/Write Memory (RWM)**
   **(e) Read-Only Memory (ROM)**

*Solution:*
(a) *Volatile Memory:* Any type of memory that requires the application of *electrical power* in order to store information is called volatile memory. If the electrical power is removed, all information stored in the memory will be lost. Many semiconductor memories are *volatile*, while all magnetic memories are *non-volatile*, which means they can store information *without* electrical power.

(b) *Random Access Memory* (RAM): Memory in which the *actual physical location* of a memory word has no effect on how long it takes to read from or write into that location is called 'random access memory' (RAM). In other words, *the access time is the same for any address in memory.* Most semiconductor memories are RAMs.

(c) *Sequential Access Memory* (SAM): A type of memory in which *the access time is not constant,* but varies depending on the address location is called sequential-access memory. A particular stored word is found by *sequencing through* all address locations until the desired address is reached. This produces access times which are much longer than those for random access memories. *Examples* of SAM devices include magnetic tape, disk, and magnetic bubble memory.

(d) *Read/Write Memory* (RWM): Any memory that can be read from or written into *with equal ease* is called read/write memory (RWM).

(e) *Read-Only Memory (ROM):* A broad class of semiconductor memories designed for applications where *the ratio of read operations to write operations is very high* is called read-only memory (ROM). Technically a ROM can be written into (programmed) *only once,* and this operation is normally performed at the factory. Thereafter, information *can only be read* from the memory. Other types of ROM are actually *read-mostly memories (RMM)* which can be written into *more than once,* but the write operation is more complicated than the read operation and it is not performed very often. *All ROM is nonvolatile* and will store data when electrical power is removed.

### 15.4 *Differentiate* between SAM and RAM.

*Solution:*

To illustrate the difference between SAM (Sequential Access Memory) and RAM (Random Access Memory) consider the situation where you have recorded 60 minutes of songs on an audio tape cassette. When you want to get to a particular song, you have to rewind or fast forward the tape until you find it. The process is relatively *slow,* and the amount of time required depends on *where* on the tape the required song is recorded. This is SAM, since you have to *sequence through* all the intervening information until you find what you are looking for.

The RAM counterpart to this would be a juke box, where you can quickly select *any* song by punching in the appropriate code and it takes the *same* time no matter *what* song you select.

### 15.5 What memory *stores* more bits: a 5M × 8 memory, or a memory that stores 1M words at a word size of 16 bits?

*Solution:*

$$5M \times 8 = 5 \times 1,048,576 \times 8 = 41,943,040 \text{ bits}$$
$$1M \times 16 = 1,048,576 \times 16 = 16,777,216 \text{ bits}$$

Hence, the 5M × 8 memory stores more bits.

### 15.6 *Distinguish* between ROM and RAM.

*Solution:*

ROM

1. ROM is a *read only* memory.
2. Data are permanently or semipermanently *stored.*
3. Data can be *read* from the memory at any time.
4. If the data are *permanently* stored, there is no write operation.
5. If the data are *semipermanently* stored, the data can be altered by special methods, but there is no write operation.
6. ROMs are *non-volatile* memories.

RAM

1. RAM is *random* access memory.
2. Has both *read and write* capability.
3. Any *storage location* in the memory can be addressed.
4. Most ROMs are also *random access* devices.
5. RAM is a *read/write* random access memory and the ROM is a *read only* random access memory.
6. RAMs are *volatile* memories.

### 15.7 *Define* the following terms:
   (a) **Static Memory Devices**
   (b) **Dynamic Memory Devices**
   (c) **Internal Memory**
   (d) **External Memory**

*Solution:*

(a) *Static Memory Devices:* Semiconductor memory *devices in which the stored data will remain permanently stored as long as power is applied* without the need for periodically rewriting the data into memory are called *static memory devices.*

(b) *Dynamic Memory Devices:* Semiconductor memory *devices in which the stored data will not remain permanently stored, even with power applied,* unless the data are periodically rewritten into memory are called dynamic memory devices. The latter operation is called a *refresh operation.*

(c) *Internal Memory:* Internal memory is also referred to as the computer's *main* or *working memory.* It stores instructions and data the CPU is currently working on. *It is the highest-speed memory in the computer and is always a semiconductor memory.*

(d) *External Memory:* External memory is also referred to as *mass storage* because it stores massive amounts of information external to the internal memory. It is *slower in speed* than internal memory and is always *non-volatile.* Magnetic tape and disk are common external memory devices.

### 15.8 Briefly *describe* the ROM family.

*Solution:*

Semiconductor ROMs are manufactured with *bipolar technology* (such as TTL) or with MOS *technology.* Figure 15.2 shows how ROMs are categorized.

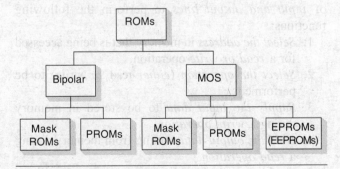

**Fig. 15.2**  *The ROM Family.*

The *mask* ROM is the type in which data are permanently stored in the memory during the manufacturing process. The *programmable* ROM, or PROM, is the type in which the data are electrically stored by the user with the aid of *specialized equipment*. Both the mask ROM and the PROM can be of either technology. The *erasable* PROM, or EPROM, is electrically programmable by the user, but the stored data can be erased either by exposure to ultraviolet light or by electrical means. The latter type is called an *electrically erasable* PROM (EEPROM) or *electrically alterable* PROM ((EAPROM). The erasable PROM is strictly a MOS device.

### 15.9 Briefly *describe* the RAM family.

*Solution:*

Figure 15.3 shows how RAMs are categorized. RAMs are also manufactured with either *bipolar* or MOS technologies. Bipolar RAMs are all *static* RAMs; that is the storage elements used in memory are latches, so data can be stored for an indefinite period of time as long as the power is on. Some MOS RAMs are of the static type and some are *dynamic* RAMs. A dynamic memory is one in which data are stored on capacitors which require periodic recharging (*refreshing*) to retain the data.

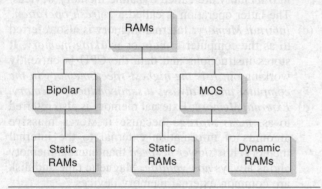

**Fig. 15.3**   *The RAM Family.*

### 15.10 What are the basic *operating principles* that are the same for all memory systems?

*Solution:*

Every memory system requires several different types of *input and output lines* to perform the following functions:

1. *Select the address* in memory that is being accessed for a *read or write* operation.
2. *Select the operation* (*either* read *or* write) to be performed.
3. *Supply the input data* to be stored in memory during a *write operation.*
4. *Hold the output data* coming from memory during a *read operation.*
5. *Enable (or disable) the memory* so that it will (or will not) respond to the address inputs and read/write command.

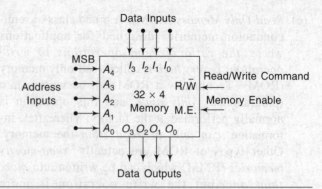

**Fig. 15.4**   *A Simplified Diagram of a 32 × 4 Memory.*

Figure 15.4 illustrates these basic functions in a simplified diagram of a 32 × 4 memory that stores *thirty two 4-bit words*. Since the *word size* is 4-bits, there are four *data input lines*, $I_0$ to $I_3$, and four *data output lines*, $O_0$ to $O_3$. During a *write operation* the data to be stored in a memory is applied to the data input lines. During a *read operation* the word being read from memory appears at the data output lines.

Since this memory stores 32 *words,* it has 32 different *storage locations* and, therefore, 32 different *binary addresses* ranging from 00000 to 11111 (decimal 0 to 31). Thus there are five *address inputs*, $A_0$ to $A_4$. To *access* one of the memory locations for a read or write operation, the 5-bit *address code* for that particular location is applied to the address inputs. In general, $N$ address inputs are required for a memory that has a capacity fo $2^N$ words.

The $R/\overline{W}$ input *controls* which memory operation is to take place: read (R) or write (W). Since there is no bar over the $R$, this indicates that the *read* operation occurs when $R/\overline{W} = 1$. The bar over W indicates that the write operation takes place when $R/\overline{W} = 0$.

Many memory systems have some means for *completely disabling* all or part of the memory so that it will not respond to other inputs. This is represented in Fig. 15.4 as the MEMORY ENABLE inputs. It is shown as a active HIGH input that enables the memory to operate normally when it is kept HIGH. A LOW on this input disables the memory so that it will not respond to the address and $R/\overline{W}$ inputs. This type of input is particularly useful when several memory modules are combined to form a large memory.

### 15.11 With the help of a simplified illustration, explain the READ and WRITE *operations.*

*Solution:*

A simplified illustration for the read and write operations on the 32 × 4 memory is given in Fig. 15.5. Part(a) shows the data word 0100 being *written into* the memory register *at address location* 00011. This data word would have been applied to the memory's *data input lines,* and *replaces* the data previously stored at address 00011.

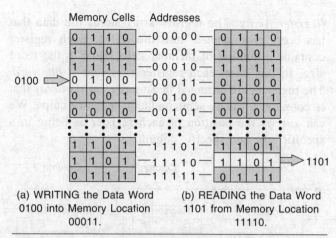

(a) WRITING the Data Word 0100 into Memory Location 00011.

(b) READING the Data Word 1101 from Memory Location 11110.

**Fig. 15.5** *The READ and WRITE Operations on the 32 × 4 Memory.*

Part(b) shows the data word 1101 being *read from* address 11110. This data would appear at the memory's *data output lines.* After the read operation, the data word 1101 is still stored in address 11110. In other words, *the read operation does not change the stored data.*

**15.12 With the help of diagrams** *explain* **the following:**
**(a) Bipolar ROM cells**
**(b) MOS ROM cells**

*Solution:*
Most IC ROMs utilize the *presence or absence* of a transistor connection at a *ROW/COLUMN junction* to represent a 1 or 0. ROMs can either be bipolar or MOS.

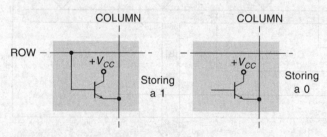

**Fig. 15.6** *Bipolar ROM Cells.*

(a) *Bipolar Cells:* Figure 15.6 shows bipolar ROM cells. The *presence* of a connection from a ROW line to the *base* of a transistor represents a 1 at that location because when the ROW line is taken HIGH, all transistors with a base connection to that ROW line turn ON and connect the HIGH (1) to the associated COLUMN lines. At the ROW/COLUMN junctions where there is an *absence* of base connections, COLUMN lines remain LOW (0) when the ROW is addressed.

(b) MOS *Cells:* Figure 15.7 illustrates MOS ROM cells. They are basically the same as the bipolar ROM cells except that they are made using MOSFETs (metal oxide semiconductor field-effect transistors). *The presence or absence of a gate*

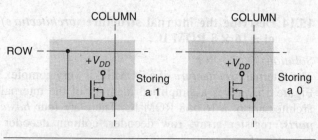

**Fig. 15.7** *MOS ROM Cells.*

*connection at a junction permanently stores a 1 or 0.*

**15.13 Illustrate a 16 × 8-bit ROM** *array.* **Explain.**

*Solution:*

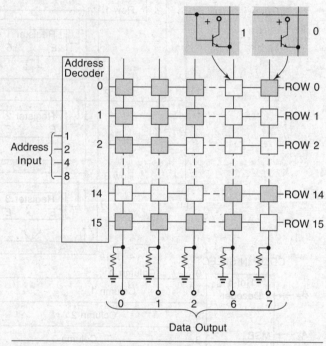

**Fig. 15.8** *A 16 × 8-Bit ROM Array.*

Figure 15.8 shows a small, simplified ROM array. The *light squares* represent stored 1s, and the *dark squares* represent stored 0s. The basic *read operation* is as follows:

When the binary address code is applied to the address input, the corresponding ROW line goes HIGH. This HIGH is connected to the COLUMN lines through the transistors at each junction (cell) *where a 1 is stored.* At each cell where a 0 is stored, the COLUMN line stays LOW because of the terminating resistor. *The COLUMN lines form the data output. The eight data bits stored in the selected ROW appear on the output lines.*

The ROM in Fig. 15.8 is organised into 16 addresses, each of which stores 8 data bits. Thus, it is a 16 × 8 (*16 by 8*) ROM, and its total capacity is 128 bits.

## 15.14  Describe the internal structure (*architecture*) of a 16 × 8 ROM IC.

*Solution:*

The internal *architecture* of a ROM IC is very complex. Figure 15.9 gives a simplified diagram of the internal architecture of a 16 × 8 ROM IC. There are four *basic parts:* register array, row decoder, column decoder, output buffers.

*Register Array:* The register array stores the data that has been *programmed* into the ROM. Each register contains a number of memory cells equal to the word size. In this case, each register stores an *8-bit word.* The registers are arranged in a *square matrix array* that is common to many semiconductor memory chips. We can *specify* the position of each register as being in a specific row and specific column.

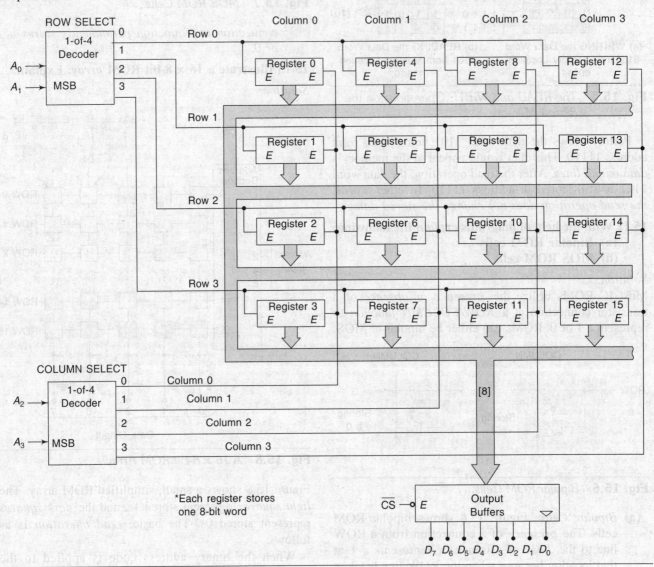

**Fig. 15.9**  *Architecture of 16 × 8 ROM.*

The eight *data outputs* of each register are connected to an internal *data bus* that runs through the entire circuit. Each register has two *enable inputs* (E); both of which have to be HIGH in order for the register's data to be placed on the bus.

*Address Decoders:* The applied address code $A_3A_2A_1A_0$ determines which register in the array will be *enabled* to place its 8-bit data word on to the bus. Address bits $A_1A_0$ are fed to a 1-of-4 decoder which activates one

row-select-line, and address bits $A_3A_2$ are fed to a second 1-of-4 decoder which activates one *column-select line.* Only one register will be selected by the address inputs using *both* the row and the column inputs, and this one will be *enabled.*

*Output Buffers:* The register that is enabled by the address inputs will place its data on the *data bus.* This data is fed into the output buffers, which will pass the data to the external *data outputs,* provided that $\overline{CS}$ is

LOW. If $\overline{CS}$ is HIGH, the output buffers are in the Hi-Z state, and $D_7$ through $D_0$ will be floating.

## THREE-STATE BUFFERS

The three-state outputs are indicated on logic symbols by a *small inverted triangle* ($\nabla$), Fig. 15.10, and are used for *compatibility with bus structures* such as those found in microprocessor-based systems.

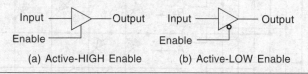

(a) Active-HIGH Enable     (b) Active-LOW Enable

**Fig. 15.10**   *Three-state Buffer Symbols.*

*Physically*, a *bus* is a set of conductive paths that serve to *interconnect* two or more functional components of a system or diverse systems. *Electrically*, a *bus* is a collection of voltages, levels, and signals that allow the various devices connected to the bus to *work together properly*.

A microprocessor is connected to memories and input/output devices by certain *bus structures*. This is shown in Fig. 15.11. An *address bus* allows the microprocessor to address the memories, and the *data bus* provides for transfer of data between the microprocessor, the memories and the input/output devices. The *control bus* allows the microprocessor to control data flow and timing for various components. The physical bus is symbolically represented by wide lines with arrow heads indicating *direction of data movement*.

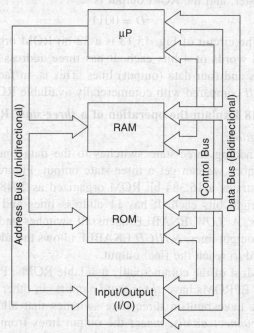

**Fig. 15.11**   *Block Diagram of a Basic Microcomputer System with Bus Interconnections.*

Many microprocessors, memories, and other integrated circuit functions have three-state buffers that serve to *interface* with the buses. This is necessary when two or more devices are connected to a *common bus*. To prevent the devices from *interfering* with each other, three-state buffers are used to *disconnect* all devices *except* the ones that are communicating at any given time.

**15.15 Describe the *working* of a diode ROM. What are its *drawbacks*?**

*Solution:*
Figure 15.12 illustrates a diode ROM. Each *horizontal row* is a register or memory location. The $R_0$ location contains three diodes, the $R_1$ register has one diode, and so on. The *output* of the ROM is the word.

$$D = D_3 D_2 D_1 D_0$$

In switch position 0, a high voltage turns *on* the diodes in the $R_0$ register; all other diodes are *off*. This means that a HIGH output appears at $D_2$, $D_1$, and $D_0$. Therefore, the *word stored* at memory location 0 is

$$D = 0111$$

When the switch is moved to position 1, the diode in the $R_1$ register conducts, forcing $D_3$ to go HIGH. Because all other diodes are off, the output of the ROM becomes

$$D = 1000$$

**Table 15.1** *Diode ROM*

| Register | Address | Word |
|----------|---------|------|
| $R_0$ | 0 | 0111 |
| $R_1$ | 1 | 1000 |
| $R_2$ | 2 | 1011 |
| $R_3$ | 3 | 1100 |
| $R_4$ | 4 | 0110 |
| $R_5$ | 5 | 1001 |
| $R_6$ | 6 | 0011 |
| $R_7$ | 7 | 1110 |

So the contents of memory location 1 are 1000. Table 15.1 shows the *contents of memory location* for different positions of the switch.

With discrete circuits we can *change* the contents of a memory location by *adding* or *removing* diodes. With intergrated circuits, the manufacturer *stores* the words at the time of fabrication. In either case, *the words are permanently stored once the diodes are wired in place.*

The diode ROM has many *drawbacks*. Their logic levels are *marginal*. The diode ROM also suffers in that it has *very little drive capability*. The diode ROMs *do not need input and output buffering* when working with systems that contain data and address buses.

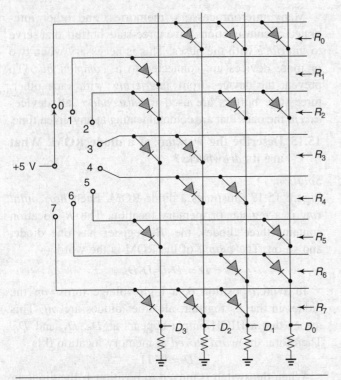

**Fig. 15.12**    *Diode ROM*

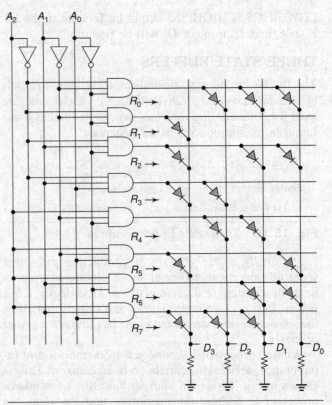

**Fig. 15.13**    *ROM with On-Chip Decoding.*

**15.16** *Distinguish* **between the address and contents of a memory location.**

*Solution:*
The address and contents of a memory location are two different things. The *address* of a memory location is the same as the *subscript* of the register storing the word. Register 0 has address 0 and *contents* 0111; register 1 has address 1 and contents 1000; register 2 has address 2 and contents 1011; and so on.

The idea of addresses applies to ROMs of any size. For example, a ROM with 256 memory locations has decimal addresses running from 0 to 255. A ROM with 1024 memory locations has decimal addresses from 0 to 1023.

**15.17 Explain the idea of *on-chip decoding*.**

*Solution:*
Rather than *switch-selecting* the memory location, IC manufacturers use *on-chip decoding*. Figure 15.13 illustrates the idea behind on-chip decoding.

The three inputs pins ($A_2$, $A_1$, and $A_0$) supply the *binary address* of the stored word. Then a 1-of-8 decoder produces a HIGH output to one of the registers. For instance, if

$$ADDRESS = A_2A_1A_0 = 100$$

the 1-of-8 decoder applies a HIGH voltage to the $R_4$ register, and the ROM output is

$$D = 0110$$

If you change the address word to

$$ADDRESS = A_2A_1A_0 = 110$$

the 1-of-8 decoder applies a HIGH voltage to the $R_6$ register, and the ROM output is

$$D = 0011$$

The circuit of Fig. 15.13 is a 32-bit ROM organized as 8 words of 4 bits each. It has three address (input) lines and four data (output) lines. This is, in fact, very *small* compared with commercially available ROMs.

**15.18 Explain the operation of a *three-state* ROM.**

*Solution:*
By adding three-state switches to the data lines of a memory we can get a three-state output. Figure 15.14 illustrates a 16,384-bit ROM organized as 2048 words of eight bits each. It has 11 address lines and 8 data lines. A *LOW* ENABLE opens all switches and *floats* the output lines. A *HIGH* ENABLE allows the addressed word to reach the final output.

Most of the commercially available ROMs, PROMs, and EPROMs have *three-state outputs*. In other words, they have built-in three-state switches that allow you to *connect or disconnect* the output lines from a data bus.

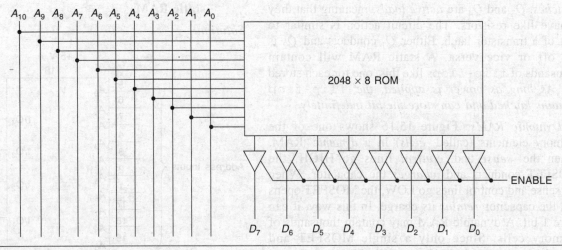

$A_{10}$ $A_9$ $A_8$ $A_7$ $A_6$ $A_5$ $A_4$ $A_3$ $A_2$ $A_1$ $A_0$

2048 × 8 ROM

ENABLE

$D_7$ $D_6$ $D_5$ $D_4$ $D_3$ $D_2$ $D_1$ $D_0$

**Fig. 15.14** *Three-State ROM.*

**15.19 Explain random access (RAM) memory. What are the different types of random access memory? Explain each type.**

*Solution:*
Most main computer memories are *random access*. By random access we mean that *we can access or reach any word in memory in the same amount of time or in the same number of operations.* Thus, in a random-access memory, access time and write time are *constants*. Other memories such as discs and tapes, require *varying amounts* of time to access a word of memory depending on its location. Random access memories today are usually composed of semiconductors, while in the past main memories were predominantly magnetic core.

RAMs can be broadly classified as:
1. Core RAMs
2. Semiconductor RAMs
3. Static RAMs
4. Dynamic RAMs
5. Three-State RAMs

*1. Core RAMs:* The core RAM was the workhorse of early computers. It has the advantage of being *non-volatile*; even though you shut off the power, a core RAM continues to store data. The disadvantage of core RAMs is that they are very *expensive and harder to work* with than semiconductor memories.

*2. Semiconductor RAMs:* Semiconductor RAMs may be *static* or *dynamic*. The static RAM uses *bipolar* or MOS flip-flops and the data is retained indefinitely as long as power is applied to the flip-flop. On the other hand, a dynamic RAM uses MOSFETs and capacitors that store data. Because the capacitor charge leaks off, the stored data must be *refreshed* (recharged) every few milliseconds. In either case, the RAMs *are volatile; turn off the power and the stored data is lost.*

In the past bipolar RAMs enjoyed a definite speed advantage over MOS; but MOS technology has made greater speed improvements so that now the ranges of *access times* for MOS and TTL RAMs overlap. *ECL RAMs have the fastest access times* with some below 10 ns. *TTL* RAMs typically have access times from 20 to 60 ns, whereas MOS RAMs have access times from 30 to more than 300 ns. Faster RAMs are naturally more expensive and may have other disadvantages, such as greater dissipation of power, fewer bits of storage per chip, and less availability of types. *In general, a bipolar memory cell requires a larger area and dissipates more power than an MOS memory cell.* At present nMOS RAMs predominate, but CMOS RAMs are becoming increasingly popular for low power applications such as digital watches.

*3. Static RAMs:* MOS RAMs may be static or dynamic. *Static memories do not require attention.* Figure 15.15 shows one of the flip-flops used in a static MOS RAM.

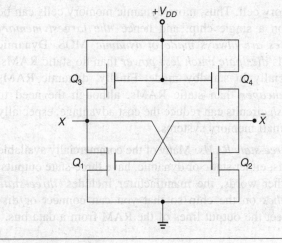

**Fig. 15.15** *Static Cell.*

In the circuit shown in Fig. 15.15 $Q_1$ and $Q_2$ act like *switches.* $Q_3$ and $Q_4$ are *active loads,* meaning that they behave like resistors. The circuit action is similar to that of a transistor latch. Either $Q_1$ conducts and $Q_2$ is cut off or vice versa. A static RAM will contain thousands of `flip-flops` like this, one for each stored bit. *As long as power is applied, the* `flip-flop` *remains latched and can store the bit indefinitely.*

*4. Dynamic RAMs:* Figure 15.16 shows one of the memory elements (called *cells*) in a *dynamic* RAM. When the *sense* and *control* lines go HIGH, the MOSFET conducts and *charges* the capacitor. When the sense and control lines go LOW, the MOSFET opens and the capacitor *retains* its charge. In this way, it can store 1 bit. A dynamic RAM may contain thousands of memory cells. Since only a single MOSFET and capacitor are needed, the dynamic RAM contains more memory cells than a comparable static RAM. In other words, *a dynamic RAM has more memory locations than a static RAM of the same physical size.*

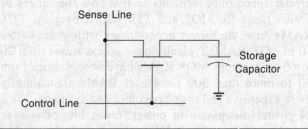

**Fig. 15.16**   *Dynamic Cell.*

Dynamic RAMs require *periodic refreshing* of the memory contents. Refreshing is usually done by periodically reading the memory location. The need for refreshing, with its accompanying support circuits, is the chief *disadvantage* of dynamic RAMs. In addition, dynamic RAMs are generally *slower* than static RAMs.

Dynamic RAMs offer three main *advantages.* Each dynamic memory cell is simpler and smaller than a static memory cell. Thus, more dynamic memory cells can be put on a single chip, and hence *the largest memory devices are always made of dynamic* MOS. Dynamic RAMs *dissipate much less power* than do static RAMs, especially in standby mode. Finally, dynamic RAMs are *cheaper* than static RAMs, although the need to *refresh* circuits can reduce the cost advantage, especially for small memory systems.

*5. Three-state RAMs:* Many of the commercially available RAMs, either static or dynamic, have three-state outputs. In other words, the manufacturer includes *three-state switches* on the chip so that you can connect or disconnect the output lines of the RAM from a data bus.

**15.20  Draw the** *pin configuration* **of the 2114 MOS static RAM.**

*Solution:*

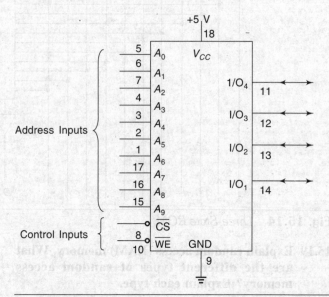

**Fig. 15.17**   *Pin Configuration of the 2114 MOS Static RAM.*

**15.21  How is data** *stored* **in the memory system of a microcomputer?**

*Solution:*
The memory system for a microcomputer consists of a large *array* of *memory cells* each holding one data bit. One cell at a time may be selected and its state read out. Alternatively, a cell may be selected and a new state written into it. *Logic circuits around the memory array govern the flow of data to or from the cells under the control of a read/write input signal.*

The process of selecting the cell is called *addressing* and the normal arrangement, where any one location in the array can be selected at anytime, is called *random access addressing*. A memory device using this form of addressing is called *random access memory* or RAM. There are two basic types of read-write RAMs which are known as *static* or *dynamic* according to the way in which the memory cells *hold* their stored data.

In a computer system it is normal to operate on *complete* words rather than individual bits so the memory system will usually be arranged as a *set of cell arrays* with one array for each data bit in the word. All the arrays are addressed in *parallel* so that a bit is selected at the same position in each array. These bits are inputs to the memory or read out from the memory *simultaneously* so that a complete word of data is transferred at a time. This is shown in Fig. 15.18.

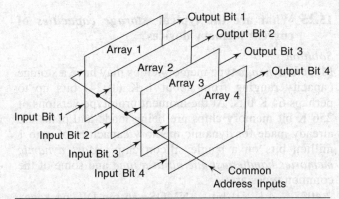

**Fig. 15.18** *Arrangement of a Group of Memory Arrays for Parallel Storage of Data Words.*

The memory may conveniently be divided into two main areas, one of which is used to *hold* the set of instructions or program whilst the other is used for *data storage* and as general working area. Single chip microcomputers often have *separate* memory arrays for program and data and these are addressed independently by the CPU. General purpose microprocessors usually have a *common* address scheme for both program and data memory although some types do provide extra *control signals* to indicate whether program or data memory is being accessed, thus allowing separate *addressing schemes* to be used if desired.

## 15.22 How does *addressing* work in a RAM?

*Solution:*
One way of *addressing* individual cells within a RAM would be to have a *separate select line for each cell*. Whilst this is feasible for a small number of cells, it is impractical for more than 40 to 50 cells due to the number of address wires needed.

To *reduce* the number of address lines RAM *devices have their cells arranged as an array of rows and columns* as shown in Fig. 15.19. Here 16 cells are

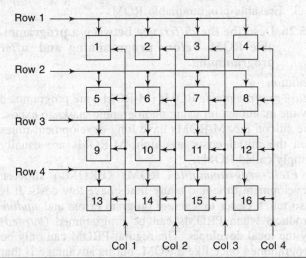

**Fig. 15.19** *Random Access Memory Addressing with Simple Row/Column Selection.*

arranged as four rows and four columns. All cells in a row are selected by the same *row select input* and similarly all cells in a column are selected by the same *column select input*. An individual cell is selected only when *both* its row and column inputs are activated simultaneously. The *data input* is fed in parallel to all cells in the array but will affect only the cell *selected* by the row and column address inputs. Similarly, all outputs are fed out to a common line but *only the contents of the addressed cell will be output*.

The number of address lines can be *reduced further* by using a *binary coded* address input and *decoding* this into individual row or column lines within the memory chip. This arrangement is shown in Fig. 15.20. Here the two row address lines are binary coded giving four possible combinations which, when decoded, produce the four *row select signals* for the memory array. A similar decoding scheme is used for the column address input. Now the 16-cell array has only four address input lines. Each extra address input will now double the number of cells that can be addressed. Thus 5 address inputs can access 32 cells whilst 10 lines would allow $32 \times 32$ or 1024 cells to be addressed. Only 20 address inputs will address over a million memory cells and still fit into a *practical package*.

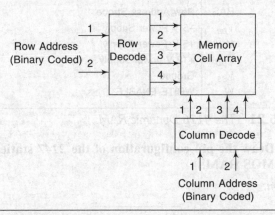

**Fig. 15.20** *Binary Coded Addressing for a Random Access Memory.*

A further *reduction* in the number of address input pins can be achieved by *multiplexing* the row and column address inputs on the *same* set of input pins. This technique is used in memory devices like *the 4116* which has 16384 memory cells.

In the 4116 the 7-bit row address is applied first to the 7 address pins and it is stored internally in a *Row Address latch*. Next the column address is applied to the same set of input pins and it is routed to the appropriate decoder within the chip to *complete* the selection of one particular cell. Two control inputs *Row Address Select* (RAS) and *Column Address Select* (CAS) are used to tell the device which address is being applied to the address input pins.

**15.23 Draw the pin configuration and pin nomenclature of the *4116* dynamic RAM.**

*Solution:*

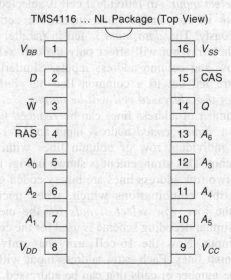

TMS4116 ... NL Package (Top View)

| | | | |
|---|---|---|---|
| $V_{BB}$ | 1 | 16 | $V_{SS}$ |
| D | 2 | 15 | $\overline{CAS}$ |
| $\overline{W}$ | 3 | 14 | Q |
| $\overline{RAS}$ | 4 | 13 | $A_6$ |
| $A_0$ | 5 | 12 | $A_3$ |
| $A_2$ | 6 | 11 | $A_4$ |
| $A_1$ | 7 | 10 | $A_5$ |
| $V_{DD}$ | 8 | 9 | $V_{CC}$ |

Pin Nomenclature

| | |
|---|---|
| $A_0$-$A_6$ | ADDRESSES |
| $\overline{CAS}$ | Column ADDRESS Strobe |
| D | Data Input |
| Q | Data Output |
| $\overline{RAS}$ | Row Address Strobe |
| $V_{BB}$ | –5 V Power Supply |
| $V_{CC}$ | +5 V Power Supply |
| $V_{DD}$ | +12 V power supply |
| $V_{SS}$ | Ground |
| $\overline{W}$ | WRITE ENABLE |

**Fig. 15.21**   *The 4116 Dynamic RAM.*

**15.24 Draw the pin configuration of the *2147* static MOS RAM.**

*Solution:*

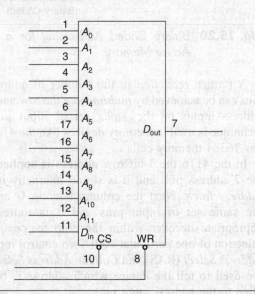

| | | | |
|---|---|---|---|
| 1 | $A_0$ | | |
| 2 | $A_1$ | | |
| 3 | $A_2$ | | |
| 4 | $A_3$ | | |
| 5 | $A_4$ | | |
| 6 | $A_5$ | 7 | |
| 17 | $A_6$ | $D_{out}$ | |
| 16 | $A_7$ | | |
| 15 | $A_8$ | | |
| 14 | $A_9$ | | |
| 13 | $A_{10}$ | | |
| 12 | $A_{11}$ | | |
| 11 | $D_{in}$ | | |
| | $\overline{CS}$   $\overline{WR}$ | | |
| | 10      8 | | |

**Fig. 15.22**   *The 2147, 4 K × 1 Static MOS RAM.*

**15.25 What are the typical *storage capacities* of current memory devices?**

*Solution:*

Modern *dynamic* type memory chips may have a storage capacity ranging from about 1 K (1024) bits up to perhaps 64 K bits. At the moment prototype versions of 256 K bit memory chips are being made and plans are already made for dynamic memory capacities of upto 1 million bits on a single silicon chip. *Most dynamic memories handle just one bit at a time* and some of the common types are:

| | | | |
|---|---|---|---|
| 4027 | 4 K × 1 bit | NMOS | 16-pin DIL package |
| 4116 | 16 K × 1 bit | NMOS | 16-pin DIL package |
| 4164 | 64 K × 1 bit | NMOS | 16-pin DIL package |

*Static* memory devices generally have *lower capacity* than dynamic types because of their more complex circuitry and typical capacities range from 256 bits to perhaps 16 K bits. An *advantage* of the static types, however, is that they do not require any additional circuitry on the board to carryout a *refresh function,* so for smaller size memory requirements they are usually more convenient than the dynamic alternative.

Many of the newer types of static RAM are organised to store words by having several arrays of cells addressed in parallel within the package. Some popular RAM types are:

| | | | |
|---|---|---|---|
| 2102 | 1 K bit (1024 × 1) | NMOS | 16-bin DIL |
| 2112 | 1 K bit (256 × 4) | NMOS | 16-pin DIL |
| 5101 | 1 K bit (256 × 4) | CMOS | 22-pin DIL |
| 2114 | 4 K bit (1024 × 4) | NMOS | 18-pin DIL |
| 6514 | 4 K bit (1024 × 4) | CMOS | 18-pin DIL |
| 4118 | 8 K bit (1024 × 8) | NMOS | 24-pin DIL |

## PROGRAMMABLE ROMS

Programmable ROMs can be divided into three major categories *depending on the way data are written into the ROM integrated circuit chip:*
  1. Mask-programmable ROMs
  2. Field-programmable ROMs
  3. Erasable-programmable ROMs

**15.26 Describe the *difference* between a programmable ROM *before* programming and *after* programming.**

*Solution:*

*Mask programmable* ROMs (M-ROMs) are programmed by the manufacturer using photographic masks to expose the silicon die. M-ROMs have long development times and the initial costs are high. M-ROMs are usually simply called ROMs.

*Field-programmable* ROMs (PROMs) shorten development time and many times have low costs. It is also much easier to *correct* program errors and *update* products when PROMs can be programmed (*burned*) by the local developer. The regular PROM can only be programmed once like a ROM, but its advantage is that it can be made in limited quantities and can be programmed in the local labor shop. The PROM is also called a *fusible-link PROM.*

The basic idea of a PROM is illustrated in Fig. 15.23. *Each memory cell contains a diode and a good fuse.* This means that all of the memory cells are storing a logical 1. This is how the PROM might look *before* programming.

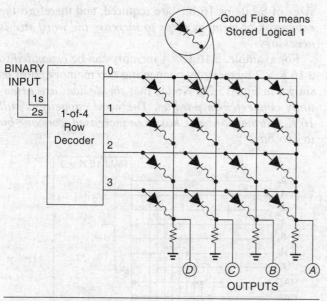

**Fig. 15.23** *A PROM before Programming. All Fuses Good (all 1s)*

The PROM in Fig. 15.24 has been programmed with seven 0s. To program or *burn* the PROM, tiny fuses must be blown as shown. A *blown fuse* in this case disconnects the diode and means a logical 0 is permanently stored in this memory cell. Because of the *permanent nature of burning* a PROM, the unit cannot be reprogrammed. A PROM of the type illustrated in Fig. 15.24 can *only* be programmed *once*.

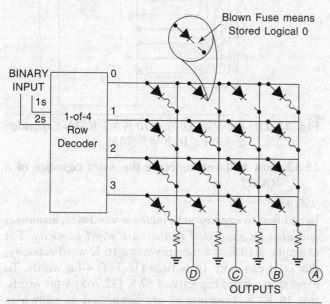

**Fig. 15.24** *PROM after Programming. Seven Fuses Blown (Seven 0s Programmed).*

*Fusible links* at the bit locations can be *burned open* by high currents. With a PROM *programmer,* the user can burn in the program and data. Once this has been done, the programming is *permanent.* In other words, *the stored contents cannot be changed.*

**15.27 Explain *erasable programmable* read-only memory (EPROM).**

*Solution:*

The EPROM is a variation of the PROM. The EPROM is programmed or burned in the local lab using a PROM *burner.* If an EPROM needs to be reprogrammed, a special *window* on top of the IC is used. Ultraviolet (UV) light is directed at the chip under the window of the EPROM for about an hour. The UV light *erases* the EPROM by *setting* all the memory cells to a logical 1. The EPROM can then be *reprogrammed.* The actual EPROM chip is *visible* through the window. These units are sometimes called *UV erasable PROMs* or *UV EPROMs.*

The EEPROM is a third variation of a programmable read-only memory. The EEPROM is an *electrically erasable* PROM also referred to as an $E^2PROM$. Since EEPROMs can be erased electrically, it is possible to *erase and reprogram* them without removing them from the circuit board. Parts of the code on the EEPROMs can be reprogrammed one byte at a time.

The *flash* EEPROM is a fourth variation of a programmable read-only memory. It is like an EEPROM in that it can be erased and reprogrammed while on the circuit board. Flash EEPROMs use a simpler storage cell, thereby allowing more memory cells on a single chip and therefore *have greater density.* Flash EEPROMs can be erased and reprogrammed faster than EEPROMs. While parts of the code can be erased and reprogrammed in an EEPROM, *the entire flash EEPROM has to be erased and reprogrammed.*

**15.28 Draw the *pin-configuration* of the TMS 4764 ROM IC.**

*Solution:*

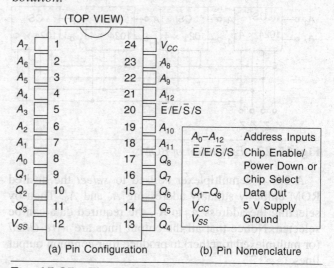

(a) Pin Configuration          (b) Pin Nomenclature

**Fig. 15.25** *The TMS 4764 ROM.*

## 15.29 Draw the pin configuration of the 2732 EPROM IC.

*Solution:*

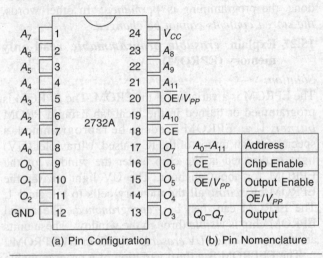

| $A_0$–$A_{11}$ | Address |
|---|---|
| $\overline{CE}$ | Chip Enable |
| $\overline{OE}/V_{PP}$ | Output Enable $\overline{OE}/V_{PP}$ |
| $Q_0$–$Q_7$ | Output |

(a) Pin Configuration    (b) Pin Nomenclature

**Fig. 15.26**   *The 2732 EPROM IC.*

## MEMORY EXPANSION

In many practical applications the required memory capacity cannot be satisfied by a single available memory IC chip. Several identical memory IC chips can be *cascaded* to provide an expanded memory of larger capacity by expanding *word size,* or by expanding *word capacity*, or by expanding both *word size and capacity.*

## 15.30 How will you *expand* a ROM?

*Solution:*

ROMs of larger sizes can be constructed by using ROMs of smaller sizes. As an example consider the construction of a 4096-bit ROM using 1024-bit ROMs. This is shown in Fig. 15.27.

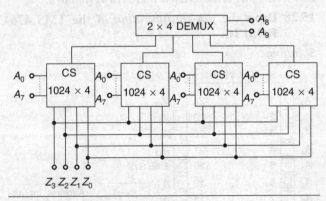

**Fig. 15.27**   *Expansion of ROM.*

A 2 × 4 demultiplexer is used to *select* the desired ROM chip, by suitably addressing $A_8$ and $A_9$. Then by selecting the address $A_0$ to $A_7$, the required data can be selected. Notice that all the output lines are *wire-ORed* (or multiplexed together) to produce four common output lines.

## 15.31 Explain how RAMs can be *expanded* to increase word size?

*Solution:*

Many RAMs are available in 1-bit and 4-bit organisations as well as larger word sizes. In many applications, word sizes of 8-bits or 16-bits are required, and therefore *the expansion of memory chips to increase the word size is necessary.*

For example, a 16 K × 1 memory can be *expanded* to a 16 K × 2 memory by connecting *two* memory chips as shown in Fig. 15.28. Notice that *the devices are essentially connected in parallel. The word capacity is still 16 K, but the word size has been increased from one bit to two bits.*

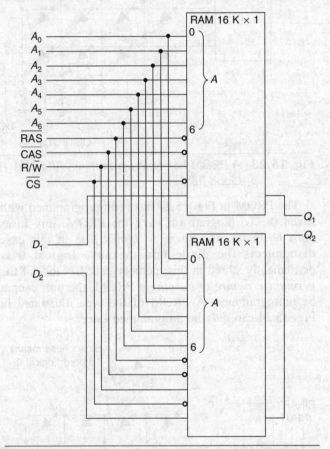

**Fig. 15.28**   *For P15.31 Two 16 K × 1 RAMs Expanded to form a 16 K × 2 RAM.*

## 15.32 How will you increase the *word capacity* of a RAM?

*Solution:*

In addition to expansion to increase word size, *memories can also be expanded to increase word capacity.* For example, a 16 K × 4 memory has a 16 K word capacity; that is, it can store 16 × 1024 (16,384) 4-bit words. To expand to a word capacity of 32 K (32,768) 4-bit words, two 16 K × 4 memories are connected as shown in Fig. 15.29. Notice that the seven multiplexed address

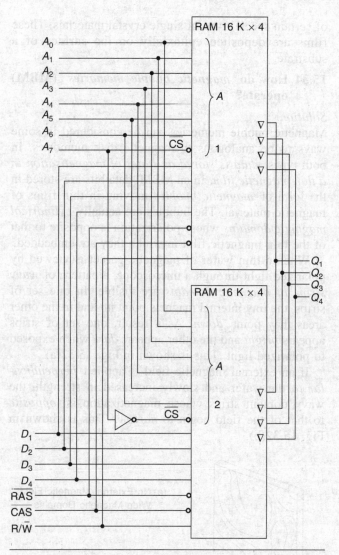

**Fig. 15.29** *Two 16 K × 4 RAMs Expanded to form a 32 K × 4 RAM.*

lines ($A_0$ through $A_6$) go to both memories and an eighth (MSB) address line, $A_7$, uses the *chip select* to enable memory 1 when it is 0 and memory 2 when it is 1. Therefore, memory address *0 through 16,383* are located in memory 1, and addresses *16,384 through 32,767* are located in memory 2. *Because both memories have three-state outputs and one memory is disabled at all times, the corresponding data lines can be connected together* as shown.

## MAGNETIC MEMORY

Magnetic memory is capable of storing larger quantities of data as compared to semiconductor memories, but the *access time* (time it takes to locate and then read or write data) is usually much more for magnetic devices. With magnetic tape or disk it takes time to *physically move* the read/write mechanism to the exact location to be written or read from.

**15.33 Explain the main features of** *magnetic-core memory.*

*Solution:*

The tiny *ferrite core* used in magnetic-core memories was the first non-volatile read/write memory. *Magnetic-core memories* were used as the central memories in computers before semiconductor memories were available. A highly magnified view of a single ferrite core is shown in Fig. 15.30(a). A typical core might measure 1/16 inches across. The ferrite core is used as a small magnet. Figure 15.30(b) shows a *write wire* threaded through the ferrite core. When current passes through the write wire in a *given direction*, the magnetic flux travels in a counterclockwise (ccw) direction. The magnetic flux direction is shown by an arrow on the core. *The ccw movement of the magnetic flux is analogous to storing a logical 1.*

Figure 15.30(c) shows the current being reversed. The magnetic flux in the core also *reverses*. The magnetic flux is now traveling in a clockwise (cw) direction in the core. *The cw movement of the magnetic flux is analogous to storing a logical 0.* With no current flow in the write wire the ferrite core is still a magnet. Depending on which direction the core was magnetized, it stores *either* a logical 0 *or* a logical 1. Figure 15.30(d) shows the ferrite core with no current flowing in the write wire. The core still has magnetic flux moving in cw direction. *This is analogous to storing a logical 0.*

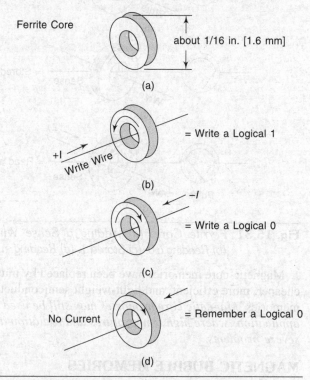

**Fig. 15.30** *Ferrite Core. (a) Size. (b) Writing a 1. (c) Writing a 0. (d) Remembering a 0.*

The *read process* requires another wire threaded through the ferrite core. The added wire is called a *sense wire*. This is shown in Fig. 15.31(a). To *read* the contents of the ferrite core, we apply a1 pulse to the core. Assuming the core is a logical 0, there will be *no change* in magnetic flux in the core. With no change in magnetic flux *no current is induced in the sense wire*. No induced pulse in the sense wire means that the core contains a 0. This is shown in Fig. 15.31(b).

Let's now assume that the core contains a logical 1, Fig. 15.31(c). This is shown with the ccw arrow on the core. To *read* the contents of the core, we apply a1 pulse in Fig. 15.31(d). The magnetic flux changes direction from ccw to cw, as shown by the arrow. *When the magnetic flux changes direction, a pulse is induced in the sensing wire.* The pulse in the sense wire tells us a logical 1 was stored in the core. The 1 which was stored in the ferrite core was *destroyed* by the read process. The core must be *restored* to the 1 state.

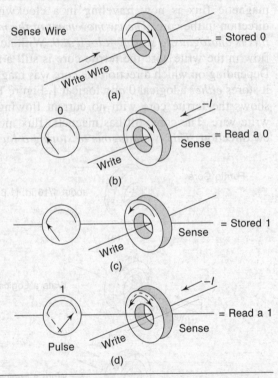

**Fig. 15.31** *Ferrite Core. (a) Adding a Sense Wire. (b) Reading a 0. (c) Stored 1. (d) Reading a 1.*

Magnetic-core memories have been replaced by much cheaper, more efficient, and light-weight semiconductor memories. *Magnetic core memories may still be used in applications where high temperatures and radiation are severe problems.*

## MAGNETIC BUBBLE MEMORIES

Magnetic bubble memories are special types of magnetic memories, which rely upon entities called *magnetic bubbles* for the storage of data. Magnetic bubbles are *strong magnetic domains* created in thin magnetic films

of certain special type of single crystal materials. These films are deposited epitaxially on the surface of a substrate.

### 15.34 How do *magnetic bubble memories* (MBM) operate?

*Solution:*

Magnetic bubble memories can be considered in some ways to be analogous to magnetic disk memories. In both types, *data is stored as states of magnetisation in a thin magnetic film*. In an MBM, data bits are stored in the form of *magnetic bubbles* moving in thin films of magnetic material. The bubbles are actually *cylindrical magnetic domains* whose polarization is opposite to that of the thin magnetic film in which they are embedded.

When a thin wafer of magnetic garnet is viewed by polarized light through a microscope, a pattern of *wavy strips of magnetic domains* are visible. In one set of strips, the tiny internal magnets point *up* and in the other areas they point *down*. As a result, one set of strips appears *bright* and the other appears *dark* when exposed to polarized light. This is shown in Fig. 15.32(a).

If an external magnetic field is applied *perpendicular to* the wafer and slowly increased in strength, the wavy domain strips whose magnetization is *opposite* to that of the field begin to *narrow*. This is shown in Fig. 15.32(b).

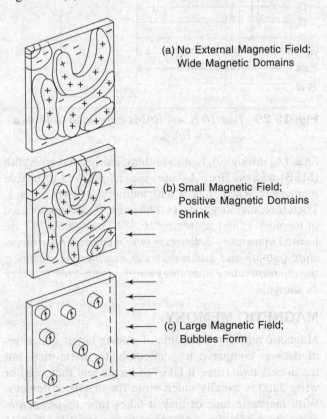

(a) No External Magnetic Field; Wide Magnetic Domains

(b) Small Magnetic Field; Positive Magnetic Domains Shrink

(c) Large Magnetic Field; Bubbles Form

**Fig. 15.32** *Creation of Magnetic Bubbles in a thin Magnetic Wafer by Applying an External Magnetic Field.*

At a certain magnitude of external field strength, all these domains suddenly *contract* into small circular areas called *bubbles*. This is shown in Fig. 15.32(c). These bubbles typically are only a few micrometers in diameter and act as tiny magnets *floating* in the external field. The bubbles can be easily *moved and controlled* within the wafer by rotating magnetic fields in the plane of the wafer, or by current carrying conductive elements.

*The presence or absence of a bubble represents a binary 1 or 0 respectively.* In the simplest MBM arrangement, *bubbles can be generated, shifted and detected in an endless-loop shift register.* The shift register is formed by a pattern of shapes that are deposited on the magnetic garnet wafer. These endless loop-shift registers provide the basis for *mass data storage.*

Basically, the data bits are stored in *several minor loops* and are transferred into *a single major loop* to be read or altered. Figure 15.33 shows a simplified diagram of the major and minor loop organizations.

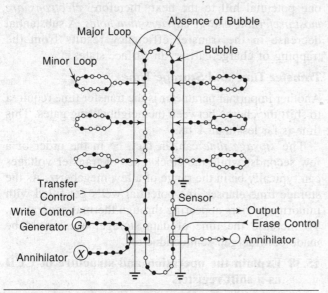

**Fig. 15.33** *Magnetic Bubble Memory (MBM) Loop Concept.*

To *write* data, bubbles enter into the major loop via a *bubble generator* from the reservoir loop (lower left corner in the figure) under control of a write command. Then from the major loop, data bits can be *transferred* into a minor loop for storage. The rotating magnetic field keeps the bubbles moving at all times. Selective field application with the various control inputs is used to produce transfers from loop to loop.

To *read* data, bits transfer from a minor loop to a major loop. They are then sensed by the detector element (as to whether they are a 1 or a 0) and the result is the output data bits. Data can also be *erased* by transferring it from the major loop to the annihilator loop (lower right corner in the figure). MBMs with a storage capacity of one million bits and higher are available.

# CHARGE COUPLED DEVICES (CCDS)

Digital data can also be stored as *charges* on capacitors. A very important type of semiconductor memory—the CCD—uses this principle to obtain *high-density storage at low power requirement levels.*

The charge-coupled device (CCD) is not a MOS process, rather it uses MOS processing to make potentially very fast (say upto 100 MHz) low power *dynamic shift registers.* Some special features of this device are:

1. there are no *transistors* on the silicon substrate.
2. *no windows* are required to be cut for diffusing dopant.
3. there are no *p-n junctions* in the structure.

Charge-coupled devices operate on the principle of generation and storage of minority carriers (a charge packet) in *potential wells,* transfer of charge packet together with potential wells along the dielectric (oxide)-semiconductor interface and its subsequent detection.

## 15.35 Explain the significance of a charge-coupled device.

*Solution:*

Charge-coupled devices have a *three layer structure* produced by the common MOS technique. They are extremely simple, (see Fig. 15.34). After oxidation of the surface of a semiconductor wafer to form a thin insulation layer, metal conductors and electrodes are suitably formed on this layer. In comparison with the process required for the manufacture of bipolar and common MOS transistor ICs, the process for the production of a CCD involves one-fourth, and half as many operations respectively. *CCDs can form the basis for memory, delay, logic and image transfer devices.*

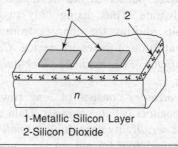

1-Metallic Silicon Layer
2-Silicon Dioxide

**Fig. 15.34** *Charge-Coupled Device.*

## 15.36 Explain in detail the operation of a charge-coupled device.

*Solution:*

Consider the operation of a device with two electrodes on the oxide layer, Fig. 15.35. A negative voltage applied to the n-type substrate must be higher than the *threshold voltage* required to form a homogeneous depletion layer at the substrate-insulator interface. Increasing the negative voltage (*storage voltage*) on an electrode 1 (gate) can produce directly under this gate a deeper

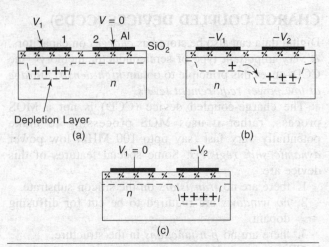

**Fig. 15.35**   *For P15.36 CCD Structure.*

layer called a *potential well* (see Fig. 15.35a). In the *storage mode,* the device can receive and store charge (minority carriers) generated in the semiconductor by an appropriate source. Because the minority carriers in the n-type silicon are holes, and the gate is negative with respect to the substrate, the gate *attracts* the holes and *retains* them in the potential well (see Fig. 15.35b).

In the *transfer mode,* the charge packet moves to a gate 2 held at a more negative voltage (*transfer voltage*) to form a yet deeper potential well under the gate. Now the holes stored under the gate *drop* into the deeper well and *flow* to the gate 2 (see Fig. 15.35c). The initial conditions of storage can be restored after removing the storage voltage from the gate and decreasing the transfer voltage on gate 2 to the storage voltage.

As soon as the storage mode is set up under the gate 2, the process of charge transfer can be extended to move the *charge packet* to the next gate and hence along the substrate. Thus, using only two levels of voltage permits shifting the charges from under one gate to the next through the entire device. *Control over the transfer of charges is made by clock pulses applied to* CCD *gates.*

The CCD *memory* consists of long rows of semiconductor capacitors called *channels.* Data are entered into a channel *serially* by depositing a *small* charge for a 0 and a *large* charge for a 1 on the capacitors. The charge packets are then *shifted* along the channel by clock signals as more data is entered *Charge movement* along the channel is illustrated in Fig. 15.36.

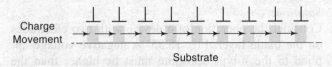

**Fig. 15.36**   *A CCD Channel.*

As with the dynamic RAM (DRAM), *the charges must be refreshed periodically.* This process is done by shifting the charge packets serially through a refresher circuit. *High density is the main advantage of CCDs.*

**15.37  What are the parameters of a charge-coupled device?**

*Solution:*
The parameters of CCDs are:
1. Transfer efficiency
2. Transfer time
3. Storage time

***Transfer Efficiency***

The process of charge transfer in a CCD can be defined by the transfer efficiency, $\eta$, which specifies a relative portion of charge being shifted in one *transfer cycle.*

$$\eta = 1 - q_1/q_r + q_1 = 1 - \varepsilon$$

Here $\varepsilon = 1 - \eta$ is the *loss factor* (transfer inefficiency); $q_1$ is the charge lost during transfer, and $q_r$ is the residual charge transferred. The *transfer efficiency* largely depends on the rate of motion of charge carriers from one potential hill to the next; therefore *electrons are most preferable charge carriers than holes.* A substantial decrease in the transfer efficiency results from the trapping of charge carriers in surface states.

***Transfer Time and Storage Time***

Another important parameter is the transfer time required to shift the charge between the neighbouring gates. This time is far less than 1 $\mu$s.

The *storage time* can, in fact, be in the order of a few seconds; while the clock rates of transfer voltages can typically be in the range of a few megahertz. As the storage time elapses, the potential wells get filled with minority carriers appearing through thermal generation. To increase the time of data storage, use should be made of wide-gap semiconductors.

**15.38  Explain the operation and structure of CCD as a shift register.**

*Solution:*
CCDs are most commonly used to perform the function of shift registers. The *control gates* of a register form an electrode system with one to four *phases.* The principle of a *three phase* CCD *shift register* is illustrated in Fig. 15.37(a). *Each third gate is connected to one and the same phase line.* First, the storage voltage $-V_2$ is applied to one group of electrodes, say 1, 4, 7 etc.; with the other electrodes kept at a lower bias voltage. The bias $-V_2$ produces potential wells under gates 1, 4, 7 etc,; with the result that the charges *injected* into the semiconductor *flow* to these wells. Assume that the charges resulting from the injection are present under the gates 1 and 7 and are absent under the gate 4.

At the next stage, the transfer voltage $|V_3| > |V_2|$ is set on the other group of electrodes, such as 2, 5, and 8, Fig. 15.37(b). Since the potential wells under these gates become *deeper*, the charges under the gates 1 and 7

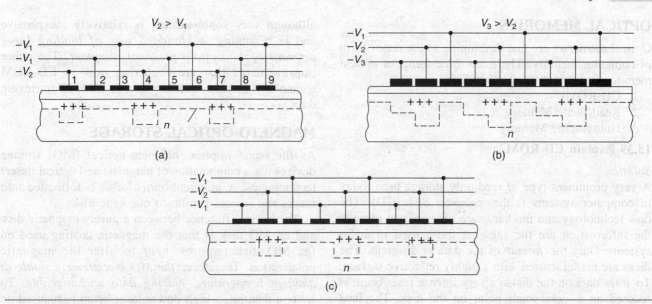

(a)

(b)

(c)

**Fig. 15.37**   *CCD as a Shift Register.*

along with the vacant state under the gate 4 will *shift* one step to the right. Further, after restoring the initial conditions of storage, Fig. 15.37(c), the potential on electrodes 2, 5, and 8 decreases to the storage voltage $-V_2$, and on the others to $-V_1$. Thus *charges (or a no charge state) can shift along through the device.* Charge carriers move from one potential well into the next by virtue of three mechanisms: self-induced drift, diffusion, and edge effect.

The *self-induced drift* results from the repulsion of charge and enables their fast transfer, but this drift occurs only at high charge densities. *Diffusion* leads to an exponential decay of charge under the transfer gate. *The edge effect* acts in the direction of charge transfer and can appreciably speed up the process. This field also causes an exponential decay of charges.

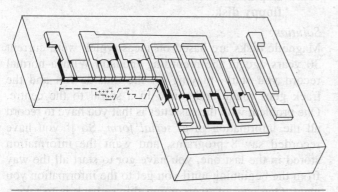

**Fig. 15.38**   *Structure of CCD as Shift Register.*

### Structure of a CCD as Shift Register

The transfer of charges from gate to gate is the primary aim one strives to achieve in all applications. But in many cases there is a need to produce a *generator of charges at the input and a detector at the output.*

It is possible to *generate* charges by several methods; for example, by forward biasing the diffused *p-n* junction in *n*-type silicon under the action of a surface avalanche breakdown in the MOS structure.

Detectors can be built around a reverse biased *p-n* junction or Schottky diode. The charge can be *detected* by changing the capacitance according to the charge stored or by changing the potential on the surface electrode with the charge change.

A shift register with 24 gates is available which can act both as a circulating storage (*memory*) and as a *controlled delay line.* This is shown in Fig. 15.35. The width of a CCD gate is not more than 10 µm, the gate capacitance is 0.4 pF, and the channel length (the centre-to-centre distance between two neighbouring gates) is equal to 10 µm. The charge transfer time is below 1 µs; the register operates in the range of a few megahertz. The CCD can also store information over a period of several seconds. The transfer voltages (voltages on the gates) range to about 10 V, which is comparatively easy to secure in silicon devices.

The *response* of a MOS IC can be raised two to ten fold using circuit engineering methods in combination with the current manufacturing methods. The former methods can increase the response by introducing additional control signals. Some circuits employ the principle of four-phase, or *multiphase locking,* to speed up the response without the power consumption or the dimensions of transistors. For example, using the design of a four-phase control circuit of somewhat increased complexity, it becomes possible to fabricate by common diffusion techniques, the shift registers with a clock rate of 10 MHz and RAMs (random access memories) with an access time of less than 10 ns.

## OPTICAL MEMORIES

Optical memories are fast developing as the major form of computer memory. There are three forms of optical memory in use at present. They are:

1. CD-ROMs
2. Read/Write Memory
3. Holographic Memory

### 15.39 Explain CD-ROM.

*Solution:*

A very prominent type of read-only storage used today in computer systems is the *compact disk* (CD). The disk technology and the hardware necessary to retrieve the information are the same as those used in audio systems. Only the *format* of the data is different. The disks are manufactured with a highly reflective surface. To *store* data on the disks, a very intense laser beam is focused on a *very* small point on the disk. The heat from this beam burns a light-diffracting pit at that point on the disk surface. Digital data (1s and 0s) are stored on the disk one bit at a time by *burning* or *not burning*. a pit into the reflective coating. The digital information is arranged on the disk as a *continuous spiral* of data points. This is shown in Figs 15.39(a) and (b). The precision of the laser beam allows very large quantities of data (over 550 Mbytes) to be stored on a small, 120-mm disk.

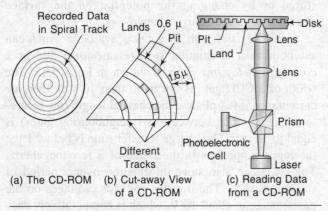

(a) The CD-ROM     (b) Cut-away View     (c) Reading Data
                        of a CD-ROM          from a CD-ROM

**Fig. 15.39** *CD-ROM.*

In order to *read* the data, a much less powerful laser beam is focused onto the surface of the disk (see Fig. 15.39(c)). At any point, the reflected light is sensed as either a 1 or a 0. This optical system is mounted on a *mechanical carriage* that moves back and forth along the radius of the disk, following the spiral of data as the disk rotates. The data retrieved from the optical system come one bit at a time in a serial data stream. The angular rotation of disk is controlled to maintain a constant rate of incoming data points. If the disk is being used for audio recording, this stream of data is converted into an analog waveform. If the disk is being used as ROM, the data are decoded into parallel bytes that computer can use. The CD player technology,

although very sophisticated, is relatively inexpensive and is becoming *a standard way of loading large amounts of data into a personal computer*. The major improvements that are occurring now in CD-ROM technology involve *quicker access time* in retrieving data.

## MAGNETO-OPTICAL STORAGE

As the name implies, magneto-optical (MO) storage devices use a combination of magnetic and optical (laser) technologies. A *magneto-optical disk* is formatted into tracks and sectors similar to magnetic disks.

The basic difference between a purely magnetic disk and an MO disk is that the magnetic coating used on the MO disk requires *heat* to alter the magnetic polarization. Therefore, *the MO is extremely stable at ambient temperature, making data unchangeable*. To *write* a data bit, a high-power laser beam is focused on a tiny spot on the disk, and the temperature of that tiny spot is raised above a temperature level called the Curie point (about 200°C). Once heated, the magnetic particles at that spot can easily have their direction (polarization) changed by a magnetic field generated by the write head. Information is *read* from the disk with a less-powerful laser than used for writing, making use of the Kerr effect where the polarity of the reflected laser light is altered depending on the orientation of the magnetic particles. Spots of one polarity represent 0s and spots of the opposite polarity represent 1s.

### 15.40 Illustrate the basic principle of a magneto-optical disk.

*Solution:*

The basic principle of a magneto-optical (MO) disk is illustrated in Fig 15.40.

### 15.41 Explain in detail the operational details of a floppy disk.

*Solution:*

Magnetic disks are based on ideas which were current 30 years ago in the recording industry. With a normal record you start playing on the outside run and the track goes round and round in a spiral to the centre. One problem with the cassettes is that you have to record all the information in a *serial form*. So if you have recorded say 8 programs, and want the information stored in the last one, you have got to start all the way from the beginning until you get to the information you want. One way of overcoming this setback is to take a *normal LP-type record approach*, where although you have got serial recording format, you have designated points called *tracks*. As there is a certain amount of random access, it is possible to 'drop in' at any point.

A magnetic disk, Fig. 15.41 is divided up into *discrete tracks* in the same way as a normal LP record. But instead of the tracks being in a spiral *they are all concentric*. A small magnetic recording head, just like a recording

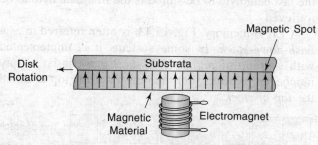

(a) Unrecorded Disk

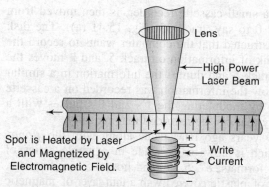

(b) Writing: A High-power Laser Beam Heats the Spot, Causing the Magnetic Particles to Align with Electromagnetic Field.

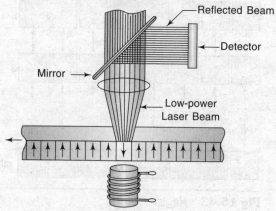

(c) Reading: A Low-power Laser Beam Reflects off of the Reversed Polarity Magnetic Particles and Polarization Shifts. If the Particles are not Reversed, the Polarization of the Reflected Beam is Unchanged.

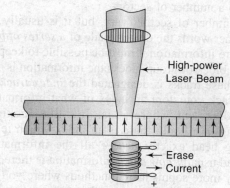

(d) Erasing: The Electromagnetic Field is Reversed as the High-Power Laser Beam Heats the Spot, Causing the Magnetic Particles to be Restored to the Original Polarity.

**Fig. 15.40** *Illustrating the Basic Principles of a Magneto-Optical Disk.*

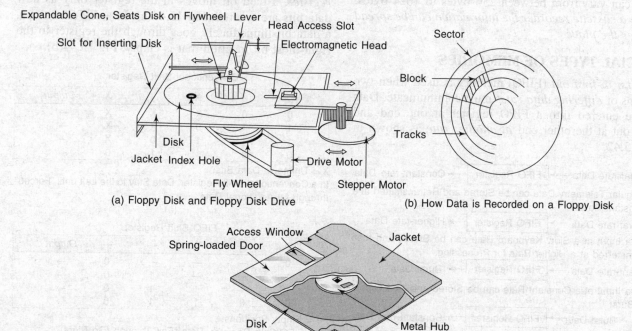

(a) Floppy Disk and Floppy Disk Drive

(b) How Data is Recorded on a Floppy Disk

(c) The 3.5 Inch Floppy Disk (Diskette) Jacket.

**Fig. 15.41** *Floppy Disk.*

head on a small cassette recorder, is then moved from say track 0 to say, track 35 (Fig. 15.41 (a)). The disk unit is instructed that the computer wants to record the next chunk of information on track 5, and it moves the head to track 5 and dumps the information in a similar way to how the information was recorded on a cassette tape, i.e. by modulating the 1's and 0's pulses with a frequency that can be recorded magnetically.

A few years ago IBM came along with the *floppy disk*, which is now being made in a whole series of different formats, 8", 5.25" and now 3.5" in diameter. If a sheet of plastic covered with a thin layer of magnetic material is spun at 300 r.p.m. it keeps relatively rigid.

The disk is split into a *series of tracks* Fig. 15.41(b) which vary from about 35 to 80. Each track is itself split into a number of sectors.

The number of sectors vary, but it is usually about 16. In other words the disk is made of a *series of blocks*. So to store information it must be possible to keep track of which block or group blocks the information is stored. One of these tracks is designated the *index tracks*, and in that track you store an index of what information is on the disk and where it is. It's like looking up something in a book; there is an index which tells the recording head exactly *where* all the information is stored and usually *how much* information is there. There are many more sophisticated methods where you might have various check digits or other information stored on the index tracks.

Any one who has used *disk drives* will have heard it *whirring away* making clanking noises. This is the head trying to find the appropriate track. The *size* of each block can vary from between 256 bytes to 1024 bytes. *Unlike a cassette recorder the information can be spread all over the place.*

## SPECIAL TYPES OF MEMORIES

The *first in-first out* (FIFO) memory is used when two systems of *differing data rates* must communicate. Data can be entered into a FIFO register at one end and taken out at the other end *at another rate* as shown in Fig. 15.42.

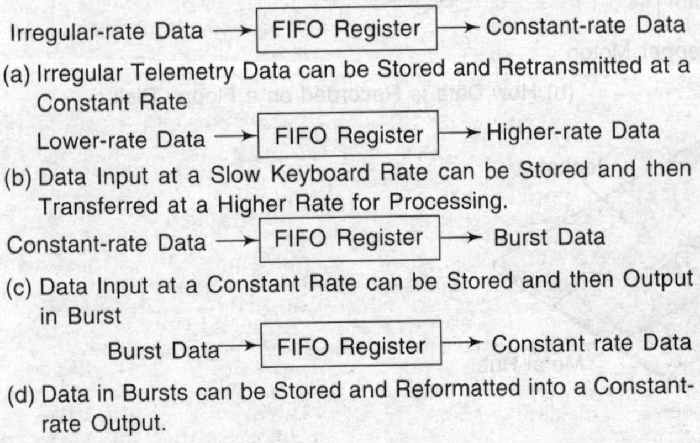

Irregular-rate Data → FIFO Register → Constant-rate Data

(a) Irregular Telemetry Data can be Stored and Retransmitted at a Constant Rate

Lower-rate Data → FIFO Register → Higher-rate Data

(b) Data Input at a Slow Keyboard Rate can be Stored and then Transferred at a Higher Rate for Processing.

Constant-rate Data → FIFO Register → Burst Data

(c) Data Input at a Constant Rate can be Stored and then Output in Burst

Burst Data → FIFO Register → Constant rate Data

(d) Data in Bursts can be Stored and Reformatted into a Constant-rate Output.

**Fig. 15.42** *FIFO Register in Data Rate Buffering Applications.*

The *last in-first out* (LIFO) memory allows data to be stored and then recalled in the *reverse order*, that is, the last data byte to be stored is the first data byte to be retrieved.

A LIFO memory, Fig. 15.43, is often referred to as a *push-down-stack*. In some systems it is implemented with a group of registers. A stack can consist of any number of registers, but the register at the top is called the *top-of-stack*.

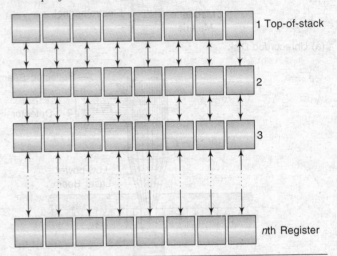

**Fig 15.43** *Register Stack.*

## 15.42 Describe a FIFO and a LIFO memory.

*Solution:*

In *FIFO memory*, the first data bit written into the memory is the first to be read out. In a *conventional register*, a data bit moves in the register only as new data bits are entered, Fig 15.44(a). In a *FIFO register*, a data bit immediately goes through the register to the right-most bit location that is empty, Fig 15.44(b).

Conventional Shift Register

| Input | X | X | X | X | Output |
|-------|---|---|---|---|--------|
| 0 | 0 | X | X | X | → |
| 1 | 1 | 0 | X | X | → |
| 1 | 1 | 1 | 0 | X | → |
| 0 | 0 | 1 | 1 | 0 | → |

X = Unknown Data Bits.
In a Conventional Shift Register, Data Stay to the Left until "Forced" through by Additional Data.

(a)

FIFO Shift Register

| Input | — | — | — | — | Output |
|-------|---|---|---|---|--------|
| 0 | — | — | — | 0 | → |
| 1 | — | — | 1 | 0 | → |
| 1 | — | 1 | 1 | 0 | → |
| 0 | 0 | 1 | 1 | 0 | → |

— = Empty Positions.
In a FIFO Shift Register, Data "Fall" through (Go Right).

(b)

**Fig. 15.44** *Comparison of a Conventional and FIFO Shift Register.*

A *LIFO memory* is commonly referred to as a push down stack, Fig. 15.45(a). A byte of data is loaded in parallel onto the top of the stack. Each successive byte *pushes* the previous one down into the next register. Data bytes are removed in the reverse order. The last byte entered is always at the top of the stack, so when it is *pulled* from the stack, the other bytes *pop up* into the next higher sections, Fig. 15.45(b).

## 15.43 What is *battery back up* and why is it needed?

*Solution:*

An important problem with the conventional read/write memory is that if the power is lost for a short period the *stored data is likely to be corrupted or completely lost*. For many applications it would be nice if the main power to the processor system could be shut down *without* losing the memory contents.

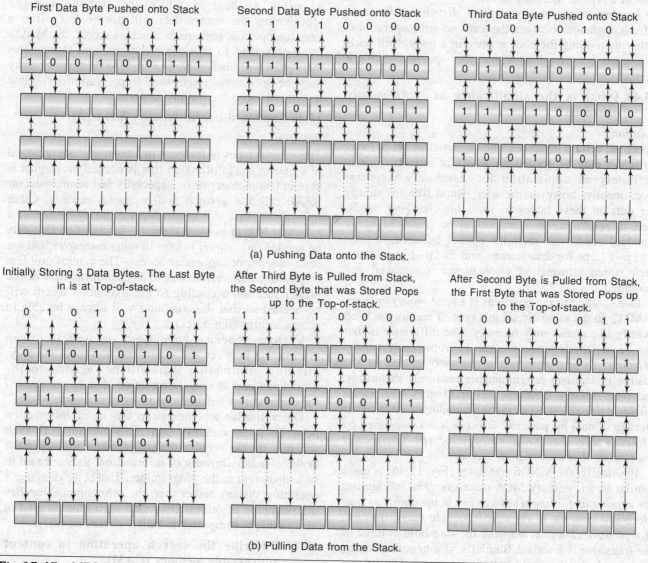

**First Data Byte Pushed onto Stack**
1 0 0 1 0 0 1 1

**Second Data Byte Pushed onto Stack**
1 1 1 1 0 0 0 0

**Third Data Byte Pushed onto Stack**
0 1 0 1 0 1 0 1

(a) Pushing Data onto the Stack.

**Initially Storing 3 Data Bytes. The Last Byte in is at Top-of-stack.**
0 1 0 1 0 1 0 1

**After Third Byte is Pulled from Stack, the Second Byte that was Stored Pops up to the Top-of-stack.**
1 1 1 1 0 0 0 0

**After Second Byte is Pulled from Stack, the First Byte that was Stored Pops up to the Top-of-stack.**
1 0 0 1 0 0 1 1

(b) Pulling Data from the Stack.

**Fig 15.45**   *LIFO Memory.*

The technique for retaining memory contents is to use what is known as *battery back-up*. Here a small battery, either dry cell or nickel cadmium rechargeable type, is used to supply power to the *memory chips alone* when the main power supply goes off. Many of the single chip microcomputers have a battery back-up facility *built into the chip* which protects the contents of some or all of the *on-chip* RAM in the event of failure of the main supply. For such a memory system

some *extra logic* and a *change over switch* are added to the normal memory system.

In the case of a CMOS *memory* where the supply current is very small, it is possible to provide memory back up for a *limited period* by using large value capacitor to supply the memory power.

Memory devices designed for use with battery back-up will usually *retain* their stored data when the supply voltage falls to perhaps *half* the normal operating level.

### 15.44 What are the methods of memory refresh?

*Solution:*

All dynamic RAMs require a *memory refresh* operation. The refresh logic can be either *internal* or *external* to the memory chip. In its simplest form the memory refresh operation *sequentially* refreshes each row of cell, one row after the other until all rows are refreshed. This is called *burst refresh* and must be repeated every 2ms to 4ms in a typical dynamic RAM.

Another basic refresh method *distributes* the row refresh operations *between* the read and write operations, rather than doing them all at once in a burst. Still each row must be refreshed within the *specified refresh period*.

### 15.45 What is the significance of *read-mostly memories*?

*Solution:*

There are certain instances when a particular set of *look-up tables* may be needed for weeks or months. This is definitely an application for *read-only memory*. Occasionally, however the user would like to *modify* the data in these tables to meet his changing needs. Here a *read/write memory* would be preferred but a standard read/write memory cannot be used, it uses `flip-flops` for data storage, and `flip-flops` loose their stored information when power is removed and reapplied.

One solution to the problems is a *read-mostly memory* (RMM). In the logic circuit this type of memory is used exactly like a read-only memory. The difference is that *the read mostly memory can be repeatedly reprogrammed to give new sets of outputs*. Instead of the fusible material in programmable read-only memories, the read- mostly memory uses transistors with *metal nitride-oxide* (MNOS) as the semiconductor element for storage of data bit patterns. *Storage is accomplished by altering the threshold voltage of the individual transistors that make up the memory*.

Physically, the MNOS transistor (Fig. 15.46) is quite similar to an ordinary MOS transistor. *The mechanism for varying its threshold voltage lies in the ability to trap electrical charges in the silicon nitride gate insulator*. If a *positive* charge is trapped, the threshold voltage of the transistor is *lowered*. Similarly, if a *negative* charge is trapped, the threshold voltage is *raised*. The former (*turn on*) represents a logic 1. The latter (*turn off*) represents a logic 0.

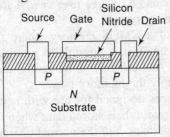

**Fig 15.46** *MNOS Transistor.*

When a number of MNOS transistors are combined into a memory array, the result of the trapped charges is to store logic 1s and 0's in a unique pattern to form a *custom programmed read only memory*. The terminology read-mostly memory is derived from the fact that at least occasionally, the memory must be written into. But *for the most part only the read function is performed*.

The read-mostly memory is *non-volatile* in that power can be removed from the transistors and then reapplied as often as desired while the trapped charges representing the binary data will not be lost. After a very long period, perhaps as much as a year, the MNOS transistors tend to lose their charges, and therein lies their *principal disadvantage*. An MNOS memory array must be *occasionally refreshed* (reprogrammed) so that it will not loose the trapped charges.

### 15.46 Explain the term *memory hierarchy*.

*Solution:*

The various types of memory in a computer are arranged in a *hierarchy*. Information that is needed *most often* is kept in fast memory or in a specially fast semiconductor RAM, called a *scratch pad* or *cache memory*. Other information that will be needed for the *operation of a program* is kept in *main memory*. Information that may be needed *only rarely* is kept in *mass memories* that are semi-random or sequential access. The central problem in *memory management* is to keep information in the proper location according to the likelihood that it will be needed so that the computer will always be able to access information quickly.

Various schemes have been devised to *swap* information between the scratchpad and main memory, bringing information that will be *needed* to the scratchpad and storing information that is *not needed* for the next few calculations in main memory.

Other similar schemes swap blocks of information between main memory and mass memory. If such schemes do not require the programmer to keep track of the *absolute location* of information, they are said to be *transparent* to the programmer. That is, the computer's operating system, rather than the programmer, handles the swapping of information. One such scheme used in many current computers is called *virtual memory*.

### 15.47 Describe the search operation in content addressable memory (CAM).

*Solution:*

Random-access memories depend upon *prior knowledge* of memory location to read out data. A *content addressable memory* (CAM) however reads out data by applying a known data set at the inputs then searching memory contents to see if there are any locations containing the same information. If there are, a *match* condition occurs and the addresses of all matching locations are made available. Normally, the content addressable memory will be organised such that some *key portion* of the data will be *searched* while the rest of the data is *ignored*.

Writing into the memory is done by *a direct address*. The determination of a write address is based either on known empty memory locations or by *searching* for locations in which data is no longer needed and then writing in those addresses.

A simplified diagram of a 16-bit CAM is shown in Fig 15.47. There are four rows in the memory, each contains four memory cells. Each row has an *individual address bit*, allowing the memory cells to be searched, read or written into.

Assume that the memory contains the data bits shown and a *search operation* is to be performed to determine if the number 5 (0101) is contained anywhere in the memory. If the *address bits* are all set to 0 and the *search data* (0101) is applied at the data input lines, a match condition will occur on all rows that contain the desired information. In this case only row 3 contains 5. If it is desired, row 3 can be read out by simply setting address bit $A2$ to a logical 1. To *write* in the memory, the write enable line is set to a logical 1 along with the selected address line. The data present at the data input lines will then be written into the selected row of the memory.

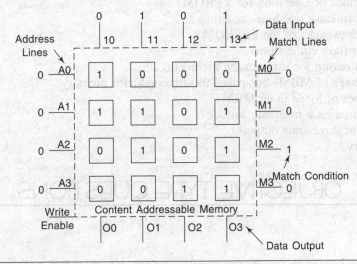

**Fig 15.47** *Search Operation in a CAM.*

## SUMMARY

➤ Digital systems with memory can *store* information.
➤ The process of entering information into memory is called *writing*.
➤ The process of retrieving information from memory is called *reading*.
➤ Each location in memory has an *address* so that it can be located.
➤ *Volatile memory* exists only as long as power supply is available.
➤ *Non-volatile memory* does not owe its existence to power supply.
➤ Present day computers mostly use *semiconductor memory*.
➤ In *random access memory* (RAM) the access time is the same for any address in memory.
➤ In *sequential access memory* (SAM) the access time is not constant.
➤ *Read only memories* (ROM) are used to store data in applications where the data changes not at all or only infrequently.
➤ *Three-state* outputs are used for compatibility with bus structures.
➤ *Mask programmable* ROM are programmed by the manufacturer.
➤ *Magnetic memory* is capable of storing large amounts of data but the access time is large.
➤ *Magnetic bubble memories* are special types of magnetic memories.
➤ Data can be stored as *charges* on capacitors.
➤ CCD memory consists of long rows of semiconductor capacitors called *channels*.
➤ *FIFO memory* is used when two systems with differing data rates must communicate.

# REVIEW QUESTIONS

1. Explain the difference between ROM and RAM.
2. Explain the difference between static and dynamic memories.
3. What is the function of the $R/\overline{W}$ input?
4. Why do some RAM chips have common input/output pins?
5. Which memory technology uses the least power ICs.
6. Why are address lines on larger memory ICs multiplexed.
7. What is meant by refreshing a dynamic RAM?
8. How do ROMs differ from PROMs ?
9. What is the normal mode of operation for a PROM?
10. What type of ROM can erase one byte at a time?
11. What are the major drawbacks of the EEPROM?
12. Where does the word flash come from?
13. What is the principal reason for using cache memory?
14. What is the disadvantage of MBMs compared to semiconductor memory?
15. What are the two types of loops in an MBM?
16. How are data bits stored on a magnetic surface?
17. What is the purpose of three-state outputs?
18. What is FIFO memory?

# OBJECTIVE TYPE QUESTIONS

## *Fill in the Blanks*

19. The _____ bus is used to specify the locations of the data stored in a memory circuit.
20. Once a memory location is selected, data travel via the _____ bus.
21. The 2114 memory IC is a 1KX4 static RAM, which means that it has_____ memory locations with _____ data bits at each location.
22. To perform a read operation with a 2147H RAM, $\overline{CS}$ must be _____ and $\overline{WE}$ must be _____ .
23. In the 2147H memory array, address lines _____ through _____ are used to select the row and _____ through _____ are used to select the column.
24. The letters RAM stand for _____ .
25. Copying information into a storage location is called _____ into memory.
26. Copying information from a storage location is called _____ from memory.
27. A RAM is also called a _____ or scratch-pad memory.
28. A disadvantage of the RAM is that it is _____ , it loses its data when the power is turned _____ .
29. The 7489 IC is a 64-bit _____ .
30. The 7489 IC can hold _____ words, each word being _____ bits wide.
31. A _____ RAM must be refreshed many times per second.
32. The 2114 RAM IC will store _____ bits of data, and each of the 1024 words is _____ bits wide.
33. Both the 7489 and 2114 memory chips are _____ RAMs.
34. The letters ROM stand for_____ .
35. Read-only memories never forget data and are called _____ memories.
36. ROM is a _____ density memory device.
37. A mask-ROM is programmed by the _____ .
38. The abbreviation NVRAM stands for _____ .
39. Battery backup SRAMs commonly use _____ battery which has a long life and maintains the data in memory when power is lost.
40. Magnetic-core memory is based on the characteristics of the tiny _____ .

41. The _____ is quiet inexpensive, reliable, and is rewritable.
42. After erasure all bits are _____ in a typical EPROM.
43. The memory of a computer is where the _____ and _____ are stored before the calculations begin.
44. The _____ and contents of a memory location are two different things.
45. With on-chip decoding, address lines can access _____ memory locations.
46. The PROM allows users to _____ their own programs and data.
47. An instrument called the PROM _____ does the storing or burning in.
48. The address bits of a static RAM _____ the memory location.
49. The write enable (WE) and chip enable (CE) select a write, read, or _____.
50. When WE is high and CE is low, you get a _____ operation.
51. A group of programs and data held permanently in a microcomputer's ROM is called _____.

## True/False Questions

State whether the following statements are True or False.
52. A volatile memory will lose its stored data when electrical power is interupted.
53. A dynamic memory will hold its data as long as electrical power is applied.
54. All ROMs are nonvolatile.
55. Semiconductor memories can only be bipolar.
56. An MROM can be programmed by the user.
57. PROMs are available in both bipolar and MOS version.
58. There is no way to erase only a portion of an EPROMs memory.
59. When memory chips are combined to form a module with a larger word size or capacity, the CS inputs of each chip are always connected together.
60. When memory chips are combined for a larger capacity, each chip is connected to the same data busline.
61. The manufacturer is the only one who can store programs and data in a ROM.
62. Because the address is in binary form, the manufacturer uses on-chip decoding to access the memory location.
63. The EPROM is ultraviolet light programmable and electrically erasable.
64. Bipolar memories are slower than MOS memories.
65. Bipolar memories are more expensive than MOS memories.
66. ROMs PROMs and EPROMs are volatile memories.
67. The memory cell of a static RAM is simpler and smaller than that of a dynamic RAM.
68. When WE and CE are both low, a read operation is performed.
69. CE high is the inactive state.

## Multiple Choice Questions

70. Which of the following memories is non-volatile memory?
    (a) ROM                          (b) PROM
    (c) ferrite core memory          (d) none of the above
71. The access time of bipolar RAM is of the order of
    (a) 20 ns        (b) 20 µs        (c) 20 ms        (d) 20 s
72. The access time of MOS RAM is of the order of
    (a) 1 ns         (b) 1 µs         (c) 1 ms         (d) 1 s
73. Which of the following memories has the highest storage capacity?
    (a) magnetic core                (b) ferrite core
    (c) semiconductor                (d) magnetic disc
74. RAM is also known as
    (a) PROM         (b) EPROM        (c) EAROM        (d) RWM
75. Memory in which the stored data is lost when power is switched off is
    (a) RAM          (b) ROM          (c) PROM         (d) ferrite core
76. A RAM is
    (a) nonvolatile memory           (b) only static memory
    (c) only dynamic memory          (d) volatile and either static or dynamic memory.

77. The density of the dynamic RAM is
    (a) more than that of the static RAM        (b) less than that of the static RAM
    (c) equal to that of the static RAM         (d) equal to or more than that of the static RAM

78. The power consumption of the dynamic RAM is
    (a) more that that of the static RAM        (b) equal to that of the static RAM
    (c) less than that of the static RAM        (d) almost zero

79. The cost of the dynamic RAM for each bit of storage is nearly
    (a) equal to that of the static RAM         (b) double that of the static RAM
    (c) five times that of the static RAM       (d) one-fifth of that of the static RAM

80. PROMs are available in
    (a) bipolar version only                    (b) MOS version only
    (c) both bipolar and MOS version            (d) none of the above

81. Periodic recharging of the memory cells at regular intervals of 3 to 8 milliseconds is required in a
    (a) ROM            (b) static RAM           (c) dynamic RAM    (d) PLA

82. The advantage of dynamic RAMs over static RAMs is
    (a) lower power consumption                  (b) high capacity
    (c) lower cost per bit                       (d) all of the above

83. Which of the following memories can be programmed by the user and then cannot be erased and reprogrammed.
    (a) ROM            (b) PROM                 (c) EPROM         (d) EEROM

84. The data bus width of a memory of size $2048 \times 8$ is
    (a) 8              (b) 10                   (c) 12            (d) 16

85. A memory has 16 bit address bus. The number of locations in the memory are
    (a) 16             (b) 32                   (c) 1024          (d) 65536

86. It is desired to have a $64 \times 8$ memory. The memories available are of $16 \times 4$ size. The number of memories required will be
    (a) 8              (b) 6                    (c) 4             (d) 2

87. Four memory chips of $16 \times 4$ size have their address buses connected together. This system will be of size
    (a) $64 \times 4$   (b) $16 \times 16$       (c) $32 \times 8$   (d) $256 \times 1$

88. The write cycle time of memory is 200ns. The maximum rate at which data can be stored is
    (a) 200 words/s    (b) $5 \times 10^3$ words  (c) $5 \times 10^6$ words/s  (d) $5 \times 10^9$ words

89. A charge coupled device is
    (a) a magnetic device                        (b) a bipolar semiconductor device
    (c) a MOS device                             (d) none of the above

90. A CCD is a
    (a) random access memory                     (b) sequentially accessed memory
    (c) content addressable memory               (d) read only memory

91. Shift registers
    (a) are sequential memories                  (b) are either static or dynamic memory
    (c) are volatile memories                     (d) have all of the above characteristics

92. A function table is required in very large numbers. The memory most suitable for this purpose would be
    (a) ROM            (b) PROM                 (c) EPROM         (d) EAROM

93. Floating gate is fabricated for making MOS
    (a) ROM            (b) PROM                 (c) EPROM         (d) EAROM

# ANSWERS

1. ROM has only a read operation; RAM has both read and write operations.
2. *Static:* the storage cells are latches and can retain data indefinitely. *Dynamic:* the storage cells are capacitors and must be refreshed periodically
3. Commands the memory to perform either a read operation or a write operation
4. To reduce pin count        5. CMOS
6. To keep the IC pin count to a minimum. They are demultiplexed by using control signals.
7. The charge on internal capacitors in the RAM is replenished

8. PROMs are field programmable ROMs are not    9. Read    10. EEPROM
11. Low density; high cost    12. Short erase and programming times    13. Economics
14. MBMs are slower than semiconductor memory (it takes longer to get data in and out)
15. Major loop; minor loop    16. Magnetized spots with specified polarities
17. Three-state allows outputs to be disconnected from bus lines.
18. In FIFO memory. the first bit (or data word) in is first one out.

| | | | |
|---|---|---|---|
| 19. Address | 20. Data | 21. 1024, 4 | 22. LOW, HIGH |
| 23. $A_0, A_5, A_6, A_{11}$ | 24. random-access memory | | 25. writing |
| 26. reading | 27. read/write | 28. volatile, off | 29. RAM |
| 30. 16, 4 | 31. dynamic | 32. 4096,4 | 33. static |
| 34. read only memory | 35. non-volatile | 36. high | 37. manufacturer |
| 38. nonvolatile, RAM | 39. lithium | 40. ferrite core | 41. flash memory |
| 42. 1s | 43. program, data | 44. address | 45. $2^n$ |
| 46. store | 47. programmer | 48. select | 49. do nothing |
| 50. read | 51. firmware | 52. True | 53. False |
| 54. True | 55. False | 56. False | 57. True |
| 58. True | 59. False | 60. True | 61. True |
| 62. True | 63. False | 64. False | 65. True |
| 66. False | 67. False | 68. False | 69. True |
| 70. (c) | 71. (a) | 72. (b) | 73. (d) |
| 74. (d) | 75. (a) | 76. (d) | 77. (a) |
| 78. (c) | 79. (d) | 80. (c) | 81. (c) |
| 82. (d) | 83. (b) | 84. (a) | 85. (d) |
| 86. (a) | 87. (b) | 88. (c) | 89. (c) |
| 90. (b) | 91. (d) | 92. (a) | 93. (c) |

# Programmable Logic Devices

## INTRODUCTION

There are practical limits to the number of *separate gates* that may usefully be put in a single package. *One of the major constraints is simply the number of pins that are required to connect to the inputs and outputs of the gates.* A circuit with 1000 separate gates, for example, would require several thousand pins and would inevitably occupy a large amount of space on a circuit board. The *external interconnections* between these pins would also require a large amount of board area.

To take full advantage of large scale integration (LSI) it is necessary to implement *not only* the gates required by a circuit, *but also* their interconnections. If this is done then only the circuit's *inputs* and *outputs* need to be brought to the outside world rather than connections to each node of the circuit. Internally connecting the gates within a package permits complex circuits to be implemented *within* a single device, but *results in a device that is dedicated to a particular function.*

## RANDOM LOGIC

Modern microprocessors, memories and interface circuits often contain thousands or tens of thousands of gates within a single chip. The *development costs* with such devices are very high and can only be justified for components that are used in very large numbers. Microprocessors are general purpose devices that can be used in a multitude of applications since their operation is determined by *software.* Similarly memory devices and several other complex components can be used in a wide range of applications, allowing them to be produced in large quantities. Unfortunately, not all electronic circuity is produced in large numbers, and in

many cases the circuits used are *unique to a particular application.* Even systems based on the use of standardized components such as microprocessors *normally require a certain amount of specialized logic to bolt the major components together.* This circuitry is often referred to as *glue logic* for obvious reasons. While the same microprocessor may be used in thousands of designs, *the glue logic varies between applications to give the system its own unique hardware characteristics.* Since the circuity tends to be specific to individual designs it is often called *random logic*, this term referring to the *selection of functions,* rather than indicating any non-casual form of operation. This random nature makes it impossible for a manufacturer to produce a single *conventional* integrated circuit that combines all the functions within a single chip.

### 16.1 What are the different types of *fuse technologies* used in PROMs?

*Solution:*

Three basic fuse technologies are used in PROMs: metal links, silicon links and PN junctions. A brief description of each of these follows:

1. *Metal links* are made of a material such as nichrome. Each bit in the memory array is represented by a separate link. *During programming the link is either blown open or left intact.* This is basically done by first addressing a given cell and then forcing a sufficient amount of current through the link to cause it to open.

2. *Silicon links* are formed by narrow notched strips of polycrystalline silicon. *Programming of these fuses requires melting of the links by passing a sufficient amount of current through them.* This

amount of current causes a high temperature at the fuse location that oxidises the silicon and forms an *insulation* around the now open link.

3. *Shorted junction* or *avalanche-induced migration* technology consists basically of two PN junctions arranged back-to-back. *During programming, one of the diode junctions is avalanched and the resulting voltage and heat cause aluminium ions to migrate and short the junction. The remaining junction is then used as a forward-biased diode to represent a data bit.*

### 16.2 What are the advantages and disadvantages of *polycrystalline silicon* for use in fuse technologies used in PROMs?

*Solution:*
*Advantages*
1. It can be *easily fabricated* during a manufacturing process involving silicon.
2. It is *easily compatible with* silicon dioxide ($SiO_2$) surface layers.
3. It can be *easily doped* to form resistors and conductors.
4. It is *compatible with* high-temperature processing.
5. It has *higher stability* than aluminium.
6. *Ease of depositing* over steep surface.

*Disadvantage*
1. Relatively *high resistivity* compared to aluminium.

### 16.3 How will you *categorise* programmable ROMs (PROMs)?

*Solution:*
ROMs can be divided into the following three major categories, depending on the way data are *written* into the ROM integrated circuit chip.
1. Mask Programmable ROMs
2. Field Programmable ROMs
3. Erasable Programmable ROMs

See Problem 15.8

## PROGRAMMABLE LOGIC DEVICES (PLDs)

In very small systems it may be possible to implement the required random logic using a handful of 7400 series TTL or 4000 series CMOS logic devices. However, *as the complexity of the system increases the number of components required becomes prohibitive.* A typical desk top computer, for example, might require only a handful of VLSI chips for the functions of the processor, memory and input/output sections, but would need more than 100 additional chips if the glue logic were implemented using simple logic circuits. *What is required is a method of providing large number of gates within a single, mass-produced device, while allowing them to be inter-connected in a manner to suit a particular application.* Devices of this type come under the general heading of *programmable logic devices* or *PLDs*.

### 16.4 What is a PLD? How are PLDs *categorized*?

*Solution:*
A *PLD* contains a large number of logic gates within a single package, but *allows a user to determine how they are interconnected.* This technology is also known as *uncommitted logic* since the gates are not committed to any specific function at the time of manufacture. The various gates within a device, and their interconnections, are arranged within one or more arrays. For this reason this form of logic is also known as *array logic*. There are many forms of array logic. Some of the most widely used are:
1. PLA     programmable logic array
2. PAL     programmable array logic
3. GAL     generic array logic
4. PROM   programmable read only memory
5. CPLD   complex programmable logic device
6. FPGA   field programmable gate array

## PROGRAMMABLE LOGIC ARRAY (PLA)

PLA combines the functions of PROM and PAL. Both the AND array and OR array are programmable. Thus it is more versatile than PROM and PAL.

### 16.5 Draw the *structure* of a simple PLA and explain with the help of an example.

*Solution:*
A combinational expression can always be represented by a series of *minterms* that may be derived directly from a truth table. For example, a system with four inputs $A$, $B$, $C$, and $D$ might have outputs $X$, $Y$, $Z$ where

$$X = \bar{A}\,\bar{B}\,\bar{C}D + \bar{A}\,\bar{B}CD$$
$$Y = \bar{A}\,\bar{B}CD + ABC\bar{D}$$
$$Z = \bar{A}\,\bar{B}\,\bar{C}D + \bar{A}BCD + ABCD$$

One way of implementing such a system is to use a number of *inverters* to produce the inverted input signals ($\bar{A}$, $\bar{B}$, $\bar{C}$ and $\bar{D}$) and then to use a series of AND *gates* and OR *gates* to generate and combine the various minterms. *A PLA has a structure that allows such functions to be produced easily.*

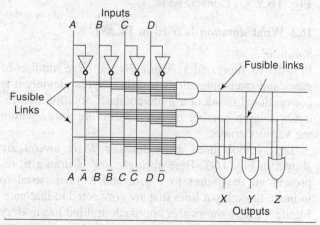

**Fig 16.1** *The Structure of a Simple PLA.*

The structure of a simple PLA is shown in Fig 16.1. This shows an arrangement with four inputs (*A*, *B*, *C*, and *D*) which are inverted to produce *four pairs of complementary inputs*. These eight signals are then each connected to the inputs of a number of AND gates *through an array of fusible links*. These fuses are initially all intact, but they may be blown selectively to determine the pattern of connections between the input signals and the AND gates. In this way *each AND gate is used to detect the input pattern corresponding to an individual minterm*. A second array of fuses is used to connect the outputs of the AND gates to a collection of OR gates. *These OR gates combine the relevant minterms to produce the various outputs*. This is illustrated in Fig. 16.2 which shows the simplified PLA in Fig. 16.1 configured to implement the system given in the above example. Here most of the fuses linking the inputs to the AND *gates* have been blown, leaving only those connecting the required signals to each gate. Similarly the fuses connected to the inputs to the OR *gates* have been *selectively blown* to produce the required three output signals.

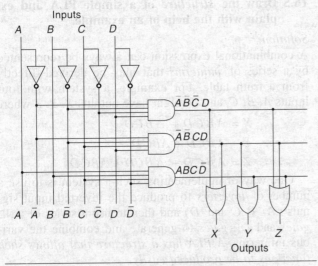

**Fig. 16.2**   *A Configured PLA.*

### 16.6 What *notation* is used in PLAs?

*Solution:*

In order to *represent symbolically* the large number of gates and interconnections within a typical device, it is conventional to adopt a more compact notation that reduces a large number of *interconnecting wires* within the various arrays.

The symbols used when drawing *logic arrays* are shown in Fig. 16.3. Here a *single line* is drawn to represent all the inputs to a gate and a *cross* used to indicate those input lines that are connected to that gate. Figure 16.3(a) shows this approach applied to an array of AND *gates* and Fig. 16.3(b) shows how it may be applied to OR *gates*.

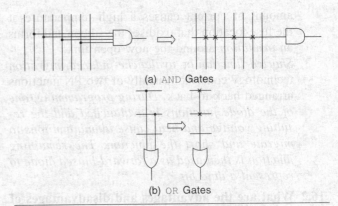

(a) AND Gates

(b) OR Gates

**Fig. 16.3**   *Logic Array Symbolic Notation.*

In the configured PLA shown in Fig. 16.2, the input signals are inverted to produce *complementary* input signals using a conventional inverter as shown Fig. 16.4(a). A disadvantage of this arrangement is that the *propagation delay* of the gate will cause the inverted input to change a short-time after the non-inverted signals. This is overcome by using a circuit that produces *both* an inverted and a non-inverted output, with equal propagation times. Such a circuit is given the symbol shown in Fig. 16.4(b).

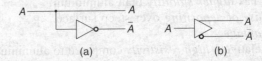

(a)                              (b)

**Fig. 16.4**   *Representation of Inverters within Logic Arrays.*

## PROGRAMMABLE ARRAY LOGIC (PAL)

PAL has some AND and OR arrays as in PROM but the input to AND gates are programmable and the inputs to OR gates are hard wired. If some AND outputs are not required they can be made 0.

### 16.7 What is the *difference* between programmable logic array (PLA) and programmable array logic (PAL)? Explain PAL in detail.

*Solution:*

*PLA is costly when the number of functions to be realized is low.* In such cases, we make use of *programmable array logic* (PAL) chips. A PAL chip is a special modification of programmable logic array (PLA) chips. In a PAL, *the AND array is programmable* as in the case of PLA, but *the OR array is fixed* i.e. the AND array contains fusible links and hence can be programmed, but the OR array connections are fixed and contain no fusible links, hence the OR array is not programmable. Figure 16.5 shows the structure of a PAL. We make use of the *same symbol* in the structure of PAL as we have done for PLA.

PALs are much *cheaper* than PLAs, hence many logic designers prefer PALs as compared to PLAs. The advantages of PLAs come into effect only when *all* of its

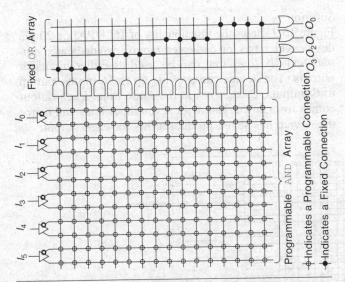

**Fig. 16.5** *A PAL with 6 Inputs, 4 Outputs and 16 Product Terms.*

individual OR gates are used in the logic design. In many situations this may not be required. In such cases, using PALs will be more economical.

PAL manufacturers compensate for the absence of a programmable OR array by providing a *range* of devices with different numbers of OR gates and with different numbers of inputs on each OR gate.

Because the OR array is *fixed* in a PAL it is common to *omit* this array from its symbolic representation. It is also common to move the inputs to the left of the diagram *to produce a circuit with the inputs on the left and outputs on the right*, as shown in Fig. 16.6.

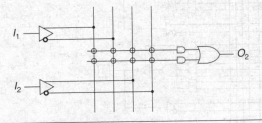

**Fig. 16.6** *A Fragment of a PAL.*

### 16.8 How can PALs be provided with increased *flexibility*?

*Solution:*
To give increased *flexibility* many PALs use a technique that permits some of their pins to be used *either* as inputs *or* as outputs. Figure 16.7 illustrates such an arrangement. Here the output from one of the OR gates of the device is passed through a *three-state inverter* before being fed to the output pin. The operation of the inverter is controlled by an *output enable* signal that is derived from the AND array in a manner similar to any other minterm. If all the fuses connected to the inputs to this AND gate are blown, its output will remain HIGH,

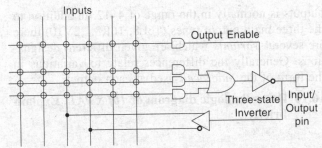

**Fig. 16.7** *A Typical PAL Input/Output Circuit.*

*enabling* the output of the inverter. This will configure this line as an output. If all the fuses connected to the inputs of this AND gate are left intact its output will remain LOW and the output of the inverter will be *disabled*, converting the pin into an *input*. The signal on the pin is used to generate *complementary signals* that are fed to the lines of the input array. Depending on the *state* of the output enable line these complementary signals may represent *either* an input signal *or* the current state of the output. In the latter case these lines may be used to allow the output of one OR gate to be *fedback* to the input of other gates. Rather than being set continuously HIGH or continuously LOW, the output enable signal can be configured *to respond to the state of lines in the input* array. This can be used to allow input signals to *enable* or *disable* an output.

The circuit in Fig. 16.7 shows the outside being controlled by a three-state inverter. A three-state non-inverting buffer could have been used in this arrangement, which would produce a functionality equivalent to that of the earlier circuits. The use of an inverting or non-inverting buffer affects the fuse map that must be used, some functions are easier to implement when an *inverter* is used, while others are easier with *a non-inverting buffer*. An *inverting buffer* is shown in the figure since this is the more common configuration.

### 16.9 How will you decode the numbering system for PALs?

*Solution:*
PALs derive their generic part name (for example 16L8 or 22V10) from their *input/output characteristics*. This is shown in Fig. 16.8.

Depending on the device, the number of array inputs varies from 16 to more than 40, while the number of

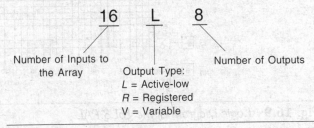

**Fig. 16.8** *The 16L8 PAL.*

outputs is normally in the range of 4–12. In addition to the three main output types (16L8, 16R8, 22V10) there are several *variants* which are given different designations. Generally the differences relate to variations in the form of the *macrocell* used at each output.

**16.10  Draw the logic diagram of *16L8 PAL*. Explain briefly**.

*Solution:*

Figure 16.9 shows the functionality of 16L8 PAL, a 20-pin device which has ten dedicated *inputs,* two dedicated *outputs* and *six lines* that can be used as either inputs or outputs. The device can provide up to 16 inputs and up to 8 outputs, though not at the same time. Each output comes from an OR gate with seven input lines and hence the device has seven product terms for each output.

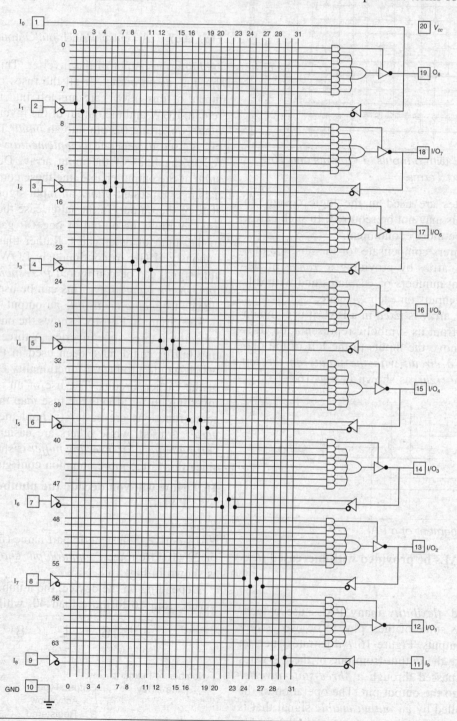

**Fig. 16.9**  *Logic Diagram of the 16L8 PAL.*

### 16.11 Draw the logic diagram of the *16R8 PAL*. Explain briefly.

*Solution:*

More sophisticated PALs replace the combinational outputs used in the 16L8 with *registered outputs with feedback. An* example of such a device is the 16R8 PAL shown in Fig. 16.10. Here each product term is *stored* into a *D* type `flip-flop` on the rising edge of a clock signal. The output from this `flip-flop` is used to generate an output signal but is also *fed back* to the input array to allow this signal to be used by other parts of the PAL. The ability of the `flip-flop` to *remember* the previous state of the device permits the implementation of a range of *sequential circuits* such as counters, shift registers and state machines.

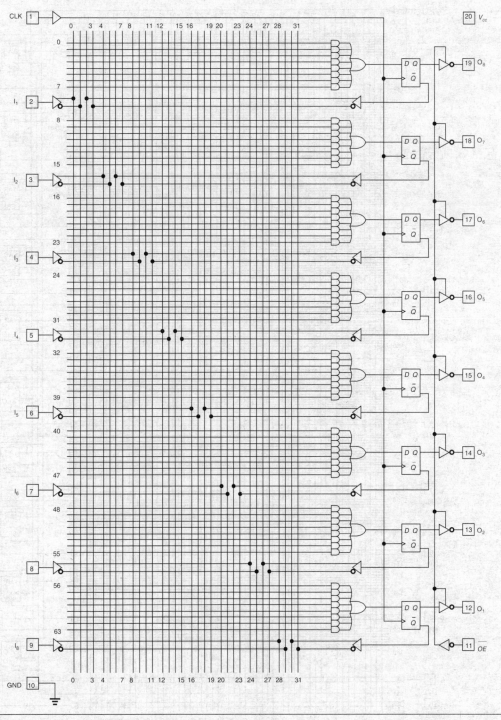

**Fig. 16.10**   *Logic Diagram of the 16R PAL with Registered Outputs.*

## 16.12 Draw the logic diagram of the *22V10 PAL*. Explain briefly.

*Solution:*

More advanced components remove the need to choose between devices with combinational outputs by providing a *variable output structure* that can be made to emulate either form. A widely used example of this type of device is the 22V10 PAL which is shown in Fig. 16.11. Here the output circuit takes the form of a *macrocell* that can be individually configured for each output. In addition to providing a combinational or registered output, the macrocell allows output to be *selectively inverted* and provides an output *enable function*. This device has 10 OR gates with inputs ranging from 8 to 16.

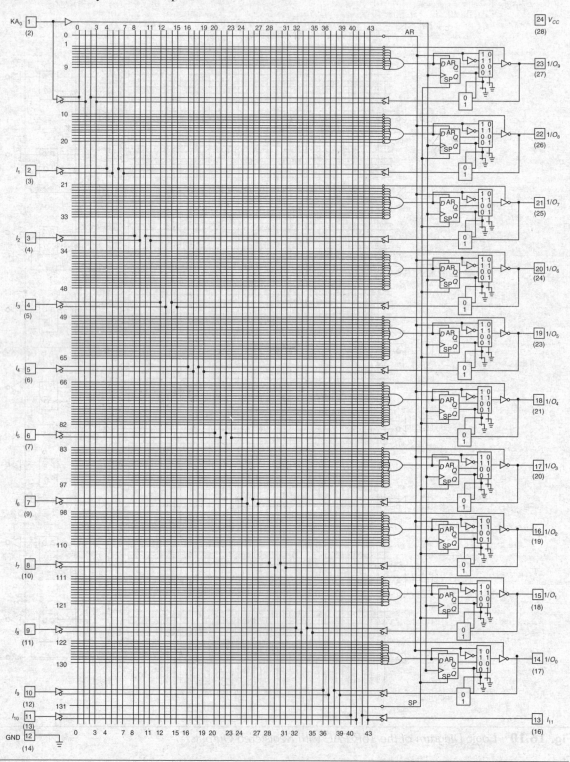

**Fig. 16.11** *Logic Diagram of the 22V10 PAL with Macrocell Outputs.*

## GENERIC ARRAY LOGIC (GAL)

PAL uses one time programmable fuse links to select the input terms which produce the AND terms. However, GAL devices use EEPROM array. Therefore, the device can be erased and reprogrammed. *The main feature of GALs is the programmable output logic macro cell (OLMC).*

**16.13 Describe *generic array logic* (GAL) and *erasable programmable logic devices* (EPLDs).**

*Solution:*
Because of their *fuse-based construction*, PALs can only be programmed once. They are therefore described as *one time programmable* (OTP) parts. The *generic-array logic* (GAL) devices are *pin compatible* with conventional PALs but use electrically erasable and programmable read only memory *(EEPROM)* technology in place of fuses to achieve reprogramability. GAL devices are intended as pin-for-pin replacements for a wide variety of PAL devices. The GAL *16V8* replaces most 20-pin PAL devices, while the *20V8* replaces most 24-pin PAL devices. Early GALs were much slower than PALs but more recent devices have *speeds* comparable with fuse-based devices.

Other *reprogrammable* PAL-like devices include *erasable PLDs* (EPLDs). These are similar to PALs, but use *erasable and programmable read only memory* (EPROM) techniques in place of fuses. This allows devices to be erased by exposure to ultraviolet light. Once erased they can then be reprogrammed. EPLDs generally offer more facilities than PALs and are more *flexible*, However they are somewhat *slower* than PALs with typical delay times of between 10 and 20 ns.

**16.14 List the commercially available *PAL devices* along with their features.**

*Solution:*
See Table 16.1

**Table 16.1** *Some Available PAL Devices*

| Device | | Inputs | | | Output | | | | Packages |
|---|---|---|---|---|---|---|---|---|---|
| | | External | Feedback | Total | Bidirectional Combinational | Registered | Combinational | Total | Pins |
| PAL | 10L8 | 10 | 0 | 10 | 0 | 0 | 8 | 8 | 20 |
| PAL | 16L8 | 10 | 6 | 16 | 6 | 0 | 2 | 8 | 20 |
| PAL | 20L8 | 14 | 6 | 20 | 6 | 0 | 2 | 8 | 24 |
| PAL | 20L10 | 12 | 8 | 20 | 8 | 0 | 2 | 10 | 24 |
| PAL | 16R4 | 8 | 8 | 16 | 4 | 4 | 0 | 8 | 20 |
| PAL | 16R6 | 8 | 8 | 16 | 2 | 6 | 0 | 8 | 20 |
| PAL | 16R8 | 8 | 8 | 16 | 0 | 8 | 0 | 8 | 20 |
| PAL | 20R4 | 12 | 8 | 20 | 4 | 4 | 0 | 8 | 24 |
| PAL | 20R6 | 12 | 8 | 20 | 2 | 6 | 0 | 8 | 24 |
| PAL | 20R8 | 12 | 8 | 20 | 0 | 8 | 0 | 8 | 24 |
| PAL | 20X4 | 10 | 10 | 20 | 6 | 4 | 0 | 10 | 24 |
| PAL | 20X8 | 10 | 10 | 20 | 2 | 8 | 0 | 10 | 24 |
| PAL | 20X10 | 10 | 10 | 20 | 0 | 10 | 0 | 10 | 24 |
| PAL | 22X10 | 12 | 10 | 22 | 10 | 10 | 0 | 10 | 24 |
| GAL | 16V8 | 8 | 8 | 16 | 8 | 8 | 8 | 8 | 20 |
| GAL | 20V8 | 12 | 8 | 20 | 8 | 8 | 8 | 8 | 24 |
| PEEL | 18CV8 | 10 | 8 | 18 | 8 | 8 | 8 | 8 | 24 |

## PROGRAMMABLE READ ONLY MEMORY (PROM)

PROM can generate any logic function of the input variables because it generates every possible AND product term. Therefore, it is useful in cases where it is required that every input combination should be available. *When the number of input variables is large a PROM becomes impractical because the number of fuses doubles for every additional input variable.*

**16.15 How will you *program* a PROM?**

*Solution:*
A PROM is normally programmed by plugging it into a special instrument called a *PROM programmer*. Basically, the programming is accomplished as shown by the simplified set up in Fig. 16.12.

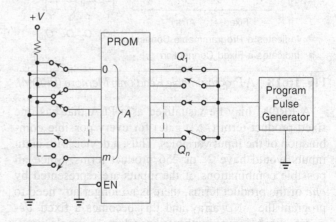

**Fig. 16.12** *Simplified PROM Programming Set up.*

An address is selected by the switch setting on the address lines, and then a pulse is applied to those output lines corresponding to bit locations where 0's are to be stored (*the PROM starts out with all 1's*). These pulses *blow the fuse links*, thus creating the desired *bit pattern*. The next address is then selected and the process is repeated. This *sequence* is done automatically by the PROM programmer.

### 16.16 Explain how a programmable read only memory is formed?

*Solution:*
Despite the *flexibility* of the PLA provided by its two programmable arrays it is often more efficient to use a *less complex configuration* with a single programmable array. A PAL arrangement can be formed by replacing the programmable OR array with a fixed series of inter connections. An alternative method of simplifying the PLA structure is to remove the programmable AND array to form a structure as shown in Fig. 16.13. This forms a *programmable read only memory* or PROM.

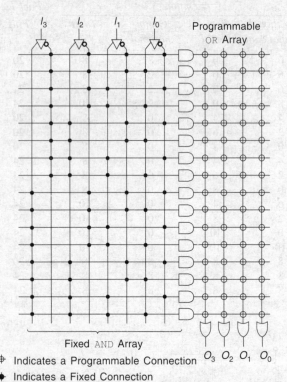

Fixed AND Array
⊕ Indicates a Programmable Connection
✦ Indicates a Fixed Connection

**Fig. 16.13**  *A Programmable Read only Memory (PROM).*

A PROM may be visualized as a PLA that has one fixed product term (AND gate) for every possible combination of the input variables. Thus, a device with eight inputs would have $2^8$ or 256 product terms. Since all possible combinations of the inputs are represented by *one* of the product terms, there is no longer any need to program the AND array and this becomes a fixed *decoder*. Each input combination selects a single AND

gate and the OR array is used to determine which of the various outputs is activated (taken HIGH) for that input combination. *The pattern written into the OR array therefore determines the output pattern that will be produced for each possible set of inputs.*

PROMs were one of the earliest forms of array logic and predate both PLAs and PALs. However, the use of a full decoder is inefficient for most logic applications and *they are more commonly used for the storage of program or data, rather than to implement logic functions.* When used in this way the input pattern represents the *address* and the corresponding pattern in the OR array represents the *stored data*. When devices of this type are designed for program or data storage they are more often referred to as ROM.

### 16.17 Use a 32 × 8 bipolar PROM to form the following functions:
$$f_1 = \Sigma m\ (0, 2, 5, 6, 8)$$
$$f_2 = \Sigma m\ (4, 5, 6, 8, 9)$$
$$f_3 = \Sigma m\ (6, 7, 8, 10, 13, 17, 22, 23)$$

*Solution:*
Since we need only three outputs, we shall assign the output data bits as:
$$f_1 = D_0, \quad f_2 = D_1 \quad \text{and} \quad f_3 = D_2$$
The remaining output data bits will be left open. Next, make a list of all the locations of the PROM (Fig. 16.14).

| Location | Contents | Location | Contents |
|---|---|---|---|
| 00 | 0000 0001 | 16 | 0000 0000 |
| 01 | 0000 0000 | 17 | 0000 0100 |
| 02 | 0000 0001 | 18 | 0000 0000 |
| 03 | 0000 0000 | 19 | 0000 0000 |
| 04 | 0000 0010 | 20 | 0000 0000 |
| 05 | 0000 0011 | 21 | 0000 0000 |
| 06 | 0000 0111 | 22 | 0000 0100 |
| 07 | 0000 0100 | 23 | 0000 0100 |
| 08 | 0000 0111 | 24 | 0000 0000 |
| 09 | 0000 0010 | 25 | 0000 0000 |
| 10 | 0000 0100 | 26 | 0000 0000 |
| 11 | 0000 0000 | 27 | 0000 0000 |
| 12 | 0000 0000 | 28 | 0000 0000 |
| 13 | 0000 0100 | 29 | 0000 0000 |
| 14 | 0000 0000 | 30 | 0000 0000 |
| 15 | 0000 0000 | 31 | 0000 0000 |

(a) Table

(b) Logic Diagram

**Fig. 16.14**  *Using PROMs for Random Logic.*

*Each minterm of the expressions represents its own address*. Minterm $m_4$, for example represents the address 4 on the table. Next, where a minterm is *present* within an expression, place a 1 in the table corresponding to that bit. Expression $f_2$, for example, includes minterm 5. Therefore, place a 1 in bit $D_1$ of address 5. Where a minterm is not present, place a 0 within the corresponding data word. Figure 16.14 shows the completed table and the resulting logic diagram.

## COMPLEX PROGRAMMABLE LOGIC DEVICES (CPLDs)

PLAs, PALs and GALs are often collectively referred to as simple programmable logic devices or SPLDs. Complex PLDs can be thought of as an arrangement of several SPLDs within a single chip. CPLDs are correctly the subject of a great deal of development work and the capabilities of these devices are increasing rapidly.

### 16.18 Draw the block diagram of a typical *CPLD*.

*Solution:*
PLAs, PALs and equivalent *reprogrammable devices* such as GALs and EPLDs are often collectively referred to as *simple programmable logic devices* (SPLDs). *Complex PLDs* can be thought of as an arrangement of several SPLDs within a single chip. In addition to providing a large number of array elements they also provide a powerful method of *interconnecting* inputs and outputs to allow fairly complex circuits to be implemented within a single package. The block diagram of a typical CPLD configuration is given in Fig. 16.15.

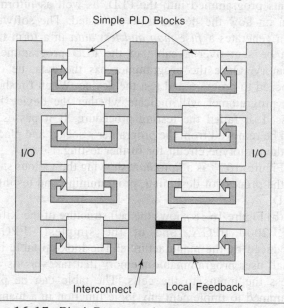

**Fig. 16.15** *Block Diagram of a Typical CPLD.*

CPLDs are normally implemented using EPROM or EEPROM techniques rather than fuses and are thus reprogrammable. EEPROM parts have the advantage of *in-circuit reprogrammability*, allowing their functionality to be changed without the devices being removed from the board. This is particularly useful when performing *system upgrades*.

At present devices with several thousands of gates are available, with delay times of only a few seconds. The propagation delay time can be *predicted* while implementing the design. A single CPLD might typically be used to implement a mixture of registers, decoders, multiplexers and counters. For example, a 32-bit counter can be produced using a single device.

### 16.19 Explain the term antifuse.

*Solution:*
An *antifuse* is a programmable element invented by Actel Corporation and is named as *programmable low impedance circuit element* (PLICE). It is normally an open device in which electrical connection is established by the application of a programmable voltage. The antifuse is a vertical, two-terminal structure. It consists of a polysilicon layer on top. N+ doped silicon on the bottom, and an oxide-nitrite-oxide dielectric layer in-between. The size of an antifuse is about 1.8 $\mu m^2$. It has a low resistance, typically 500 $\Omega$ when *programmed* and over 100 M$\Omega$ when in the *unprogrammed* state. The antifuse is a very attractive alternative to EPROM, EEPROM, or RAM for use as a programmable element in a large programmable gate array. *It is a one time programmable device.*

## FIELD PROGRAMMABLE GATE ARRAY (FPGA)

Research and development engineers have been making huge efforts to increase the *functional capabilities* of PLDs. FPGAs have been developed with this aim. The number of equivalent gates in PLDs is about 1000 or so. In FPGAs the number of equivalent gates can be 10000 or so. The architecture of FPGAs is different from that of other PLDs.

### 16.20 Illustrate and discuss the architecture of FPGAs.

*Solution:*
FPGAs take the form of a two-dimensional array of logic cells. These may be arranged in rows, or, more commonly in a *rectangular grid* as shown in Fig. 16.16. The size of the array varies considerably, with *small devices* having about 64 cells, while larger *devices* may have more than 1000 cells. Between the cells of the array run groups of vertical and horizontal *channels* that can be used to route signals through the circuit. *Programmable switches* are used to interconnect these conductors and so provide point-to-point connections.

The programmable switches within FPGAs may be either one time programmable (OTP) or reprogrammable. OTP parts are based on the use of *antifuses* rather than the conventional fuses used in PALs.

*Reprogrammability* is achieved by replacing each antifuse with a transistor switch (a MOSFET). The *state*

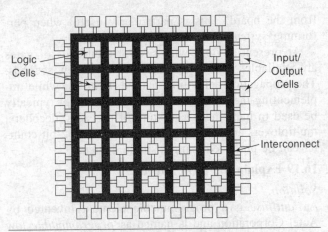

**Fig. 16.16**  *A Simplified FPGA Arrangement*

of the switch is then determined by a memory element that can be set either to open or to close the switch. You can visualize this memory element as a bistable element. This technique is referred to as a *static random access memory* (SRAM) approach and has the *advantage* that the contents of the memory can be changed as often as desired. The device is therefore completely reprogrammable. One *disadvantage* of this approach is that the content of the memory is volatile, and is lost when the power is removed. To overcome this problem the states of the various interconnections must be loaded from some nonvolatile memory (ROM or computer disk) when power is first applied.

FPGAs are particularly useful when implementing systems that require *on-chip memory* or that benefit from distributed architecture. Modern FPGAs operate at very high speeds, but are generally not as fast as PALs or CPLDs. Also, their propagation delay times are greatly affected by the *route* taken by the signals within the chips. This makes it very difficult to predict a circuit's performance before it is completed. This is in marked contrast to PALs and CPLDs where delay times are totally predictable.

**16.21 (a) Draw the flowchart of PLD design, programming and test process.**

**(b) Explain briefly the configurable Logic Block of a Xilinx XC 2000 FPGA.**

*Solution:*

(a) When PLDs were first introduced the logic designer would develop a *fuse map* that showed which fuses to blow and send it off to the PROM, PAL or FPLA manufacturer. The manufacturer would then program the device according to the fuse map, test it and send it to the designer. In recent years the availability of relatively inexpensive programming equipment has made it convenient for users to program their own PLDs. There are *universal programmers* on the market that can program most common PROMs, PALs, and FPLAs. The device to be programmed is plugged into a socket on the programmer, and the programmer will *program and test* the device according to data that have been supplied by the user.

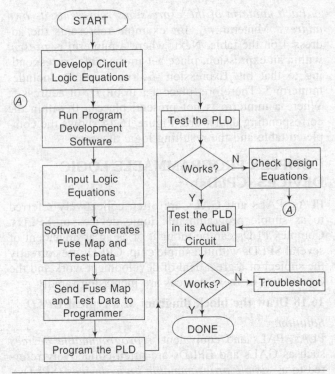

**Fig. 16.17**  *Flowchart of PLD Design Programming and Test Process.*

The programming and test data are typically developed using commonly available *software* that will run on standard PCs. Using this software, the user enters data into the computer describing the logic functions he wants programmed into the PLD, as well as information on how the device is to be tested. The software then generates a *fuse map and test data* in a form that can be sent over a cable to the PLD programmer's memory. Once the programmer has the data, he can proceed to program and test the device. When finished, the programmer will indicate whether the device has passed or failed the testing procedure. If it passes, it can be removed from the programer's socket and placed in the prototype circuit for further testing.

Figure. 16.17 is a *flowchart* showing the various steps in the process of designing, programming and testing a PLD.

(b) Figure 16.18 shows the cell structure of the Xilinx XC 2000 FPGA, one of the simplest FPGAs produced by the manufacturers. The look-up table is a small user programmable memory that takes as its address the inputs to the cells. The table can be programmed to implement any logic function in a manner similar to a PROM. More sophisticated devices have much more complex logic cells that may contain several `flip-flops`, several look-up tables and a selection of other logic gates. The versatility of this arrangement, and the very flexible interconnection mechanism, allow complex circuits to be implemented within a single chip.

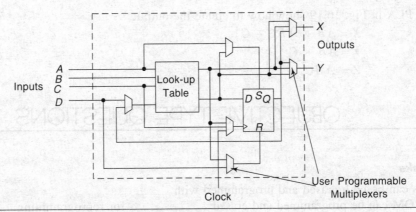

**Fig. 16.18** *The Configurable Logic Block of a Xilinx XC 2000 FPGA.*

## SUMMARY

> ➢ PLDs can be used to generate a desired logic function.
> ➢ PLDs can be classified as PLA, PAL, GAL, PROM, CPLD and FPGA.
> ➢ In a PLA both AND array and OR array are programmable.
> ➢ In a PAL only AND array is programmable, whereas the OR array is hard wired.
> ➢ GAL has input term matrix, AND gates and output macrocells.
> ➢ CPLD is an arrangement of several simple PLDs within a single chip.
> ➢ FPGA has high component density. Logic cell array is one type of FPGA.

## REVIEW QUESTIONS

**Test your understanding**

1. What is a PLD?
2. What does an X represent on a PLD diagram?
3. What does a dot represent on a PLD diagram?
4. How does the architecture of a PAL differ from that of a PROM?
5. How does the architecture of FPLA differ from that of PROMs and PALs?
6. What capability does a polarity fuse give a PLD designer?
7. Name two advantages of GAL devices over PAL devices.
8. Name two software packages that are used to implement PLD circuits.
9. Name the three modes of operation for a GAL 16V8A

## SUPPLEMENTARY PROBLEMS

**Test your understanding**

10. Implement the function
$$X = \bar{A}\,\bar{B}C + A\,B\,\bar{C} + \bar{B}C$$
$$Y = \bar{A}\,\bar{B}C + A\,B\,\bar{C}$$
$$Z = \bar{B}C$$

11. Illustrate a PLA with six inputs, four outputs and 16 product terms.
12. Draw the block diagram of a field programmable logic array.
13. How does a polarity fuse function?
14. Use a bipolar $32 \times 8$ PROM to implement the following equations:
$$f_1 = \Sigma m\ (2,\ 3,\ 6,\ 16,\ 26) + d\ (4,\ 5)$$
$$f_2 = \Sigma m\ (6,\ 7,\ 8,\ 10,\ 13,\ 14) + d\ (30,\ 31)$$
$$f_3 = \Sigma m\ (10,\ 11,\ 12,\ 13,\ 25) + d\ (0,\ 1,\ 3,\ 31)$$

15. Given the PLA in Fig. 16.19 show how to create the output
$$X = A\bar{B} + \bar{A}\bar{B}C + C$$
$$Y = A\bar{B} + \bar{C}$$
$$Z = \bar{A}\bar{B}C$$

# OBJECTIVE TYPE QUESTIONS

Test your
understanding

## Fill in the Blanks

16. EEPROMs can be both erased and programmed with _____.
17. The EEPROM can be programmed and erased _____ for reprogramming.
18. An EPROM is an _____ PROM.
19. A PAL consists of _____.
20. Using the one line conventions for PLDs, a dot signifies fuses that are _____.
21. A single PLD can be used to implement several _____ expressions.
22. An advantage that basic PLA architecture has over basic PAL architecture is that PLA has _____ OR gates at its output.
23. PLD technology is also known as _____ logic.
24. A single line is drawn to represent all the _____ to a gate.
25. A _____ is used to indicate those input lines that are connected to that gate.
26. In a FPGA channels can be used to _____ the signals through the circuit.
27. As the complexity of a system increases the number of components required becomes _____.
28. Programming of fuses requires _____ of links.
29. PLD allows the user to determine how logic gates are _____.
30. A PLA has a structure that allows _____ expressions to be produced easily.
31. In a PLA the OR gates combine the relevant _____ to produce the various outputs.
32. In a PLA the _____ arrays contain fusible links.
33. The macrocell allows the output to be _____ inverted and provides an output enable function.

## True/False Questions

State whether the following statements are True or False.
34. PROM is once programmable.
35. RMM can be read and written to multiple times.
36. CAM is unique in that data is accessed based on the address, rather than on the contents of the memory.
37. A PLA is a form of encoder in which the outputs have a fixed logic output.
38. Memory registers can also be stacked.
39. A PAL chip is a special modification of the PLA chip.
40. In a PAL the AND array is fixed and the OR array is programmable.
41. A PAL can be used as a dynamic memory.
42. With a PROM Programmer the PROM starts out with all 0s.
43. An antifuse is reprogrammable.
44. Polycrystalline silicon has lower stability than aluminium.
45. In a PLA each AND gate is used to detect the input pattern corresponding to an individual minterm.
46. PALs can only be programmed once.
47. GAL devices are not pin compatible with conventional PALs.
48. OTP parts are based on the use of antifuses.

## Multiple Choice Questions

49. A PLA is a
    (a) SSI device       (b) MSI device       (c) LSI device       (d) VLSI device
50. The capacity or size of a PLA is specified by the
    (a) number of inputs                    (b) number of product terms
    (c) number of outputs                   (d) all of the above

51. A PROM is
    (a) mask programmed
    (c) OTP
    (b) erasable by UV radiations
    (d) reprogrammable

52. A PLA
    (a) is mask programmable
    (c) can be programmed by the user
    (b) is field programmable
    (d) can be erased and programmed.

53. A field programmable logic array
    (a) cannot be programmed by a user
    (c) can be erased by the user
    (b) can be programmed by a user only once
    (d) is reprogrammable.

54. A PLA consists of
    (a) AND matrix
    (c) invert/non-invert matrix
    (b) OR matrix
    (d) all of the above.

55. Fusible link is associated with
    (a) RAM        (b) ROM        (c) PROM        (c) EPROM

56. RWM is the same as
    (a) RAM        (b) ROM        (c) PROM        (d) EAROM

57. A PLA can be used
    (a) to realize combinational logic
    (c) as a dynamic memory
    (b) to realize sequential logic
    (d) as a microprocessor

# ANSWERS

1. An IC that contains a large number of gates, FFs, and registers whose interconnections can be modified by the user to perform specific functions.
2. An intact fuse
3. A hard wired connection
4. The PAL has a programmable AND array; the PROM has a programmable OR array.
5. A FPLA contains both programmable AND and OR arrays.
6. To invert or not invert the device outputs.
7. Erasable and reprogrammable
8. Development software; programming software
9. Simple, complex, registered output.
10. (See Fig. 16.19)
11. (See Fig. 16.20)

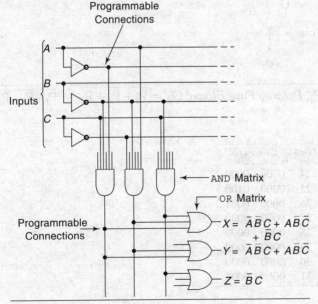

**Fig. 16.19** *Solution for Problem 10.*

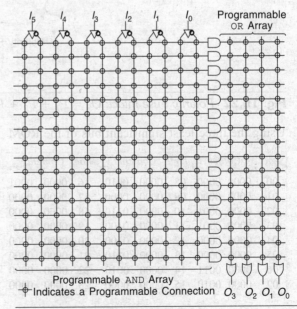

**Fig. 16.20** *Solution for Problem 11.*

12. (See Fig. 16.21)

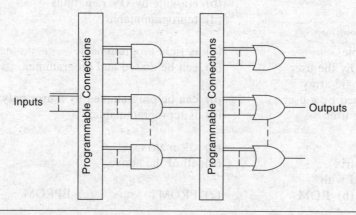

**Fig. 16.21** *Solution for Problem 12.*

13. Many PLDs include a programmable polarity feature that provides the option of *inverting* any of the output functions. When the fuse is intact (logic 0), the EXOR will pass the OR gate with *no inversion*, when the fuse is open (logic 1), the EXOR will *invert* the OR gate output. (See Fig. 16.22)

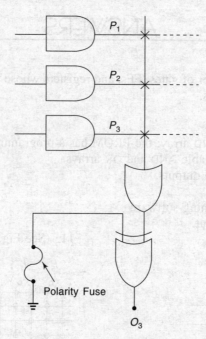

Polarity Fuse

$O_3$

**Fig. 16.22** *Polarity Fuse Intact:* $O_3 = P_1 + P_2 + P_3$, *Polarity Fuse Blown:* $O_3 = \overline{P_1 + P_2 + P_3} = \bar{P_1} \cdot \bar{P_2} \cdot \bar{P_3}$.

14. Using the three least significant bits of the ROM

| Loc. | Contents | Loc. | Contents | Loc. | Contents | Loc. | Contents |
|------|----------|------|----------|------|----------|------|----------|
| 00 | 0000 0000 | 08 | 0000 0010 | 16 | 0000 0001 | 24 | 0000 0000 |
| 01 | 0000 0000 | 09 | 0000 0000 | 17 | 0000 0000 | 25 | 0000 0100 |
| 02 | 0000 0001 | 10 | 0000 0110 | 18 | 0000 0000 | 26 | 0000 0001 |
| 03 | 0000 0001 | 11 | 0000 0100 | 19 | 0000 0000 | 27 | 0000 0000 |
| 04 | 0000 0000 | 12 | 0000 0100 | 20 | 0000 0000 | 28 | 0000 0000 |
| 05 | 0000 0000 | 13 | 0000 0110 | 21 | 0000 0000 | 29 | 0000 0000 |
| 06 | 0000 0011 | 14 | 0000 0010 | 22 | 0000 0000 | 30 | 0000 0000 |
| 07 | 0000 0010 | 15 | 0000 0000 | 23 | 0000 0000 | 31 | 0000 0000 |

15. (See Fig. 16.23)

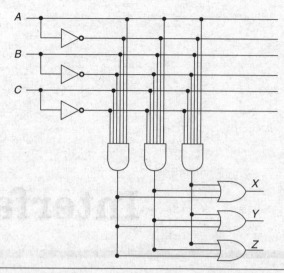

**Fig. 16.23** *Solution for Problem 15.*

| | | | |
|---|---|---|---|
| 16. Electrical pulses | 17. In circuit | 18. Erasable | 19. AND and OR gates |
| 20. Left in tact | 21. SOP | 22. Programmable | 23. Uncommitted |
| 24. Inputs | 25. Cross | 26. Route | 27. Prohibitive |
| 28. Melting | 29. Interconnected | 30. Combinational | 31. Minterms |
| 32. AND | 33. Selectively | 34. True | 35. True |
| 36. False | 37. False | 38. True | 39. True |
| 40. False | 41. False | 42. False | 43. False |
| 44. False | 45. True | 46. True | 47. False |
| 48. True | 49. (c) | 50. (d) | 51. (c) |
| 52. (a) | 53. (b) | 54. (d) | 55. (c) |
| 56. (d) | 57. (a) | | |

# Interfacing

## INTRODUCTION

There are many system problems that require connecting a digital portion of a system to an analog component. This 'meeting of the circuits' is called an *interface*. The dictionary definition of an interface is "*a common boundary between two parts of matter or space*". In the case of digital circuits, the two parts of matter or space can be interpreted to mean *two physical or functional electronic units*. Hence, an interface circuit could be one that *transmits and receives* digital data, say between two separate electronic chassis; or it might be one that *converts analog* information to digital data or vice versa. Some of the most common types of interface circuits likely to be encountered include buses, line drivers and receivers, digital-to-analog (D/A) and analog-to digital (A/D) converters, concepts of series and parallel transfer and the UART and RS 232 C interface devices.

### 17.1 Explain Nyquist's *sampling theorem.*

*Solution:*

In order to obtain a picture of the *changes* in a varying quantity it is necessary to take measurements. This process is referred to as *sampling*. If a quantity is changing *rapidly* we will need to take samples more frequently than if it changes *slowly*. Obviously the required *sampling rate* would be determined by the most rapidly changing or, in other words, the highest frequency, components within a signal.

Nyquist's sampling theorem states that *the sampling rate must be greater than twice the highest frequency present in the signal being sampled*. It also states that under these circumstances none of the information within

the signal is lost by sampling. In other words, *it is possible to reconstruct completely the original signal from the samples*.

$$f_s \geq 2f_m \qquad (17.1)$$

where $f_s$ is the frequency with which sampling is done, and $f_m$ is the *maximum frequency* of the analog signal.

Sampling can be done by applying the analog signal to the input of a *MOS switch*, and applying sampling pulses to its gate.

### 17.2 How will you express analog voltages in binary?

*Solution:*

Any analog voltage can be expressed as a binary word by *assigning voltage weights to each bit position*. For example, consider a 4-bit word. Voltage values of 8, 4, 2 and 1 can be assigned to each bit position as follows:

| Binary word | Voltage |
|---|---|
| 0000 | 0 |
| 0001 | 1 |
| 0010 | 2 |
| 0011 | 3 |
| 0100 | 4 |
| . . . . | . . . |
| . . . . | . . . |
| 1101 | 13 |
| 1110 | 14 |
| 1111 | 15 |

*Each successive binary count* represents 1/15th of the entire voltage.

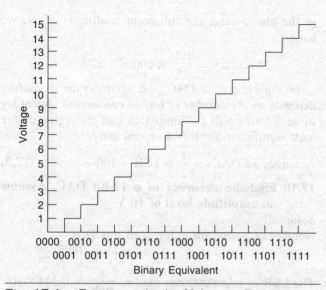

**Fig. 17.1**  *Expressing Analog Voltage in Binary.*

Thus, if a voltage of 13.6 V must be represented, 1110, a binary 14, is *as close as* we could come. A graph of these voltages versus their *binary equivalents* is shown in Fig. 17.1. Note that this is a *step process—voltage is resolvable only into discrete binary words.*

If this concept were extended to 8 bits, each successive binary count would be equal to 1/255 of the total. We can say that the *resolution* of this system is 1/255 or 0.392% of full scale. In general, the percent resolution is

$$\%R = \frac{1}{2^N - 1} \times 100 \qquad (17.2)$$

## D/A CONVERTERS

Digital-to-analog conversion involves translation of digital information into *equivalent* analog information. For a D/A converter to be useful, there has to be *a meaningful representation of the digital quantity as an analog representation.* A D/A converter is sometimes considered as a *decoding device.* D/A conversion is a straight forward process and is *considerably easier* than A/D conversion. In fact, a D/A converter is usually an *integral part* of any A/D converter.

### 17.3  What is the *percent resolution* of a 5-bit digital-to-analog converter (DAC)?

*Solution:*
The maximum number that can be represented using 5 bits is

$$11111_2 = 31_{10}$$

Therefore, the percent resolution is

$$\% R = \frac{1}{2^N - 1} \times 100 = \frac{1}{2^5 - 1} \times 100 = 3.23\%$$

### 17.4  Comment upon 'The trade-off is *precision of output versus cost*'.

*Solution:*
Since the resolution problem introduces *error* into the system, it is desirable to use as many bits as possible. However, *component value tolerances must be less than the percent resolution to introduce a minimum of error.* Therefore, the greater the number of bits used, the more precise the resistors in the D/A must be. The trade-off is precision of output versus cost.

### 17.5  Draw a table of percent resolution versus number of bits.

*Solution:*

| Number of bits | Percent resolution |
|---|---|
| 4 | 6.67 |
| 6 | 1.75 |
| 8 | 0.392 |
| 10 | 0.976 |
| 12 | 0.0244 |
| 14 | 0.00610 |
| 16 | 0.00153 |

## BINARY WEIGHTED DACs

If we scale the input resistors with a binary weighting factor, each *input* can made to provide a binary-weighted amount of current, and the *output* voltage will represent the *sum* of all the binary-weighted input currents.

### 17.6  A 6-bit converter has a maximum precision supply voltage of 20 V. Provide the following information for the unit:
   (a)  What *voltage change* does each LSB represent?
   (b)  What voltage does 100110 represent?

*Solution:*
(a) Each bit represents $1_2/111111_2$ or 1/63rd of the total of 20 V. Therefore, each LSB change represents

$$E = \frac{1}{63} \times 20$$

$$= 0.317 \text{ V}$$

(b) The binary number $100110_2$ equals $38_{10}$. Therefore, a 100110 represents

$$E = \frac{100110_2}{111111} \times 20_{10}$$

$$= \frac{38}{63} \times 20$$

$$= 12.06 \text{ V}$$

**17.7 Find the *binary equivalent weight* of each bit in a 4 bit system. *Check*.**

*Solution:*

The LSB has a weight of 1/15 or 1 part in 15.
The second LSB has a weight of 2/15.
The third LSB has a weight of 4/15.
The fourth LSB has a weight of 8/15.

*Check:*  *The sum of the weights must equal 1.*
1/15 + 2/15 + 4/15 + 8/15 =15/15 =1.

**17.8 Draw the *block diagram* of a D/A converter. Explain**.

*Solution:*

To *convert* a digital signal to analog, it is necessary to treat each bit in *binary weighted manner*. The block diagram of such a device is shown in Fig. 17.2. The *reference voltage source* feeds a precisely regulated voltage to the *voltage switches*. Upon receipt of a *convert* signal, binary data is clocked into the *register*, with each bit assigned a weighted value of current or voltage. These binary signals from the input register next feed *voltage switches* which provide one of two possible outputs: 0 V or the precision voltage (source voltage). Thus, they are equivalent to an ordinary SPDT switch controlled by the binary signals from the register. The switches feed a resistive *summing network* which converts each bit into its weighted current value and sums them for a total current. This total value is then fed to the *amplifier*, which performs two functions, current to voltage *conversion* and *scaling*, so that the output voltage of the *D/A* converter will be the proper value.

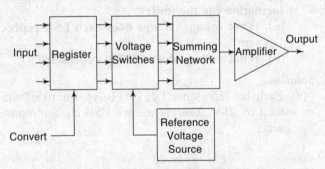

**Fig. 17.2**  *Block Diagram Digital-to-analog Converter.*

**17.9  Define and explain the term *accuracy* of DACs.**

*Solution:*

*Accuracy is defined as the nearness of a measured value to the true value.* For example, if the true value of a voltage level is 12 V, and its measured value using an instrument is 11.9 V we say that there is an *error* of 0.1 V in the measurement. *This error may be expressed as a percentage with reference to the full-scale (or, maximum) reading of the instrument. If*

in the above case, the full-scale reading is 15 V, we have

$$\text{Accuracy} = \frac{0.1}{15} \times 100 = 0.67\%$$

*In the case of a DAC, the accuracy of a reading depends on the number of bits of conversion.* Accuracy in such cases will be limited to half the value of the least significant bit. It is assumed that

$$\text{Accuracy of DACs} = \frac{1}{2} \times \text{LSB} \times 100\% \qquad (17.3)$$

**17.10 Find the *accuracy* of a 12-bit DAC. Assume an amplitude level of 10 V**.

*Solution:*
Number of *quantization levels* of this DAC
$$= 2^{12} = 4096$$

The LSB of this DAC can read $= \dfrac{1}{4096} = 0.244 \times 10^{-3}$

The *smallest reading* possible is $0.244 \times 10^{-3} \times 10$
$$= 2.44 \text{ mV}$$

For the 12-bit DAC, accuracy $\quad = \dfrac{1}{2} \times \dfrac{100}{4096}$
$$= 0.122 \times 10^{-3} \times 100$$
$$= 0.0122\%$$

## OPERATIONAL AMPLIFIERS

The resistive ladder networks work well for driving *very high impedance* circuits. However, if an attempt is made to drive a *low-impedance circuit*, there is insufficient drive from the `flip-flops` that supply voltages to the individual resistors, and a *degradation* of voltage levels occurs. *Uniform known voltage levels are a prerequisite for proper operation of the resistive ladder network. Operational amplifiers provide the necessary impedance matching and buffering as well amplification of the analog voltage swings to achieve the well-behaved voltage levels.*

**17.11 How does an *op- amp* work?**

*Solution:*
Most D/A and A/D circuits require the use of an *operational amplifier* (op-amp) for *signal conditioning*. Three characteristics of op-amps make them an almost *ideal amplifier:* (1) very high input impedance, (2) very high voltage gain and (3) very low output impedance. A basic op-amp circuit is shown in Fig. 17.3.

The symbol for the op-amp is the same as that for a comparator but when it is connected as shown in Fig. 17.3, it provides a much different function. The basic theory involved in the operation of the op-amp circuit in Fig. 17.3 is as follows:

1. The impedance looking into the (+) and (−) *input terminals* is assumed to be infinite; therefore $I_{in}$ (+), (−) = 0 A.

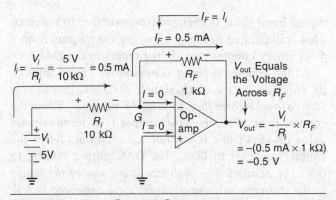

**Fig. 17.3** *Basic Op-amp Operation.*

2. Point $G$ is assumed to be at the *same* potential as the (+) input; therefore, point $G$ is at 0 V called *virtual ground*. (Virtual means 'in effect' but not actual. It is at 0 V, but it cannot sink current.)
3. With point $G$ at 0 V, there will be 5 V across the 10 kΩ resistor, causing 0.5 mA to flow.
4. The 0.5 mA cannot flow *into* the op-amp; therefore, it flows *up* through the 1 kΩ resistor.
5. Because point $G$ is at virtual ground, and because $V_{out}$ is measured with respect to ground, $V_{out}$ is equal to the voltage across the 1 kΩ resistor, which is –0.5 V.

**17.12 Find $V_{out}$ in Fig. 17.4.**

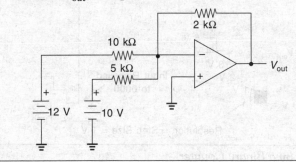

**Fig. 17.4**

*Solution:*

$$I_{10\ k\Omega} = \frac{12\ V}{10\ k\Omega} = 1.2\ mA$$

$$I_{5\ k\Omega} = \frac{10\ V}{5\ k\Omega} = 2\ mA$$

$$I_{2\ k\Omega} = 1.2\ mA + 2\ mA = 3.2\ mA$$
$$V_{out} = -(3.2\ mA \times 2\ k\Omega) = -6.4\ V$$

**17.13 With the help of a suitable illustration, describe the working of a *binary-weighted digital-to-analog converter*.**

*Solution:*
If we scale the input resistors with a *binary weighting factor*, each input can be made to provide a binary-weighted amount of current, and the output voltage will represent the sum of all the binary-weighted input currents, as shown in Fig. 17.5.

| $D_3$ | $D_2$ | $D_1$ | $D_0$ | $V_{out}(-V)$ |
|---|---|---|---|---|
| 0 | 0 | 0 | 0 | 0 |
| 0 | 0 | 0 | 1 | 1 |
| 0 | 0 | 1 | 0 | 2 |
| 0 | 0 | 1 | 1 | 3 |
| 0 | 1 | 0 | 0 | 4 |
| 0 | 1 | 0 | 1 | 5 |
| 0 | 1 | 1 | 0 | 6 |
| 0 | 1 | 1 | 1 | 7 |
| 1 | 0 | 0 | 0 | 8 |
| 1 | 0 | 0 | 1 | 9 |
| 1 | 0 | 1 | 0 | 10 |
| 1 | 0 | 1 | 1 | 11 |
| 1 | 1 | 0 | 0 | 12 |
| 1 | 1 | 0 | 1 | 13 |
| 1 | 1 | 1 | 0 | 14 |
| 1 | 1 | 1 | 1 | 15 |

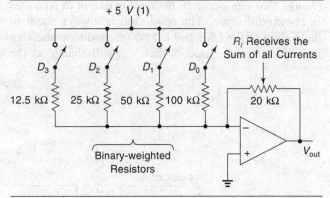

**Fig. 17.5** *Binary-weighted Digital-to-analog Converter.*

The 20 kΩ resistor *sums* the currents that are provided by closing any of the switches $D_0$ to $D_3$. The resistors are *scaled* in such a way as to provide a binary-weighted amount of current to be summed by the 20 kΩ resistor. Closing $D_0$ causes 50 μA to flow through the 20 kΩ creating –1.0 V at $V_{out}$. Closing each successive switch *doubles* the amount of current of the previous switch.

*Coming up with accurate resistances over such a large range of values is very difficult. This limits the practical use of this type of D/A converter for any more than 4-bits conversions.*

**17.14 Determine the voltage at $V_{out}$ in Fig. 17.5 if the binary equivalent $10_{10}$ is input to switches $D_3$ to $D_0$.**

*Solution:*

$$10_{10} = 1010_2\ (\text{switches } D_3 \text{ and } D_1 \text{ are closed})$$

$$I_3 = \frac{5\ V}{12.5\ k\Omega} = 0.4\ mA$$

$$I_1 = \frac{5\ V}{50\ k\Omega} = 0.1\ mA$$

$$V_{out} = -[(0.4\ mA + 0.1\ mA) \times 20\ k\Omega] = -10\ V.$$

*The negative sign is present because the summing amplifier is a polarity-inverting amplifier.*

**17.15 A 5-bit *D/A converter* produces $V_{out}$ = 0.2 V for a digital input of 00001. Find the value of $V_{out}$ for an input of 11111.**

*Solution:*

Obviously 0.2 V is the *weight of the LSB*. Thus, the weights of the other bits must be 0.4 V, 0.8 V, 1.6 V and 3.2 V, respectively. For a digital input of 11111, then, the value of $V_{out}$ will be

$$V_{out} = 3.2\ V + 1.6\ V + 0.8\ V + 0.4\ V + 0.2\ V$$
$$= 6.2\ V.$$

**17.16 Explain in detail the term *full-scale output*.**

*Solution:*

Resolution of a D/A converter is defined as *the smallest change that can occur in the analog output as a change in the digital input*. The resolution is always equal to the weight of the LSB and is also referred to as the *step size*, since it is the amount that $V_{out}$ will change as the digital input value is changed from one step to the next. This is illustrated in Fig. 17.6 where the outputs from a 4-bit binary counter provide the inputs to the DAC.

As the counter is being *continuously cycled* through its 16 states by the clock signal, *the DAC output is a staircase waveform that goes up 1V per step*. When the counter is at 1111, the DAC output is at its maximum value of 15 V; this is its *full scale output*. When the counter recycles to 0000, the DAC output returns to 0 V. *The resolution or step size is the size of the jumps in the staircase waveform; in this case each step is 1 V.*

In general for an *N*-bit DAC, the *number of different levels* will be $2^N$, and the *number of steps* will be $2^N - 1$.

$$\text{Analog output} = K \times \text{digital input} \qquad (17.4)$$

The digital input is equal to the number of the step. *K* is the amount of voltage (or current) per step, and the analog output is the product of the two.

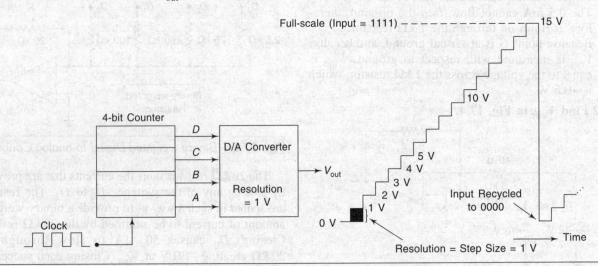

**Fig. 17.6** *Output Waveforms of DAC as Inputs are Provided by a Binary Counter.*

**17.17 A 10-bit DAC has a step size of 10 mV. Determine the full-scale output voltage and the percentage resolution.**

*Solution:*

$$\%\ \text{resolution} = \frac{\text{step size}}{\text{Full Scale (FS)}} \times 100$$

with 10 bits there will be $2^{10} - 1 = 1023$ steps of 10 mV each. The full scale output will be 10 mV $\times$ 1023 = 10.23 V and

$$\%\ \text{resolution} = \frac{10\ mV}{1023} \times 100\% \approx 0.1\%$$

**17.18 Illustrate a DAC using *BCD input code*.**

*Solution:*

Many DACs use a BCD input code where *4-bit code groups are used for each decimal digit*. Figure 17.7 illustrates an 8-bit (two-digit) converter of this type.

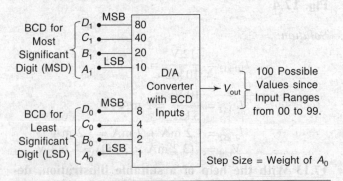

**Fig. 17.7** *DAC using BCD Input Code. This Converter Accepts a 2-digit Input and Generates 100 Possible Analog Output Values.*

Each 4-bit code group can range from 0000 to 1001, and so *the BCD inputs represent decimal numbers from 00 to 99*. Within each code group the *weights* of the different bits are in the normal binary proportions (1, 2,

4, 8), but the *relative weights* of each code group are different by a factor of 10. Figure 17.7 shows the relative weights of the various bits. Note that the bits that make up the *BCD* code for the *most significant digit* (MSD) have a relative weight, that is *10 times* that of the corresponding bits of the *least significant digit* (LSD).

**17.19 If the *weight* of $A_0$ is 0.1 V in Fig. 17.7 find the following values:**
  **(a) Step size,**
  **(b) full-scale output and percentage resolution**
  **(c) $V_{out}$ for $D_1C_1B_1A_1 = 0101$ and $D_0C_0B_0A_0 = 1000$.**

*Solution:*
  (a) Step size is the weight of the LSB of the LSD, 0.1 V.
  (b) There are 99 steps since there are two *BCD* digits. Thus, *full scale output* is $99 \times 0.1 = 9.9$ V. The *percentage resolution* is

$$\frac{\text{Step size}}{\text{F.S.}} \times 100\% = \frac{0.1}{9.9} \times 100\% \approx 1\%$$

We could also have used Eq. 17.2 to calculate percentage resolution.

  (c) The *exact weights* in volts are listed below.

| MSD | | | | LSD | | | |
|---|---|---|---|---|---|---|---|
| $D_1$ | $C_1$ | $B_1$ | $A_1$ | $D_0$ | $C_0$ | $B_0$ | $A_0$ |
| 8.0 | 4.0 | 2.0 | 1.0 | 0.8 | 0.4 | 0.2 | 0.1 |

One way to find out $V_{out}$ for a given input is to *add the weights of all bits that are* 1s. Thus, for an input of 0101 1000, we have

$$V_{out} = \overbrace{4\ \text{V}}^{C_1} + \overbrace{1\ \text{V}}^{A_1} + \overbrace{0.8\text{V}}^{D_0} = 5.8\ \text{V}$$

An easier way is to realize that the *BCD input code* represents $58_{10}$ and the step size is 0.1, so that

$$V_{out} = (0.1\ \text{V}) \times 58 = 5.8\ \text{V}$$

**17.20 A certain 12- bit *BCD* digital-to-analog converter has a *full- scale output* of 9.99 V. Determine the**
  **(a) percent resolution,**
  **(b) converter's step size.**

*Solution:*
  (a) Twelve bits correspond to three decimal digits; that is, decimal numbers from 000 to 999. Therefore, the output of this DAC has 999 *possible steps* from 0 V to 9.99 V. Thus, we have

$$\% \text{ resolution} = \frac{1}{999} \times 100\% \approx 0.1\%$$

  (b) Step size $= \dfrac{9.99\ \text{V}}{999}$

$$= 0.01\ \text{V}$$

**17.21 Explain *bipolar DACs*.**

*Solution:*
Some DACs are designed to produce both *positive and negative* values, such as –10 to +10 V. This is generally done by using the binary input as a *signed number* with the MSB as the sign bit (*0 for +* and *1 for –*). Negative input values are often represented in 2's-complement form, although the true magnitude form is also used by some DACs. For example, suppose that we have a 6-bit bipolar DAC that uses the *2's-complement* system and has a resolution of 0.2 V. The binary input values range from 100000 (–32) to 011111 (+31) to produce analog outputs in the range from –6.4 to +6.2 V. There are 63 steps ($2^6 – 1$) of 0.2 V between these positive and negative limits.

## R/2R DACs

The use of binary-weighted resistors to produce the proper weighting of each bit has some practical limitations. The biggest problem is the large difference in resistor values between the LSB and the MSB. With the current IC fabrication technology, it is very difficult to produce resistance values over a wide resistance range that maintains an accurate ratio especially with variations in temperature. For this reason it is preferable to have a circuit that uses resistances that are fairly close in value. One of the most widely used DAC circuits that satisfies this requirement is the R/2R ladder network, where the resistance values span a range of only 2 to 1.

**17.22 Explain in detail the operation of *R/2R* digital-to-analog converter.**

*Solution:*
The method for D/A conversion that is most often used in integrated circuit D/A converters is known as the *R/2R ladder circuit*. In this circuit, *only* two resistor values are required, which lends itself nicely to the fabrication of ICs with a *resolution* of 8, 10, or 12 bits, and even higher.

Figure 17.8 illustrat a 4-bit D/A R/2R converter. To form converters with higher resolution, all that needs to be done is to *add* more R/2R resistors and switches to the left of $D_3$. Commercially available DACs with resolutions of 8, 10, and 12 bits are commonly made this way.

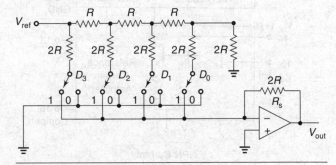

**Fig. 17.8** *The R/2R Ladder D/A Converter.*

In Fig. 17.8 the 4-bit digital information to be converted to analog is entered on the $D_0$ to $D_3$ switches. In an actual *IC switch*, each current path is controlled by a semiconductor switch such as the *CMOS transmission gate*. The arrangement of the circuit is such that *as the switches are moved to the position, they cause a current to flow through the summing resistor, $R_S$, that is proportional to their binary equivalent value. Each successive switch position is worth double the previous one.*

The circuit which is designed in the shape of a *ladder* is an ingenious way to form a *binary-weighted current-division circuit*. Keep in mind:

1. The (−) input to op-amp is *virtual ground*, and any current that reaches this point will continue to flow-past it, up through the summing resistor, $R_S$.
2. The resistance of and the current through each rung of the ladder is *unaffected* by the position of any of the data switches, $D_3$ to $D_0$.
3. With the data switch in the 0 *position*, the bottom of the corresponding resistor is connected to *ground*.
4. With the data switch in the 1 position, the bottom of the corresponding resistor is connected to *virtual* ground, which acts the same as ground.

## 17.23 Describe the *DAC-0808 family*.

*Solution:*
The National Semiconductor DAC-0807, and DAC-0806 are members of a very popular family of *8-bit monolithic DACs*. All three of these devices share the same operating principles, packaging, and pin designations. The pin configuration of DAC-0808/7/6 is shown in Fig. 17.9.

The major parameter that differentiates the three versions of this device is *accuracy*. The *DAC-0808* has a full 8-bit accuracy, ±1/2 LSB, while the DAC 0807 effectively has 7-bit accuracy. Thus, in terms of absolute

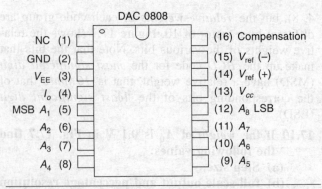

**Fig. 17.9**   *Pin Configuration of the DAC-0808.*

error, the output of the DAC-0807 may vary ± 3/4 LSB from the expected output level. Finally, the DAC-0806 has 6-bit accuracy therefore, its output may vary ±1 LSB from the expected level. For convenience, the DAC-0808/7/6 is referred to as a DAC-0808. Typically, the DAC-0808 has a setting time of 150 ns. The inputs are TTL and CMOS compatible, and it can operate with power-supply voltages that range from ± 4.5 to ± 18 V.

## 17.24 Give the block diagram, pin configuration, and typical application of the MC1408 D/A converter.

*Solution:*
*One very popular and inexpensive 8-bit DAC is the DAC 0808 and its equivalent, the MC1408.* A block diagram and pin configuration of the IC are given in Fig. 17.10(a) and (b). A typical application of the IC is given in Fig. 17.10(c).

The circuit in Fig. 17.10(c) is set up to *accept an 8-bit digital input and provide a 0 to +10 V analog output*. A reference current ($I_{ref}$) is required for the D/A and is provided by the 10 V, 5 kΩ combination shown. The negative reference (pin 15) is then tied to ground via an equal size (5 kΩ) resistor.

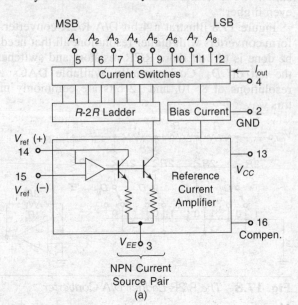

(a)

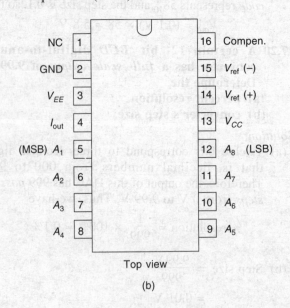

Top view

(b)

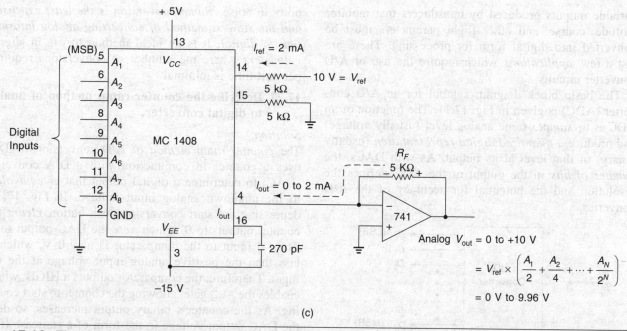

**Fig. 17.10** *The MC 1408A D/A Converter, (a) Block Diagram, (b) Pin Configuration, (c) A Typical Application of the DAC IC-MC1408.*

The 2 mA reference current dictates the *full-scale output current* ($I_{out}$) to also be approximately 2 mA. To calculate the *actual output current* use the formula:

$$I_{out} = I_{ref} \times \left(\frac{A_1}{2} + \frac{A_2}{4} + \cdots + \frac{A_8}{256}\right) \qquad (17.5)$$

[For example, with all inputs ($A_1$ to $A_8$) HIGH, $I_{out} = I_{ref} \times (0.996)$]. To convert an output current to an output voltage, a *series resistor* could be connected from pin 4 to ground, and the output taken across the resistor. This method is simple, but it may cause *inaccuracies* as various size loads are connected to it.

A more accurate method uses an op-amp such as the 741 shown in Fig. 17.10(c). The output current flows through $R_F$, which develops an output voltage equal to $I_{out} \times R_F$. *The range of output voltage can be changed by changing $R_F$ and is limited only by the specifications of the op-amp used.*

**17.25 Determine $I_{out}$ and $V_{out}$ in Fig. 17.10(c) if the following *binary strings* are input at $A_1$ to $A_8$: (a) 1111 1111, (b) 1001 1011.**

*Solution:*

(a)  $I_{out} = I_{ref} \times \left(\frac{A_1}{2} + \frac{A_2}{4} + \cdots + \frac{A_8}{256}\right)$

$= 2\,\text{mA}\left(\frac{1}{2} + \frac{1}{4} + \frac{1}{8} + \frac{1}{16} + \frac{1}{32} + \frac{1}{64} + \frac{1}{128} + \frac{1}{256}\right)$

$= 2\,\text{mA} \times \dfrac{255}{256} = 1.99\,\text{mA}$

and  $V_{out} = I_{out} \times R_F$

$= 1.99\,\text{mA} \times 5\,\text{k}\Omega$

$= 9.96\,\text{V}$

(b)  $I_{out} = 2\,\text{mA} \times \left(\frac{1}{2} + \frac{1}{16} + \frac{1}{32} + \frac{1}{128} + \frac{1}{256}\right)$

$= 2\,\text{mA} \times \dfrac{155}{256} = 1.21\,\text{mA}$

and  $V_{out} = I_{out} \times R_F$

$= 1.21\,\text{mA} \times 5\,\text{k}\Omega$

$= 6.05\,\text{V}$

## A/D CONVERSION (ADCs)

ADCs are used for the *conversion of analog signals into digital signals*. All digital systems have ADCs as part of their structure. There are several types of ADCs available in the form of *IC chip* in the market.

**17. 26 Describe *analog-to digital* (A/D) conversion. What are its *applications*?**

*Solution:*

Computers and other digital systems are used extensively for the analysis and processing of signals that are actually *continuously variable*. A *digital voltmeter* is an example of a device that processes an analog voltage and produces a numerical representation of that voltage on its display. Sophisticated *image processing systems* convert the continuous shading and colors of images into a digital form that is then processed by a computer, in order to enhance the image. For the computerized *flight control systems* of a jet fighter, the continuously variable outputs produced by transducers that monitor altitude, course, and other flight parameters must be converted into digital form for processing. These are just a few *applications* which require the use of A/D converter circuits.

The basic block diagram symbol for an A/D converter (ADC) is given in Fig. 17.11. The function of an ADC is to *sample* some analog level (usually voltage) and produce a *quantized digital representation* (usually binary) of that level at its output. As with DACs, the *number of bits* in the output of the ADC defines the resolution and the potential for accuracy of the A/D converter.

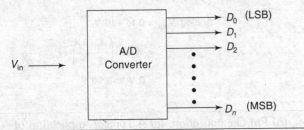

**Fig. 17.11**   *Symbols for an n-bit A/D Converter.*

## COUNTER-RAMP ADC

Much of the information provided by a digital system exists first in *analog form*, requiring *conversion* to digital. There are many methods by which this must be done, with varying conversion rates, cost, and suscepti-

bility to noise. *Ramp conversion is the least expensive and the slowest method of converting analog information to digital.* It is an ideal method to use in *digital voltmeters* where the number of conversions required per unit time is minimal.

### 17.27  Describe the counter-ramp method of analog to digital converter.

*Solution:*
The *counter-ramp method* of A/D conversions (ADC) uses a counter in conjunction with a D/A converter (DAC) to determine a digital output that is *equivalent* to the unknown analog input voltage. In Fig. 17.12, depressing the start conversion push button *clears* the counter outputs to 0, which *sets* the DAC output to 0. The (–) input to the comparator is now 0 V, which is less than the positive analog input voltage at the (+) input. Therefore, the comparator outputs a HIGH, which enables the AND gate, allowing the counter to start counting. As the counter's binary output increases, so does the DAC output voltage in the form of a staircase (this ADC is also known as the *staircase ADC*).

When the staircase voltage *reaches and then exceeds* the analog input voltage, the comparator output goes LOW, *disabling* the clock and stopping the counter. The counter output at that point is equal to the binary number that caused the DAC to output a voltage slightly greater than the analog input voltage. *Thus, we have the binary equivalent of the analog voltage.*

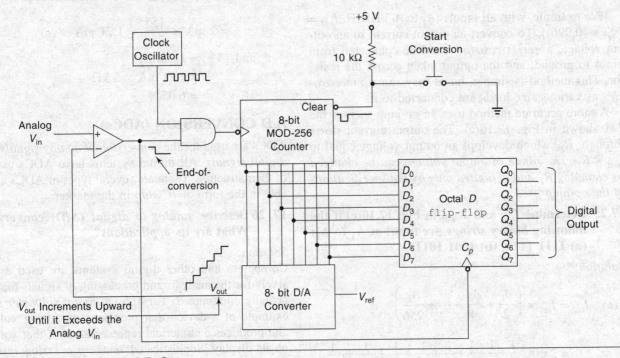

**Fig. 17.12**   *Counter-ramp A/D Converter.*

The *HIGH-to-LOW transition* of the comparator is also used to trigger the *D* flip-flop to *latch on* to the binary number at that instant. To perform another conversion, the start push button is depressed again and the process repeats. The result from the *previous* conversion remains in the *D* flip-flop until the next *end-of-conversion* HIGH-to-LOW edge comes along.

To change the circuit to perform *continuous conversions* the end-of-conversion line could be tied back to the clear input of the counter. *A short delay* needs to be inserted into this new line, however, to allow the *D* flip-flop to read the binary number before the counter is reset. Two inverters placed end to end in the line will produce a sufficient delay.

**17.28 Discuss the *advantages* and *disadvantages* of counter-ramp conversion.**

*Solution:*
*Advantages*
1. The principle is *simple and straight forward*.
2. It is *very easy to construct* this ADC.
3. This basic principle is *employed in many advanced ADCs*.
*Disadvantages*
1. *Only increasing voltages* can be measured.
2. The system is *very slow*.
3. This may be *mainly used to read dc voltages*.
4. Practically, the system *comes to rest only when $V_d$ (digital voltage) > $V_a$ (analog voltage)*. This sets an error in reading as shown in Fig. 17.13.

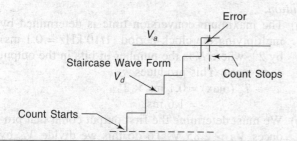

**Fig. 17.13** *Waveform of the Counter-ramp ADC.*

**17.29 Determine the minimum *conversion interval* of an ADC using an eight-stage counter with a clock frequency of 2 MHz.**

*Solution:* An eight stage counter has $2^8$-*count levels*. At a clock rate of 2 MHz, the *count period*:

$$T = \frac{1}{f} = \frac{1}{2 \times 10^6} = 0.5 \text{ μs}.$$

Maximum count interval = $T \times N = 256 \times 0.5$ μs = 128 μs. This is the time period taken for one conversion.

**17.30 Find the *resolution* of a 12-stage ADC.**

*Solution:*

$$\text{Percent resolution} = \frac{1}{2^{12}} \times 100 = 0.0244\%$$

**17.31 Determine the *resolution* of the 12-stage ADC if $V_{FS} = 10.24$ V.**
*Solution:*

$$\text{Voltage resolution} = \frac{10.24}{2^{12}-1} = 2.5 \text{ mV}.$$

**17.32 What is the conversion time of a staircase ADC?**
*Solution:*
Maximum conversion time of staircase ADC = $2^N/f$ where $N$ is the number of stages or bits and $f$ is the clock frequency. If the *average conversion time* is preferred, the definition changes to:
Average conversion time

$$= \frac{1}{2} \text{ (maximum conversion time)} = \frac{2^N-1}{f}$$

## SUCCESSIVE APPROXIMATION TECHNIQUE

The counter ramp technique has one major drawback. If the maximum possible positive voltage were to be converted in a 6-bit converter, the *conversion process* would require $2^6 = 64$ steps to complete—one for each possible count of the binary counter. *Thus, the counter ramp is extremely slow.* A method that greatly reduces the conversion time is the successive approximation technique. *This method successively approximates the input voltage by factors of two, to very rapidly converge to the correct answers* Instead of 64 steps, the successive approximation techniques requires only six steps to perform the same 6-bit conversion.

**17.33 Explain the working of a *successive approximation* ADC (SA-ADC).**
*Solution:*
The block schematic of the SA-ADC is given in Fig. 17.14. Some portion of the SA-ADC is similar to the counter-ramp ADC. This includes the comparator, the DAC and the binary display. The main part of the SA-ADC is the *successive approximation register* (SAR). This is a complex circuitry and performs several operations at the same time.

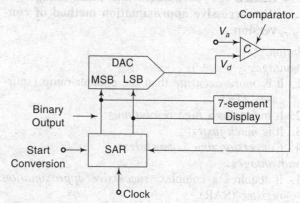

**Fig. 17.14** *Successive Approximation ADC.*

The analog data to be converted is applied to the comparator $C$. The fed back voltage $V_d$ is compared with the analog voltage $V_a$ and the output of the comparator is applied to SAR. *Initially, $V_d$ is set at half of the full-scale voltage.* If the full-scale voltage, for example is 15 V, $V_d$ will be 7.5 V to start with. The comparator then searches for whether $V_a$ is more (or, less) than $V_d$. If $V_a > V_d$, the SAR registers a 1 as its MSB. If $V_a < V_d$, the SAR registers a 0 as its MSB. The SAR then puts a 1 in the *next lower-significant bit* position automatically by itself, and the DAC converts this to an analog-equivalent voltage $V_d$, corresponding to the new value of the binary in the counter. If the input is still greater, a 1 is registered in the next lower significant bit; otherwise a 0 is registered. *This process is continued till the input is fully converted to binary.*

As an illustration, assume $V_{FS} = 15$ V. Let a voltage of 10 V be applied to the input of $C$ (i.e. $V_a = 10$ V). Initially, the SAR MSB = 1, all the lower significant bits being 0's. If we assume a 4-bit converter, the reading of the *SAR* would then be 1000. This corresponds to *decimal 8*, and $V_d = 8$ V now. As $V_a$ (10 V) $> V_d$ (8 V), the MSB retains its 1, and the next significant bit is made 1 by the SAR. The SAR now reads 1100, which corresponds to $V_d = 12$ V. Since $V_d$, now, is greater than $V_a$, the second-significant bit is made 0 by the SAR, instead of a 1. The binary counter now becomes 1000 again. But the SAR, on the third clock pulse, registers a 1 for the third bit, and the display reads 1010, which corresponds to *decimal 10* V. As the voltages $V_a$ and $V_d$ are now *equal*, the conversion stops. The method of *narrowing in* on the unknown analog input voltage is much improved. The conversion is fast. The *conversion time* of the successive approximation ADC is given by

$$N \times \frac{1}{f}$$

where

$N$ = number of bits, and

$f$ = clock frequency.

**17.34  Discuss the *advantages and disadvantages* of the successive approximation method of conversion.**

*Solution:*
*Advantages*
  1. It is *more accurate* than the counter-ramp (staircase) ADC.
  2. It maintains a *high resolution.*
  3. It is *much faster.*
  4. *Conversion time is much less.*
*Disadvantages*
  1. It requires a complex *successive approximation register* (SAR).
  2. It is *costly*, as it contains more components.

**17.35  Determine the conversion time of an SA-ADC for 12-bit resolution, at 2.5 MHz.**

*Solution:*

$$\text{Conversion time} = \frac{N}{f} = \frac{12}{2.5 \times 10^6}$$

$$= 4.8 \ \mu s.$$

**17.36  The DAC in Fig. 17.15 has $V_{FS} = 10.00$ V, the clock PRF = 10 kHz and the LOW-to-HIGH transition of the START input is synchronized with the rising edge of the clock. Determine:**
  **(a)** *the maximum conversion time.*
  **(b)** **the** *output count* **and** *conversion time* **for** $V_{in} = 2.85$ V.

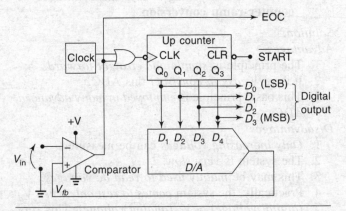

**Fig. 17.15**

*Solution:*
  (a) The maximum conversion time is determined by multiplying the clock period (1/10 kHz = 0.1 ms) by $2^N$, where $N$ is the number of bits in the output code word. This produces
  $$T_c \ (\text{max}) = 0.1 \ \text{ms} \times 2^4$$
  $$= 1.6 \ \text{ms}.$$
  (b) We must determine the first output count that produces $V_{fb} > 2.85$ V. To do this we divide $V_{in}$ by the value of 1 LSB and round up to the next higher integer. This produces the decimal equivalent of the binary output. Here, we obtain
  $$\frac{2.85 \ \text{V}}{0.625 \ \text{V}} = 4.56$$
  Output count = $5_{10} = 0101_2$

## LINEAR RAMP (SINGLE-SLOPE) ADC

Probably the most important single reason for investigating other methods of conversion is to *determine ways to reduce the conversion time.* If a very short conversion time is not a requirement, there are other methods of A/D conversion that are simpler to implement and much more economical. Basically, these techniques involve *comparison* of the unknown input voltage with a reference voltage that begins at zero and increases *linearly* with time. The time required for the reference voltage to increase to the value of the unknown voltage is directly proportional to the magnitude of the unknown voltage, and this time period is measured with a digital counter. This is referred to as a *single-ramp* method since the reference voltage is sloped like a ramp.

### 17.37 Describe linear-ramp (*single-slope*) ADC.

*Solution:*

If a *very short conversion time* is not a requirement, there are other methods of A/D conversion that are simpler to implement and much more economical. Basically, these techniques involve *comparison* of the unknown input voltage with a reference voltage that begins at zero and increases *linearly* with time. The time required for the reference voltage to increase to the value of the unknown voltage is *directly proportional* to the magnitude of the unknown voltage and this *time period* is measured with a digital counter. This is referred to as a *single-ramp method*, since the reference voltage is *sloped* like a ramp. A variation on this method involves using an op-amp integrating circuit in a *dual-ramp configuration*. The dual-ramp (dual slope) method is very popular, and widely used in digital voltmeters and digital panel meters. It *offers good accuracy good linearity and very good noise rejection characteristics*.

Figure 17.16(a) shows a relatively simple ADC that uses a *ramp generator* as comparison-signal. The analog data $V_a$ is compared with a linear ramp-voltage $V_r$ in a comparator $C$. The output of $C$, when $V_a > V_r$ is used to stop the count of the digital binary counter as shown in Fig. 17.16(b). At the command of the *start* pulse, both the linear ramp generator and the binary counter start operation. The binary counter goes on counting the clock pulses from a clock generator, till the *stop* command from the comparator stops the count.

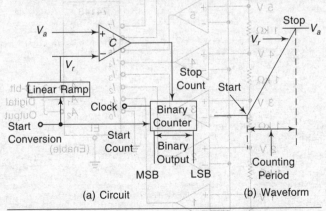

**(a) Circuit**

**(b) Waveform**

**Fig. 17.16** *Linear-ramp (single-slope) ADC.*

### 17.38 Discuss the *advantages* and *disadvantages* of single-slope ADC.

*Solution:*
*Advantages*
1. Very *simple* circuitry.
2. Quite *fast*, as no conversion from digital to analog is required.
3. Lower cost (*economical*).

*Disadvantages*
1. *Precise adjustments* of ramp (slope) signal and clock frequency required.
2. *Poor conversion efficiency*.
3. *Poor resolution*.

## DUAL-SLOPE ADC

A variation of single slope method *involves using an operational amplifier integrating circuit in a dual slope configuration*. The dual-ramp method is very popular, and widely used in digital voltmeters and digital panel meters. *It offers good accuracy, good linearity, and very good noise-rejection characteristics*.

### 17.39 Discuss linear ramp (*dual slope*) ADC.

*Solution:*
The *dual-slope ADC* overcomes the problems of the single-slope ADC. Figure 17.17 shows the schematic representation of the dual-slope ADC and Fig. 16.22 shows the *charging and discharging intervals* of the ADC.

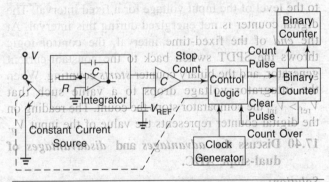

**Fig. 17.17** *Schematic Representation of the Dual-slope ADC.*

We charge a capacitor $C$ for a *fixed duration* (Fig. 17.18). This means that the integrator capacitor will charge to a voltage level depending on the value of the input analog voltage. After the *charging interval* is over, the integrator capacitor is allowed to discharge at a uniform rate through a constant current circuit. Depending on the level to which the capacitor had been initially charged, the *discharge time* varies as shown in Fig. 17.18, and hence the binary counter's counting time

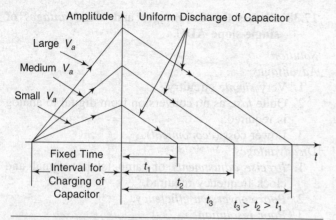

**Fig. 17.18**   *Charge-discharge Intervals of Capacitor.*

varies. This then reads the input voltage in terms of the *count duration*. The larger this duration, the more the count.

In Fig. 17.17, there is a toggle switch that connects the input data and the constant-current generator to the integrator, *alternately*. This toggle switch is controlled by a *control-logic* circuit. The output of the integrator is applied to a comparator, which gives a *stop command* once its output exceeds the reference voltage $V_{ref}$. The control logic controls the clock, *start count* and *clear count* pulses of the binary counter, as well as the single-pole double-throw (SPDT) toggle switch.

At the *start command* the integrator starts charging to the level of the input voltage for a fixed interval. The digital counter is not energized during this interval. At the *end* of the fixed-time interval, the control logic throws the SPDT switch back to the constant-current generator, and the binary counter *starts* counting. When the integrator voltage drops to a value such that $V_{ref} > V_{int}$ the comparator stops the count. The reading on the digital counter represents the value of the input $V_a$.

**17.40 Discuss the *advantages* and *disadvantages* of dual-slope ADC.**

*Solution:*

*Advantages*

1. *Clock frequency drift* is compensated for, as the same clock and integrator are used to perform conversions during the positive and negative intervals of the count period.
2. The above reason also *increases accuracy*.
3. Setting the clock rate and reference-input value can give *desired scaling* of the counter output.
4. The counter can be designed to be in binary, *BCD*, or any other *desired display form*.
5. *Low conversion time*.

*Disadvantages*

1. *Complicated circuitry*.
2. *Higher cost*.

## FLASH ADCs

*The flash converter is the highest-speed ADC available, but it requires much more circuitry than the other types.* For example, a 6-bit flash ADC requires 63 analog comparators, while an 8-bit unit requires 255 comparators. The large number of comparators has limited the size of flash converters. IC flash converters are commonly available in 2-8-bit units and most manufacturers offer 9 and 10-bit units as well.

**17.41 Explain the operation of a *parallel-encoded* ADC.**

*Solution:*

The parallel-encoded flash converter is *the highest-speed ADC available, but it requires much more circuitry than the other types.* For example, a 6-bit flash ADC requires 63 analog comparators, while an 8-bit unit requires 255 comparators and a 10-bit comparator requires 1023 comparators. The large number of comparators has limited the size of flash converters. IC flash converters are currently available in 2-8 bit units, and most manufacturers predict that 9- and 10-bit units will hit the market soon.

In this method, Fig. 17.19, several comparators are set up, each at a *different* voltage reference level with their outputs driving a *priority encoder*. The voltage-divider network in Fig. 17.19 is designed to drop 1 V across each resistor. This sets up a *voltage reference* at each comparator input in 1 V steps.

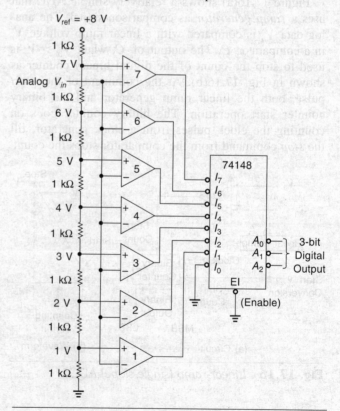

**Fig. 17.19**   *Parallel-encoded (Flash) 3-bit ADC.*

When $V_{in} = 0$ V, the + input on all seven comparators will be higher than the – input, so they will all output a HIGH. In this case $\bar{I}_0$ is the only active-LOW input that is *enabled*, so the 74148 will output an active-LOW binary 0(111). When $V_{in}$ exceeds 1.0 V comparator 1 will output a LOW. Now $\bar{I}_0$ and $\bar{I}_1$ are *both enabled*, but because it is a *priority encoder*, the output will be a binary 1 (110). As $V_{in}$ increases further, each successive comparator outputs a LOW. *The highest input that receives a LOW is encoded into its binary equivalent output.*

The A/D converter in Fig. 17.19 is set up to convert analog voltages in the range from 0 to 7 V. *The range* can be scaled higher or lower, depending on the input voltage levels that are expected. The *resolution* of this converter is only 3 bits, so it can only differentiate between eight different analog input levels. To expand to 4-bit resolution, eight more comparators are required to differentiate the 16 different voltage levels. *Circuit complexity becomes a real problem when using parallel encoding for high resolution conversion.* However, a big advantage of parallel encoding is its high speed. The *conversion speed* is limited only by the propagation delay of the comparators and encoder (less than 20 ns total).

### 17.42 Discuss the *advantages* and *disadvantages* of flash converter.

*Solution:*
*Advantages*
1. *The fastest conversion process* (governed only by the propagation delay of the gates)
2. *Highest accuracy.*
3. *Highest possible resolution* by increasing the number of comparators.

*Disadvantages*
1. Very *complicated circuit.*
2. *Cost* is directly proportional to the number of comparators used.
3. Number of comparators depends on the *resolution* required.

### 17.43 Explain *multiplexing technique* so that one ADC may be time-shared.

*Solution:*
When analog inputs from several sources are to be converted, a *multiplexing technique* can be used so that one ADC may be *time-shared*. The basic scheme is illustrated in Fig. 17.20 for a *four-channel acquisition system*.

*Rotary switch S* is used to switch each analog signal to the input of the ADC, one at a time in sequence. The *control circuitry* controls the switch position according to the *select address bits*, $A_1$, $A_0$, from the mod-4 counter. For example, with $A_1 A_0 = 00$, the switch connects $V_{A0}$ to the *ADC* input; $A_1 A_0 = 01$ connects

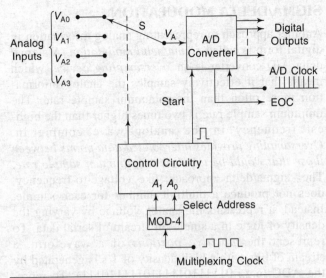

**Fig. 17.20** *Conversion of Four Analog Inputs by Multiplexing.*

$V_{A1}$ to the *ADC* input, and so on. Each input channel has a specific *address code* which when present, connects that channel to the ADC. The operation proceeds as follows:

1. With select address = *00*, $V_{A0}$ is *connected* to the *ADC* input.
2. The control circuits *generates* a START pulse to *initiate* the conversion of $V_{A0}$ to its digital equivalent.
3. When the conversion is complete, (end of conversion) (EOC) *signals* that the ADC output data are ready. Typically, these data will be transferred to a computer over a *data bus.*
4. The multiplexing clock *increments* the select address to *01* which connects $V_{A1}$ to the ADC.
5. Steps 2 and 3 are *repeated* with the digital equivalent $V_{A1}$ now present at the ADC outputs.
6. The multiplexing clock *increments* the select address to *10* and $V_{A2}$ is connected to the ADC.
7. Steps 2 and 3 are *repeated* with the digital equivalent of $V_{A2}$ now present at the ADC outputs.
8. The multiplexing clock *increments* the select address to *11*, and $V_{A3}$ is connected to the ADC.
9. Steps 2 and 3 are *repeated* with the digital equivalent of $V_{A3}$ now present on the ADC outputs.

The multiplexing clock controls the *rate* at which the analog signals are sequentially switched into the ADC. The maximum rate is determined by the *delay time* of the switches and the *conversion time* of the ADC. The switch delay time can be minimized by using semiconductor switches as the *CMOS bilateral switch*. It may be necessary to connect a *sample-and-hold* circuit at the input of the *ADC* if the analog inputs will change significantly during the *ADC* conversion time.

# SIGMA/DELTA MODULATION

Another approach to representing analog information in digital form is called *sigma/delta modulation*. A sigma/delta A/D converter is an *oversampling device*, which means that it effectively samples the analog information more often than the minimum sample rate. The minimum sample rate is two times higher than the highest frequency in the analog wave coming in. *Oversampling provides interpolated data points between those that would be taken at the minimum sample rate.* The sigma/delta approach, like voltage-to-frequency, does not produce a multibit number for each sample. Instead, it represents the analog voltage by varying the density of logic in a single-bit stream of serial data. To represent the *positive portions* of a waveform, a stream of bits with a high density of 1's is generated by the ADC (e.g., 01111101111110111110111). To repre-

sent the *negative portions,* a lower density of 1's (i.e., a higher density of 0's) is generated (e.g., 000100010000010000010).

# INTERFACING LOGIC FAMILIES

Often the need arises to interface (connect) between the various TTL and CMOS families. You have to make sure that a HIGH out of a TTL gate looks like a HIGH to the input of a CMOS gate and vice versa. The same holds true for the LOW logic levels. You have also to make sure that the driving gate can sink or source enough current to meet the input current requirements of the gate being driven.

**17.44  What problems arise when interfacing standard 7400 series TTL to a 4000 B series CMOS?**

*Solution:*

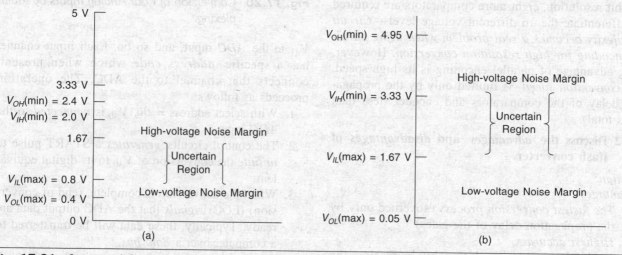

**Fig. 17.21**  *Input and Output Voltage Specifications: (a) 7400 Series TTL (b) 4000B series CMOS (5 V; Supply).*

*There is no problem for the LOW-level output,* because the TTL guarantees a maximum LOW-level output of 0.4 V and the CMOS will accept any voltage up to 1.67 V $\left(\frac{1}{3}V_{CC}\right)$ as a LOW-level input. But for the HIGH level, the TTL may output as little as 2.4 V as a HIGH. The CMOS expects at least 3.33 V as a HIGH-level input. Therefore, 2.4 V is unacceptable, because it falls within the *uncertain region.* However, a pull-up resistor can be connected between the CMOS input to $V_{CC}$, as shown in Fig. 17.22 to solve the HIGH-level input problem.

The 10 kΩ resistor is used to *raise* the output of the TTL gate closer to 5 V when it is in a HIGH output state. With $V_{out1}$, HIGH, the voltage at $V_{in2}$ will be *almost* 5 V because current in the 4069B is so LOW (≈1 μA) that the voltage drop across the 10 kΩ is *insignificant,* leaving almost 5.0 V at $V_{in2}$ ($V_{in2}$ = 5 V – 1 μA × 10 kΩ = 4.99 V).

The other thing to look at when interfacing is *the current levels of all gates that are involved.* The 7404

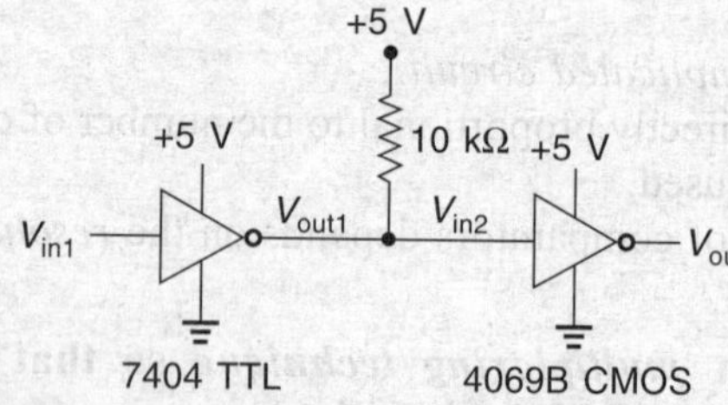

**Fig. 17.22**  *Using a pull up Resistor to Interface TTL to CMOS.*

can *sink* ($I_{OL}$) 16 mA, which is easy enough for the $I_{IL}$ of the 4069B (1 μA) plus the current from the 10 kΩ resistor (5 V/10 kΩ = 0.5 mA). $I_{OH}$ of the 7404 (– 400 μA) is no problem either, *because with pull-up resistor the 7404 will not have to source current.*

**17.45  What problems arise when driving TTL from CMOS?**

*Solution:*
When driving TTL from CMOS, the *voltage levels* are no problem because the CMOS will output about 4.95 V

for a HIGH and 0.05 V for a LOW which is easily interpreted by the TTL gate.

*The current levels* can be a real concern because 4000B CMOS has severe output current limitations (The 74 C and 74HC series have much better output current capabilities, however). Figure 17.23 shows the input/output currents that flow when interfacing CMOS to TTL.

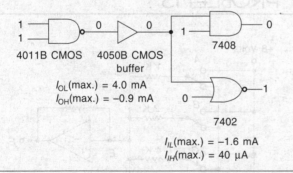

**Fig. 17.23** *Current when Interfacing CMOS to TTL.*

For the HIGH output condition (Fig. 17.23a), the 4069B CMOS can source a maximum current of 0.51 mA which is *enough* to supply the HIGH-level input current ($I_{IH}$) to one 7404 inverter. But for the LOW output condition the 4069B can also sink only 0.51 mA, which is *not enough* for the 7404 LOW-level input current ($I_{IL}$).

Most of the 4000B series has the same problem of *low-output drive current capability*. To alleviate this problem, two special gates, the *4050 buffer* and the *4049 inverting buffer*, are specifically designed to provide high output current to solve many interfacing problems. They have drive capabilities of $I_{OL}$= 4.0 mA and $I_{OH}$ = –0.9 mA which is enough to drive two 74XX TTL loads, as shown in Fig. 17.24.

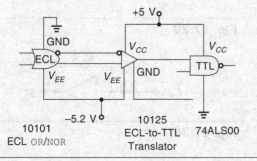

**Fig. 17.24** *Using the 4050B Buffer to Supply Sink and Source Currents to Two Standard TTL Loads.*

## 17.46 What problem arises when interfacing families that have different supply voltages?

*Solution:*
The 4000B series can use anywhere from +3 to 15 V for a supply, and the ECL series uses –5.2 V for a supply, for example. *The problem of interfacing logic families that have different power supplies is solved by using level-shifter ICs.* Figure. 17.25 shows the connections for interfacing 15 V CMOS to 5 V TTL.

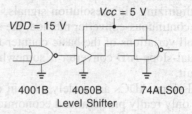

**Fig. 17.25** *Using a Level Shifter to Convert 0 V/15 V Logic to 0 V/5 V Logic.*

The 4050B *level shifting buffer* is powered from a 5 V supply and can actually accept 0 V/15 V logic levels at the input, and at the output correspondinglogic levels are 0 V/5 V. For an inverter function, use the 4049B instead of the 4050B.

The reverse conversion, 5 V TTL to 15 V CMOS, is accomplished with 4504B CMOS level shifter, as shown in Fig. 17.26. The 4504B *level-shifting buffer* requires two power supply inputs: the 5 V $V_{CC}$ supply to enable it to recognize the 0 V/5 V *input levels* and the 15 V supply to enable it to provide 0.V/15 V *output levels*.

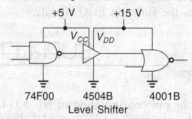

**Fig. 17.26** *Level Shifting 0 V/5 V TTL Logic to 0 V/15 V CMOS Logic.*

## 17.47 How will you interface ECL to TTL and vice versa?

*Solution:*
Interfacing 0 V/5 V logic levels to –5.2 V/0 V ECL requires another set of level shifters (or *translators*): the ECL 10125 and the ECL 10124, whose connections are shown in Fig. 17.27.

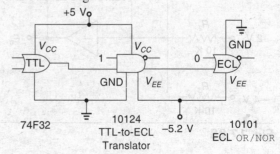

**Fig. 17.27** *Circuit Connections for Translating between TTL and ECL Levels.*

## SUMMARY

■■■■■■■

> ➤ Digital-to-analog conversion is most easily accomplished with the help of resistance networks.
> ➤ The binary ladder has definite advantages over the resistance divider.
> ➤ The complete D/A converter consists of a binary ladder (usually) and a `flip-flop` register to hold the digital input information.
> ➤ The simultaneous method for analog-to-digital conversion is very fast but becomes cumbersome for more than a few bits of resolution.
> ➤ The counter-type A/D converter is somewhat slower but represents a much more reasonable solution for digitizing high-resolution signals.
> ➤ The continuous-converter method, the successive-approximation method, and the section-counter method are all variations of the basic counter-type A/D converter which lead to a much faster conversion time.
> ➤ A dual-slope A/D converter is somewhat slower but offers excellent accuracy in a relatively inexpensive circuit.
> ➤ Dual-slope ADCs are widely used in digital voltmeters.
> ➤ The only really practical and economical way to build DACs and ADCs is to make use of commercially available MSI circuits.

■■■■■■■

## REVIEW QUESTIONS

1. Why is it difficult to build an accurate 8-bit binary-weighted D/A converter?
2. What is the fastest method of A/D conversion?
3. What is the advantage of smaller (finer) resolution?
4. What is the advantage of R/2R ladder DACs over those that use binary-weighted register?
5. Why are voltage DACs generally slower than current DACs?
6. Why must interfaces to common buses be made with three-state devices?
7. State the major advantage and disadvantage of a flash converter.
8. What is the function EOC signal?

## SUPPLEMENTARY PROBLEMS

9. Draw the pin configuration of NE 5034.
10. Give the pin configuration of ADC-0801 converter.
11. Compute the output voltage for the circuit in Fig. 17.28.
12. Assume switches $A$, $B$, $C$, $D$ of Fig. 17.29 are 0110. Compute the output voltage
13. Compute the gain of the op-amp shown in Fig. 17.29. What is its output voltage if $E_{in}$ = 3.2 V?
14. Describe the working of voltage switches.

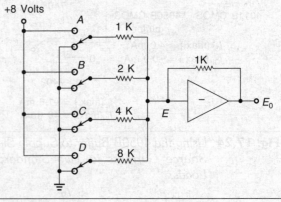

**Fig. 17.29**

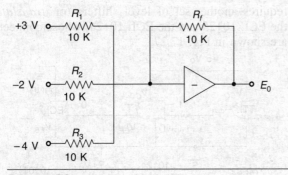

**Fig. 17.28**

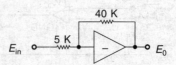

**Fig. 17.30**

# OBJECTIVE TYPE QUESTIONS

## Fill in the Blanks

15. The input impedance to an operational amplifier is assumed to be _____.
16. The voltage difference between the (+) input and (–) input is approximately _____ volts.
17. If the first three resistors in a binary-weighted D/A converter are 30, 60 and 120 K$\Omega$, the fourth resistor, used for $D_0$ input must be _____ ohms.
18. The resolution of a DAC or ADC specifies the _____.
19. One difficulty in building a high-resolution, 10-bit parallel-encoded ADC is that it would take _____ comparators to complete the design.
20. The sampling rate must be greater than _____ the highest frequency present in the signal being _____.
21. In a _____ process, voltage is resolvable into discrete binary words.
22. The summing amplifier is a _____ amplifier.
23. Some DACs are designed to produce both _____ and _____ values.
24. Ideally, the output of a DAC will be _____ when the binary input is _____.
25. Monolithic converters are relatively _____.
26. The SAR performs several _____ at the same time.
27. A single-slope ADC is quite _____.
28. A parallel-encoded ADC requires much more _____ than other types.
29. Flash conversion is the _____ conversion process.

## True/False Questions

State whether the following statements are True or False.
30. Resolution in a D/A converter is equal to the number of steps: $2^N - 1$.
31. Accuracy is defined as the nearness of a measured value to the true value.
32. A flash ADC does not contain a DAC.
33. The percentage resolution increases as the number of bits is increased.
34. The percentage resolution of a DAC depends only on the number of bits.
35. The conversion time of a SAC increases as the analog voltage increases.
36. Transducers are devices that convert physical quantities into electrical quantities.
37. Hybrid converters are generally quite cheap.
38. To build an R/2R D/A converter, you would need at least eight different resistor sizes.

## Multiple Choice Questions

39. The equivalent weight of the LSB in a 4-bit variable resistive divider DAC is.
    (a) 1/4.      (b) 1/16      (c) 1/15      (d) 1/32
40. For a 4-input resistive divider (0 = 0 V, 1 = + 10 V) the analog output voltage for a digital input of 1101 is.
    (a) $7\frac{1}{3}$ V      (b) 13 V      (c) $8\frac{2}{3}$ V      (d) 11.01 V
41. A 4-bit resistor divider DAC uses 80 K$\Omega$ resistor for MSB. The resistor value for LSB is.
    (a) 160 k$\Omega$      (b) 40 k$\Omega$      (c) 20 k$\Omega$      (d) 10 k$\Omega$
42. For a 5-bit resistive divider network, the weight assigned to MSB is
    (a) 1/31      (b) 1/32      (c) 8/31      (d) 16/32.
43. In a binary R/2R ladder DAC, the input resistance for each input is
    (a) $R$      (b) $2R$      (c) $3R$      (d) $4R$
44. The percentage resolution of a 10-bit ADC is nearly
    (a) 1%      (b) 0.01%      (c) 0.1%      (d) 10%

# ANSWERS

1. Because finding precision resistors over such a large range of values would be very difficult.
2. Flash (simultaneous)
3. It produces a greater number of possible analog outputs between zero and full scale.
4. It only uses two different sizes of resistors.
5. Because of the response time of the op-amp current-to-voltage converter.
6. So that all devices except those communicating at any given time can be disconnected from the bus.
7. Major advantage is conversion speed; major disadvantage is the number of required circuit components for practical realisation.
8. Tells us when conversion is complete and digital equivalent of $V_A$ is at register output.
9.                                                   10.

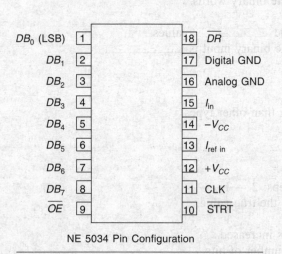

NE 5034 Pin Configuration

**Fig. 17.31**

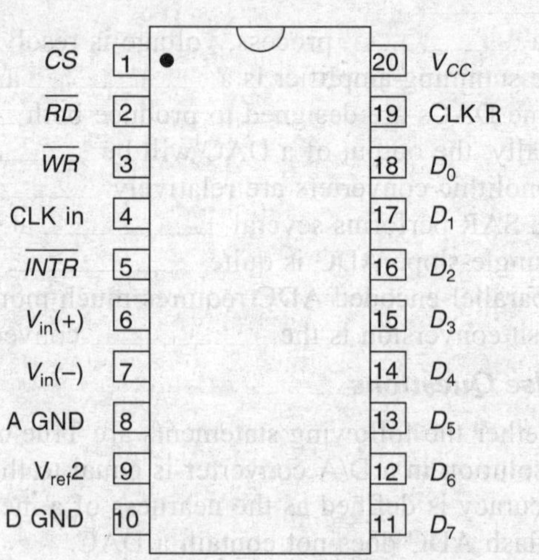

ADC-0801 Pin Configuration

**Fig. 17.32**

11. 3.00 V           12. 6.00 V           13. $A_v = \dfrac{40k}{5k}$,   $E_0 = 25.6$ V

14. The simplest scheme for a voltage switch is an integrated circuit containing a field effect transistor. This is shown in Fig. 17.33.

    With a HIGH logic level on the input, $Q_1$ will cut-off and $Q_2$ turn on, grounding the output. With a LOW level on the input, $Q_2$ will cut-off and $Q_1$ turn on, connecting $V_{ref}$ to the output. Thus, the device outputs $V_{ref}$ or ground to the resistance network connected to the output.

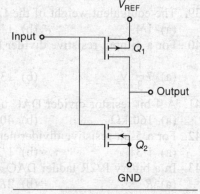

**Fig. 17.33** *Voltage Switch.*

15. infinite                 16. 0                 17. 240 k$\Omega$
18. number of bits at the input or output           19. 1023.
20. twice, sampled            21. Step
22. Polarity inverting        23. Positive, negative       24. Zero, all 0's
25. Inexpensive             26. Operations            27. Fast
28. Circuitry                  29. Fastest               30. False
31. True                       32. True                  33. False
34. True                       35. False               36. True
37. False                      38. False              39. (c)
40. (c)                        41. (d)                 42. (d)
43. (c)                        44. (c)

# Microprocessor Basics

## INTRODUCTION

In the early days, all digital integrated citcuits were *integrated copies* of the discrete component circuitry they replaced. They were made of resistors and bipolar transistors diffused into a single *chip* of silicon and only a very few individual logic elements (gates, flip-flop, etc.) could be built into a *package*. Therefore, a typical digital system employing these circuits consisted of a very large number of *separate packages*.

As bipolar semiconductor technologists learned how to increase the *complexity* of the circuit in each package, *integrated circuits* employing *p*-channel and *n*-channel MOSFETs were introduced. The *MOS technologies* opened the way to integrating thousands of transistors on a single chip and enabled circuits of an *unprecedented complexity* to be contained in a single small package.

At this stage a very difficult problem arose. A great deal of money is needed to design and produce one complex LSI circuit. If a large number of each particular integrated circuit is ultimately to be produced, the development cost can be *spread* over a sufficiently large number of units to become *insignificant*. In addition, it is important to note that semiconductor manufacture is essentially a *mass production* undertaking, as the more the integrated circuits of one type that can be produced the lower the production cost per unit.

The potential advantages of large scale integration were in danger of *not being fully realised* because it was found that as the complexity of an integrated circuit was increased the more *specialised* became its uses. *What was needed was a universal digital integrated circuit that could be used in an unlimited number of different applications.* That universal IC was developed and was called the *microprocessor* (μP).

## MICROPROCESSOR

Any conventional digital circuit consists of a number of gates and flip-flops connected in such a way as to perform the required function. Such a circuit accepts *digital inputs,* performs some kind of *processing* and provides *digital outputs*. The function performed by many digital systems is determined by the *way* in which the various gates and flip-flops are *interconnected*.

The microprocessor differs from the *hardwired* digital circuit in that the function performed is determined by a *sequence of instructions* which are stored in a *memory* in much the same way as a conventional digital computer. *A change in the program will alter the function carried out by the microprocessor.*

All microprocessors can be divided into *four basic sections*: a memory, an input/output unit, a control unit and an arithmetic logic unit. The entire operation of such a system can be likened to that of a man adding up numbers written on a sheet of paper and writing the result on the same piece of paper.

In this analogy the sheet of paper becomes the *peripheral device*—the source and destination of the data to be processed. The man's eyes are the *input* system enabling the numbers to be read into the memory.The man's hand forms the *output* unit enabling the results of a calculation to be written down. The *memory* of both the men and machine perform the same function—both store the sequence of instructions (algorithm) for performing addition. The part of the brain which performs the addition can be likened to the *arithmetic logic unit* and the brain's co-ordinating centre to the machine's *control unit.*

## 18.1  What is a *microprocessor*?

*Solution:*

A microprocessor is a large scale integrated (LSI) circuit which contains the complex digital logic required for the *central processing unit* (CPU) of a digital computer. A set of perhaps two or three LSI devices making up a CPU may also be called a microprocessor.

By itself a microprocessor is virtually useless and other circuits must be added around it to produce a *working* digital computer. A microprocessor package is shown in Fig. 18.1.

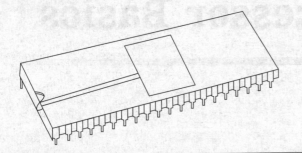

**Fig. 18.1**   *A Microprocessor Package.*

At the heart of the computer is the CPU itself which contains all the logic circuits that govern the *timing and operation* of the computer and perform the *arithmetic and logic functions*.

Outside the CPU there is a memory section which *stores* the data to be processed and also *holds* a list of instructions, called the *program*, which tells the CPU what to do.

The computer must be able to communicate with the outside world and this is done through input and output channels called *ports*. These ports allow the computer to *accept data from* various input sources, such as a switch or keyboard and *output data to* a printer, a plotter or a visual display unit (VDU).

## MICROCOMPUTER

The term microcomputer is used to indicate a small size computer system consisting of the three basic units: CPU, memory and input/output interface. A microcomputer in most cases refers to an interconnection of LSI components. A microcomputer can be used as a low-cost, general-purpose computer to provide processing capabilities similar to those of any other computer system.

### 18.2  How does a microcomputer *differ* from a micro-processor?

*Solution:*

The name *microcomputer* is used to describe any small computer system which uses a *microprocessor* as its CPU. Normally a microcomputer uses several integrated circuits, popularly referred to as *chips* because each is constructed on a tiny slice or chip of silicon. Sometimes all of the components for the microcomputer are contained within a single integrated circuit and this type of device is called a *single chip microcomputer* to differentiate it from the more common microprocessor device.

A single chip microcomputer contains the control and arithmetic circuits making up the CPU, some memory for data and instructions and a set of input and output signal lines for communication with the outside world. Single chip microcomputers are ideal for use in small *dedicated systems* since they produce a very simple hardware system and reduce the size and cost of the complete product.

An example of the application of a single chip microcomputer is in the familiar electronic pocket calculator. Other common applications are in electronic toys and in domestic appliance controllers.

### 18.3  How are the *program instructions* made up?

*Solution:*

The instructions for the processor consist of a *string* of numbers which are stored as *binary data words* in the memory section of the microcomputer system. Every instruction contains an operation code or *opcode* which defines the type of operation the CPU has to perform when the instruction is executed. Typical operations might be LOAD, STORE, ADD, INCREMENT, and so on.

Each different opcode is represented in the memory by a unique number so we might have the number 96 for a LOAD instruction whilst 97 could be a STORE instruction.

Apart from the opcode most instructions will also have an *operand* which occupies the next one or two words in the memory following the opcode word. This operand may represent data to be processed by the instruction or an address which gives the memory location of either some data or another instruction.

Although the instruction opcode is just a number in the memory it is common practice to use a *mnemonic code* for it when the program is written on paper. This makes the program easier for a human programmer to understand. Thus the opcode for 'Load a number into the accumulator' might be written as LDA. Similarly data and addresses associated with the opcode may also be given names to make the program easier to follow. The general idea is shown in Fig. 18.2 which shows both the mnemonic list and actual memory contents for a section of program for a Motorola-6800 microprocessor.

In a general purpose microprocessor there might be 50–200 different opcodes to define available operations. In practice there may be several different versions of an instruction such as LOAD, each having a different opcode and operating in a different way when executed.

The majority of processor types have an 8-bit word for the instruction opcode but some processors use 16-bit words for program instructions. In these 16-bit processors the opcode occupies *only a part* of the complete instruction word and other parts of the word may define various options and provide address information.

Mnemonic Listing

| LDAA | NUMBER 1 | Load Number 1 to Accumulator |
| ADDA | 5 · | Add 5 to Accumulator |
| ASLA | | Shift Accumulator Left by 1 bit |
| SUBA | NUMBER 2 | Subtract Numbers 2 from Accumulator |
| STAA | RESULT | Store Accumulator to result Location |

NUMBER 1 Stored at 0211 in Memory, NUMBER 2 at 212 2nd Result to be Placed in Locations 213

Program as Stored in Memory

| Memory Address(hex) | Memory Contents (hex) | |
|---|---|---|
| 0100 | B6 | LDAA op code |
| 0101 | 02 | ⎫ Address 0211 |
| 0102 | 11 | ⎭ |
| 0103 | 8B | ADDA op code |
| 0104 | 05 | Data 5 |
| 0105 | 48 | ASLA op code |
| 0106 | Bo | SUBA op code |
| 0107 | 02 | ⎫ Address 0212 |
| 0108 | 12 | ⎭ |
| 0109 | B7 | STAA op code |
| 010A | 02 | ⎫ Address 0213 |
| 010B | 13 | ⎭ |

**Fig. 18.2** *Typical Segment of Machine Code Program for 6800 Type Microprocessor Showing How it is Stored in Memory.*

### 18.4 How does *word length* affect a microprocessor?

*Solution:*

For simple control applications such as coin operated machines, toys, calculators, and appliance controllers a *4-bit word* is very convenient. A word of this length can readily provide the digits from 0 to 9 plus 5 or 6 additional codes which may define the type of operation to be carried out. Many of the single chip microcomputers, such as the Texas Instruments TMS 1000 series, use a 4-bit word for data, although the instructions may still use 8-bit words.

For applications involving the handling of text information and for general purpose desk top or personal computers it is usual to have an 8-bit data word. Popular microprocessors such as the Intel 8085, Motorola 6800 and 6809 series, Zilog Z 80 and the MOS technology 6500 series all use *8-bit words* for both data and instructions.

When the processor is to be used in a large system or has very complex calculations to perform there is an advantage in using *16-bit or even 32-bit word length*.

An advantage of using the larger word is that where as 8-bit processors normally use 2 or 3 bytes for each instruction, a 16-32-bit machine can use just one word

which saves time in setting up and executing the instructions. *In general, the longer word length machines tend to be faster in operation and more efficient.*

## MICROPROCESSOR ORGANISATION

To guarantee a wide range of acceptability, a microprocessor must provide an internal organisation suited to a wide range of applications. The organisations of commercial microprocessors differ from each other, but they all have the comon property of a CPU. As such they are capable of interpreting instruction codes received from memory and of performing data processing tasks specified by a program. They also respond to external control commands and generate control signals for external modules to use.

### 18.5 What is microprocesor *architecture*?

*Solution:*

The *internal arrangement* of a microprocessor or microcomputer device is called its *architecture*. The logic of a microprocessor is extremely complex so an architecture diagram will usually show only the main *functional blocks* of the logic system. The diagram will show all of the *working registers* that may be used by instructions in the program.

Figure 18.3 shows the architecture of a typical *general-purpose microprocessor* similar to that which might be used in a popular computer system such as the APPLE, PET or Sinclair ZX81.

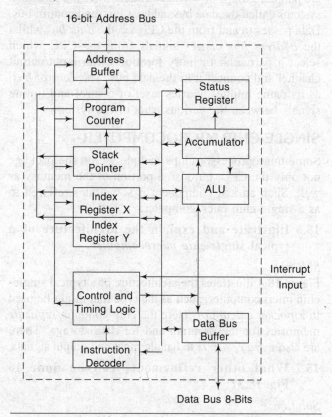

**Fig. 18.3** *Internal Architecture of a Typical 8-bit Microprocessor.*

The logic can be broadly divided into one part which *controls* the sequence of operations and another which *processes* data by carrying out arithmetic or logical operations. These two sections are closely *linked* and in some cases their functions tend to *overlap*.

At the heart of the *control section* is a register called the *program counter*. The program counter register is used to hold the address of memory location that contains the opcode for the *next* instruction to be executed. The opcode data is held in an *instruction register* during execution and an *instruction decoder* sets up the required logic sequence within the CPU to perform the required operations.

Other parts of the control system include a stack, or a *stack pointer register*, an *index register* or *data pointer register*, and some logic to handle *interrupt* operations where an external signal can be used to influence the flow of program execution.

*Processing* of data is carried out by an *arithmetic and logic unit* (ALU) working in association with a register called the *accumulator*. Some processors, such as the Motorola 6800 series, have two accumulator registers. Associated with the accumulator is a *status register* in which the individual bits are used to indicate the *state* of the processor.

*Communication* between the CPU memory and input/output ports is carried out over a series of *buses* which are parallel groups of wires. Normally there are three bus systems called the data bus, address bus, and control bus. Data passes to and from the CPU via the *data bus* whilst the *address bus* carries signals from the CPU which select a particular memory location or an input/output channel and connect it to the data bus. The *control bus*, as its name implies, carries a set of control and timing signals between the various parts of the system.

## SINGLE-CHIP MICROCOMPUTER

Some microprocessor chips include within the package not only the CPU, but also a portion of the memory as well. Such an LSI component is sometimes referred to as a single-chip microcomputer.

### 18.6 Illustrate and explain the architecture of a typical *single-chip microcomputer*.

*Solution:*
Figure 18.4 illustrates the architecture of a typical single-chip microcomputer, such as the type that might be used in a *pocket calculator*. Here the chip contains *separate* memories for the program and for data storage. There are also *extra registers* to handle input and output signals.

### 18.7 What other refinements can be done to Fig. 18.3?

*Solution:*
Another section of logic which may be shown on the architecture of Fig. 18.3 is the *clock generator* which

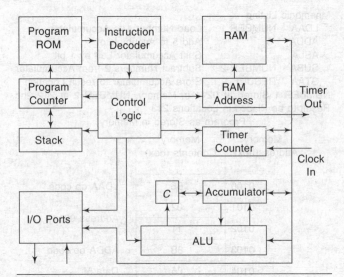

**Fig. 18.4** *Architecture of a Typical Single-chip Microcomputer.*

provides the master timing for the microprocessor. The *address register*, which drives the address bus, may also be shown. Many single-chip microcomputers have separate address registers and bus systems for program and data memory and data address may be set up by programing instructions.

### 18.8 How are *instructions* executed?

*Solution:*
The first step in executing an instruction is that the address held in the program counter is placed on the address bus. This *selects* the memory location which the opcode of the instruction to be executed contains. The opcode is *read* from memory and *transferred* via the data bus to the instruction register. The opcode is *decoded* by the CPU control logic which then sets up the internal logic paths and the timing sequence required to execute the instruction.

At this point the program counter is *updated* to provide the address of the next instruction. Some instructions will consist simply of an opcode and in such cases the program counter is simply *increased by one*. Other instructions will have an operand of one or two bytes which will always follow the opcode. In such cases the program counter is *incremented by two or three* to point to the next opcode in memory. Sometimes the instruction operand will provide the address of the next instruction to be executed and the operand data is transferred *directly* from the data bus into the program counter register.

Once the opcode has been decoded and any operands dealt with, the instruction is executed and the process continues with the instruction selected by the new contents of the program counter.

The operation of the CPU whilst executing an instruction normally takes up two or more *CPU clock periods*. The first step of loading and decoding the opcode is called the instruction *fetch cycle* and the last cycle is normally the *execution cycle*. Loading of operands will take up further cycles. Some processors, such as the 6800 and 6500 series, have a very simple two-phase clock with internal CPU operations occurring during phase 1 and data bus access during phase 2. Thus a simple instruction will use two clock cycles, the first *fetching* the opcode and the second *executing* the instruction. Other processors have more complex *timing schemes* where a complete operation consists of several instruction cycles each of which may use a different number of clock cycles according to the type of action being carried out. Fetch and execute cycle is shown in Fig. 18.5.

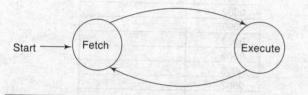

**Fig. 18.5** *Fetch and Execute Cycle.*

### 18.9 Illustrate, with the help of an example, an *ALU adding two operands*.

*Solution:*

For example, Fig. 18.6 shows an 8-bit number from *accumulator A* being added to an 8-bit number from the *data register*. The result of this addition (sum) is put into an accumulator, replacing, the original operand that was stored there. *When an ALU performs an operation on two operands, the result of the operation always goes into an accumulator and replaces the previous operand.* Therefore, the accumulator *not only* stores an operand prior to manipulation by the ALU, *but also* stores the result of the operation after the operation has been performed. The data register temporarily stores a byte of data that is to be put onto the data bus or has been taken off the data bus.

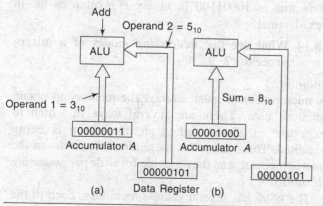

(a)

(b)

**Fig. 18.6** *Example of an ALU Adding Two Operands; (a) the ALU Adding $011_2$ and $101_2$, (b) The Sum ($1000_2$) being Put into the Accumulator.*

### 18.10 Explain microprocessor/memory *interaction*.

*Solution:*

The microprocessor is connected to a memory with the *address bus* and *data bus*. In addition, there are certain *control signals* that must be sent between the microprocessor and the memory, such as read/write controls. This is illustrated in Fig. 18.7.

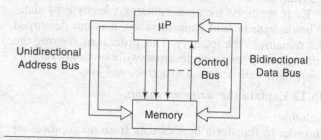

**Fig. 18.7** *Microprocessor/Memory Interaction.*

The address bus is *unidirectional*, meaning the address data bits go only one way—from the micro processor to the memory. There is no need for the memory to send any address information to the micro-processor ($\mu P$). The data bus is *bidirectional*, so information can travel either to or from the micro-processor memory.

### 18.11 Explain the *read operation*.

*Solution:*

To transfer a byte of data from the memory to the microprocessor, a *read operation* must be carried out. With reference to Fig. 18.8, to begin, the program counter contains the 16-bit address of the byte to be read from the memory. This address is *located* into the address register and put onto the address bus. The program counter advances by one (*increments*) to the next address and waits.

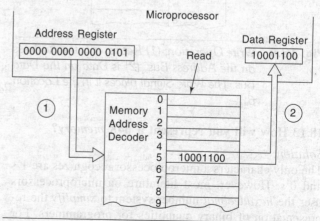

**Fig 18.8** *Read Operation; (1) Shows Address $5_{10}$ being Put on The Address Bus Followed by a Read Signal, (2) Shows the Contents of Address $5_{10}$ in Memory Put on the Data and Stored in a Data Register.*

Once the *address code* is on the bus, the microprocessor control unit sends a *read signal* to the memory. At the memory, the address bits are *decoded* and the desired memory location is *selected*. The read signal causes the *contents* of the selected address to be put on the data bus. The data byte is then loaded into the data register to be used by the µP. This completes the *read operation*.

Each memory location contains one byte of data. When a byte is read from memory, it is not destroyed but remains in the memory. This process of *copying* the contents of a memory location without destroying its contents is called *non-destructive read out*.

### 18.12 Explain the *write operation*.

*Solution:*

In order to transfer a byte of data from microprocessor to the memory, a *write operation* is required. With reference to Fig. 18.9, the memory is *addressed* in the same way as in the read operation. A data byte being held in the data register is put onto the data bus and the microprocessor sends the memory a write signal. This causes the byte on the data bus to be *stored* at the selected location in the memory as specified by the 16-bit *address code*. The existing contents of that particular memory location are *replaced* by the new data byte. This completes the write operation.

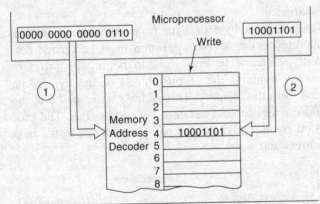

**Fig. 18.9**  *Write Operation; (1) Represents the Address on the Address Bus, (2) is Data on the Data Bus. The Write Signal places it in the Location $6_{16}$.*

### 18.13 How will you represent a *64K memory*?

*Solution:*

The only characters a microprocessor recognizes are 1's and 0's. However, most literature on microprocessors uses the *hexadecimal* number system to *simplify* the representation of binary quantities for programmers. For example, the binary address 1110001011010011 can be written as E2D3 in hexadecimal. This is shown in Fig. 18.10.

The hexadecimal number system simplifies the representation of binary quantities for programmers.

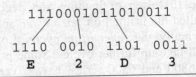

**Fig. 18.10**

A *16-bit address* can have a *minimum* hexadecimal value of $0000_{16}$ and a *maximum* hexadecimal values of $FFFF_{16}$. With this notation, a 64K memory (actually 65,536) can be shown in a block form as in Fig. 18.11.

| Address (hexadecimal) | Contents |
|---|---|
| 0000 | |
| 0001 | |
| 0002 | |
| 0003 | |
| 0004 | |
| 0005 | |
| 0006 | |
| 0007 | |
| 0008 | |
| 0009 | |
| 000A | |
| 000B | |
| 000C | |
| FFFB | |
| FFFC | |
| FFFD | |
| FFFE | |
| FFFF | |

**Fig. 18.11**  *Representation of a 64K Memory.*

A *data byte* can also be represented in hexadecimal. A data byte can be either an instruction, an operand, or an address. A data byte is 8bits and can represent decimal numbers from $0_{10}$ to $255_{10}$, or it can represent upto 256 instructions. For example, a *microprocessor code* that is 10001100 in binary is written as 8C in hexadecimal.

### 18.14 What are the *addressing modes* of a microprocessor?

*Solution:*

A microprocessor must *address* the memory to obtain or store data. There are several ways in which to *generate* an address when an instruction is being executed. These are called the *addressing modes* of the microprocessor, and they provide for wide *programming flexibility*.

The *6800* has several addressing modes. Each of the instructions available to the microprocessor has a certain addressing mode associated with it. These are—inherent, immediate, direct, extended, relative and indexed.

**18.15 How does the *arithmetic and logic unit* of a microprocessor work?**

*Solution:*

Virtually all *processing of numbers* in a CPU is carried out in the arithmetic and logic unit (*ALU*) which works in conjunction with a special register called the *accumulator*. The general arrangement of this part of a CPU is shown in Fig. 18.12.

The ALU itself is a *complex logic array* which can carry out operations such as Add, Shift, And, Increment etc. There are two *data inputs* to the ALU, one of which comes from the accumulator, whilst the other may be taken, via the data bus, from memory or another CPU register. The result of the operation is written into the accumulator *replacing* its previous contents. A single bit extension to the accumulator is used to save any

carry bit produced by the arithmetic logic operation in the ALU.

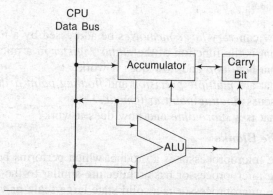

**Fig. 18.12** *Basic Arrangement of the Arithmetic and Logic Unit of A Computer.*

# SUMMARY

- ➤ A microprocessor (μP) is a sophisticated, sequential, digital circuit that is designed to follow a sequence of instructions called a program.
- ➤ The program is stored in memory devices that are connected to the microprocessor.
- ➤ In order to run a program, the microprocessor fetches an instruction from memory, then executes it, then fetches the next instruction, executes it, and so on.
- ➤ The execution of some instructions involves reading in data values from input devices.
- ➤ Some instructions cause the microcomputer to write data values to output devices.
- ➤ Data values can also be stored in and retrieved from memory devices that are connected to the microprocessor.
- ➤ The microprocessor is connected to the memory and I/O devices by a group of wires called the data bus.
- ➤ An address bus, connected from the microprocessor to the memory and I/O devices, carries a number that specifies the location in memory of the instruction or data that the microprocessor is trying to access.
- ➤ A set of control signals form the timing and control bus. They coordinate data transfer and indicate what type of data should currently be on the data bus.
- ➤ A microprocessor along with a memory system and I/O devices make up a microcomputer.
- ➤ Microcomputers can be made up of a single chip that is embedded in a product, such as a microwave oven or a VCR, for the purpose of controlling the operation of the device.

# REVIEW QUESTIONS

**Test your understanding**

1. What is a CPU?
2. What is meant by interfacing in a computer system?
3. What are the five basic units in a computer?
4. Explain the difference between a microprocessor and a microcomputer?
5. Name the three major sections of a MPU?
6. What is the function of the program counter?
7. What two types of information are stored in computer words?
8. What is the advantage of a larger-word-size computer?
9. What is an opcode?
10. What is an operand address?
11. What is an instruction mnemonic?
12. What generally takes place during a fetch cycle? During an execute cycle?

# SUPPLEMENTARY PROBLEMS

13. How can *very large memories* be addressed by a microprocessor?
14. What is the function of the *status register* in a microprocessor?
15. What is a *loop* and how does it work?
16. What are *multiple precision* and *floating point arithmetic?*
17. Discuss *floating point arithmetic.*
18. What is a *subroutine* and how does it work?

## Fill in the Blanks

19. The microprocessor is a product which performs both _____ and _____ functions.
20. The microprocessor has architecture similar to the _____ computer's.
21. The microprocessor is a solid-state large scale-or very large scale-integrated (LSI or VLSI) _____.
22. Each improvement in architecture increases the microprocessor's _____ and _____.
23. Four-bit microprocessors use a _____ and are _____.
24. Microcontrollers are microprocessors with memory and _____ .
25. The microprocessor is a microprocessing unit in a _____ .
26. Data processing is the microprocessor's _____ function.
27. The ALU must wait for _____ to be placed in certain places.
28. The _____ is a set of instructions for processing the data.
29. In order to process data, the microprocessor must have _____ .
30. Control logic tells the microprocessors how to _____ and _____ the program.
31. When you change the microprocessor's _____ you change what it does to the data.
32. The microprocessor can do nothing by _____ .
33. A microprocessor does not include _____ circuits.
34. The microprocessor's fetch-and-execute cycle is used to get and carry out _____ .
35. The ALU is used to do _____ .
36. You can change what a microprocessor will do by changing the _____ in memory.
37. One of the most common measurements of a microprocessor's power is its. _____ .
38. A 8-bit word is a very common word length. It is called a _____ .
39. Microprocessors (except the 8080) require a _____ regulated power supply.
40. Microprocessors transfer data or instructions between the MPU and memory (or I/O) via a _____ data bus.
41. The program counter (PC) is the register that holds the address of the _____ program instruction.
42. The accumulator is the register(s) associated with the _____ operation and sometimes _____ operations.
43. The individual bits in the status register are called _____ .
44. General purpose registers may be used to temporarily _____ data or _____ an address.
45. The index register is used to hold the address of an _____ when the indexed address mode is used.
46. The stack pointer (SP) is a specialized register that keeps track of the _____ memory location in the stack.
47. An _____ is the technique used to fetch the desired operand during the execution of an instruction.
48. Most 8-bit microprocessors use _____ address buses.
49. Most 8-bit MPUs use _____ data lines.
50. A microprocessor system has three buses: address, _____ , and _____ .

## True/False Questions

State whether the following statements are True or False.
51. The microprocessor is a data processing unit.
52. The ALU can by itself move data from place to place.
53. For each instruction in memory, the microprocessor goes through two fetch-and-execute cycles.
54. The microprocessor is never a complete, working product by itself.
55. The bit size of a microprocessor is sometimes referred to as its word size.
56. The stack is a reserved area in RAM used for permanent storage of data, return addresses, and contents of registers.

57. The stack is used during subroutine calls and interrupts.
58. When viewed from the top, pin 1 is immediately clockwise from the index mark.
59. The flags are most closely associated with the instruction decoder.

### Multiple Choice Questions

60. The number of programmable 8-bit registers of 6800 are
    (a) 2             (b) 3             (c) 4             (d) 5
61. The number of programmable 16-bit registers of 6800 are
    (a) 2             (b) 3             (c) 4             (d) 5
62. The number of programmable 8-bit registers of 6800 which can also be used as 16-bit register pair are
    (a) 2             (b) 3             (c) 4             (d) 1
63. The number of temporary registers of 6800 which are not programmable are
    (a) 2             (b) 3             (c) 1             (d) 4
64. The number of accumulators in 6800 are
    (a) 2             (b) 3             (c) 1             (d) 4
65. The value of Program Counter of 6800 at power-on are after reset is
    (a) 0000                                  (b) FFFEH
    (c) User programmable          (d) FFFF
66. The width of the instruction register of 6800 is
    (a) 8             (b) 4             (c) 16             (d) 32
67. The number of flags available in 6800 are
    (a) 6             (b) 5             (c) 4             (d) 7

# ANSWERS

1. Control and arithmetic/logic unit combined
2. The synchronization of digital information transmission between the computer and external I/O devices.
3. Input, output, arithmetic/logic, control, memory
4. The microprocessor is the CPU portion of the microcomputer
5. Timing and control, register, ALU
6. Keeps track of instruction addresses
7. Data and instructions
8. Executes programs at a faster rate
9. A binary code that represents the operation to be performed by the CPU.
10. The address of the data to be operated on as the CPU executes the instruction called for by the opcode
11. A short abbreviation for the operation
12. During a fetch cycle, the CPU fetches the opcode and the operand address from memory. During the execute cycle, the CPU executes the operation called for by the opcode.
13. For a typical 8-bit microprocessor the address bus will have 16-bits allowing access to upto 65536 (64K) words of memory. For most purposes, of course, this is perfectly adequate, but sometimes it may be desirable to have access to a *larger memory space*. One technique for achieving this is to use a *segmented memory system*.

    In a segmented memory system a register is set aside as a *segment number register* and this is used to provide the more significant bits of the complete memory address. Thus if an 8-bit segment register were used the effective memory address would become 24bits wide and would consist of 256 segments of 64K each. To access data within another segment of memory the processor would have to set up new word in the segment register prior to making the memory access.

    Some 16-bit microprocessors such as the Z8000 also use segmented addressing but in this case the segment registers are located *within* the CPU and may be *directly* acted upon by the program instructions.
14. All microprocessors have some form of *status register* which shows the *current state* of the CPU. Each bit in this register is used as a *flag* to signal that a particular condition exists within the processor system. Sometimes this register is called the flag or *condition code register*.

    Figure 18.13 shows the *allocation* of bits in the status register of the *Motorola 6800 microprocessor*. Bit 3 is the zero or *Z bit* which, *when set at 1*, indicates that the result of the last operation was zero. If the Z bit is *set at* 0 then the result was not zero. A 1 in the bit 4 position indicates that the result was a negative number. This bit is called the negative or *N bit* and a 0 here indicates a positive result.

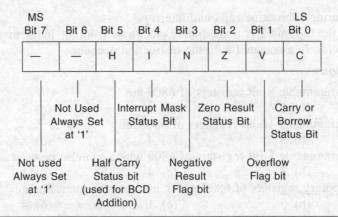

**Fig. 18.13** *The Condition Code or Status Register of a 6800 Microprocessor and the Functional Allocation of its Data Bits.*

During an arithmetic operation, such as add or subtract, a *carry* or *borrow* may be produced and this is indicated by the *C or carry bit*. If the previous instruction involves shifting the pattern of bits in the accumulator, or another register, the *C* bit may be set to the state of the bit that was pushed out from the end of the register.

Another condition that can occur during an arithmetic operation is *overflow* where the result of the operation is outside the range of numbers that can be represented by the computer word. This condition is signalled by the *V bit* in the 6800 status register. Other types of processor may define this as the *O or overflow bit*. The overflow condition occurs when arithmetic is being carried out on *signed numbers* and for an 8-bit processor this would mean that the result was greater than 127 or more negative than 127. Apart from the normal carry bit the 6800 has an extra carry bit (*H*) which indicates that a carry occurred from bit 3 to 4 during an add instruction. The *H* bit is used when BCD numbers are being handled.

Other status register bits may be used to *enable or disable* interrupt operations. The 6502 processor uses a status register bit to *change* its arithmetic operations from the normal binary mode to a mode which handles BCD numbers.

Some status register bits, such as carry, overflow and interrupt, can be *directly set or reset* by program instructions as well as being affected by the results of executing arithmetic or logic operations.

15. In almost all programs there will be occasions *where a sequence of instructions must be executed a number of times in succession.* The actual sequence may range from just one or two instructions upto a complete section of the program. This type of operation is called a *loop*.

    Before a loop section is reached a register or memory location is set to the *number of times* the loop is to be executed. Next the loop itself *starts* and the first instruction is labelled or its address is noted. The main body of the loop is similar to any other section of the program. At the *end* of the loop sequence the count stored in the register or memory is *decremented* and the result *tested for zero*. If the result is not zero the program *branches back* to the first instruction of the loop sequence which is then *executed again*. If the result is *zero* the required number of *passes* has been made and the program continues with the *next* instruction. The basic program flow is shown in Fig. 18.14.

    A loop can be used to provide a simple *time delay* and the time will then be the *execution time* of the instructions in the loop, including the test and branch instructions, multiplied by the number of times the loop is executed.

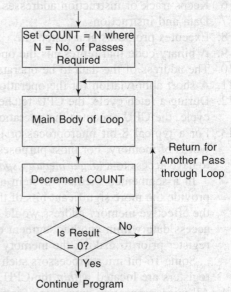

**Fig. 18.14** *Basic Program for a Loop Operation.*

16. With an 8-bit CPU the *range* of numbers that can be handled directly by the accumulator is 0 to 255 or alternatively –127 to +127 for signed numbers. Larger numbers can be handled by dealing with the numbers as a *series of 8bit segments.*

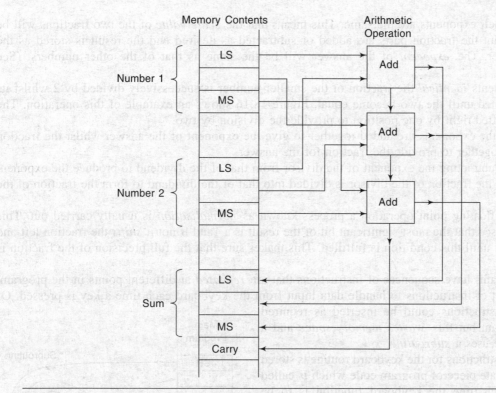

Memory Contents          Arithmetic
                         Operation

**Fig. 18.15**  *Addition of Two 24-bit Numbers Each Stored as Three 8-bit Words.*

Suppose we decide to use 24-bit numbers. For an 8-bit CPU this is a *triple precision* number. The two numbers will be stored in memory as two sets of three 8-bit words as shown in Fig. 18.15. At the start, one of the least significant words is loaded and the least significant part of the second number added to it. This result is now stored as the *least significant word* of the result. Next the two middle sections of the numbers are added taking into account any *carry* produced by the first addition and this result is stored as the *middle word* of the result. Finally the most significant parts are added, again carrying into account any carry from the previous addition and this result is stored as the *most significant part* of the answer. Finally any carry produced may need to be stored in a fourth word of the answer.

Subtraction of numbers in several sections may be carried out in a similar fashion to addition provided that the *borrow* is taken account of between each successive subtraction operation. Similar techniques may be used for multiplication and divison.

Where fractions are to be handled it is usual to employ some form of *floating point arithmetic system*.

In a floating point scheme each number is divided up into two elements. One part is a *fraction* ranging in value from 0 to 1. It provides the *basic numerical value* and determines the *precision* of the results. The second part of the number is the *exponent*. The exponent can be a number representing the *power of 2* by which the fraction must be multiplied to obtain the *actual value* of the number.

In the fraction, the bit to the *right* of the sign bit represents the value 0.5 and *successive bits* moving to the right represent 0.25, 0.125, 0.0625 and so on. It is also possible to have the fraction represented as a BCD number in which case *each successive digit* would be equivalent to tens, hundredths and so on.

Where *BCD* is used for the fraction then the exponent will be a decimal one, i.e. it is a *power of 10* rather than a power of 2. Use of decimal exponent and fraction is useful if the results have to be printed out.

17. When the numbers are represented in *floating point form* the sequence of operations for arithmetic becomes more *complex*. Suppose we take *addition* and *subtraction*. Before the actual addition or subtraction can be carried out the two numbers must

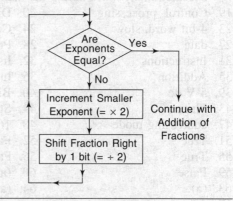

**Fig. 18.16**  *Flowchart of Loop for Equating Exponents Prior to Floating Point Add or Subtract.*

be *adjusted* so that their exponents are the same. This means that the *scale value* of the two fractions will be the same. At this point the fraction parts are added or subtracted as desired and the result is stored as the *fraction* of the answer. The *exponent* of the answer will be the same as that of the other numbers. (See Fig. 18.16)

To make the exponents *identical* the fraction of the smaller number is successively divided by 2 whilst its exponent is incremented until the two become equal. Figure 18.16 shows an example of this operation. The fraction is simply shifted right by one position to provide the division by two.

For *multiplication* the exponents are added together to give the exponent of the answer whilst the fraction parts are multiplied together to provide the fraction for the answer.

*Division* involves subtracting the exponent of the divisor from that of the dividend to produce the exponent of the quotient whilst the fraction of the divisor is divided into that of the dividend to form the fraction of the quotient.

At the end of any floating point operation a process known as *normalisation* is usually carried out. This effectively checks to see that the most significant bit of the result is a 1 and if not it *shifts* the fraction left and *corrects* the exponent until this condition is fulfilled. This makes sure that the full precision of the fraction is being used.

18. Most computer programs have sequences of instructions that are *repeated* at different points in the program. An example is the set of instructions to handle data input from the keyboard each time a key is pressed. Of course this set of instructions could be inserted as required throughout the program but this *wastes memory space* and a more efficient routine uses a *subroutine*.

The sequence of instructions for the keyboard routine is stored in memory as a separate piece of program code which is called a subroutine and each time the keyboard function is to be executed a special Jump to Subroutine (JSR) instruction is inserted into the main program. For some processors a *CALL* instruction is used instead of JSR. The JSR or CALL instruction has as its operand the starting address of the subroutine code. Each time the JSR instruction is encountered a jump is made to the *first* instruction of the subroutine sequence and execution of the subroutine commences. The *last* instruction in the subroutine is an RTS or Return from Subroutine or RET instruction. This RTS instruction causes execution of the main program to be resumed at the instruction immediately following JSR or CALL. Each time the subroutine function is required this *sequence of events* occurs with program execution jumping from the main program to the subroutine and back again. This is shown in Fig. 18.17.

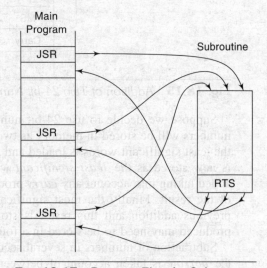

**Fig. 18.17**   *Program Flow for Subroutines.*

The advantage of using a subroutine is that although the sequence of instructions of the subroutine may be executed *many times* during the main program it is stored *only once* in the memory thus saving space.

| | | | |
|---|---|---|---|
| 19. Control, processing | 20. Digital | 21. Microcircuit | 22. Speed, computing power |
| 23. 4-bit word, slow | 24. Communication | 25. Microcircuit | 26. Main |
| 27. data | 28. Program | 29. Control logic | 30. Decode, execute |
| 31. Instructions | 32. Itself | 33. Memory | 34. Instructions |
| 35. Addition | 36. Instructions | 37. Word length | 38. Byte |
| 39. 5 V dc | 40. Bidirectional | 41. Next | 42. ALU, I/O |
| 43. Flags | 44. Store, hold | 45. Operand | 46. Next available |
| 47. addressing mode | 48. 16-bit | 49. Eight | 50. Data, control |
| 51. True | 52. False | 53. False | 54. True |
| 55. True | 56. False | 57. True | 58. False |
| 59. False | 60. (a) | 61. (b) | 62. (d) |
| 63. (a) | 64. (a) | 65. (b) | 66. (a) |
| 67. (a) | | | |

# Logic Operations— Comparison Chart

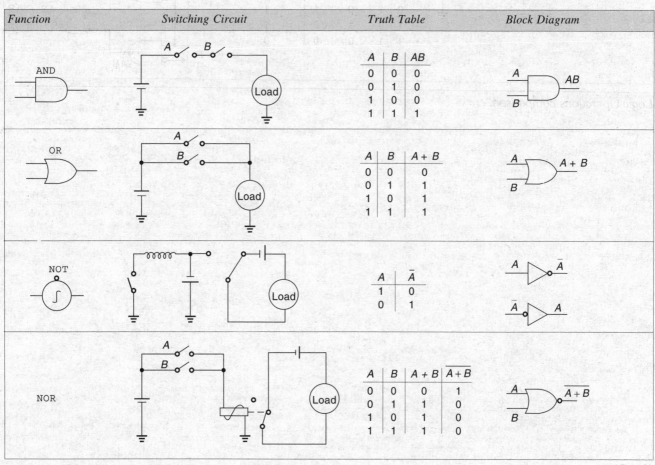

| Function | Switching Circuit | Truth Table | | | | Block Diagram |
|---|---|---|---|---|---|---|
| AND | | $A$ | $B$ | $AB$ | | |
| | | 0 | 0 | 0 | | |
| | | 0 | 1 | 0 | | $AB$ |
| | | 1 | 0 | 0 | | |
| | | 1 | 1 | 1 | | |
| OR | | $A$ | $B$ | $A + B$ | | |
| | | 0 | 0 | 0 | | |
| | | 0 | 1 | 1 | | $A + B$ |
| | | 1 | 0 | 1 | | |
| | | 1 | 1 | 1 | | |
| NOT | | $A$ | $\bar{A}$ | | | |
| | | 1 | 0 | | | |
| | | 0 | 1 | | | |
| NOR | | $A$ | $B$ | $A + B$ | $\overline{A+B}$ | |
| | | 0 | 0 | 0 | 1 | |
| | | 0 | 1 | 1 | 0 | $\overline{A+B}$ |
| | | 1 | 0 | 1 | 0 | |
| | | 1 | 1 | 1 | 0 | |

*(Contd.)*

*(Contd.)*

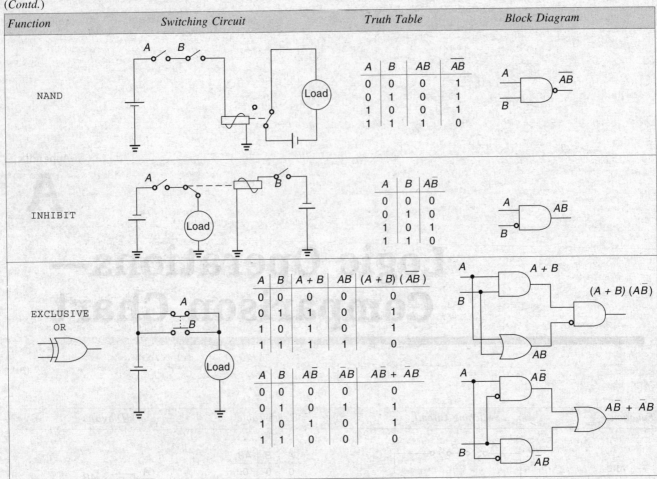

| Function | Switching Circuit | Truth Table | Block Diagram |
|---|---|---|---|

**NAND**

| $A$ | $B$ | $AB$ | $\overline{AB}$ |
|---|---|---|---|
| 0 | 0 | 0 | 1 |
| 0 | 1 | 0 | 1 |
| 1 | 0 | 0 | 1 |
| 1 | 1 | 1 | 0 |

**INHIBIT**

| $A$ | $B$ | $A\overline{B}$ |
|---|---|---|
| 0 | 0 | 0 |
| 0 | 1 | 0 |
| 1 | 0 | 1 |
| 1 | 1 | 0 |

**EXCLUSIVE OR**

| $A$ | $B$ | $A + B$ | $AB$ | $(A + B)\,(\overline{AB})$ |
|---|---|---|---|---|
| 0 | 0 | 0 | 0 | 0 |
| 0 | 1 | 1 | 0 | 1 |
| 1 | 0 | 1 | 0 | 1 |
| 1 | 1 | 1 | 1 | 0 |

| $A$ | $B$ | $A\overline{B}$ | $\overline{A}B$ | $A\overline{B} + \overline{A}B$ |
|---|---|---|---|---|
| 0 | 0 | 0 | 0 | 0 |
| 0 | 1 | 0 | 1 | 1 |
| 1 | 0 | 1 | 0 | 1 |
| 1 | 1 | 0 | 0 | 0 |

*Logic Operations-comparison.*

# Digital ICs

**Table B.1** *TTL Devices*

| Number | Function |
|---|---|
| 7400 | Quad 2-input NAND gates |
| 7401 | Quad 2-input NAND gates (open collector) |
| 7402 | Quad 2-input NOR gates |
| 7403 | Quad 2-input NOR Gates (open collector) |
| 7404 | Hex inverters |
| 7405 | Hex inverters (open collector) |
| 7406 | Hex inverter buffer-driver |
| 7407 | Hex buffer-drivers |
| 7408 | Quad 2-input AND gates |
| 7409 | Quad 2-input AND gates (open collector) |
| 7410 | Triple 3-input NAND gates |
| 7411 | Triple 3-input AND gates |
| 7412 | Triple 3-input NAND gates (open collector) |
| 7413 | Dual Schmitt triggers |
| 7414 | Hex Schmitt triggers |
| 7416 | Hex inverter buffer-drivers |
| 7417 | Hex buffer-drivers |
| 7420 | Dual 4-input NAND gates |
| 7421 | Dual 4-input AND gates |
| 7422 | Dual 4-input NAND gates (open collector) |
| 7423 | Expandable dual 4-input NOR gates |
| 7425 | Dual 4-input NOR gates |
| 7426 | Quad 2-input TTL-MOS interface NAND gates |
| 7427 | Triple 3-input NOR gates |
| 7428 | Quad 2-input NOR buffer |
| 7430 | 8-input NAND gate |
| 7432 | Quad 2-input OR gates |
| 7437 | Quad 2-input NAND buffers |
| 7438 | Quad 2-input NAND buffers (open collector) |
| 7439 | Quad 2-input NAND buffers (open collector) |
| 7440 | Dual 4-input NAND buffers |
| 7441 | BCD-to-decimal decoder-Nixie driver |
| 7442 | BCD-to-decimal decoder |
| 7443 | Excess 3-to-decimal decoder |

*(Contd.)*

**Table B.1** *(Contd.)*

| Number | Function |
|---|---|
| 7444 | Excess Gray-to-decimal decoder |
| 7445 | BCD-to-decimal decoder-driver |
| 7446 | BCD-to-seven segment decoder-drivers (30 V output) |
| 7447 | BCD-to-seven segment decoder-drivers (15 V output) |
| 7448 | BCD-to-seven segment decoder-drivers |
| 7450 | Expandable dual 2-input 2-wide AND-OR-INVERT gates |
| 7451 | Dual 2-input 2-wide AND-OR-INVERT gates |
| 7452 | Expandable 2-input 4-wide AND-OR gates |
| 7453 | Expandable 2-input 4-wide AND-OR-INVERT gates |
| 7454 | 2-input 4-wide AND-OR-INVERT gates |
| 74153 | Dual 4/1 multiplexer |
| 74154 | 4-line-to-16-line decoder-demultiplexer |
| 74155 | Dual 2/4 demultiplexer |
| 74156 | Dual 2/4 demultiplexer |
| 74157 | Quad 2/1 data selector |
| 74160 | Decade counter with asynchronous clear |
| 74161 | Synchronous 4-bit counter |
| 74162 | Synchronous 4-bit counter |
| 74163 | Synchronous 4-bit counter |
| 74164 | 8-bit serial shift register |
| 74165 | Parallel-load 8-bit serial shift register |
| 74166 | 8-bit shift register |
| 74173 | 4-bit three-state register |
| 74174 | Hex *F* flip-flop with clear |
| 74175 | Quad *D* flip-flop with clear |
| 74176 | 35-MHz preset table decade counter |
| 74177 | 35-MHz preset table binary counter |
| 74179 | 4-bit parallel-access shift register |
| 74180 | 8-bit odd-even parity generator-checker |
| 74181 | Arithmetic-logic unit |
| 74182 | Look-ahead carry generator |
| 74184 | BCD-to-binary converter |
| 74185 | Binary-to-BCD converter |

*(Contd.)*

**Table B.1**   *(Contd.)*

| Number | Function |
|--------|----------|
| 74189 | Three-state 64-bit random-access memory |
| 7455 | Expandable 4-input 2-wide AND-OR-INVERT gates |
| 7459 | Dual 2-3 input 2-wide AND-OR-INVERT gates |
| 7460 | Dual 4-input expanders |
| 7461 | Triple 3-input expanders |
| 7462 | 2-2-3-3 input 4-wide expanders |
| 7464 | 2-2-3-4 input 4-wide AND-OR-INVERT gates |
| 7465 | 4-wide AND-OR-INVERT gates (open collector) |
| 7470 | Edge-trigged JK flip-flop |
| 7472 | JK master-slave flip-flop |
| 7473 | Dual JK master-slave flip-flop |
| 7474 | Dual *D* flip-flop |
| 7475 | Quad latch |
| 7476 | Dual JK master-slave flip-flop |
| 7480 | Gates full-adder |
| 7482 | 2-bit binary full-adder |
| 7483 | 4-bit binary full-adder |
| 7485 | 4-bit magnitude comparator |
| 7486 | Quad Exclusive-OR gate |
| 7489 | 64-bit random-access read-write memory |
| 7490 | Decade counter |
| 7491 | 8-bit shift register |
| 7492 | Divide-by-12 counter |
| 7493 | 4-bit binary counter |
| 7494 | 4-bit shift register |
| 7495 | 4-bit right-shift-left-shift register |
| 7496 | 5-bit parallel-in-parallel-out shift register |
| 74100 | 4-bit bistable latch |
| 74104 | JK master-slave flip-flop |
| 74105 | JK master-slave flip-flop |
| 74107 | Dual JK master-slave flip-flop |
| 74109 | Dual JK positive-edge-triggered flip-flop |
| 74116 | Dual 4-bit latches with clear |
| 74121 | Monostable multivibrator |
| 74122 | Momostable multivibrator with clear |
| 74123 | Monostable multivibrator |
| 74125 | Three-state quad bus buffer |
| 74126 | Three-state quad bus buffer |
| 74132 | Quad Schmitt trigger |
| 74136 | Quad 2-input Exclusive-OR gate |
| 74141 | BCD-to-decimal decoder-driver |
| 74142 | BCD counter-latch-driver |
| 74145 | BCD-to-decimal decoder-driver |
| 74147 | 10/4 priority encoder |
| 74148 | Priority encoder |
| 74150 | 16-line-to-1-line multiplexer |
| 74151 | 8-channel digital multiplexer |
| 74152 | 8-channel data selector-multiplexer |
| 74190 | Up-down decade counter |
| 74191 | Synchronous binary up-down counter |
| 74192 | Binary up-down counter |
| 74193 | Binary up-down counter |
| 74194 | 4-bit directional shift register |
| 74195 | 4-bit parallel-access shift register |
| 74196 | Presettable decade counter |
| 74197 | Presettable binary counter |
| 74198 | 8-bit shift register |

*(Contd.)*

**Table B.1**   *(Contd.)*

| Number | Function |
|--------|----------|
| 74199 | 8-bit shift register |
| 74221 | Dual one-shot Schmitt trigger |
| 74251 | Three-state 8-channel multiplexer |
| 74259 | 8-bit addressable latch |
| 74276 | Quad JK flip-flop |
| 74279 | Quad debouncer |
| 74283 | 4-bit binary full adder with fast carry |
| 74284 | Three-state 4-bit multiplexer |
| 74285 | Three-state 4-bit multiplexer |
| 74365 | Three-state hex buffers |
| 74366 | Three-state hex buffers |
| 74367 | Three-state hex buffers |
| 74368 | Three-state hex buffers |
| 74390 | Individual clocks with flip-flops |
| 74393 | Dual 4-bit binary counter |

## DIGITAL IC SPECIFICATIONS

The following pages list the functional and electrical characteristics of the popular *54/74 series* of digital ICs.

Functional specifications tell what an IC does, what decisions it makes. These specifications are often expressed with the help of a truth table or formula.

Remember that *positive logic* is where logic 1 is positive with respect to logic 0, *negative logic*, where logic 1 is negative with respect to logic 0. Of course, which type of logic is to be employed is the designer's choice. This choice will affect the very nature of some logic circuits. For example, the NAND gates of the type 7400 IC become NOR gates if negative logic is employed. One may assume that positive logic is employed, however, unless something is said to the contrary. Generally, as here, *the logic gates are identified in terms of positive logic*. Thus, the 7400 is referred to as a quad 2-input NAND gate. In some publications, you may see the same gate referred to as a NAND/NOR gate. The gate may assume either function, and the author is covering both cases.

The *functional specifications* given here include information on the applications and special features of the various circuits. For a complete understanding of these applications and features, refer to the appropriate discussions elsewhere in this text.

The *electrical specifications* include loading information, power dissipation, and speed. The figures given are typical, under normal operating conditions. The loading data, as has already been explained, tells how many circuits of a certain kind may be driven by another given circuit. Unless otherwise noted, *all TTL gate outputs can drive up to 10 inputs, a total input load current of 16 mA*.

For most semiconductors, the power rating tells how much power the device may absorb as heat without malfunctioning. For ICs, the power rating simply tells how much power the device consumes. We are interested in this primarily because it tells us how much power our power supply must provide. The power consumed by most of these devices is small, but in digital systems where large numbers of ICs are used, the power requirements can become appreciable. *The power figures given here tell the typical power usage per package.*

The operating speed of most logic devices is expressed as a *propagation delay time:* $t_{PHL}$ is the time required for a decision to change from high to low, and $t_{PLH}$ is the time required for a decision to change from low to high. For all *sequential circuits,* such as `flip-flops`, counters, and registers, the delay is the time from a clock pulse to a response in the $Q$ or $\overline{Q}$ output.

For sequential circuits, we are frequently more interested in the maximum *toggle rate.* This is the maximum clock frequency that can be used with a sequential device, and as you will see, it is expressed in megahertz.

*Positive supply voltage* is applied to pin 7 and *ground* to pin 14 of most 14-pin TTL ICs; pins 8 and 16 are used on 16-pin ICs. Exceptions to this general rule are noted on the data sheets. For power, you can use a +5 V supply, but three 1.5 V flashlight batteries connected in series to make +4.5 V will work just as well for experimenting. Never use four batteries when experimenting, since that would produce +6 V which exceeds the maximum +5.5 V rating. Higher voltages may be applied to the collectors of some buffer gates having open-collector outputs (see data sheets).

## 7400
### QUAD 2-INPUT NAND GATE

This device consists of four 2-input NAND gates. Each gate may be used as an inverter, or two gates may be cross-coupled to form bistable circuits.

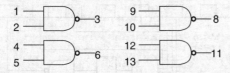

**Fig. B.1**

| | |
|---|---|
| Positive logic: | NAND |
| Negative logic: | NOR |
| Total power dissipation: | 40 mW |
| Propagation delay time: | 13 nsec |

## 7401
### QUAD 2-INPUT NAND GATE

#### *(Open Collector)*

This device consists of four 2-input NAND gates with no output pull-up circuits. It can be used where the wired-OR function is required, or for driving discrete components.

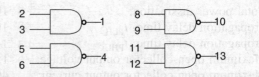

**Fig. B.2**

| | |
|---|---|
| Positive logic: | NAND |
| Negative logic: | NOR |
| Total power dissipation: | 40 mW |
| Propagation delay time: | 35 nsec |
| Maximum open-collector output voltage: | 5.5 V |
| Maximum open-collector output current: | 16 mA |

## 7402
### QUAD 2-INPUT NOR GATE

This device consists of four 2-input NOR gates. Each gate may also be used to make an inverter, or two gates may be cross-coupled to form bistable circuits.

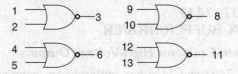

**Fig. B.3**

| | |
|---|---|
| Positive logic: | NOR |
| Negative logic: | NAND |
| Total power dissipation: | 60 mW |
| Propagation delay time: | 13 nsec |

## 7404
### HEX INVERTER

This device offers six independent inverting gates in a single package. Each gate consists of a single input driving an output inverter.

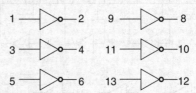

**Fig. B.4**

| | |
|---|---|
| Total power dissipation: | 60 mW |
| Propagation delay time: | 13 nsec |

## 7406, 7416
### HEX INVERTER BUFFER/DRIVER

#### *(Open-Collector High-Voltage Outputs)*

The 7406 and 7416 hex inverter buffer drivers feature standard TTL inputs with inverted high-voltage, high-current, open-collector outputs for interface with MOS logic, lamps, or relays.

| | |
|---|---|
| Total power dissipation: | 160 mW |
| Propagation delay time, $t_{PLH}$: | 10 nsec |
| Propagation delay time, $t_{PHL}$: | 14 nsec |
| Maximum open-collector output voltage: | 15 V |
| Maximum open-collector output current: | 40 mA |

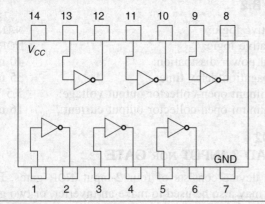

**Fig. B.5.**

# 7407, 7417
## HEX BUFFER/DRIVER

### *(Open-Collector High-Voltage Outputs)*

The 7407 and 7417 hex buffer/driver features standard TTL inputs with non-inverted high-voltage, high-current open-collector outputs for interface with MOS logic, lamps, and relays.

| | |
|---|---|
| Total power dissipation: | 120 mW |
| Propagation delay time, $t_{PLH}$: | 6 nsec |
| Propagation delay time, $t_{PHL}$: | 20 nsec |
| Maximum open-collector output voltage: | 30 V (7407) |
| | 15 V (7417) |
| Maximum open-collector output current: | 40 mA |

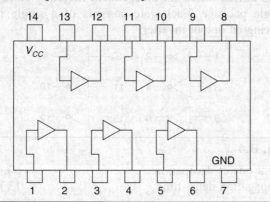

**Fig. B.6**

# 7410
## TRIPLE 3-INPUT NAND GATE

| | |
|---|---|
| Positive logic: | NAND |
| Negative logic: | NOR |
| Total power dissipation: | 30 mW |
| Propagation delay time: | 10 nsec |

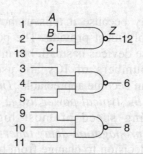

**Fig. B.7**

# 7413
## DUAL NAND SCHMITT TRIGGER

This consists of two identical Schmitt trigger circuits in monolithic IC form. Each circuit functions as a 4-input NAND gate, but because of the Schmitt action, the gate has different input threshold levels for positive- and negative-going signals. The *hysteresis*, or *back-lash*, is the difference between the two threshold levels and is typically 900 mV.

An important design feature of the 7413 is built-in temperature compensation. This insures very high stability of the threshold levels and the hysteresis over a very wide temperature range. Typically, the hysteresis changes by 3% over the temperature range of –55 to 125 °C, and the upper threshold changes by 1% over the same range. The 7413 can be triggered from the slowest of input ramps and still give clean, jitter-free output signals.

| | |
|---|---|
| Total power dissipation: | 80 mW |
| Propagation delay time, $t_{PLH}$: | 18 nsec |
| Propagation delay time, $t_{PHL}$: | 15 nsec |

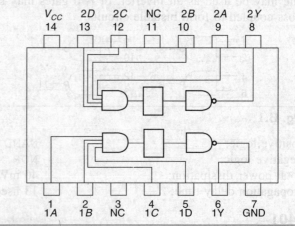

**Fig. B.8**

# 7420
## DUAL 4-INPUT NAND GATE

This device consists of two 4-input NAND gates. These gates may be cross-coupled to form an R-S flip-flop.

| | |
|---|---|
| Positive logic: | NAND |
| Negative logic: | NOR |
| Total power dissipation: | 20 mW |
| Propagation delay time: | 13 nsec |

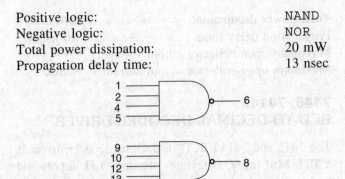

**Fig. B.9**

## 7426
## QUAD 2-INPUT NAND BUFFER

### (Open-Collector High-Voltage Output)

The 7426 quad 2-input NAND gate features standard TTL inputs with high-voltage open-collector outputs for interface with MOS logic, lamps, and relays.

| | |
|---|---|
| Total power dissipation: | 40 mW |
| Propagation delay time, $t_{PLH}$: | 16 nsec |
| Propagation delay time, $t_{PHL}$: | 11 nsec |
| Maximum open-collector output voltage: | 15 V |
| Maximum open-collector output current: | 16 mA |

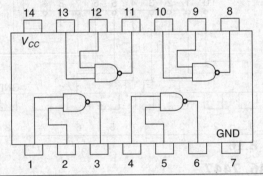

**Fig. B.10**

## 7430
## 8-INPUT NAND GATE

This device is an 8-input NAND gate. It is useful when processing a large number of variables, such as in encoders and decoders.

| | |
|---|---|
| Positive logic: | NAND |
| Negative logic: | NOR |
| Total power dissipation: | 10 mW |
| Propagation delay time: | 13 nsec |

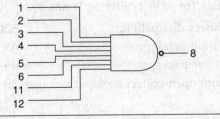

**Fig. B.11**

## 7437, 7438
## QUAD 2-INPUT NAND BUFFER

### (Open-Collector Output)

The 7437 is a NAND gate similar to the 7400 except that it will drive three times as many loads. The 7438 is an open-collector type, similar to 7403.

The 7437 and 7438 contain four 2-input NAND gates. The 7437 has a guaranteed fan-out of 30 loads. The 7438 has an open-collector output for wired-AND applications, but still retains the high sink-current capability of the 7437.

| | |
|---|---|
| Total power dissipation: | 100 mW |
| Propagation delay time, $t_{PLH}$: | 10 nsec |
| Propagation delay time, $t_{PHL}$: | 14 nsec |
| Output loading factor: | 30 (7437) |
| Maximum open-collector output voltage: | 5.5 V (7438) |
| Maximum open-collector output current: | 48 mA (7438) |

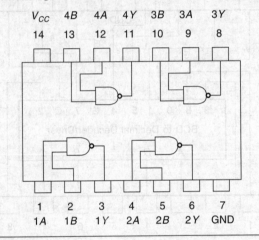

**Fig. B.12**

## 7440
## DUAL 4-INPUT NAND BUFFER

This device consists of two 4-input NAND power gate circuits. Each gate is designed for driving 30 input loads.

| | |
|---|---|
| Positive logic: | NAND |
| Negative logic: | NOR |
| Output loading factor: | 30 |
| Total power dissipation: | 50 mW |
| Propagation delay time: | 13 ns |

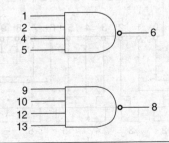

**Fig. B.13**

## 7441
## BCD-TO-DECIMAL DECODER/DRIVER

The 7441 Nixie decoder/driver is a 1-out-of-10 decoder which has been designed to provide the necessary high-voltage characteristics required for driving gas-filled cold-cathode indicator tubes. It may also be utilized in driving relays or other high-voltage interface circuitry.

The element is designed using TTL techniques and is therefore completely compatible with DTL and TTL elements. The specially designed output drivers provide the necessary stable output state. There are no input codes where all outputs are off, or where more than one out put can be turned on.

Total power dissipation:                 80 mW
Maximum open-collector output voltage:   60 V
Maximum open-collector output current:   7 mA

Total power dissipation:                 340 mW
Propagation delay time:                  20 nsec
Maximum open-collector output voltage:   55 V
Maximum open-collector output current:   7 mA

## 7445, 74145
## BCD-TO-DECIMAL DECODER/DRIVER

The 7445 and 74145 BCD-to-decimal decoder/driver is a TTL MSI array. It features standard TTL inputs and high-voltage, high-current outputs.

Total power dissipation:                 215 mW
Propagation delay time:                  60 nsec
Maximum open-collector output voltage:   30 V (7445)
                                         15 V (74145)
Maximum open-collector output current:   80 mA

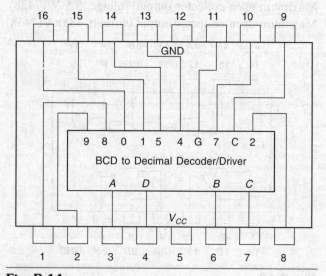

**Fig. B.14**

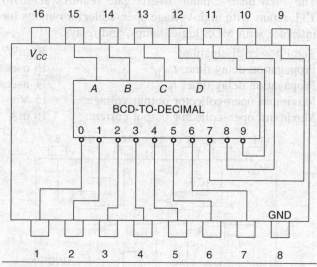

**Fig. B.16**

## 7442
## BCD-TO-DECIMAL DECODER

The 7442 BCD-to-decimal decoder is a TTL MSI array utilized in decoding and logic conversion applications. The 7442 decodes a 4-bit BCD number into 1 of 10 outputs.

## 7446, 7447
## BCD-T0-7-SEGMENT DECODER/DRIVER

The 7446 and 7447 BCD-to-7-segment decoder driver ICs are TTL monolithic devices consisting of the necessary logic to decode a BCD code to 7-segment readout plus selected signs.

Incorporated in this device is a blanking circuit allowing leading- and trailing-zero suppression. Also included is a lamp test control to turn 'on' all segments.

The 7446 and 7447 provide open-collector output transistors for directly driving lamps.

Total power dissipation:                 320 mW
Propagation delay time:                  45 nsec
Current per package:                     43 mA
Maximum open-collector output voltage:   30 V (7446)
                                         15 V (7447)

Maximum open-collector output current:   40 mA

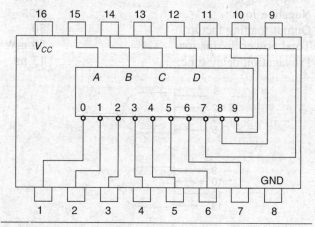

**Fig. B.15**

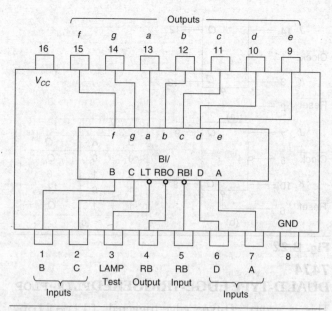

**Fig. B.17**

## 7448
## BCD-TO-7-SEGMENT DECODER/DRIVER

The 7448 BCD-to-7-segment decoder/driver is a TTL monolithic device consisting of the necessary logic to decode a BCD code to 7-segment readout plus selected signs.

Incorporated in this device is a blanking circuit allowing leading- and trailing-zero suppression. Also included is a lamp test control to turn on all segments.

The 7448 has a 2k pullup resistor on the outputs to provide sufficient source current to drive interface elements.

| | |
|---|---|
| Total power dissipation: | 265 mW |
| Propagation delay time: | 45 nsec |
| Maximum low-level output current: | 6.4 mA |

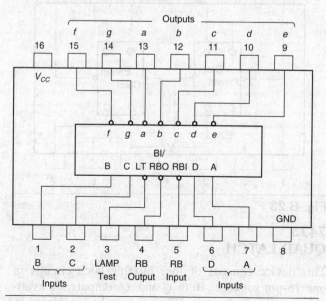

**Fig. B.18**

## 7450
## EXPANDABLE DUAL 2-WIDE 2-INPUT AND-OR-INVERT GATE

This device consists of two AND-OR-invert gates, one of which is OR expandable. Each gate is made up of two 2-input AND gates ORed together and inverted. Up to four 7460 expander gates may be ORed with the device at the expander points.
Positive logic:

$$(A \cdot B) + (C \cdot D) + \text{(expanders)}$$

Negative logic:

$$(A + B) \cdot (C + D) \cdot \text{(expanders)}$$

| | |
|---|---|
| Total power dissipation: | 28 mW |
| Propagation delay time: | 13 nsec |

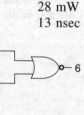

**Fig. B.19**

## 7470
## J-K FLIP-FLOP

The 7470 is an edge-triggered J-K flip-flop, featuring gated inputs, direct clear and preset inputs, and complementary $Q$ and $\bar{Q}$ outputs. Input information is transferred to the outputs on the positive edge of the clock pulse.

Direct-coupled clock triggering occurs at a specific voltage level of the clock pulse. After the clock input threshold voltage has been passed, the gated inputs are locked out.

This flip-flop is ideally suited for medium- and high-speed applications. It can be used to obtain a significant saving in system power dissipation and package count where input gating is required.

| | |
|---|---|
| Total power dissipation: | 65 mW |
| Operating frequency: | 35 MHz |

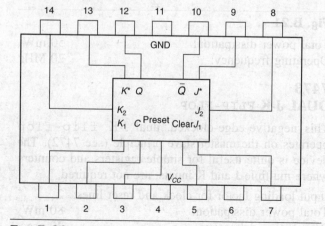

**Fig. B.20**

## 7472
### J-K MASTER/SLAVE FLIP-FLOP

These J-K flip-flops are based on the master/slave principle. Each flip-flop has AND gate inputs for entry into the master section which is controlled by the clock pulse. The clock pulse also regulates the state of the coupling transistors which connect the master and slave sections. The sequence of operation is as follows:

1. Isolate slave from master.
2. Enter information from AND gate inputs to master.
3. Disable AND gate inputs.
4. Transfer information from master to slave.

$t_n$ = bit time before clock pulse
$t_{n+1}$ = bit time after clock pulse

**Truth Table**

| $t_n$ | | $t_{n+1}$ |
|---|---|---|
| J | K | Q |
| 0 | 0 | $Q_n$ |
| 0 | 1 | 0 |
| 1 | 0 | 1 |
| 1 | 1 | $\bar{Q}_n$ |

(a)

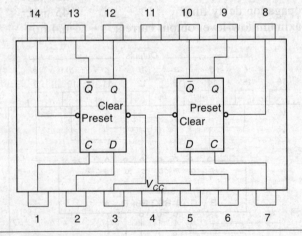

(b)

**Fig. B.21**

Total power dissipation:    50 mW
Operating frequency:    20 MHz

## 7473
### DUAL J-K FLIP-FLOP

This negative-edge-clocked, dual J-K flip-flop operates on the master/slave principle (see 7472). The device is quite useful for simple registers and counters where multiple J and K inputs, are not required.

Input loading factor for clock and reset lines: 2
Total power dissipation:    80 mW
Propagation delay time:    30 nsec
Operating frequency:    15 MHz

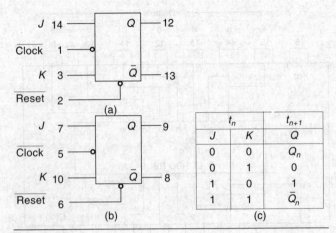

**Fig. B.22**

## 7474
### DUAL D-TYPE EDGE-TRIGGERED FLIP-FLOP

This is a dual *D*-type edge-triggered flip-flop, featuring direct clear and preset inputs and complementary $Q$ and $\bar{Q}$ outputs. Input information is transferred to the $Q$ output on the positive-going edge of the clock pulse.

Clock triggering occurs at a voltage level of the clock pulse, and is not directly related to the transition time of the positive-going pulse. After the clock input threshold voltage has been passed, the data input ($D$) is locked out.

A low input to the preset terminal sets $Q$ to logic 1. A low input to the clear input sets $Q$ to logic 0. Preset and clear are independent of the clock input.

Total power dissipation:    86 mW
Operating frequency:    25 MHz

**Fig. B.23**

## 7475
### QUAD LATCH

This device consists of four bistable latch circuits in one 16-pin package. Both $Q$ and $\bar{Q}$ outputs are available on all four devices. When the strobe (enable) is in the logic 1 state, the $Q$ output will follow the state of the data input. When the strobe goes to the logic 0 state, the $Q$ output will retain the state of the data input at the time of the transition from the logic 1 state.

Input loading factor for $D$: 2
Input loading factor for strobe: 4
Total power dissipation: 160 mW
Propagation delay time: 30 ns

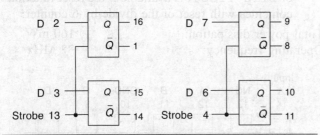

**Fig. B.24**

## 7476
### DUAL J-K MASTER-SLAVE FLIP-FLOP

This J-K flip-flop is based on the master/slave principle (see 7472). Inputs to the master section are controlled by the clock pulse. The clock pulse also regulates the state of the coupling transistors which connect the master and slave sections.

A low input to the preset terminal sets $Q$ to logic 1. A low input to the clear terminal sets $Q$ to logic 0. Clear and preset are independent of the clock input.

Total power dissipation: 100 mW
Operating frequency: 20 MHz

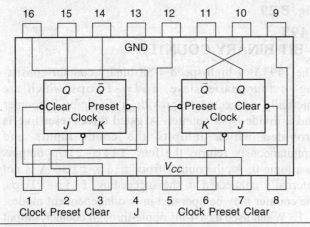

**Fig. B.25**

## 7486
### QUAD 2-INPUT EXCLUSIVE-OR GATE

The 7486 quad 2-input exclusive-OR gate is a TTL element providing the function $A \oplus B = A\bar{B} + \bar{A}B$ at the output

Total power dissipation: 150 mW
Propagation delay time: 18 nsec

| Inputs | | Output |
|---|---|---|
| A | B | Y |
| 0 | 0 | 0 |
| 0 | 1 | 1 |
| 1 | 0 | 1 |
| 1 | 1 | 0 |

(a)

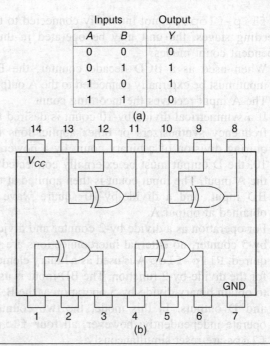

(b)

**Fig. B.26**

## 7489
### 64-BIT READ/WRITE MEMORY (RAM)

The 7489 is a TTL 64-bit read/write random-access memory, organized as 16 words of 4 bits each. The 7489 is ideally suited for application as scratch pads and high-speed buffer memories.

Words are selected through a 4-input binary decoder when the chip select input (CE) is at logic 0. Data is written into the memory when *read enable* (RE) is at logic 0, and read from the memory when RE is at logic 1.

Total-power dissipation: 380 mW
Read time: 35 nsec
Write time: 50 nsec

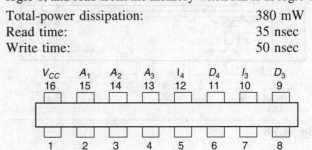

**Fig. B.27**

## 7490
### DECADE COUNTER

The 7490 is a high-speed decade counter, consisting of four master/slave flip-flops internally connected to provide a divide-by-2 counter and a divide-by-5 counter. Gated direct-reset lines are provided to inhibit count inputs and return all outputs to a logic 0 or to a binary-coded decimal (BCD) count of 9. As the output from flip-flop A is not internally connected to the succeeding stages, the unit may be operated in three independent count modes:

1. When used as a BCD decade counter, the BD input must be externally connected to the A output. The A input receives the incoming count.

2. If a symmetrical divide-by-10 count is desired for frequency synthesizers or other applications requiring division of a binary count by a power of 10, the D output must be externally connected to the A input. The input count is then applied at the BD input, and a divide-by-10 square wave is obtained at output A.

3. For operation as a divide-by-2 counter and divide-by-5 counter, no external interconnections are required. Flip-flop A is used as a binary element for the divide-by-2 function. The BD input is used to obtain binary divide-by-5 operation at the B, C, and D outputs. In this mode, the two counters operate independently; however, all four flip-flops are reset simultaneously.

Total power dissipation:          160 mW
Operating frequency:              32 MHz

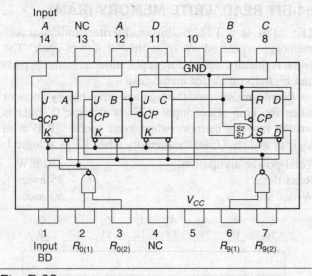

**Fig. B.28**

## 7492
## DIVIDE-BY-TWELVE COUNTER

The 7492 is a high-speed 4-bit binary counter consisting of four master/slave flip-flops which are internally connected to provide a divide-by-2 counter and a divide-by-6 counter. A gated direct reset line is provided which inhibits the count inputs and simultaneously returns the four flip-flop outputs to a logic 0. As the output from flip-flop A is not internally connected to the succeeding flip-flops, the counter may be operated in two independent modes:

1. When used as a divide-by-12 counter, output A must be externally connected to input BD. The

input count pulses are applied to input A. Simultaneous division of, 2, 6, and 12 are performed at the A, C, and D outputs.

2. When used as a divide-by-6 counter, the input count pulses are applied to input BC. Simultaneously, frequency division of 3 and 6 are available at the C and D outputs. Independent use of flip-flop A is available if the reset function coincides with reset of the divide-by-6 counter.

Total power dissipation:          160 mW
Operating frequency:              32 MHz

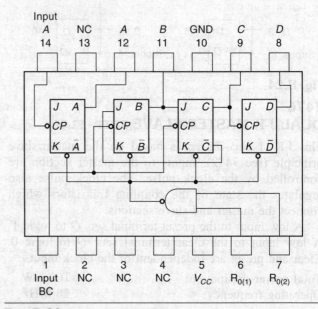

**Fig. B.29**

## 7493
## 4-BIT BINARY COUNTER

The 7493 is a high-speed 4-bit binary counter consisting of four master/slave flip-flops which are internally connected to provide a divide-by-2 counter and a divide-by-8 counter. A gated direct reset line is provided which inhibits the count inputs and simultaneously returns the four flip-flop outputs to a logic 0. As the output from flip-flop A is not internally connected to the succeeding flip-flops, the counter may be operated in two independent modes:

1. When used as a 4-bit ripple-through counter, output A must be externally connected to input B. The input count pulses are applied to input A. Simultaneous divisions of 2, 4, 8, and 16 are performed at the A, B, C, and D outputs.

2. When used as a 3-bit ripple-through counter, the input count pulses are applied to input B. Simultaneous frequency divisions of 2, 4, and 8 are available at the B, C, and D outputs. Independent use of flip-flop D is available if the reset function coincides with reset of the 3-bit ripple-through counter.

Total power dissipation:  160 mW
Operating frequency:  32 MHz

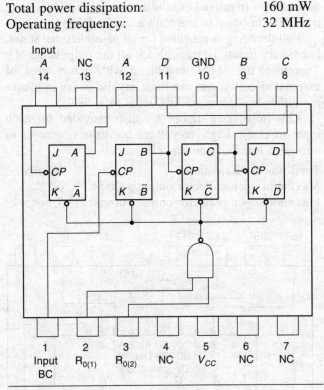

**Fig. B.30**

## 7495
## 4-BIT RIGHT/LEFT SHIFT REGISTER

The 7495 is a universal 4-bit shift register designed with standard TTL techniques. The circuit layout consists of four R-S master/slave flip-flops, four AND-OR-invert gates, and six inverters configured to form a versatile register which will perform right-shift/left shift or parallel-in/parallel-out operations. These operations are controlled by input level to the mode control.

Right-shift operations are performed when a logic 0 level is applied to the mode control. Serial data is entered at the serial input (pin 1) and shifted one position right on each clock-1 pulse. In this mode, clock-2 and parallel inputs A through D are inhibited.

Parallel-in/parallel-out operations are performed when a logic-1 level is applied to the mode control. Parallel data is entered at parallel inputs A through D and is transferred to the data outputs A through D on each clock-2 pulse. In this mode, left-shift operations may be implemented by externally tying the output of each flip-flop to the parallel input of the previous flip-flop; with serial inputs, data is entered at input D.

Information must be present at the inputs prior to clocking, and transfer of data occurs on the falling edge of the clock pulse.

Total Power dissipation:  195 mW
Operating frequency:  25 MHz

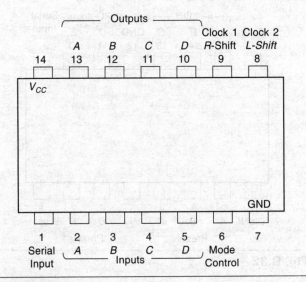

**Fig. B.31**

## 7496
## 5-BIT SHIFT REGISTER

This shift register consists of five R-S master/slave flip-flops connected to perform parallel-to-serial-to-parallel conversion of binary data. Since both inputs and outputs to all flip-flops are accessible, parallel-in/parallel-out or serial-in/serial-out operation may be performed.

All flip-flops are simultaneously set to the logic 0 state by applying a logic 0 voltage to the clear input. This condition may be applied independent of the state of the clock input.

The flip-flops may be independently set to the logic 1 state by applying a logic 1 to both the preset input of the specific flip-flop and the common preset input. The common preset input is provided to allow flexibility of either setting each flip-flop independently or setting two or more flip-flops simultaneously. Preset is also independent of the state of the clock input or clear input.

Transfer of information to the output pins occurs when the clock input goes from a logic 0 to a logic 1. Since the flip-flops are R-S master/slave circuits, the proper information must appear at the R-S inputs of each flip-flop prior to the rising edge of the clock input voltage waveform. The serial input provides this information to the first flip-flop, while the outputs of the subsequent flip-flops provide information for the remaining R-S inputs. The clear input must be at a logic 1 and the preset input must be at a logic 0 when clocking occurs.

Total power dissipation:  240 mW
Operating frequency:  10 MHz

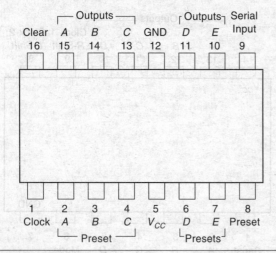

**Fig. B.32**

## 74107
### DUAL J-K MASTER/SLAVE FLIP-FLOP

The 74107A J-K flip-flop is based on the master/slave principle (see 7472). Inputs to the master section are controlled by the clock pulse. The clock pulse also regulates the state of the coupling transistors which connect the master and slave sections.

Total power dissipation:          100 mW
Operating frequency:          20 MHz

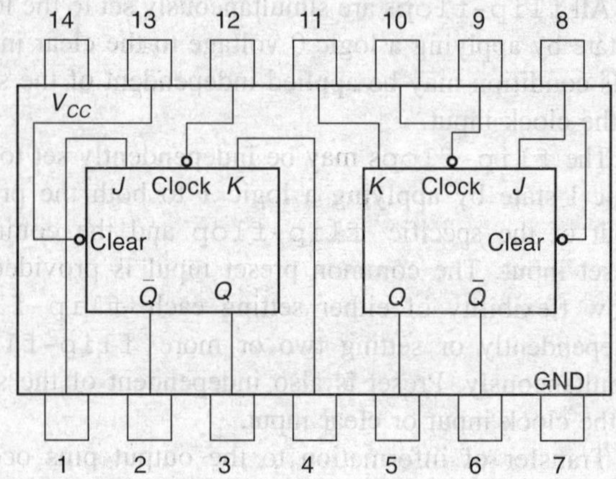

**Fig. B.33**

## 74141
### BCD-TO-DECIMAL DECODER/DRIVER

This is a BCD-to-decimal decoder designed specifically to drive cold-cathode indicator tubes. This decoder dem-

onstrates an improved capability to minimize switching transients in order to maintain a stable display.

Full decoding is provided for all possible input states. For binary inputs 10 through 15, all the outputs are off. Therefore, the 74141, combined with a minimum of external circuitry, can use these invalid codes in blanking either leading or trailing zeros in a display.

Low-impedance diodes are also provided for each input to clamp negative-voltage transitions in order to minimize transmission-line effects.

Total power dissipation:          80 mW
Maximum open-collector output voltage:          60 V
Maximum open-collector output current:          7 mA

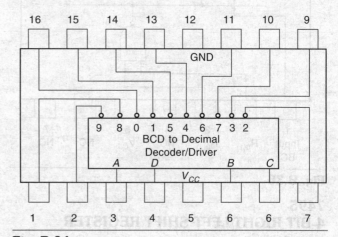

**Fig. B.34**

## 74150
### 16-LINE-TO-1-LINE DATA SELECTOR/MULTIPLEXER

The 74150 is a 1-of-16 data selector which performs parallel-to-serial data conversion. The unit incorporates an enable circuit for chip select. This allows multiplexing from *n* lines to one line.

The 74150 is provided with a strobe input which when set to logic 0 enables the function of these multiplexers.

This data selector/multiplexer is fully compatible for use with other TTL or DTL circuits. A fan-out to 20 normalized series 74 loads is provided in the logic 1 state to facilitate connection of unused inputs to used inputs.

Total power dissipation:          200 mW
Propagation delay time (select) time:          22 nsec

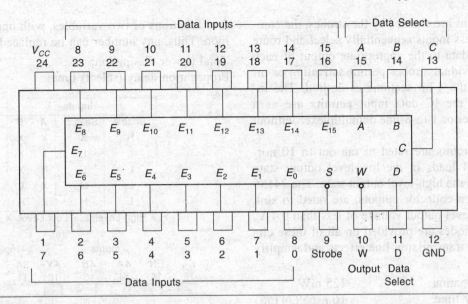

**Fig. B.35**

## 74151
### 8-LINE-TO-1-LINE DATA SELECTOR/MULTIPLEXER

The 74151 is a 1-of-8 data selector which performs parallel-to-serial data conversion. The unit incorporates an enable circuit for chip select. This allows multiplexing from *n* lines to one line. Both true and complement outputs are available.

| Total power dissipation: | 145 mW |
|---|---|
| Propagation delay (select) time: | 19 nsec |

**Fig. B.36**

## 74153
### DUAL 4-LINE-TO-1-LINE DATA SELECTOR/MULTIPLEXER

Each of these monolithic data selector/multiplexers contains inverters and drivers to supply fully complemen-tary on-chip binary-decoding and data selection. Separate strobe inputs are provided for each of the two 4-line sections.

These data selector/multiplexers are fully compatible for use with most TTL and DTL circuits. A fan-out to 20 series 74 loads is provided in the high-level state to facilitate connection of unused inputs to used inputs.

| Total power dissipation: | 180 mW |
|---|---|
| Propagation delay (select) time: | 17 nsec |

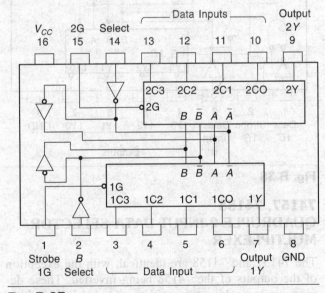

**Fig. B.37**

## 74155, 74156
### DUAL 2-LINE-TO-4-LINE DECODER/DEMULTIPLEXER

These monolithic TTL circuits feature dual 1-line-to-4-line demultiplexers with individual strobes and com-mon binary address inputs, all in a single 16-pin package.

When both sections are enabled by the strobes, the common binary address inputs sequentially select and route associated input data to the appropriate output of each section. The individual strobes permit activating or inhibiting each of the 4-bit sections as desired. The inverter following the IC data input permits use as a 3-to-8-line decoder or 1-to-8-line demultiplexer without external gating.

The 74155 circuits are rated to fan out to 10 normalized series 74 loads in the low-level output state and to 20 loads in the high-level output state. The 74156 circuits, with open-collector outputs, are rated to sink 16 mA at a low-level output voltage of less than 0.4 V. Input clamping diodes are provided on all of these circuits to minimize transmission-line effects and simplify system design.

Total power dissipation:          125 mW
Propagation delay time:          16 nsec (74155)
                                           21 nse (74156)

four functions of two variables, with one variable common. Thus, any number can be replaced.

Total power dissipation:          150 mW
Propagation delay (select) time:          14 nsec

| Inputs | | | | Output Y |
|---|---|---|---|---|
| *Enable* | *Select* | *A* | *B* | *74157* |
| H | X | X | X | L |
| L | L | L | X | L |
| L | L | H | X | H |
| L | H | X | L | L |
| L | H | X | H | H |

H = High Level, L = Low Level, X = Irrelevant

(a)

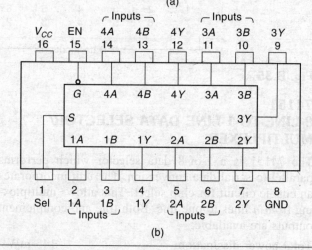

(b)

**Fig. B.39**

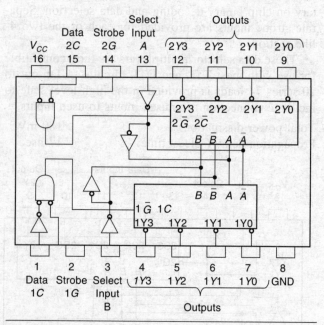

**Fig. B.38**

## 74157, 74158
## QUADRUPLE 2-INPUT DATA SELECTOR/ MULTIPLEXER

The 74157 and 74158 are identical, with the exception of the outputs of the 74158 being inverted. These devices are logical implementations of a 4-pole/2-position switch, with the position of the switch being set by the logic levels supplied to the one select input. When the enable input (E) is high, all outputs are low, regardless of the other inputs.

The devices provide the ability, in one package, to select 4 bits of either data or control from two sources. By proper manipulation of the inputs, it can generate

## 74160, 74161, 74162, 74163
## SYNCHRONOUS 4-BIT COUNTER

These synchronous, presettable counters feature an internal carry look-ahead for application in high-speed counting schemes. The 74160 and 74162 are decade counters; the 74161 and 74163 are binary counters. Synchronous operation is provided by having all `flip-flops` clocked simultaneously, so that the output changes coincide with each other. This mode of operation eliminates the output counting spikes which are normally associated with asynchronous (ripple clock) counters. A buffered clock input triggers the four J-K master/slave `flip-flops` on the rising (positive-going) edge of the clock input waveform.

All inputs are diode-clamped to minimize transmission-line effects, thereby simplifying system design. A full fan-out to 10 normalized series 74 loads is available from each of the outputs in the low-level state. A fan-out of 20 normalized series 74 loads is provided in the high-level state to facilitate connection of unused inputs.

Total power dissipation:          305 mW
Operating frequency:          25 MHz

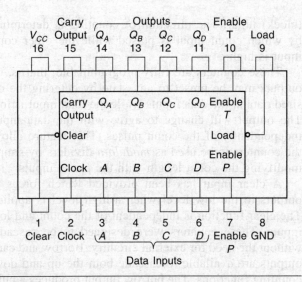

**Fig. B.40**

# 74164
## 8-BIT PARALLEL-OUT SERIAL SHIFT REGISTER

These 8-bit shift registers feature gated serial inputs and an asynchronous clear. The gated serial inputs (A and B) permit complete control over incoming data. A low at either or both of the inputs inhibits entry of new data and resets the first flip-flop to the low level at the next clock pulse. A high level on both inputs sets the first flip-flop to a high level at the next clock pulse. Data at the serial inputs may be changed while the clock is high. Information will be entered only on the low-to-high level transition of the clock input.

| | |
|---|---|
| Total power dissipation: | 167 mW |
| Maximum clock frequency: | 25 MHz |

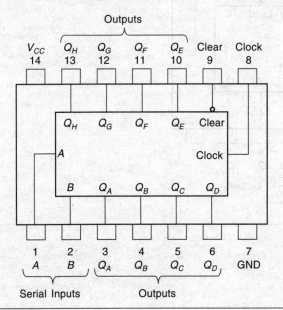

**Fig. B.41**

# 74165
## PARALLEL-LOAD 8-BIT SHIFT REGISTER

The 74165 is an 8-bit serial shift register that shifts data to the right when clocked. Parallel-in access to each stage is made available by eight individual, direct data inputs which are enabled by a low level at the shift/load input. These registers also feature gated clock inputs and complementary outputs from the 8th bit.

Clocking is accomplished through a 2-input NOR gate, permitting one input to be used as a clock-inhibit function. Holding either of the clock inputs high inhibits clocking, and holding either clock input low with the load input high enables the other clock input. The clock-inhibit input should be changed to the high level only while the clock input is high. Parallel loading is inhibited as long as the load input is high. When taken low, data at the parallel inputs is loaded directly into the register independently of the state of the clock.

| | |
|---|---|
| Total power dissipation: | 210 mW |
| Maximum clock frequency: | 25 MHz |

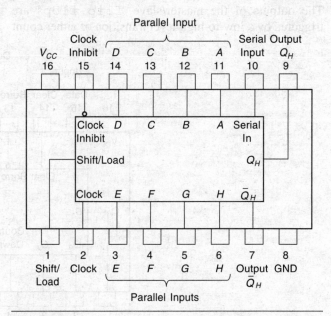

**Fig. B.42**

# 74180
## 8-BIT ODD/EVEN PARITY GENERATOR/CHECKER

The 74180 8-bit odd/even parity generator and checker is a TTL monolithic array, featuring gating logic arranged to generate or check odd or even parity.

| | |
|---|---|
| Total power dissipation: | 170 mW |
| Propagation delay time: | 35 nsec |

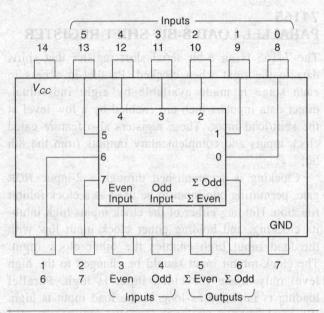

**Fig. B.43**

## 74192
## SYNCHRONOUS DECADE UP/DOWN COUNTER

The outputs of the master/slave `flip-flops` are triggered by a low-to-high level transition of either count (clock) input. The direction of counting is determined by which count input is pulsed while the other count input is high.

These counters are fully programmable; that is, the outputs may be preset to any state by entering the desired data at the data inputs while the load input is low. The output will change to agree with the data inputs independently of the count pulses. This feature allows the counters to be used as *modulo-n* dividers by simply modifying the count length with the preset inputs.

A clear input has been provided which forces all outputs to the low level when a high level is applied. The clear function is independent of the count and load inputs. These counters were designed to be cascaded without the need for external circuitry. Borrow and carry outputs are available to cascade both the up and down counting functions. The borrow output produces a pulse equal in width to the countdown input when the counter underflows. Similarly, the carry output produces a pulse equal in width to the countup input when an overflow condition exists. The counters can then be easily cascaded by feeding the borrow and carry outputs to the countdown and countup inputs, respectively, of the succeeding counter.

| | |
|---|---|
| Total power dissipation: | 325 mW |
| Maximum count frequency: | 32 MHz |

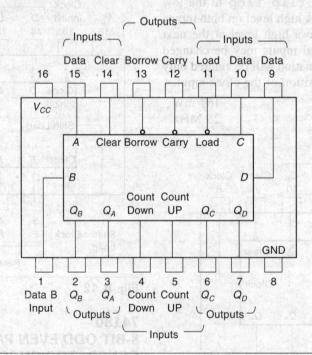

**Fig. B.44**

# Linear Integrated Circuits

## 555 TYPE TIMER

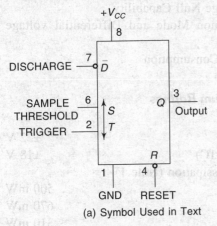

(a) Symbol Used in Text

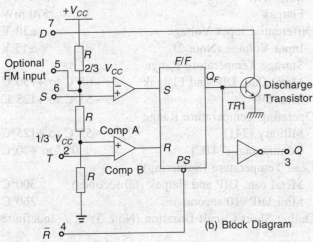

(b) Block Diagram

**Fig. C.1**  *555 Timer.*

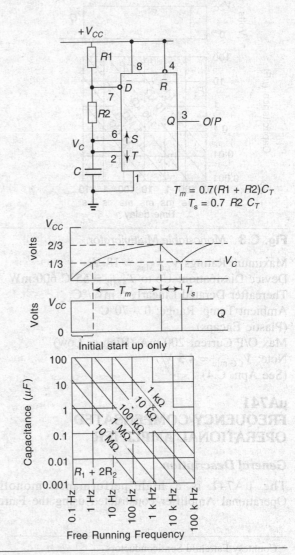

$$T_m = 0.7(R1 + R2)C_T$$
$$T_s = 0.7\, R2\, C_T$$

**Fig. C.2**  *Astable Multivibratior.*

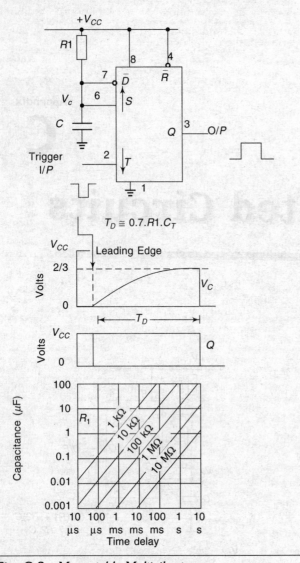

$$T_D \cong 0.7.R1.C_T$$

**Fig. C.3** *Monostable Multivibrator.*

Maximum Ratings $V_{CC \, Max}$ = 18 V
Device Dissipation: Up to $T_{AMB}$ = 55°C 600 mW
Thereafter Derated Linearly 5 mW/°C
Ambient Temp. Range: 0 – 70°C
(Plastic Encaps).
Max O/P Current 200 mA (High or Low)
Note: $V_{CC \, min}$ = 4.5 V
(See Apn. C.4)

# μA741
# FREQUENCY-COMPENSATED
# OPERATIONAL AMPLIFIER

## General Description

The μA741 is a high performance monolithic
Operational Amplifier constructed using the Fairchild

---

\* Countesy Fairchild Semiconductors

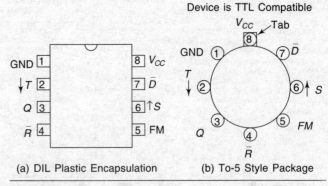

(a) DIL Plastic Encapsulation    (b) To-5 Style Package

**Fig. C.4**

Planar\* epitaxial process. It is intended for a wide range
of analog applications. High comon mode voltage range
and absence of "latch-up" tendencies make the μA741
ideal for use as a voltage follower. The high gain and
wide range of operating voltage provides superior
performance in integrator, summing amplifier, and
general feedback applications.

- No Frequency Compensation Required
- Short Circuit Protection
- Offset Voltage Null Capability
- Large Common Mode and Differential voltage ranges
- Low Power Consumption
- No Latch Up

### Absolute Maximum Ratings

| | |
|---|---|
| Supply Voltage | |
| Military (741) | ±22 V |
| Commercial (741C) | ±18 V |
| Internal Power Dissipation (Note 1) | |
| Metal Can | 500 mW |
| DIP | 670 mW |
| Mini DIP | 310 mW |
| Flatpak | 570 mW |
| Differential Input Voltage | ±30 V |
| Input Voltage (Note 2) | ±15.V |
| Storage Temperature Range | |
| Metal Can, DIP and Flatpak | –65°C to +150°C |
| Mini DIP | –55°C to +125°C |
| Operating Temperature Range | |
| Military (741) | –55°C to +125°C |
| Commercial (741C) | 0°C to +70°C |
| Lead Temperature (Soldering) | |
| Metal can, DIP and flatpak (60 seconds) | 300°C |
| Mini DIP (10 seconds) | 260°C |
| Output Short Citcuit Duration (Note 3) | Indefinite |

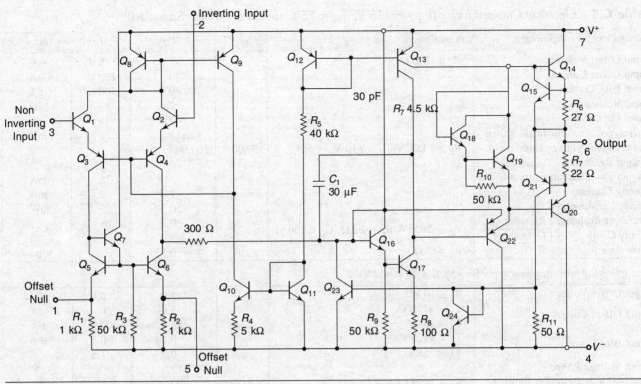

**Fig. C.5**  *Equivalent Circuit.*

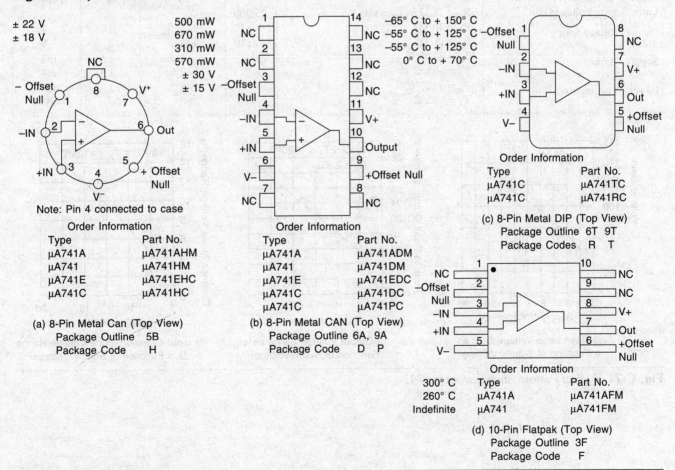

**Fig. C.6**  *Connection Diagram.*

**Table C.1** *Electrical Characteristics ($V_S = \pm 15$ V, $T_A = 25°C$ unless otherwise Specified)*

| Parameters (see definition) | | Conditions | Min. | Typ. | Max. | Units |
|---|---|---|---|---|---|---|
| Input Offset Voltage | | $R_S \leq 10$ kΩ | | 1.0 | 5.0 | mV |
| Input Offset Current | | | | 20 | 200 | nA |
| Input Bias Current | | | | 80 | 500 | nA |
| Input Resistance | | | 0.3 | 2.0 | | MΩ |
| Input Capacitance | | | | 1.4 | | pF |
| Offset Voltage Adjustment Range | | | | ±15 | | mV |
| Large Signal Voltage Gain | | $R_L \geq 2$ kΩ, $V_{OUT} = \pm10$ V | 50,00 | 200,000 | | |
| Output Resistance | | | | 75 | | Ω |
| Output Short Circuit Current | | | | | 25 | mA |
| Supply Current | | | | 1.7 | 2.8 | mA |
| Power Consumption | | | | 50 | 85 | mW |
| Transient Response | Risetime | $V_{IN} = 20$ mV, $R_L = 2$ kΩ, $C_L < 100$ pF | | 0.3 | | μs |
| (Unity Gain) | Over shoot | | | 5.0 | | % |
| Slew Rate | | $R_L > 2$kΩ | | 0.5 | | V/μs |

The following specifications apply for $-55°C < T_A < +125°C$:

| Parameters (see definition) | Conditions | Min. | Typ. | Max. | Units |
|---|---|---|---|---|---|
| Input Offset Voltage | $R_S \leq 10$ kΩ | | 1.0 | 6.0 | mV |
| Input Offset Current | $T_A = +125°C$ | | 7.0 | 200 | nA |
| | $T_A = -55°C$ | | 85 | 500 | nA |
| Input Bias Current | $T_A = +125°C$ | | 0.03 | 0.5 | μm |
| | $T_A = -55°C$ | | 0.3 | 1.5 | |
| Input Voltage Range | | ±12 | ±13 | | V |
| Comon Mode Rejection Ratio | $R_S \leq 10$ kΩ | 70 | 90 | | dB |
| Supply Voltage Rejection Ratio | $R_S \leq 10$ kΩ | | 30 | 150 | μV/V |
| Large Signal Voltage Gain | $R_L \geq 2$k Ω, $V_{OUT} = \pm10$ V | 25,000 | | | |
| Output Voltage Swing | $R_L \geq 10$ kΩ | ±12 | ±14 | | V |
| | $R_L \geq 2$k Ω | ±10 | ±13 | | V |
| Supply Current | $T_A = +125°C$ | | 1.5 | 2.5 | mA |
| | $T_A = -55°C$ | | 2.0 | 3.3 | mA |
| Power Consumption | $T_A = +125°C$ | | 45 | 75 | mW |
| | $T_A = -55°C$ | | 60 | 100 | mW |

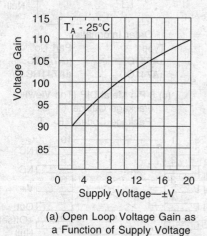

(a) Open Loop Voltage Gain as
a Function of Supply Voltage

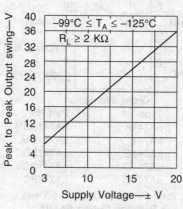

(b) Output Voltage Swing as a
Function of Suply Voltage

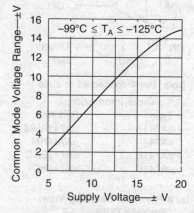

(c) Input Common Mode Voltage Range
as a Function of Supply Voltage

**Fig. C.7** *Typical Performance Curves for 741*

# Interfacing Devices

## 1-BUS LINE SYSTEM

A bus-line system is a special *interface system* in which all the instruments are connected *in parallel* to a number of communication lines as illustrated in principle by Fig. D.1. The *advantage* of such a system is that interconnecting cable problems have effectively been eliminated and that *additional units can easily be added*. However, complications have been created: for example, if it is required to transfer information from instrument *A* to instrument *C*, a number of *arrangements* must be made.

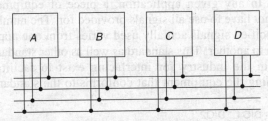

**Fig. D.1** *Four-line Interconnecting Bus.*

1. Instrument *A* must be set ready to *supply* the data to the line. *It must be addressed as a talker.*
2. Instrument *C* must be set ready to *receive* the data *it must be addressed as a listener.*
3. All other instruments must be *set passive*.
4. If a series of data has to be transferred, steps must be taken to ensure that no new data is supplied by the talker before the current set has been *completely accepted* by the listener. *This is taken care of by the handshake or data byte transfer control procedure.*
5. All instruments must understand a number of *general statements* and *commands* such as 'message starts, 'memory ends', and 'attention please'.

To oversee such an arrangement it is apparent that *some kind of controller is required to regulate traffic between the various instruments via the bus.*

## 2-IEC BUS

This is a system with 16 parallel lines, which are divided into three groups according to the function as shown in Fig. D.2. Eight of the lines form the data bus which is used for transferring measuring data, addresses and programming data. Three lines are used for direct communication between a *talker* and *listeners*, a process correctly termed the data-byte transfer control but more commonly referred to as the *handshake function*. The remaining five lines are used for the general *interface management messages*, that is, *management between the controller and the controlled.*

## 3-IEEE 488 (GPIB) BUS

The GPIB is defined by IEEE Std 488 and is therefore sometimes known as the *IEEE-488 bus*. This is a standard for interfacing with programmable instrumentation or control systems. It is an eight-bit system that operates to 1 MHz and can drive up to 20 meter lines.

The standard defines three basic classes of devices that can be connected to the GPIB: *talker, listener,* and *controller*. There can also be devices that are combinations of these basic types.

An important application of the GPIB is in the interconnection of several test instruments to form an *automated test system*. Examples of *talkers* in this application are devices that produce information, such as digital multimeters and frequency counters. Examples of *listeners* are display devices and programmable instruments such as signal generators, and power supplies. A programmable multimeter, for example, can

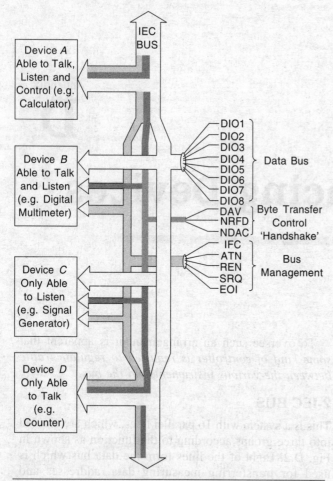

**Fig. D.2**    *IEC Bus System for Interconnecting Instruments.*

be *both* a talker and a listener. It functions as a talker when outputting voltage measurements and as a receiver when receiving program instructions. The *controller* is a device that determines when the other devices can use the bus.

Physically the GPIB consists of a 24-wire shielded cable. Eight lines carry *data,* eight lines carry *control signals* (commands) and eight are reserved for *grounds*. The eight commands are divided into three *data byte transfer controls* and five *interface management lines*. The standard connector diagram is shown in Fig. D.3.

## 4-RS232C

The most widely used device for *serial data communications* is the RS232C standard as identified by the Electronic Industries Association (EIA). This standard is used for *interface* between data terminal equipment and data communication equipment. Interfacing a computer and a peripheral device, such as a printer or CRT, would be one application.

Basically, RS-232C specifies a 25-pin connector and assigns serial signals to specific pins on the connector. Data rates up to 20 kilobaud can be accommodated under this specification. Four types of data bytes are defined: data signals, control signals, timing signals and ground.

A logic 1 signal is defined as a voltage between $-3$ V and $-25$ V. A logic 0 is between $+3$ V and $+25$ V. Control signals are considered to be OFF if in the negative range (a *logic 1* in this case) and they are considered to be ON if in the positive range (a *logic 0* in this case). *There can be no voltages between $-3$ V and $+3$ V*. Special IC devices are available to translate from RS-232C levels to TTL and CMOS levels and vice versa.

Of the 25 signal lines defined by the RS-232C standard, 2 are *grounds*, 4 are *data signals*, 12 are *control signals*, and 3 are *timing signals*. Each signal has a particular nomenclature, abbreviation, and pin assignment. In any given application, a piece of equipment does not have to use all signals provided for. The number of specified signals actually used varies from one application to another. This standard as well as other standards used in the industry for interfacing exist to facilitate matching the equipment that conforms to the standard.

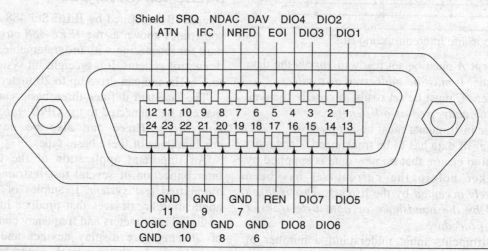

**Fig. D.3**    *IEEE-488 (GPIB) Standard Connector.*

# 6800 Microprocessor

## MICROPROCESSOR FUNDAMENTALS

Any conventional digital circuit consists of a number of gates and flip-flops connected in such a way as to perform the required function. Such a circuit accepts digital inputs, performs some kind of processing and provides digital outputs. The function performed by many digital systems is determined by the way in which the various gates and flip-flops are interconnected.

## PROGRAMMING

The microprocessor differs from the "hardwired" digital circuit in that the function performed is determined by a sequence of instructions which are stored in a memory in much the same way as a conventional digital computer. A change in the program will alter the function carried out by the microprocessor.

## PRACTICAL MICROPROCESSORS

To enable readers to more fully grasp the details involved in microprocessor system design, one microprocessor—the Motorola M6800—will be described.

The Motorola M6800 is a family of six integrated circuits that can be interconnected in a variety of different ways. The set comprises the microprocessor itself (MPU), a Random Access Memory (RAM), a Read Only Memory (ROM), a Peripheral Interface Adapter (PIA), an Asynchronous Communications Interface Adapter (ACI$_A$) and a Low-speed Modem (LSM).

## SECTIONS

All microprocessors can be divided into four basic sections: a memory, an input/output unit, a control unit and an arithmetic logic unit. The entire operation of such a system can be compared to a man adding up numbers written on a sheet of paper and writing the result on the same piece of paper.

In this analogy the sheet of paper becomes the peripheral device—the source and destination of the data to be processed. The man's eyes are the input system enabling the numbers to be read into the memory. The man's hand forms the output unit enabling the results of a calculation to be written down. The memory of both the man and machine perform the same function—both store the sequence of instructions (algorithm) for performing addition. The part of the brain which performs the addition can be compared to the arithmetic logic unit and the brain's co-ordinating centre to the machine's control unit.

## BYTES

In the Motorola microprocessor, instructions and alphanumeric data are represented by 8-bit binary words, called bytes, which are stored in the memory. Each location within the memory has a numerical address (in the same way as houses in a street) and each location is capable of holding one byte of information.

With one byte (eight bits) it is possible to count up to the equivalent of 256 in decimal and, therefore, with one byte it is possible to individually address up to 256 memory locations. For the majority of microprocessor applications much greater memory capacity is required, therefore all the registers within the microprocessor concerned with addressing have a length of 16 bits.

This means that up to 65,536 separate locations within memory can be addressed (since a 16-bit binary word can have a value of up to this figure in decimal). Every location within memory will hold one 8-bit binary word, which means that the memory can consist of $65,536 \times 8 = 524,288$ bits. However, there is no need to have a memory as large as this to make the MPU function.

## HEXADECIMAL CODING

In binary, memory location number 'one' would be referred to as location 0000000000000001, location number 'two' would be 0000000000000010 and location 32,769 would be 1000000000000001, which, you will agree, is all rather tedious.

To avoid using such long strings of 1s and 0s, the hexadecimal code is often used when referring to numbers within the MPU, as conversion between binary and hexadecimal is easier to perform and more convenient than conversion between binary and decimal.

The conversion between binary and hexadecimal first involves splitting the binary word up into blocks of 4-bits as follows:

01101101 becomes 0110 1101

**Table E.1**  *Hexadecimal Code*

| Decimal | | Binary | | Hexadecimal |
|---|---|---|---|---|
| 0 | = | 0000 | = | 0 |
| 1 | = | 0001 | = | 1 |
| 2 | = | 0010 | = | 2 |
| 3 | = | 0011 | = | 3 |
| 4 | = | 0100 | = | 4 |
| 5 | = | 0101 | = | 5 |
| 6 | = | 0110 | = | 6 |
| 7 | = | 0111 | = | 7 |
| 8 | = | 1000 | = | 8 |
| 9 | = | 1001 | = | 9 |
| 10 | = | 1010 | = | A |
| 11 | = | 1011 | = | B |
| 12 | = | 1100 | = | C |
| 13 | = | 1101 | = | D |
| 14 | = | 1110 | = | E |
| 15 | = | 1111 | = | F |

Each block of four bits has 16 possible values. In the decimal system we only have ten symbols to use (0 to 9) so, in the hexadecimal system, counting continues using letters of the alphabet as follows:

Returning to our earlier example, 01101101 in hexadecimal is equal to:

01101101

0110    1101

6      D   (from Table 1)

In other words 0110101 is equivalent to 6D in hexadecimal. If you wish to work it out you will find that 6D in hexadecimal is equivalent to 109 in decimal.

Using the hexadecimal system is confusing at first. Numbers like CF2C do not seem to make much sense. However, after a little practice working in 16s with the hexadecimal system, it becomes as familiar as working in tens.

## SIMPLIFIED VIEW

A much simplified block diagram of the Motorola microprocessor is shown in Fig. E.1. The blocks labelled programme counter, stack pointer and index register are all registers capable of holding 2 bytes (16 bits) which are used to hold the addresses of instructions or data stored in the memory.

Accumulators *A* and *B* are each 1 byte registers which are primarily used to hold data for and from the arithmetic logic unit. The instruction register is used to hold an instruction (1 byte) which is decoded and used to produce the control, routing and timing signals which are necessary to carry out the instruction.

## EXAMPLE SEQUENCE

With the aid of Fig. E.1 and Fig. E.2 it is possible to trace a complete sequence of events within the microprocessor.

Figure E.2 shows a number of memory locations containing instructions which are to be performed by the microprocessor. For convenience the instructions are shown in hexadecimal instead of binary. To the left of the memory locations are the four digit hexadecimal memory location addresses. On the right of the memory locations are the plain English explanations of the instructions stored in the memory locations.

The program counter is set to the address of the first instruction in the programme which is situated at memory location 0001. This is done by loading the programme counter with the number 0001.

The address in the program counter is sent to the memory along the address bus and, as a result, the contents of memory location 0001 are sent to the MPU along the data bus to be stored in the instruction register. The program counter is now incremented by 1 to 0002.

The content of the instruction register (86—the instruction to load accumulator *A* with data represented by the byte in the next memory location) is decoded and the control system causes the byte addressed by the program counter to be transferred along the data bus from memory to accumulator *A* in the MPU. The program counter is again incremented (now holds 0003) and accumulator *A* holds the numerical value 05 (hexadecimal).

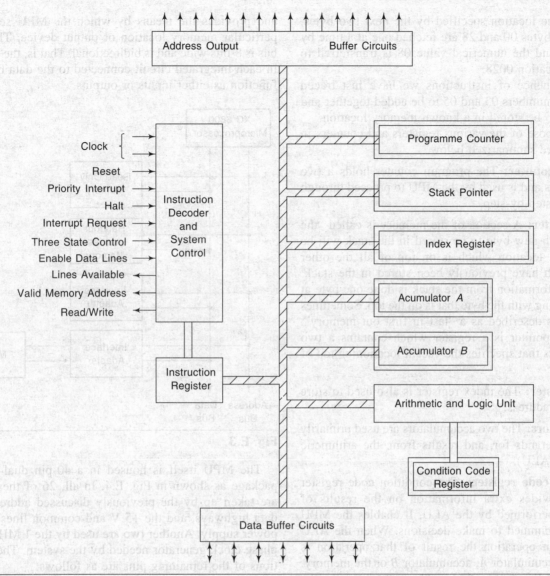

**Fig. E.1**

| | | |
|---|---|---|
| 0001 | 86 | Load Accumulator A with |
| 0002 | 05 | the Number 05 (Hex) |
| 0003 | B9 | Add Contents of Accumulator |
| 0004 | 00 | *A* to the Contents of the |
| 0005 | 27 | Memory Location 0027. |
| 0006 | B7 | Store the Contents of Accumulator |
| 0007 | 00 | *A* at Memory |
| 0008 | 28 | Location 0028 |
| | | |
| 0027 | 03 | Operand |
| 0028 | 08 | Result |

**Fig. E.2**

## NEXT INSTRUCTION

The MPU fetches the next instruction from memory that is addressed by the program. This is B9—an instruction which causes the numerical value contained in accumulator *A* to be added to the content of the memory location specified in the following two bytes of the instr-

uction and to place the result of the addition in accumulator *A*. The program counter is incremented to 0004.

The MPU fetches the first byte of the second operand address (00) from memory location 0004, increments the programme counter to 0005 and fetches the second byte of the address (27) from location 0005. The program counter is incremented to 0006.

The MPU now holds the first operand (05) in accumulator *A*, holds the address 0027, which is the location of the second operand, and has the instruction to add (B9) in the instruction register. The MPU fetches the data at address 0027 (the numerical value 03), adds it to accumulator *A* and stores the result in accumulator *A*.

Having completed instruction B9, the MPU fetches the next instruction (B7) addressed by the programme counter and then increments the programme counter. Instruction B7 will cause the contents of accumulator *A* (the result of the addition of 05 and 03) to be transferred to the location specified by the next two bytes. These two bytes 00 and 28 are fetched one at a time by the MPU and the numerical value 08 is transferred to memory location 0028.

The sequence of instructions we have just traced caused the numbers 03 and 05 to be added together and the result to be stored in a known memory location.

The purpose of the various registers and counters in the MPU are summarized below.

**Program counter:** The program counter holds a two byte address and is used by the MPU to proceed through a program step-by-step.

**Stack pointer:** A section of the memory is called "the stack". Each new byte to be stored in the stack will be stored at a location which is on top of all the other bytes which have previously been stored in the stack. Reading information from the stack is done one byte at a time starting with the byte that is on the top. Sometimes the stack is described as a "last in first out memory". The stack pointer is a register which contains a two byte address that specifies the vacant location on top of the stack.

**Index register:** The index register is also used to store a two byte address.

**Accumulators:** The two accumulators are used primarily to hold operands for, and results from, the arithmetic logic unit (ALU).

**Condition code register:** The condition code register (CCR) provides extra information on the results of operation performed by the ALU. It enables the MPU to be programmed to make decisions. When the ALU performs an operation the result of that operation is stored in accumulator *A*, accumulator *B* or the memory.

Additionally, various `flip-flops` (or bits) may be set in the CCR to indicate that, for instance, the result is negative, the result is zero or that overflow occurred. Two bits are set aside to indicate if a carry (or half carry) has occurred and one bit is called the "Interrupt Mask Bit".

It is possible, under program control, to examine (or test) the state of individual bits within the CCR following an operation. For example, bit *N* in the CCR is set to "1" if the result of an operation is negative. A programmer could say:

A. Carry out instructions 1, 2 and 3.
B. Instruction 4. Does bit $N = 1$? (bit test). If $N = 0$ return to instruction 1. If $N = 1$ proceed with instruction 5. In other words, the sequence of instructions being carried out by the machine was made dependent on the sign of the result through the use a CCR bit test.

Figure E.3 shows the main interconnections in a typical MPU system. The address bus is 16-bits wide

and provides the means by which the MPU selects a particular memory location or output device. The data bus is 8-bits wide and is bidirectional. That is, the buffers in each integrated circuit connected to the data bus can function as either inputs or outputs.

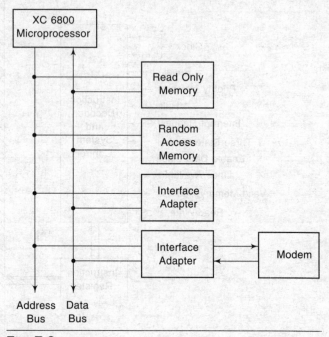

**Fig. E.3**

The MPU itself is housed in a 40-pin dual-in-line package as shown in Fig. E.4. In all, 26 of these pins are taken up by the previously discussed address and data highways, and the +5 V and common lines of the power supply. Another two are used by the 1 MHz two-phase clock generator needed by the system. The functions of the remaining pins are as follows:

**Pin 2. HALT :** When this input is taken to logic "0" all activity in the machine is stopped.

**Pin 39. Three-state control:** A logic '1' input on this pin will cause all of the address bus buffers and the Read/Write line (pin 34) to go into a high impedance state—in other words turning them off. External equipment can now use the address bus to directly access the memory without involving the MPU in the process (Direct Memory Access—DMA).

**Pin 34. Read/Write:** The MPU has two basic modes of operation—read and write. In the read mode the MPU is in a condition to accept information from either the memory or from input/output devices. In the write mode the MPU will send out information to either the memory or the input/output circuits. The MPU informs the rest of the system that it is in the read mode by applying logic '1' to the read/write output.

When the MPU is in the write mode the read/write output is at logic "0". Normally, when the MPU is in

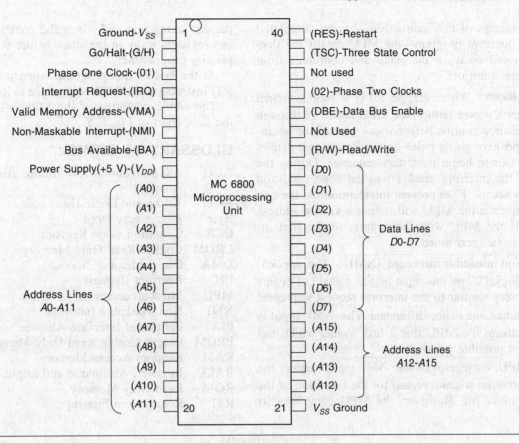

Ground-$V_{SS}$ | 1 — 40 | (RES)-Restart
Go/Halt-(G/H) — (TSC)-Three State Control
Phase One Clock-(01) — Not used
Interrupt Request-(IRQ) — (02)-Phase Two Clocks
Valid Memory Address-(VMA) — (DBE)-Data Bus Enable
Non-Maskable Interrupt-(NMI) — Not Used
Bus Available-(BA) — (R/W)-Read/Write
Power Supply(+5 V)-($V_{DD}$) — (D0)

MC 6800 Microprocessing Unit

Address Lines A0-A11 (A0)–(A11), pins 20, 21

Data Lines D0-D7
Address Lines A12-A15
$V_{SS}$ Ground

**Fig. E.4**

the stand by mode (waiting for work) the read/write output will be logic "1". When either the HALT input is at logic "0" (machine halted) or the three-state control input is high (DMA), the MPU read/write output will be put into a high-impedance state.

**Pin 5. Valid memory address (VMA):** When the MPU has placed a memory address on the address bus, the VMA output goes to logic "1". This signal is used for control purposes.

**Pin 36. Data bus enable:** When this input is in the logic "0" state the data bus driver circuits are held in a high impedance state for DMA applications. Normally this input is driven by the clock. Additionally, the data bus drivers within the MPU are also disabled internally every time the MPU goes into the read condition.

**Pin 7. Highway available:** This output normally in the logic "0" state unless either the HALT line is at logic "0" (halt machine) or the MPU has just executed an instruction to "wait." In both of these two conditions the Highway available output will go to logic "1"— indicating to other circuits the MPU has stopped and that the address highway is vacant, and all "three-state" output drivers will be put in their high impedance condition. The MPU is removed from the "wait" state when a valid interrupt occurs (see later).

**Pin 4. Interrupt request (IRQ):** A logic "0" on the IRQ input will cause the following sequence of events:

1. The MPU will complete the instruction it is currently processing.
2. The Interrupt mask bit in the condition code register is examined. If this bit is "1" it means that the processor is processing a previously requested interrupt and the MPU will, therefore, ignore the new interrupt request until it has completed all the instructions in the interrupt programme it is currently servicing. If the Interrupt mask bit is at logic "0", the MPU enters an interrupt routine.
3. The contents of the index register, program counter, accumulators and the condition code register are stored in the memory in the previously mentioned stack.
4. The MPU now responds to the interrupt request (having ensured that all the information it was processing has been safely stored away) by setting the mask interrupt bit to logic "1". This ensures that the MPU cannot respond to any new interrupt request.
5. The MPU now addresses a known location in memory where the first instruction for the interrupt service program will have been previously stored.
6. The last instruction in the interrupt program will be RTI (Return from Interrupt).

7. On receipt of this instruction—having completed the interrupt program—the MPU recalls the data it stored away in the stack and continues from where it left off.

**Pin 40.   Reset :** Whenever the MPU is first switched on, or after a power failure, the MPU has to go through an initialisation routine before it can commence operations. A positive going pulse on the Reset input causes the processor to begin its restart sequence. During the sequence the interrupt mask bit in the code condition register is set to "1" to prevent interruption. At the end of the sequence the MPU will output a known address to provide the MPU with the address of the first instruction to be  performed.

**Pin 6.   Non maskable interrupt  (NMI) :** The application of a logic "0" on this input begins a chain of events which is very similar to the interrupt request sequence, but which has one major difference. The NMI Input is used to inform the MPU that a task awaits which has the highest possible priority.

The MPU, on receipt of the NMI signal, enters the interrupt routine without regard for the condition of the interrupt mask bit. However, the MPU completes its present instruction and stores the contents of the various registers away in the stack before starting the high priority programme.

At the end of this program, when it encounters the RTI instruction, the MPU will return to its previous task.

The whole operation of the MPU is summarised in the flow chart of Fig. E.5.

## GLOSSARY OF TERMS...

| | |
|---|---|
| ACI$_A$ | Asynchronous Communications Interface Adapter |
| ACU | Arithmetic Logic Unit |
| Byte | 8-bit binary word |
| CCR | Condition Code Register |
| CROM | Control Read Only Memory |
| DMA | Direct Memory Access |
| IRQ | Interrupt Request |
| MPU | Microprocessor |
| NMI | Non Maskable Interrupt |
| PIA | Peripheral Interface Adapter |
| PROM | Programmable Read Only Memory |
| RAM | Random Access Memory |
| RALU | Register, Arithmetic and Logic Unit |
| ROM | Read Only Memory |
| RTI | Return from Interrupt |

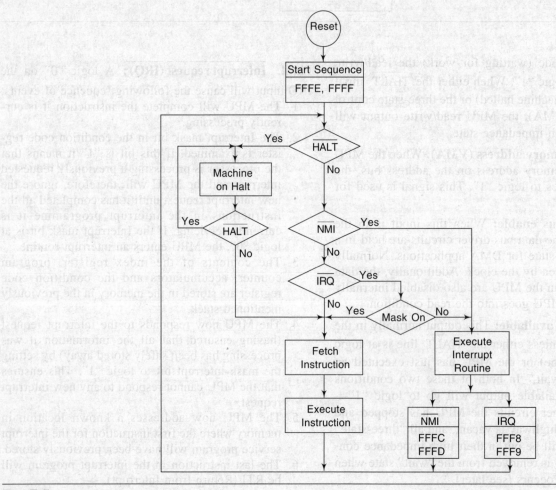

**Fig. E.5**

# Glossary

**Ten (10) Percent Point** A point on a rising or falling waveform that is equal to 0.1 times its highest value.

**Two's (2's) Complement** The binary number that results when 1 is added to the 1's complement.

**Triple five (555) Timer** A digital timing circuit that can be connected as either an astable or a monostable circuit.

**Ninety (90) Percent Point** A point on a rising or falling waveform that is equal to 0.9 times its highest value.

**A/D Conversion** The process of converting an analog input voltage to a number of equivalent digital output levels.

**Access time** In general, the delay time measured from chip enable (or address) until valid data appears at the output.

**Active Load** A transistor that acts as a load for another transistor.

**Active-Low** Normally, a signal must be high to do something. Active-low refers to the opposite concept: a signal must be low to cause something to happen or to indicate that something has happened.

**Active Power Dissipation** The power dissipation of a device under switching conditions. It differs from static power dissipation because of the large current spikes during output transitions.

**ADC** Analog-to-digital converter.

**Address** Selection of a cell in a memory array for a read or a write operation.

**AND Gate** A gate with two or more inputs. The output is high only when all inputs are high.

**Assert** To activate. If an input line has a bubble on it, you assert the input by making it low. If there is no bubble, you assert the input by making it high.

**Astable** Having two output states, neither of which is stable.

**Asynchronous** Independent of clocking. The output can change without having to wait for a clock pulse.

**Base** The number of digits or basic symbols in a number system. The decimal system has a base of 10 because it uses 10 digits. Binary has a base of 2, octal a base of 8, and hexadecimal a base of 16.

**BCD** A binary-coded decimal.

**Binary Numbers** A number code with base 2 that uses only the digits 0 and 1 to represent quantities.

**Bipolar** Having two types of charge carriers: free electrons and holes.

**Bistable** Having two stable states.

**Bistable Multivibrator** Another term for an RS flip-flop.

**Bit** An abbreviated form of binary digit. Instead of saying that 10110 has five binary digits, we can say that it has 5 bits.

**Buffer Register** A group of memory elements, often flip-flops, that can store a binary word.

**Bus** A group of wires that transmits binary data. The data bus of a first-generation microcomputer has eight wires, each carrying 1 bit. This means that the data bus can transmit 1 byte at a time. Typically, the byte represents an instruction or data word that is moved from one register to another.

**Byte** A binary number with 8 bits.

**Capacity** The total number of bits that can be stored in a memory.

**Chip** A small piece of semiconductor material. Sometimes chip refers to an IC device including its pins.

**Chip** An integrated circuit. A piece of semiconductor material with a micro-miniature circuit on its surface.

**Clock** A periodic waveform (usually a square wave) that is used as a synchronizing signal in a digital system

**Clock Cycle Time** The time period of a clock signal.

**Clock Stability** A measure of the frequency stability of a waveform; usually given in parts per million (ppm).

**CMOS Inverter** A push-pull connection of p- and n-channel MOSFETs.

**Compatibility** Ability of the output of one device to drive the input of another device.

**Contact Bounce** Opening and closing of a set of contacts as a result of the mechanical bounce that occurs when the device is switched.

**D/A Conversion** The process of converting a number of digital input signals to one equivaient analog output voltage.

**DAC** Digital-to-analog converter.

**Data Selector** A synonym for multiplexer.

**De Morgan's First Theorem** In words, the complement of a logical sum equals the logical product of the complements. In terms of circuit, a NOR gate is equivalent to a bubbled AND gate.

**De Morgan's Second Theorem** In words, the complement of a logical product equals the logical sum of the complements. In terms of circuits, a NAND gate is equivalent to a bubbled OR gate.

**Decoder** A circuit that is similar to a demultiplexer, except there is no data input. The control input bits produce one active output line.

**Decoding Gate** A logic gate whose output is high (or low) only during one of the unique states of a counter.

**Demultiplexer** A circuit with one input and many outputs.

**Differential Linearity** A measure of the variation in size of the input voltage to an A/D converter which causes the converter to change from one state to the next.

**Digit** A basic symbol used in a number system. The decimal system has 10 digits, 0 through 9.

**Don't Care Condition** An input-output condition that never occurs during normal operation. Since the condition never occurs, you can use an $X$ on the Karnaugh map. This $X$ can be a 0 or a 1, whichever you prefer.

**Dual Circuit** Given a logic circuit, you can find its dual as follows. Change each AND (NAND) gate to an OR (NOR) gate, change each OR (NOR) gate to an AND (NAND) gate, and complement all input-output signals.

**Duty Cycle** For a periodic, rectangular waveform, the ratio of time the signal is high to the time period of the signal.

**Dynamic Memory** A memory whose contents must be restored periodically.

**Edge Triggering** A circuit responds only when the clock is in transition between its two voltage states.

**EPROM** An erasable programmable read-only memory. With this device, the user can erase the stored contents with ultraviolet light and electrically store new data. EPROMs are useful during project development where programs and data are being perfected.

**Equivalent Binary Weight** The value assigned to each bit in a digital number, expressed as a fraction of the total. The values are assigned in binary fashion according to the sequence $1, 2, 4, 8, ..., 2^n$, where $n$ is the total number of bits.

**Even Parity** A binary number with an even number of 1's.

**Exclusive-OR Gate** A gate that producers a high output only when an odd number of inputs is high.

**Fall Time** The time required for a signal to transition from 90% of its maximum value down to 10% of its maximum.

**Fanout** The maximum number of TTL loads that a TTL device can reliably drive.

**Field-Programmable** A PROM that can be programmed by the user.

**Flip-Flop** An electronic circuit that has two stable states.

**Full-Adder** A logic circuit with three inputs and two outputs. The circuit adds 3 bits at a time, giving a sum and a carry output.

**Gate** A digital circuit with one or more input voltages but only one output voltage.

**Glitch** An undesired positive or negative pulse appearing at the output of a logic gate.

**Glitch** Very narrow positive or negative pulse that appears as an unwanted signal.

**Half-Adder** A logic circuit with two inputs and two outputs. It adds 2 bits at a time, producing a sum and a carry output.

**Hard Saturation** Using enough base current to ensure saturation under all operating conditions. A guideline for hard saturation is to design for a base current of one-tenth the collector saturation current.

**Hardware** The electronic, magnetic, and mechanical devices used in a computer or digital system.

**Hexadecimal** Refers to number system with a base of 16. The hexadecimal system has digits 0 through 9, followed by $A$ through $F$.

**Hold Time** The minimum amount of time that data must be present after the clock trigger arrives.

**Interface** The way a driving device is connected to a loading device. All the circuitry between the output of a device and the input of another device.

**Inverter** A gate with only one input and a complemented output.

**Karnaugh Map** A drawing that shows all the fundamental products and the corresponding output values of a truth table.

**Latch** Another term for an RS flip-flop.

**LED** A light-emitting diode.

**Logic Circuit** A digital circuit, a switching circuit, or any kind of two-state circuit that duplicates mental processes.

**Logic Clip** A device attached to a 14-or 16-pin DIP. The LEDs in this troubleshooting tool indicate the logic states of the pins.

**Logic Probe** A troubleshooting device that indicates the state of a signal line.

**Logic Pulser** A troubleshooting device that generates brief voltage pulses. The typical logic pulser has a push-button switch that produces a single pulse for each closure. More advanced logic pulsers can generate a pulser train with a specified number of pulses.

**Low-power Schottky TTL** A modification of standard TTL in which larger resistances and Schottky diodes are used. The larger resistances decrease the power dissipation, and the Schottky diodes increase the speed.

**LSB** Least -significant bit.

**Magnitude** The absolute or unsigned value of a number.

**Mask-Programmable** A PROM that can be programmed only by the manufacturer.

**Matrix Addressing** Selection of a single cell in a rectangular array of cells by choosing the intersection of a single row and a single column.

**Memory Cell** The circuit used to store a single bit of information in a semiconductor memory chip.

**Microprocessor** A digital IC that combines the arithmetic and control sections of a computer.

**Milliman's Theorem** A theorem from network analysis which states that the voltage at any node in a resistive network is equal to the sum of the currents entering the node divided by the sum of the conductances connected to the node, all determined by assuming that the voltage at the node is zero.

**Modulus** Defines the number of states through which a counter can progress.

**Monostable** A circuit that has two output states, only one of which is stable.

**MSB** Most-significant bit.

**Multiplexer** A circuit with many inputs but only one output.

**Natural Count** The maximum number of states through which a counter can progress. Given by $2^n$, where $n$ is the number of flip-flops in the counter.

**Negative True** A signal is negative true when the voltage is low.

**Nibble** A binary number with 4 bits.

**Noise Immunity** The amount of noise voltage that an input can tolerate without causing a false change in output state.

**Nonvolatile Storage** A method whereby a loss of power will not result in a loss of stored data.

**Octal** Refers to a number system with a base of 8, that is, one that uses 8 digits. Normally, these are 0, 1, 2, 3, 4, 5, 6 and 7.

**Octet** Eight adjacent 1's in a $2 \times 4$ shape on a Karnaugh map.

**Odd Parity** A binary number with an odd number of 1's.

**One-shot** Another term for a monostable circuit.

**OR Gate** A gate with two or more inputs. The output is high when any input is high.

**Overflow** An unwanted carry that produces an answer outside the valid range of the numbers being represented.

**Overlapping Groups** Using the same 1 more than once when looping the 1's of a Karnaugh map.

**Pair** Two horizontally or vertically adjacent 1's on a Karnaugh map.

**PAL** A programmable array logic (sometimes written PLA, which stands for programmable logic array). In either case, it is a chip with a programmable AND array and a fixed OR array.

**Parallel Counter** A synchronous counter in which all flip-flops change states simultaneously since all clock inputs are driven by the same clock.

**Parallel Shift** Data bits are shifted simultaneously with a single clock transition.

**Parity Generation** An extra bit that is generated and attached to a binary number, so that the new number has either even or odd parity.

**Positive True** A signal is positive true when the voltage is high.

**Presettable Counter** A counter incorporating logic such that it can be preset to any desired state.

**Product-of-sums Equation** A Boolean equation that is the logical product of logical sums. This type of equation applies to an OR-AND circuit.

**Product-of-sums Equation** The logical product of those fundamental sums that produce output 1's in the truth-table. The corresponding logic circuit is an OR-AND circuit, or the equivalent NOR-NOR circuit.

**PROM** A programmable read-only memory. A type of chip that allows the user to program it with a PROM programmer that burns fusible links at the diode cross points. Once the data is stored, the programming is permanent. PROMs are useful for small production runs.

**Propagation Delay** The amount of time it takes for the output to change states after an input trigger.

**Quad** Four horizontal, vertical, or rectangular 1's on a Karnaugh map.

**Quantization Error** The error inherent in any digital system due to the size of the LSB.

**RAM** Random-access memory.

**Read Operation** The act of detecting the contents of a memory.

**Redundant Group** A group of 1's on a Karnaugh map that are all part of other groups. You can eliminate any redundant group.

**Register Capacity** Determined by the number of `flip-flops` in the register. There must be one `flip-flop` for each binary bit; the register capacity is $2^n$, where $n$ is the number of `flip-flops`.

**Ring Counter** A basic shift register with direct feedback such that the contents of the register simply circulate around the register when the clock is running.

**Ripple Counter** An asynchronous counter in which each `flip-flop` is triggered by the output of the previous `flip-flop`.

**Rise Time** The time required for a signal to transition from 10% of its maximum value up to 90% of its maximum.

**ROM** A read-only memory. An IC that can store many binary numbers at locations called addresses. ROMs are expensive to manufacture and are used only for large production runs where the cost of the mask can be recovered by sales.

**SAR** Sequential approximation register, used in a sequential ADC.

**Saturation Delay Time** The time delay encountered when a transistor tries to come out of the saturation region. When the base drive switches from high to low, a transistor cannot instantaneously come out of hard saturation: extra carriers must first flow out of the base region.

**Schmitt Trigger** A digital circuit that produces a rectangular output. The input waveform may be sinusoidal, triangular, distorted, and so on. The output is always rectangular.

**Serial Shift** Data bits are shifted one after the other in a serial fashion with one bit shifted at each clock transition. Therefore, $n$ clock transitions are needed to shift an $n$-bit binary number.

**Setup Time** The minimum amount of time required for data inputs to be present before the clock arrives.

**Shift Counter** A basic shift register with inverse feedback such that a cyclic counter is formed.

**Shift Register** A group of `flip-flops` connected in such a way that a binary number can be shifted into or out of the `flip-flops`.

**Sink** A place where something is absorbed. When saturated, the lower transistor in a totem-pole output acts as a current sink because conventional charges flow through the transistor to ground.

**Soft Saturation** Driving a transistor with the minimum base current needed to produce saturation.

**Software** A program or programs. The instructions that tell a computer how to process the data.

**Source** The upper transistor of a totem-pole output acts as a source because conventional flow is out of the emitter into the load.

**Speed-up Capacitor** Whenever you use a voltage divider, the stray capacitance across the output resistor will slow down the switching speed unless you add a capacitor across the input resistor. This capacitor speeds up the charging of the stray capacitance across the output of the voltage divider.

**Standard TTL** The basic TTL design. It has a power dissipation of 10 mW per gate and a propagation delay time of 10 ns.

**Static Memory** A memory capable of storing data indefinitely, provided there is no loss of power.

**Static Power Dissipation** The product of dc voltage and current.

**Strobe** An input that disables or enables a circuit.

**Sum-of-products Equation** A Boolean equation that is the logical sum of logical products. This type of equation applies to an `AND-OR` circuit.

**Synchronous** When outputs change states in time with a clock. A clock signal must be present in order for the outputs to change states.

**Three-state TTL** A modified TTL design that allows us to connect outputs directly. Earlier computers used open-collector devices with their buses, but the passive pull-up severely limited the operating speed. By replacing open-collector devices with three-state devices, we can significantly reduce the switching time needed to change from the low state and the output state. The result is faster data changes on the bus, which is equivalent to speeding up the operation of a computer.

**Timing Diagram** A picture that shows the input-output waveforms of a logic circuit.

**Transistor-Transistor Logic (TTL)** A family of digital devices which is produced as integrated circuits (ICs) in 14-, 16-, 20-, and 24-pin dual-in-line packages (DIPs).

**Truth Table** A table that shows all of the input-output possibilities of a logic circuit.

**TTL Clock** A circuit that generates a clock waveform that is compatible with standard TTL logic circuits.

**Two-state Operation** The use of only two points on the load line of a device, resulting in all voltages being either low or high.

**Up-Down Counter** A basic counter, synchronous or asynchronous, that is capable of counting in either an upward or a downward direction.

**Volatile Storage** A method of storing information whereby a loss of power will result in a loss of the data stored.

**Weight** Refers to the decimal value of each digit position of a number. For decimal numbers, the weights are 1, 10, 100, 1000 … working from the decimal point to the left. For binary numbers the weights are 1, 2, 4, 8 … to the left of the binary point. With octal numbers, the weights become 1, 8, 64, …. to the left of the octal point.

**Write Operation** The act of storing information in a memory.

# Bibliography

1 Bannister, BR, and White Head, DG *Fundamentals of Digital Systems*, McGraw-Hill Book Co., New York.

2 Barna, A., and Porat, DI, *Integrated Circuits in Digital Electronics*, John Wiley and Sons, New York, 1973.

3 Bartee, TC, *Digital Computer Fundamentals*, 3rd ed., McGraw-Hill Book Co., New York, 1972.

4 Blakeslee, TR, *Digital Design with Standard MSI and LSI* John Wiley and Sons Inc., New York, 1979.

5 Chang, HY, Manning, EG, and Metze, G, *Fault Diagnosis of Digital Systems*, John Wiley and Sons, New York, 1970.

6 Chu, Y, *Digital Computer Design Fundamentals*, McGraw-Hill Book Co., New York, 1962.

7 Fletcher, WL, *An Engineering Approach to Digital Design*, Prentice-Hall Inc., Englewood Cliffs, New Jersey, 1980.

8 Floyd, L, *Digital Fundamentals*, Charles E Merrill Publishing Co.

9 Gothman, H, *Digital Electronics—An Introduction to Theory and Practice*, 2nd ed, Prentice-Hall Inc., Englewood Cliffs, New Jersey, 1982.

10 Hall, DV, *Microprocessors and Digital Systems*, McGraw-Hill Book Co., New York, 1980.

11 Hill, FJ, and Peterson, G.R., *Digital Systems, Hardware, Organization and Design*, John Wiley and Sons, New York, 1973.

12 Hill, FJ, and Peterson, GR, *Introduction to Switching Theory and Logical Design*, John Wiley and Sons, New York, 1974.

13 Hillburn, JL, and Julich, PN, *Microcomputers/Microprocessors—Hardware, Software and Applications*, Prentice-Hall, Englewood Cliffs, Jersey, 1976.

14 Jain, RP, *Modern Digital Electronics*, Tata McGraw-Hill Publishing Company, New Delhi 1984.

15 Kline, RM, *Digital Computer Design*, Prentice-Hall Inc., Englewood Cliffs, New Jersey, 1977.

16 Kohavi, Z, *Switching and Finite Automata Theory*, 2nd ed. McGraw-Hill Book Co., New York, 1978.

17 Lee, C, *Digital Circuits and Logic Design*, Prentice-Hall Inc., Englewood Cliffs, New Jersey, 1976.

18 Leventhal, LA, *Introduction to Microprocessors: Software, Hardware and Programming*, Prentice-Hall Inc., Englewood cliffs, New Jersey, 1980.

19 Malvino, AP, *Digital Computer Electronics*, McGraw-Hill Book Co., New York.

20 Malvino, AP, and Leach, DP, *Digital Principles and Applications*, McGraw-Hill Book Co., New York.

21 Mano, M, *Digital Logic and Computer Design*, Prentice-Hall Inc., Englewood Cliffs, New Jersey, 1979.

22 Marcus, MP, *Switching Circuits for Engineers*, 3rd ed Prentice-Hall, Englewood Cliffs, New Jersey, 1975.

23 Mathur, AP, *Introduction to Microprocessors* Tata McGraw-Hill, New Delhi, 1992.

24 McCluskey, EJ, Jr, *Introduction to the Theory of Switching Circuits*, McGraw-Hill Book Co., New York, 1965.

25 Millman, J, *Microelectronics: Digital and Analog Circuits and Systems*, McGraw-Hill Book company, New York, 1979.

26 Millman, J, and Halkias, CC, *Integrated Electronics*, McGraw-Hill, New York, 1972.

27 Millman, J, and Taub H, *Pulse Digital and Switching Waveforms*, McGraw-Hill Book Co., New York, 1965.

28 Morris, RL, and Miller, JR, *Designing with TTL Integrated Circuits*, McGraw-Hill Book Co., New York, 1974.

29 Nagle, HT, Jr, Carrol, BD, and Irwin, JD, *An Introduction to Computer Logic*, Prentice-Hall Inc., Englewood Cliffs, New Jersey, 1975.

30 Rhyne, VT, *Fundamentals of Digital System Design,* Prentice-Hall Inc., Englewood Cliffs, New Jersey, 1973.

31 Scarlitt, JA, *Transistor Logic and its Interconnections,*—Van Nostrand Reinhold Co., New York, 1972.

32 Schilling, DL, and Belove, C, *Electronics Circuits—Discrete and Intergrated*, McGraw-Hill Book Co., New York.

33 Taub, H, and Schilling, D, *Digital Intergrated Electronics,* McGraw-Hill Book Co., New York, 1977.

34 Texas Instruments Staff, *Designing with TTL Integrated Circuit,* McGraw-Hill Book Company, New York, 1971.

35 Tocci, R.J., *Digital Systems*, 5th ed., Prentice-Hall Inc., Englewood Cliffs, New Jersey, 1991.

# Index of ICs

# Index